MTH 1100/1105 FUNDAMENTALS OF ALGEBRA AND INTERMEDIATE ALGEBRA

MTH 1100/1105 Fundamentals of Algebra and Intermediate Algebra

Custom Edition for Troy University

Taken from:
Beginning and Intermediate Algebra, Fifth Edition
by Margaret L. Lial, John Hornsby and Terry McGinnis

Cover Art: Courtesy of Photodisc/Getty Images.

Taken from:

Beginning and Intermediate Algebra, Fifth Edition
by Margaret L. Lial, John Hornsby and Terry McGinnis
Copyright © 2012, 2008, 2004, 2000 by Pearson Education, Inc.
Published by Addison-Wesley
San Francisco, California 94111

This special edition published in cooperation with Pearson Learning Solutions.

Pearson Learning Solutions, 501 Boylston Street, Suite 900,
Boston, MA 02116
A Pearson Education Company
www.pearsoned.com

Printed in the United States of America

1 2 3 4 5 6 7 8 9 10 V092 16 15 14 13 12

000200010271672630

ML

ISBN 10: 1-256-79309-4
ISBN 13: 978-1-256-79309-0

To Callie, Kurt, Clayton, and Grady—
Welcome to our family.

Marge, John, and Terry

Contents

Week one (handwritten annotation)

Linear Equations in Two Variables   175

Exponents and Polynomials   231

Factoring and Applications   295

Rational Expressions and Applications   357

Graphs, Linear Equations, and Functions   425

Inequalities and Absolute Value   565

Roots, Radicals, and Root Functions   599

Quadratic Equations, Inequalities, and Functions   669

It is with pleasure that we offer the fifth edition of *Beginning and Intermediate Algebra*. With each new edition, the text has been shaped and adapted to meet the changing needs of both students and educators, and this edition faithfully continues that process. As always, we have taken special care to respond to the specific suggestions of users and reviewers through enhanced discussions, new and updated examples and exercises, helpful features, updated figures and graphs, and an extensive package of supplements and study aids. We believe the result is an easy-to-use, comprehensive text that is the best edition yet.

Students who have never studied algebra—as well as those who require further review of basic algebraic concepts before taking additional courses in mathematics, business, science, nursing, or other fields—will benefit from the text's student-oriented approach. Of particular interest to students and instructors will be the NEW Study Skills activities and Now Try Exercises.

This text is part of a series that also includes the following books:

▶ *Beginning Algebra,* Eleventh Edition, by Lial, Hornsby, and McGinnis

▶ *Intermediate Algebra,* Eleventh Edition, by Lial, Hornsby, and McGinnis

▶ *Algebra for College Students,* Seventh Edition, by Lial, Hornsby, and McGinnis

NEW IN THIS EDITION

We are pleased to offer the following new student-oriented features and study aids:

Lial Video Library This collection of video resources helps students navigate the road to success. It is available in MyMathLab and on Video Resources on DVD.

MyWorkBook This helpful guide provides extra practice exercises for every chapter of the text and includes the following resources for every section:

▶ Key vocabulary terms and vocabulary practice problems

▶ Guided Examples with step-by-step solutions and similar Practice Exercises, keyed to the text by Learning Objective

▶ References to textbook Examples and Section Lecture Videos for additional help

▶ Additional Exercises with ample space for students to show their work, keyed to the text by Learning Objective

Study Skills Poor study skills are a major reason why students do not succeed in mathematics. In these short activities, we provide helpful information, tips, and strategies on a variety of essential study skills, including *Reading Your Math Textbook, Tackling Your Homework, Taking Math Tests,* and *Managing Your Time.* While most of the activities are concentrated in the early chapters of the text, each has been designed independently to allow flexible use with individuals or small groups of students, or as a source of material for in-class discussions. (See pages 48 and 223.)

Now Try Exercises To actively engage students in the learning process, we now include a parallel margin exercise juxtaposed with each numbered example. These all-new exercises enable students to immediately apply and reinforce the concepts and skills presented in the corresponding examples. Answers are conveniently located on the same page so students can quickly check their results. (See pages 3 and 87.)

Revised Exposition As each section of the text was being revised, we paid special attention to the exposition, which has been tightened and polished. (See Section 1.4 Real Numbers and the Number Line, for example.) We believe this has improved discussions and presentations of topics.

Specific Content Changes These include the following:

▷ We gave the exercise sets special attention. There are over 1000 new and updated exercises, including problems that check conceptual understanding, focus on skill development, and provide review. We also worked to improve the even-odd pairing of exercises.

▷ Real-world data in over 150 applications in the examples and exercises have been updated.

▷ There is an increased emphasis on the difference between expressions and equations, including a new Caution at the beginning of Section 2.1. Throughout the text, we have reformatted many example solutions to use a "drop down" layout in order to further emphasize for students the difference between simplifying expressions and solving equations.

▷ We increased the emphasis on checking solutions and answers, as indicated by the new *CHECK* tag and ✓ in the exposition and examples.

▷ The presentation on solving linear equations in Sections 2.1–2.3 now includes five new examples and corresponding exercises.

▷ Section 2.6 includes entirely new discussion and examples on percent, percent equations, and percent applications, plus corresponding exercises.

▷ Section 3.4 on writing and graphing equations of lines provides increased development and coverage of the slope-intercept form, including two new examples.

▷ Section 6.5 includes new coverage of simplifying rational expressions with negative exponents.

▷ Section 7.3 Introduction to Functions from the previous edition has been expanded and split into two sections.

▷ Presentations of the following topics have also been enhanced and expanded:

Dividing real numbers involving zero (Section 1.6)
Solving applications involving consecutive integers and finding angle measures (Section 2.4)
Solving formulas for specified variables (Sections 2.5 and 6.7)
Using interval notation (Section 2.8)
Graphing linear equations in two variables (Section 3.2)
Dividing polynomials (Section 4.7)
Factoring trinomials (Section 5.2)
Solving quadratic equations by factoring (Sections 5.6 and 11.1)
Solving systems of linear equations with decimal coefficients (Section 8.2)

Solving systems of linear equations in three variables (Section 8.4)
Graphing linear inequalities in two variables (Section 9.3)
Solving quadratic equations by substitution (Section 11.4)
Evaluating expressions involving the greatest integer (Section 13.1)
Graphing hyperbolas (Section 13.3)
Evaluating factorials and binomial coefficients (Section 14.4)

HALLMARK FEATURES

We have included the following helpful features, each of which is designed to increase ease-of-use by students and/or instructors.

Annotated Instructor's Edition For convenient reference, we include answers to the exercises "on page" in the *Annotated Instructor's Edition,* using an enhanced, easy-to-read format. In addition, we have added approximately 30 new Teaching Tips and over 40 new and updated Classroom Examples.

Relevant Chapter Openers In the new and updated chapter openers, we feature real-world applications of mathematics that are relevant to students and tied to specific material within the chapters. Examples of topics include Americans' personal savings rate, the Olympics, and student credit card debt. Each opener also includes a section outline. (See pages 1, 85, and 175.)

Helpful Learning Objectives We begin each section with clearly stated, numbered objectives, and the included material is directly keyed to these objectives so that students and instructors know exactly what is covered in each section. (See pages 2 and 130.)

Popular Cautions and Notes One of the most popular features of previous editions, we include information marked ⚠ CAUTION and NOTE to warn students about common errors and emphasize important ideas throughout the exposition. The updated text design makes them easy to spot. (See pages 2 and 56.)

Comprehensive Examples The new edition of this text features a multitude of step-by-step, worked-out examples that include pedagogical color, helpful side comments, and special pointers. We give increased attention to checking example solutions—more checks, designated using a special *CHECK* tag, are included than in past editions. (See pages 87 and 333.)

More Pointers Well received by both students and instructors in the previous edition, we incorporate more pointers in examples and discussions throughout this edition of the text. They provide students with important on-the-spot reminders and warnings about common pitfalls. (See pages 192 and 281.)

Updated Figures, Photos, and Hand-Drawn Graphs Today's students are more visually oriented than ever. As a result, we have made a concerted effort to include appealing mathematical figures, diagrams, tables, and graphs, including a "hand-drawn" style of graphs, whenever possible. (See pages 188 and 261.) Many of the graphs also use a style similar to that seen by students in today's print and electronic media. We have incorporated new photos to accompany applications in examples and exercises. (See pages 109 and 176.)

Relevant Real-Life Applications We include many new or updated applications from fields such as business, pop culture, sports, technology, and the life sciences that show the relevance of algebra to daily life. (See pages 116 and 541.)

Emphasis on Problem-Solving We introduce our six-step problem-solving method in Chapter 2 and integrate it throughout the text. The six steps, *Read, Assign a Variable, Write an Equation, Solve, State the Answer,* and *Check,* are emphasized in boldface type and repeated in examples and exercises to reinforce the problem-solving process for students. (See pages 108 and 337.) We also provide students with PROBLEM-SOLVING HINT boxes that feature helpful problem-solving tips and strategies. (See pages 139 and 338.)

Connections We include these to give students another avenue for making connections to the real world, graphing technology, or other mathematical concepts, as well as to provide historical background and thought-provoking questions for writing, class discussion, or group work. (See pages 195 and 251.)

Ample and Varied Exercise Sets One of the most commonly mentioned strengths of this text is its exercise sets. We include a wealth of exercises to provide students with opportunities to practice, apply, connect, review, and extend the algebraic concepts and skills they are learning. We also incorporate numerous illustrations, tables, graphs, and photos to help students visualize the problems they are solving. Problem types include writing ✐, graphing calculator ▦, multiple-choice, true/false, matching, and fill-in-the-blank problems, as well as the following:

▶ *Concept Check* exercises facilitate students' mathematical thinking and conceptual understanding. (See pages 96 and 196.)

▶ *WHAT WENT WRONG?* exercises ask students to identify typical errors in solutions and work the problems correctly. (See pages 208 and 335.)

▶ *Brain Busters* exercises challenge students to go beyond the section examples. (See pages 119 and 246.)

▶ *RELATING CONCEPTS* exercises help students tie together topics and develop problem-solving skills as they compare and contrast ideas, identify and describe patterns, and extend concepts to new situations. These exercises make great collaborative activities for pairs or small groups of students. (See pages 209 and 264.)

▶ *TECHNOLOGY INSIGHTS* exercises provide an opportunity for students to interpret typical results seen on graphing calculator screens. Actual screens from the TI-83/84 Plus graphing calculator are featured. (See pages 210 and 336.)

▶ *PREVIEW EXERCISES* allow students to *review* previously-studied concepts and *preview* skills needed for the upcoming section. These make good oral warm-up exercises to open class discussions. (See pages 92 and 199.)

Special Summary Exercises We include a set of these popular in-chapter exercises in selected chapters. They provide students with the all-important ***mixed* review problems** they need to master topics and often include summaries of solution methods and/or additional examples. (See pages 247 and 404.)

Extensive Review Opportunities We conclude each chapter with the following review components:

▶ A **Chapter Summary** that features a helpful list of **Key Terms,** organized by section, **New Symbols, Test Your Word Power** vocabulary quiz (with answers immediately following), and a **Quick Review** of each section's contents, complete with additional examples (See pages 224–226.)

▶ A comprehensive set of **Chapter Review Exercises,** keyed to individual sections for easy student reference, as well as a set of **Mixed Review Exercises** that helps students further synthesize concepts (See pages 227–228.)

▶ A **Chapter Test** that students can take under test conditions to see how well they have mastered the chapter material (See page 229.)

▶ A set of **Cumulative Review Exercises** (beginning in Chapter 2) that covers material going back to Chapter 1 (See page 230.)

Glossary For easy reference at the back of the book, we include a comprehensive glossary featuring key terms and definitions from throughout the text. (See pages G-1 to G-8.)

SUPPLEMENTS

For a comprehensive list of the supplements and study aids that accompany *Beginning and Intermediate Algebra,* Fifth Edition, see pages xix–xxi.

ACKNOWLEDGMENTS

The comments, criticisms, and suggestions of users, nonusers, instructors, and students have positively shaped this textbook over the years, and we are most grateful for the many responses we have received. Thanks to the following people for their review work, feedback, assistance at various meetings, and additional media contributions:

Barbara Aaker, *Community College of Denver*
Viola Lee Bean, *Boise State University*
Kim Bennekin, *Georgia Perimeter College*
Dixie Blackinton, *Weber State University*
Tim Caldwell, *Meridian Community College*
Sally Casey, *Shawnee Community College*
Callie Daniels, *St. Charles Community College*
Cheryl Davids, *Central Carolina Technical College*
Robert Diaz, *Fullerton College*
Chris Diorietes, *Fayetteville Technical Community College*
Sylvia Dreyfus, *Meridian Community College*
Lucy Edwards, *Las Positas College*
Sabine Eggleston, *Edison College*
LaTonya Ellis, *Bishop State Community College*
Jacqui Fields, *Wake Technical Community College*
Beverly Hall, *Fayetteville Technical Community College*
Sandee House, *Georgia Perimeter College*
Lynette King, *Gadsden State Community College*
Linda Kodama, *Windward Community College*
Ted Koukounas, *Suffolk Community College*
Karen McKarnin, *Allen County Community College*
James Metz, *Kapi′olani Community College*
Barbara Meyers, *Cameron University*

Jean Millen, *Georgia Perimeter College*
Molly Misko, *Gadsden State Community College*
Jane Roads, *Moberly Area Community College*
Lisa Scott, *Texas Wesleyan University*
Melanie Smith, *Bishop State Community College*
Linda Smoke, *Central Michigan University*
Erik Stubsten, *Chattanooga State Technical Community College*
Tong Wagner, *Greenville Technical College*
Sessia Wyche, *University of Texas at Brownsville*

Special thanks are due the many instructors at Broward College who provided insightful comments.

Over the years, we have come to rely on an extensive team of experienced professionals. Our sincere thanks go to these dedicated individuals at Addison-Wesley, who worked long and hard to make this revision a success: Chris Hoag, Maureen O'Connor, Michelle Renda, Adam Goldstein, Kari Heen, Courtney Slade, Kathy Manley, Stephanie Green, Lin Mahoney, and Mary St. Thomas.

We are especially grateful to Callie Daniels for her excellent work on the new Now Try Exercises. Abby Tanenbaum did a terrific job helping us revise real-data applications. Kathy Diamond provided expert guidance through all phases of production and rescued us from one snafu or another on multiple occasions. Marilyn Dwyer and Nesbitt Graphics, Inc., provided some of the highest quality production work we have experienced on the challenging format of these books.

Special thanks are due Jeff Cole, who continues to supply accurate, helpful solutions manuals; David Atwood, who wrote the comprehensive *Instructor's Resource Manual with Tests;* Beverly Fusfield, who provided the new MyWorkBook; Beth Anderson, who provided wonderful photo research; and Lucie Haskins, for yet another accurate, useful index. De Cook, Shannon d'Hemecourt, Paul Lorczak, and Sarah Sponholz did a thorough, timely job accuracy checking manuscript and page proofs. It has indeed been a pleasure to work with such an outstanding group of professionals.

As an author team, we are committed to providing the best possible text and supplements package to help instructors teach and students succeed. As we continue to work toward this goal, we would welcome any comments or suggestions you might have via e-mail to math@pearson.com.

Margaret L. Lial
John Hornsby
Terry McGinnis

STUDENT SUPPLEMENTS

Student's Solutions Manual

▶ By Jeffery A. Cole, *Anoka-Ramsey Community College*

▶ Provides detailed solutions to the odd-numbered, section-level exercises and to all Now Try Exercises, Relating Concepts, Summary, Chapter Review, Chapter Test, and Cumulative Review Exercises

ISBNs: 0-321-71565-9, 978-0-321-71565-4

NEW Video Resources on DVD featuring the Lial Video Library

▶ Provides a wealth of video resources to help students navigate the road to success

▶ Available in MyMathLab (with optional subtitles in English)

▶ Includes the following resources:

Section Lecture Videos that offer a new navigation menu for easy focus on key examples and exercises needed for review in each section (with optional subtitles in Spanish and English)

Solutions Clips that feature an instructor working through selected exercises marked in the text with a DVD icon 🌐

Quick Review Lectures that provide a short summary lecture of each key concept from Quick Reviews at the end of every chapter in the text

Chapter Test Prep Videos that include step-by-step solutions to all Chapter Test exercises and give guidance and support when needed most—the night before an exam. Also available on YouTube (searchable using author name and book title)

ISBNs: 0-321-71572-1, 978-0-321-71572-2

NEW MyWorkBook

▶ Provides Guided Examples and corresponding Now Try Exercises for each text objective

▶ Refers students to correlated Examples, Lecture Videos, and Exercise Solution Clips

▶ Includes extra practice exercises for every section of the text with ample space for students to show their work

▶ Lists the learning objectives and key vocabulary terms for every text section, along with vocabulary practice problems

ISBNs: 0-321-71573-X, 978-0-321-71573-9

INSTRUCTOR SUPPLEMENTS

Annotated Instructor's Edition

▶ Provides "on-page" answers to all text exercises in an easy-to-read margin format, along with Teaching Tips and extensive Classroom Examples

▶ Includes icons to identify writing 🖉 and calculator 🖳 exercises. These are in the Student Edition also.

ISBNs: 0-321-71569-1, 978-0-321-71569-2

Instructor's Solutions Manual

▶ By Jeffery A. Cole, *Anoka-Ramsey Community College*

▶ Provides complete solutions to all text exercises, including all Classroom Examples and Now Try Exercises

ISBNs: 0-321-71566-7, 978-0-321-71566-1

Instructor's Resource Manual with Tests

▶ By David Atwood, *Rochester Community and Technical College*

▶ Contains two diagnostic pretests, four free-response and two multiple-choice test forms per chapter, and two final exams

▶ Includes a mini-lecture for each section of the text with objectives, key examples, and teaching tips

▶ Provides a correlation guide from the fourth to the fifth edition

ISBNs: 0-321-71567-5, 978-0-321-71567-8

PowerPoint® Lecture Slides

▶ Present key concepts and definitions from the text

▶ Available for download at www.pearsonhighered.com/irc

ISBNs: 0-321-71571-3, 978-0-321-71571-5

TestGen® (www.pearsonhighered.com/testgen)

▶ Enables instructors to build, edit, print, and administer tests using a computerized bank of questions developed to cover all text objectives

▶ Allows instructors to create multiple but equivalent versions of the same question or test with the click of a button

▶ Allows instructors to modify test bank questions or add new questions

▶ Available for download from Pearson Education's online catalog

ISBNs: 0-321-71568-3, 978-0-321-71568-5

STUDENT SUPPLEMENTS

InterAct Math Tutorial Website
http://www.interactmath.com

▶ Provides practice and tutorial help online

▶ Provides algorithmically generated practice exercises that correlate directly to the exercises in the textbook

▶ Allows students to retry an exercise with new values each time for unlimited practice and mastery

▶ Includes an interactive guided solution for each exercise that gives helpful feedback when an incorrect answer is entered

▶ Enables students to view the steps of a worked-out sample problem similar to the one being worked on

INSTRUCTOR SUPPLEMENTS

Pearson Math Adjunct Support Center

(http://www.pearsontutorservices.com/math-adjunct.html)

▶ Staffed by qualified instructors with more than 50 years of combined experience at both the community college and university levels

Assistance is provided for faculty in the following areas:

▶ Suggested syllabus consultation

▶ Tips on using materials packed with your book

▶ Book-specific content assistance

▶ Teaching suggestions, including advice on classroom strategies

---

Available for Students and Instructors

MyMathLab® Online Course (Access code required.)

MyMathLab® is a text-specific, easily customizable online course that integrates interactive multimedia instruction with textbook content. MyMathLab gives instructors the tools they need to deliver all or a portion of their course online, whether their students are in a lab setting or working from home.

▶ **Interactive homework exercises,** correlated to the textbook at the objective level, are algorithmically generated for unlimited practice and mastery. Most exercises are free-response and provide guided solutions, sample problems, and tutorial learning aids for extra help.

▶ **Personalized homework** assignments can be designed to meet the needs of the class. MyMathLab tailors the assignment for each student based on their test or quiz scores so that each student's homework assignment contains only the problems they still need to master.

▶ **Personalized Study Plan,** generated when students complete a test or quiz or homework, indicates which topics have been mastered and links to tutorial exercises for topics students have not mastered. Instructors can customize the Study Plan so that the topics available match their course content.

▶ **Multimedia learning aids,** such as video lectures and podcasts, animations, and a complete multimedia textbook, help students independently improve their understanding and performance. Instructors can assign these multimedia learning aids as homework to help their students grasp the concepts.

▶ **Homework and Test Manager** lets instructors assign homework, quizzes, and tests that are automatically graded. They can select just the right mix of questions from the MyMathLab exercise bank, instructor-created custom exercises, and/or TestGen® test items.

▶ **Gradebook,** designed specifically for mathematics and statistics, automatically tracks students' results, lets instructors stay on top of student performance, and gives them control over how to calculate final grades. They can also add offline (paper-and-pencil) grades to the gradebook.

- ▶ **MathXL Exercise Builder** allows instructors to create static and algorithmic exercises for their online assignments. They can use the library of sample exercises as an easy starting point, or they can edit any course-related exercise.

- ▶ **Pearson Tutor Center** (www.pearsontutorservices.com) access is automatically included with MyMathLab. The Tutor Center is staffed by qualified math instructors who provide textbook-specific tutoring for students via toll-free phone, fax, email, and interactive Web sessions.

Students do their assignments in the Flash®-based MathXL Player, which is compatible with almost any browser (Firefox®, Safari™, or Internet Explorer®) on almost any platform (Macintosh® or Windows®). MyMathLab is powered by CourseCompass™, Pearson Education's online teaching and learning environment, and by MathXL®, our online homework, tutorial, and assessment system. MyMathLab is available to qualified adopters. For more information, visit our website at www.mymathlab.com or contact your Pearson representative.

MathXL® Online Course (access code required)

MathXL® is an online homework, tutorial, and assessment system that accompanies Pearson's textbooks in mathematics or statistics.

- ▶ **Interactive homework exercises,** correlated to the textbook at the objective level, are algorithmically generated for unlimited practice and mastery. Most exercises are free-response and provide guided solutions, sample problems, and learning aids for extra help.

- ▶ **Personalized homework** assignments are designed by the instructor to meet the needs of the class, and then personalized for each student based on their test or quiz results. As a result, each student receives a homework assignment that contains only the problems they still need to master.

- ▶ **Personalized Study Plan,** generated when students complete a test or quiz or homework, indicates which topics have been mastered and links to tutorial exercises for topics students have not mastered. Instructors can customize the available topics in the study plan to match their course concepts.

- ▶ **Multimedia learning aids,** such as video lectures and animations, help students independently improve their understanding and performance. These are assignable as homework, to further encourage their use.

- ▶ **Gradebook,** designed specifically for mathematics and statistics, automatically tracks students' results, lets instructors stay on top of student performance, and gives them control over how to calculate final grades.

- ▶ **MathXL Exercise Builder** allows instructors to create static and algorithmic exercises for their online assignments. They can use the library of sample exercises as an easy starting point or the Exercise Builder to edit any of the course-related exercises.

- ▶ **Homework and Test Manager** lets instructors create online homework, quizzes, and tests that are automatically graded. They can select just the right mix of questions from the MathXL exercise bank, instructor-created custom exercises, and/or TestGen test items.

The new, Flash®-based MathXL Player is compatible with almost any browser (Firefox®, Safari™, or Internet Explorer®) on almost any platform (Macintosh® or Windows®). MathXL is available to qualified adopters. For more information, visit our website at www.mathxl.com, or contact your Pearson representative.

Using Your Math Textbook

Your textbook is a valuable resource. You will learn more if you fully make use of the features it offers.

General Features

▶ **Table of Contents** Find this at the front of the text. Mark the chapters and sections you will cover, as noted on your course syllabus.

▶ **Answer Section** Tab this section at the back of the book so you can refer to it frequently when doing homework. Answers to odd-numbered section exercises are provided. Answers to ALL summary, chapter review, test, and cumulative review exercises are given.

▶ **Glossary** Find this feature after the answer section at the back of the text. It provides an alphabetical list of the key terms found in the text, with definitions and section references.

▶ **List of Formulas** Inside the back cover of the text is a helpful list of geometric formulas, along with review information on triangles and angles. Use these for reference throughout the course.

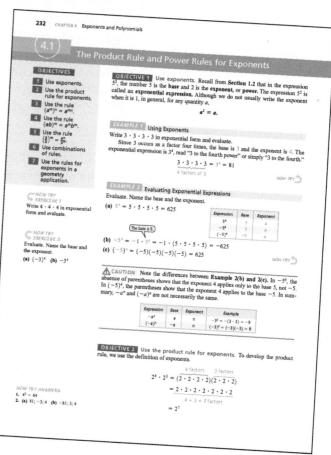

Specific Features

▶ **Objectives** The objectives are listed at the beginning of each section and again within the section as the corresponding material is presented. Once you finish a section, ask yourself if you have accomplished them.

▶ **Now Try Exercises** These margin exercises allow you to immediately practice the material covered in the examples and prepare you for the exercises. Check your results using the answers at the bottom of the page.

▶ **Pointers** These small shaded balloons provide on-the-spot warnings and reminders, point out key steps, and give other helpful tips.

▶ **Cautions** These provide warnings about common errors that students often make or trouble spots to avoid.

▶ **Notes** These provide additional explanations or emphasize important ideas.

▶ **Problem-Solving Hints** These green boxes give helpful tips or strategies to use when you work applications.

Find an example of each of these features in your textbook.

The Real Number System

The personal savings rate of Americans has fluctuated over time. It stood at a hefty 10.8% of after-tax income in 1984, but dropped to −0.5% by 2005 when Americans actually spent more than they earned. This was the first negative savings rate since the Great Depression of the 1930s. In recent years, Americans have spent less and saved more, and personal savings rates have returned to positive territory, reaching 6.9% in May 2009. (*Source:* U.S. Bureau of Economic Analysis.)

In this chapter, we examine *signed numbers* and apply them to situations such as the personal savings rate of Americans in **Exercise 115** of **Section 1.5.**

Fractions

In everyday life, the numbers seen most often are the **natural numbers,**

$$1, 2, 3, 4, \dots,$$

the **whole numbers,**

$$0, 1, 2, 3, 4, \dots,$$

and **fractions,** such as

$$\frac{1}{2}, \quad \frac{2}{3}, \quad \text{and} \quad \frac{15}{7}.$$

The parts of a fraction are named as shown.

$$\text{Fraction bar} \rightarrow \frac{4}{7} \begin{array}{l} \leftarrow \text{Numerator} \\ \leftarrow \text{Denominator} \end{array}$$

The fraction bar represents division $\left(\frac{a}{b} = a \div b\right).$

A fraction is classified as being either a **proper fraction** or an **improper fraction.**

Proper fractions $\dfrac{1}{5}, \dfrac{2}{7}, \dfrac{9}{10}, \dfrac{23}{25}$ Numerator is **less than** denominator. Value is less than 1.

Improper fractions $\dfrac{3}{2}, \dfrac{5}{5}, \dfrac{11}{7}, \dfrac{28}{4}$ Numerator is **greater than or equal to** denominator. Value is greater than or equal to 1.

A **mixed number** is a single number that represents the sum of a natural number and a proper fraction.

$$\text{Mixed number} \rightarrow 5\frac{3}{4} = 5 + \frac{3}{4}$$

OBJECTIVE 1 **Learn the definition of *factor*.** In the statement $3 \times 6 = 18$, the numbers 3 and 6 are called **factors** of 18. Other factors of 18 include 1, 2, 9, and 18. The result of the multiplication, 18, is called the **product.** We can represent the product of two numbers, such as 3 and 6, in several ways.

$$3 \times 6, \quad 3 \cdot 6, \quad (3)(6), \quad (3)6, \quad 3(6) \qquad \text{Products}$$

We *factor* a number by writing it as the product of two or more numbers. Factoring is the reverse of multiplying two numbers to get the product.

Multiplication   Factoring

$$3 \cdot 6 = 18 \qquad\qquad 18 = 3 \cdot 6$$

Factors Product   Product Factors

NOTE In algebra, a raised dot $\cdot$ is often used instead of the $\times$ symbol to indicate multiplication because $\times$ may be confused with the letter x.

A natural number greater than 1 is **prime** if it has only itself and 1 as factors. "Factors" are understood here to mean natural number factors.

$$2, 3, 5, 7, 11, 13, 17, 19, 23, 29, 31, 37 \qquad \text{First dozen prime numbers}$$

A natural number greater than 1 that is not prime is called a **composite number.**

4, 6, 8, 9, 10, 12, 14, 15, 16, 18, 20, 21   First dozen composite numbers

By agreement, the number 1 is neither prime nor composite.

Sometimes we must find all **prime factors** of a number—those factors which are prime numbers.

NOW TRY
EXERCISE 1
Write 60 as the product of prime factors.

EXAMPLE 1 Factoring Numbers

Write each number as the product of prime factors.

(a) 35

Write 35 as the product of the prime factors 5 and 7, or as

$$35 = 5 \cdot 7.$$

(b) 24

We show a factor tree on the right. The prime factors are circled.

Divide by the least prime factor of 24, which is 2.	$24 = 2 \cdot 12$
Divide 12 by 2 to find two factors of 12.	$24 = 2 \cdot 2 \cdot 6$
Now factor 6 as $2 \cdot 3$.	$24 = 2 \cdot 2 \cdot 2 \cdot 3$

All factors are prime.

NOW TRY

NOTE When factoring, we need not start with the least prime factor. No matter which prime factor we start with, we will *always* obtain the same prime factorization. Verify this in **Example 1(b)** by starting with 3 instead of 2.

OBJECTIVE 2 Write fractions in lowest terms. Recall the following **basic principle of fractions,** which is used to write a fraction in *lowest terms.*

Basic Principle of Fractions

If the numerator and denominator of a fraction are multiplied or divided by the same nonzero number, the value of the fraction is not changed.

A fraction is in **lowest terms** when the numerator and denominator have no factors in common (other than 1).

Writing a Fraction in Lowest Terms

Step 1 Write the numerator and the denominator as the product of prime factors.

Step 2 Divide the numerator and the denominator by the **greatest common factor,** the product of all factors common to both.

NOW TRY ANSWER
1. $2 \cdot 2 \cdot 3 \cdot 5$

**NOW TRY
EXERCISE 2**
Write $\frac{30}{42}$ in lowest terms.

EXAMPLE 2 Writing Fractions in Lowest Terms

Write each fraction in lowest terms.

(a) $\frac{10}{15} = \frac{2 \cdot 5}{3 \cdot 5} = \frac{2 \cdot 1}{3 \cdot 1} = \frac{2}{3}$

The factored form shows that 5 is the greatest common factor of 10 and 15. Dividing both numerator and denominator by 5 gives $\frac{10}{15}$ in lowest terms as $\frac{2}{3}$.

(b) $\frac{15}{45}$

By inspection, the greatest common factor of 15 and 45 is 15.

$$\frac{15}{45} = \frac{15}{3 \cdot 15} = \frac{1}{3 \cdot 1} = \frac{1}{3}$$

Remember to write 1 in the numerator.

If the greatest common factor is not obvious, factor the numerator and denominator into prime factors.

$$\frac{15}{45} = \frac{3 \cdot 5}{3 \cdot 3 \cdot 5} = \frac{1 \cdot 1}{3 \cdot 1 \cdot 1} = \frac{1}{3}$$ The same answer results.

NOW TRY

⚠ **CAUTION** When writing fractions like $\frac{15}{45}$ from **Example 2(b)** in lowest terms, be sure to include the factor 1 in the numerator.

OBJECTIVE 3 Multiply and divide fractions.

Multiplying Fractions

If $\frac{a}{b}$ and $\frac{c}{d}$ are fractions, then $\frac{a}{b} \cdot \frac{c}{d} = \frac{a \cdot c}{b \cdot d}$.

That is, to multiply two fractions, multiply their numerators and then multiply their denominators.

EXAMPLE 3 Multiplying Fractions

Find each product, and write it in lowest terms.

(a) $\frac{3}{8} \cdot \frac{4}{9} = \frac{3 \cdot 4}{8 \cdot 9}$ Multiply numerators. Multiply denominators.

$= \frac{3 \cdot 4}{2 \cdot 4 \cdot 3 \cdot 3}$ Factor the denominator.

$= \frac{1}{2 \cdot 3}$ Divide numerator and denominator by 3 · 4, or 12.

Remember to write 1 in the numerator.

$= \frac{1}{6}$ Lowest terms

NOW TRY ANSWER
2. $\frac{5}{7}$

NOW TRY
EXERCISE 3

Find each product, and write it in lowest terms.

(a) $\dfrac{4}{7} \cdot \dfrac{5}{8}$ (b) $3\dfrac{2}{5} \cdot 6\dfrac{2}{3}$

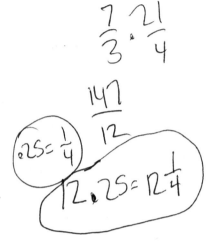

(b)

Think: $4 \cdot 5 = 20$, and $20 + 1 = 21$, so $5\dfrac{1}{4} = \dfrac{21}{4}$.

$$2\dfrac{1}{3} \cdot 5\dfrac{1}{4} = \dfrac{7}{3} \cdot \dfrac{21}{4} \qquad \text{Write each mixed number as an improper fraction.}$$

Think: $3 \cdot 2 = 6$, and $6 + 1 = 7$, so $2\dfrac{1}{3} = \dfrac{7}{3}$.

$$= \dfrac{7 \cdot 21}{3 \cdot 4} \qquad \text{Multiply numerators. Multiply denominators.}$$

$$= \dfrac{7 \cdot 3 \cdot 7}{3 \cdot 4} \qquad \text{Factor the numerator.}$$

Think: $\dfrac{49}{4}$ means $49 \div 4$.

$$\begin{array}{r} 12 \\ 4\overline{)49} \\ 4 \\ \hline 9 \\ 8 \\ \hline 1 \end{array} \quad \text{gives} \quad 12\tfrac{1}{4}.$$

$$= \dfrac{49}{4}, \quad \text{or} \quad 12\dfrac{1}{4} \qquad \text{Write in lowest terms and as a mixed number.}$$

NOW TRY

NOTE Some students prefer to factor and divide out any common factors *before* multiplying.

$$\dfrac{3}{8} \cdot \dfrac{4}{9} = \dfrac{3}{2 \cdot 4} \cdot \dfrac{4}{3 \cdot 3} \qquad \text{Example 3(a)}$$

$$= \dfrac{1}{2 \cdot 3} \qquad \text{Divide out common factors. Multiply.}$$

$$= \dfrac{1}{6} \qquad \text{The same answer results.}$$

Number	Reciprocal
$\frac{3}{4}$	$\frac{4}{3}$
$\frac{11}{7}$	$\frac{7}{11}$
$\frac{1}{5}$	5, or $\frac{5}{1}$
9, or $\frac{9}{1}$	$\frac{1}{9}$

A number and its reciprocal have a product of 1. For example,

$$\tfrac{3}{4} \cdot \tfrac{4}{3} = \tfrac{12}{12} = 1.$$

Two fractions are **reciprocals** of each other if their product is 1. See the table in the margin. Because division is the opposite (or inverse) of multiplication, we use reciprocals to divide fractions.

Dividing Fractions

If $\dfrac{a}{b}$ and $\dfrac{c}{d}$ are fractions, then $\qquad \dfrac{a}{b} \div \dfrac{c}{d} = \dfrac{a}{b} \cdot \dfrac{d}{c}.$

That is, to divide by a fraction, multiply by its reciprocal.

As an example of why this method works, we know that $20 \div 10 = 2$ and also that $20 \cdot \dfrac{1}{10} = 2$. The answer to a division problem is called a **quotient.** For example, the quotient of 20 and 10 is 2.

EXAMPLE 4 Dividing Fractions

Find each quotient, and write it in lowest terms.

(a) $\dfrac{3}{4} \div \dfrac{8}{5} = \dfrac{3}{4} \cdot \dfrac{5}{8} = \dfrac{3 \cdot 5}{4 \cdot 8} = \dfrac{15}{32}$ Make sure the answer is in lowest terms.

Multiply by the reciprocal of the second fraction.

NOW TRY ANSWERS
3. (a) $\frac{5}{14}$ (b) $\frac{68}{3}$, or $22\frac{2}{3}$

(b) $\dfrac{3}{4} \div \dfrac{5}{8} = \dfrac{3}{4} \cdot \dfrac{8}{5} = \dfrac{3 \cdot 8}{4 \cdot 5} = \dfrac{3 \cdot 4 \cdot 2}{4 \cdot 5} = \dfrac{6}{5}, \quad \text{or} \quad 1\dfrac{1}{5}$

NOW TRY
EXERCISE 4

Find each quotient, and write it in lowest terms.

(a) $\dfrac{2}{7} \div \dfrac{8}{9}$ (b) $3\dfrac{3}{4} \div 4\dfrac{2}{7}$

(c) $\dfrac{5}{8} \div 10 = \dfrac{5}{8} \div \dfrac{10}{1} = \dfrac{5}{8} \cdot \dfrac{1}{10} = \dfrac{5 \cdot 1}{8 \cdot 10} = \dfrac{5 \cdot 1}{8 \cdot 5 \cdot 2} = \dfrac{1}{16}$

> Remember to write 1 in the numerator.

Write 10 as $\frac{10}{1}$.

(d) $1\dfrac{2}{3} \div 4\dfrac{1}{2} = \dfrac{5}{3} \div \dfrac{9}{2}$ Write each mixed number as an improper fraction.

$= \dfrac{5}{3} \cdot \dfrac{2}{9}$ Multiply by the reciprocal of the second fraction.

$= \dfrac{10}{27}$ Multiply numerators. Multiply denominators.

NOW TRY

OBJECTIVE 4 **Add and subtract fractions.** The result of adding two numbers is called the **sum** of the numbers. For example, $2 + 3 = 5$, so 5 is the sum of 2 and 3.

Adding Fractions

If $\dfrac{a}{b}$ and $\dfrac{c}{b}$ are fractions, then $\dfrac{a}{b} + \dfrac{c}{b} = \dfrac{a + c}{b}$.

That is, to find the sum of two fractions having the *same* denominator, add the numerators and *keep the same denominator.*

NOW TRY
EXERCISE 5

Find the sum, and write it in lowest terms.

$$\dfrac{1}{8} + \dfrac{3}{8}$$

EXAMPLE 5 **Adding Fractions with the Same Denominator**

Find each sum, and write it in lowest terms.

(a) $\dfrac{3}{7} + \dfrac{2}{7} = \dfrac{3 + 2}{7} = \dfrac{5}{7}$ Add numerators. Keep the same denominator.

(b) $\dfrac{2}{10} + \dfrac{3}{10} = \dfrac{2 + 3}{10} = \dfrac{5}{10} = \dfrac{1}{2}$ Write in lowest terms.   **NOW TRY**

If the fractions to be added do *not* have the same denominators, we must first rewrite them with a common denominator. For example, to rewrite $\frac{3}{4}$ as an equivalent fraction with denominator 32, think,

$$\dfrac{3}{4} = \dfrac{?}{32}.$$

We must find the number that can be multiplied by 4 to give 32. Since $4 \cdot 8 = 32$, we multiply numerator and denominator by 8.

$$\dfrac{3}{4} = \dfrac{3 \cdot 8}{4 \cdot 8} = \dfrac{24}{32}$$ $\frac{3}{4}$ and $\frac{24}{32}$ are equivalent fractions.

Finding the Least Common Denominator

To add or subtract fractions with different denominators, find the **least common denominator (LCD)** as follows.

Step 1 Factor each denominator.

Step 2 For the LCD, use every factor that appears in any factored form. If a factor is repeated, use the largest number of repeats in the LCD.

NOW TRY ANSWERS
4. (a) $\frac{9}{28}$ (b) $\frac{7}{8}$
5. $\frac{1}{2}$

Find each sum, and write it in lowest terms.

(a) $\dfrac{5}{12} + \dfrac{3}{8}$ (b) $3\dfrac{1}{4} + 5\dfrac{5}{8}$

EXAMPLE 6   Adding Fractions with Different Denominators

Find each sum, and write it in lowest terms.

(a) $\dfrac{4}{15} + \dfrac{5}{9}$

To find the least common denominator, first factor both denominators.

$$15 = 5 \cdot 3 \quad \text{and} \quad 9 = 3 \cdot 3$$

Since 5 and 3 appear as factors, and 3 is a factor of 9 twice, the LCD is

$$\overset{15}{\overbrace{}}\ \overset{9}{\overbrace{}}$$
$$5 \cdot 3 \cdot 3, \quad \text{or} \quad 45.$$

Write each fraction with 45 as denominator.

$$\frac{4}{15} = \frac{4 \cdot 3}{15 \cdot 3} = \frac{12}{45} \quad \text{and} \quad \frac{5}{9} = \frac{5 \cdot 5}{9 \cdot 5} = \frac{25}{45}$$

> At this stage, the fractions are *not* in lowest terms.

$$\frac{4}{15} + \frac{5}{9} = \frac{12}{45} + \frac{25}{45} = \frac{37}{45} \quad \text{Add the two equivalent fractions.}$$

(b) $3\dfrac{1}{2} + 2\dfrac{3}{4}$

Method 1 $3\dfrac{1}{2} + 2\dfrac{3}{4} = \dfrac{7}{2} + \dfrac{11}{4}$ Write each mixed number as an improper fraction.

> Think: $\frac{7 \cdot 2}{2 \cdot 2} = \frac{14}{4}$

$$= \frac{14}{4} + \frac{11}{4}$$ Find a common denominator. The LCD is 4.

$$= \frac{25}{4}, \quad \text{or} \quad 6\frac{1}{4}$$ Add. Write as a mixed number.

Method 2 $\begin{aligned} 3\dfrac{1}{2} &= 3\dfrac{2}{4} \\ + 2\dfrac{3}{4} &= 2\dfrac{3}{4} \end{aligned}$ Write $3\frac{1}{2}$ as $3\frac{2}{4}$. Then add vertically. Add the whole numbers and the fractions separately.

$$5\frac{5}{4} = 5 + 1\frac{1}{4} = 6\frac{1}{4}, \quad \text{or} \quad \frac{25}{4}$$ NOW TRY

The **difference** between two numbers is found by subtracting the numbers. For example, $9 - 5 = 4$, so the difference between 9 and 5 is 4.

Subtracting Fractions

If $\dfrac{a}{b}$ and $\dfrac{c}{b}$ are fractions, then $\quad \dfrac{a}{b} - \dfrac{c}{b} = \dfrac{a - c}{b}.$

That is, to find the difference between two fractions having the *same* denominator, subtract the numerators and **keep the same denominator.**

NOW TRY
EXERCISE 7

Find each difference, and write it in lowest terms.

(a) $\dfrac{5}{11} - \dfrac{2}{9}$ **(b)** $4\dfrac{1}{3} - 2\dfrac{5}{6}$

EXAMPLE 7 Subtracting Fractions

Find each difference, and write it in lowest terms.

(a) $\dfrac{15}{8} - \dfrac{3}{8} = \dfrac{15 - 3}{8}$ Subtract numerators.
Keep the same denominator.

$= \dfrac{12}{8}$

$= \dfrac{3}{2},$ or $1\dfrac{1}{2}$ Write in lowest terms and as a mixed number.

(b) $\dfrac{7}{18} - \dfrac{4}{15} = \dfrac{7 \cdot 5}{2 \cdot 3 \cdot 3 \cdot 5} - \dfrac{4 \cdot 2 \cdot 3}{2 \cdot 3 \cdot 3 \cdot 5}$ $18 = 2 \cdot 3 \cdot 3$ and $15 = 3 \cdot 5$, so the LCD is $2 \cdot 3 \cdot 3 \cdot 5 = 90$.

$= \dfrac{35}{90} - \dfrac{24}{90}$ Write the equivalent fractions.

$= \dfrac{11}{90}$ Subtract. The answer is in lowest terms.

(c) $\dfrac{15}{32} - \dfrac{11}{45}$

Since $32 = 2 \cdot 2 \cdot 2 \cdot 2 \cdot 2$ and $45 = 3 \cdot 3 \cdot 5$, there are no common factors. The LCD is $32 \cdot 45 = 1440$.

$\dfrac{15}{32} - \dfrac{11}{45} = \dfrac{15 \cdot 45}{32 \cdot 45} - \dfrac{11 \cdot 32}{45 \cdot 32}$ Find a common denominator.

$= \dfrac{675}{1440} - \dfrac{352}{1440}$ Write the equivalent fractions.

$= \dfrac{323}{1440}$ Subtract numerators. Keep the common denominator.

(d) $4\dfrac{1}{2} - 1\dfrac{3}{4}$

Method 1 $4\dfrac{1}{2} - 1\dfrac{3}{4} = \dfrac{9}{2} - \dfrac{7}{4}$ Write each mixed number as an improper fraction.

$= \dfrac{18}{4} - \dfrac{7}{4}$ Find a common denominator. The LCD is 4.

Think: $\dfrac{9 \cdot 2}{2 \cdot 2} = \dfrac{18}{4}$

$= \dfrac{11}{4},$ or $2\dfrac{3}{4}$ Subtract. Write as a mixed number.

Method 2 $4\dfrac{1}{2} = 4\dfrac{2}{4} = 3\dfrac{6}{4}$ $4\dfrac{2}{4} = 3 + 1 + \dfrac{2}{4} = 3 + \dfrac{4}{4} + \dfrac{2}{4} = 3\dfrac{6}{4}$

$\underline{-1\dfrac{3}{4} = 1\dfrac{3}{4} = 1\dfrac{3}{4}}$

$2\dfrac{3}{4},$ or $\dfrac{11}{4}$

NOW TRY

NOW TRY ANSWERS
7. **(a)** $\dfrac{23}{99}$ **(b)** $\dfrac{3}{2}$, or $1\dfrac{1}{2}$

NOW TRY
EXERCISE 8

A board is $10\frac{1}{2}$ ft long. If it must be divided into four pieces of equal length for shelves, how long must each piece be?

OBJECTIVE 5 Solve applied problems that involve fractions.

EXAMPLE 8 Adding Fractions to Solve an Applied Problem

The diagram in **FIGURE 1** appears in the book *Woodworker's 39 Sure-Fire Projects*. Find the height of the bookcase/desk to the top of the writing surface.

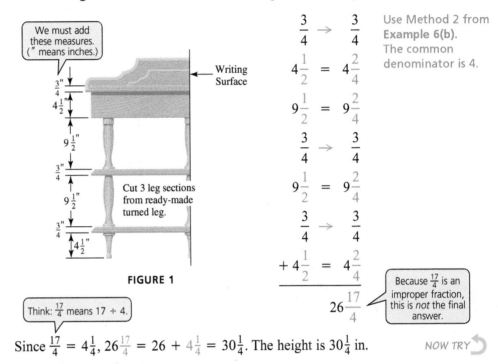

We must add these measures. (" means inches.)

← Writing Surface

Cut 3 leg sections from ready-made turned leg.

FIGURE 1

$$\frac{3}{4} \rightarrow \frac{3}{4}$$
$$4\frac{1}{2} = 4\frac{2}{4}$$
$$9\frac{1}{2} = 9\frac{2}{4}$$
$$\frac{3}{4} \rightarrow \frac{3}{4}$$
$$9\frac{1}{2} = 9\frac{2}{4}$$
$$\frac{3}{4} \rightarrow \frac{3}{4}$$
$$+4\frac{1}{2} = 4\frac{2}{4}$$
$$\overline{\qquad\quad 26\frac{17}{4}}$$

Use Method 2 from Example 6(b). The common denominator is 4.

Because $\frac{17}{4}$ is an improper fraction, this is *not* the final answer.

Think: $\frac{17}{4}$ means $17 \div 4$.

Since $\frac{17}{4} = 4\frac{1}{4}$, $26\frac{17}{4} = 26 + 4\frac{1}{4} = 30\frac{1}{4}$. The height is $30\frac{1}{4}$ in. NOW TRY

OBJECTIVE 6 Interpret data in a circle graph. In a **circle graph,** or **pie chart,** a circle is used to indicate the total of all the data categories represented. The circle is divided into *sectors*, or wedges, whose sizes show the relative magnitudes of the categories. The sum of all the fractional parts must be 1 (for 1 whole circle).

EXAMPLE 9 Using a Circle Graph to Interpret Information

Recently there were about 970 million Internet users worldwide. The circle graph in **FIGURE 2** shows the fractions of these users living in various regions of the world.

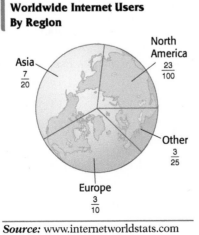

Worldwide Internet Users By Region

Asia $\frac{7}{20}$

North America $\frac{23}{100}$

Other $\frac{3}{25}$

Europe $\frac{3}{10}$

Source: www.internetworldstats.com

FIGURE 2

NOW TRY ANSWER
8. $2\frac{5}{8}$ ft

NOW TRY
EXERCISE 9

Refer to the circle graph in **FIGURE 2** on the preceding page.

(a) Which region had the least number of Internet users?

(b) Estimate the number of Internet users in Asia.

(c) How many actual Internet users were there in Asia?

(a) Which region had the largest share of Internet users? What was that share?

The sector for Asia is the largest, so Asia had the largest share of Internet users, $\frac{7}{20}$.

(b) Estimate the number of Internet users in North America.

A share of $\frac{23}{100}$ can be rounded to $\frac{25}{100}$, or $\frac{1}{4}$, and the total number of Internet users, 970 million, can be rounded to 1000 million (1 billion). We multiply $\frac{1}{4}$ by 1000. The number of Internet users in North America would be about

$$\frac{1}{4}(1000) = 250 \text{ million.}$$

(c) How many actual Internet users were there in North America?

We multiply the actual fraction from the graph for North America, $\frac{23}{100}$, by the number of users, 970 million.

$$\frac{23}{100}(970) = \frac{23}{100} \cdot \frac{970}{1} = \frac{22{,}310}{100} = 223\frac{1}{10} \quad \boxed{\text{This is reasonable, given our estimate in part (b).}}$$

Thus, $223\frac{1}{10}$ million, or 223,100,000 (since $\frac{1}{10}$ million $= \frac{1}{10} \cdot 1{,}000{,}000 = 100{,}000$), people in North America used the Internet.

NOW TRY

NOW TRY ANSWERS
9. **(a)** other
   (b) 333 million $\left(\frac{7}{20} \text{ is about } \frac{1}{3}.\right)$
   (c) $339\frac{1}{2}$ million, or 339,500,000

1.1 EXERCISES

 MyMathLab | Math XL PRACTICE | WATCH | DOWNLOAD | READ | REVIEW

⊕ *Complete solution available on the Video Resources on DVD*

Concept Check Decide whether each statement is true *or* false. *If it is false, say why.*

1. In the fraction $\frac{5}{8}$, 5 is the numerator and 8 is the denominator. T

2. The mixed number equivalent of $\frac{31}{5}$ is $6\frac{1}{5}$.

3. The fraction $\frac{7}{7}$ is proper. F

4. The number 1 is prime.

5. The fraction $\frac{13}{39}$ is in lowest terms. F

6. The reciprocal of $\frac{6}{2}$ is $\frac{3}{1}$.

7. The product of 10 and 2 is 12. F

8. The difference between 10 and 2 is 5.

Identify each number as prime, composite, *or* neither. *If the number is composite, write it as the product of prime factors.* **See Example 1.**

9. 19 P   **10.** 31 P   **11.** 30   **12.** 50

⊕ **13.** 64   **14.** 81   **15.** 1 N   **16.** 0 N

17. 57   **18.** 51   **19.** 79   **20.** 83   **21.** 124

22. 138   **23.** 500   **24.** 700   **25.** 3458   **26.** 1025

Write each fraction in lowest terms. **See Example 2.**

27. $\frac{8}{16}$ **28.** $\frac{4}{12}$ ⊕ **29.** $\frac{15}{18}$ **30.** $\frac{16}{20}$ **31.** $\frac{64}{100}$

32. $\frac{55}{200}$ **33.** $\frac{18}{90}$ **34.** $\frac{16}{64}$ **35.** $\frac{144}{120}$ **36.** $\frac{132}{77}$

37. *Concept Check* Which choice shows the correct way to write $\frac{16}{24}$ in lowest terms?

A. $\frac{16}{24} = \frac{8+8}{8+16} = \frac{8}{16} = \frac{1}{2}$

B. $\frac{16}{24} = \frac{4 \cdot 4}{4 \cdot 6} = \frac{4}{6}$

C. $\frac{16}{24} = \frac{8 \cdot 2}{8 \cdot 3} = \frac{2}{3}$

D. $\frac{16}{24} = \frac{14+2}{21+3} = \frac{2}{3}$

38. *Concept Check* Which fraction is *not* equal to $\frac{5}{9}$?

A. $\frac{15}{27}$ **B.** $\frac{30}{54}$ **C.** $\frac{40}{74}$ **D.** $\frac{55}{99}$

Find each product or quotient, and write it in lowest terms. **See Examples 3 and 4.**

39. $\frac{4}{5} \cdot \frac{6}{7}$ **40.** $\frac{5}{9} \cdot \frac{2}{7}$ **41.** $\frac{2}{3} \cdot \frac{15}{16}$ **42.** $\frac{3}{5} \cdot \frac{20}{21}$

43. $\frac{1}{10} \cdot \frac{12}{5}$ **44.** $\frac{1}{8} \cdot \frac{10}{7}$ **45.** $\frac{15}{4} \cdot \frac{8}{25}$ **46.** $\frac{21}{8} \cdot \frac{4}{7}$

47. $21 \cdot \frac{3}{7}$ **48.** $36 \cdot \frac{4}{9}$ **49.** $3\frac{1}{4} \cdot 1\frac{2}{3}$ **50.** $2\frac{2}{3} \cdot 1\frac{3}{5}$

51. $2\frac{3}{8} \cdot 3\frac{1}{5}$ **52.** $3\frac{3}{5} \cdot 7\frac{1}{6}$ **53.** $\frac{5}{4} \div \frac{3}{8}$ **54.** $\frac{7}{5} \div \frac{3}{10}$

55. $\frac{32}{5} \div \frac{8}{15}$ **56.** $\frac{24}{7} \div \frac{6}{21}$ **57.** $\frac{3}{4} \div 12$ **58.** $\frac{2}{5} \div 30$

59. $6 \div \frac{3}{5}$ **60.** $8 \div \frac{4}{9}$ **61.** $6\frac{3}{4} \div \frac{3}{8}$ **62.** $5\frac{3}{5} \div \frac{7}{10}$

63. $2\frac{1}{2} \div 1\frac{5}{7}$ **64.** $2\frac{2}{9} \div 1\frac{2}{5}$ **65.** $2\frac{5}{8} \div 1\frac{15}{32}$ **66.** $2\frac{3}{10} \div 1\frac{4}{5}$

67. *Concept Check* For the fractions $\frac{p}{q}$ and $\frac{r}{s}$, which one of the following can serve as a common denominator?

A. $q \cdot s$ **B.** $q + s$ **C.** $p \cdot r$ **D.** $p + r$

68. *Concept Check* Write a fraction with denominator 24 that is equivalent to $\frac{5}{8}$.

Find each sum or difference, and write it in lowest terms. **See Examples 5–7.**

69. $\frac{7}{15} + \frac{4}{15}$ **70.** $\frac{2}{9} + \frac{5}{9}$ **71.** $\frac{7}{12} + \frac{1}{12}$ **72.** $\frac{3}{16} + \frac{5}{16}$

73. $\frac{5}{9} + \frac{1}{3}$ **74.** $\frac{4}{15} + \frac{1}{5}$ **75.** $\frac{3}{8} + \frac{5}{6}$ **76.** $\frac{5}{6} + \frac{2}{9}$

77. $3\frac{1}{8} + 2\frac{1}{4}$ **78.** $4\frac{2}{3} + 2\frac{1}{6}$ **79.** $3\frac{1}{4} + 1\frac{4}{5}$ **80.** $5\frac{3}{4} + 1\frac{1}{3}$

81. $\frac{7}{9} - \frac{2}{9}$ **82.** $\frac{8}{11} - \frac{3}{11}$ **83.** $\frac{13}{15} - \frac{3}{15}$ **84.** $\frac{11}{12} - \frac{3}{12}$

85. $\frac{7}{12} - \frac{1}{3}$ **86.** $\frac{5}{6} - \frac{1}{2}$ **87.** $\frac{7}{12} - \frac{1}{9}$ **88.** $\frac{11}{16} - \frac{1}{12}$

89. $4\frac{3}{4} - 1\frac{2}{5}$ **90.** $3\frac{4}{5} - 1\frac{4}{9}$ **91.** $6\frac{1}{4} - 5\frac{1}{3}$ **92.** $5\frac{1}{3} - 4\frac{1}{2}$

Use the table to answer Exercises 93 and 94.

93. How many cups of water would be needed for eight microwave servings?

94. How many teaspoons of salt would be needed for five stove-top servings? (*Hint:* 5 is halfway between 4 and 6.)

	Microwave	Stove Top		
Servings	1	1	4	6
Water	$\frac{3}{4}$ cup	1 cup	3 cups	4 cups
Grits	3 Tbsp	3 Tbsp	$\frac{3}{4}$ cup	1 cup
Salt (optional)	Dash	Dash	$\frac{1}{4}$ tsp	$\frac{1}{2}$ tsp

Source: Package of Quaker Quick Grits.

The Pride Golf Tee Company, the only U.S. manufacturer of wooden golf tees, has created the Professional Tee System, shown in the figure. Use the information given to work Exercises 95 and 96. (Source: The Gazette.)

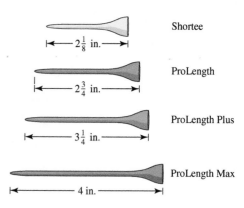

Shortee
$2\frac{1}{8}$ in.

ProLength
$2\frac{3}{4}$ in.

ProLength Plus
$3\frac{1}{4}$ in.

ProLength Max
4 in.

95. Find the difference in length between the ProLength Plus and the once-standard Shortee.

96. The ProLength Max tee is the longest tee allowed by the U.S. Golf Association's *Rules of Golf.* How much longer is the ProLength Max than the Shortee?

Solve each problem. **See Example 8.**

97. A hardware store sells a 40-piece socket wrench set. The measure of the largest socket is $\frac{3}{4}$ in. The measure of the smallest is $\frac{3}{16}$ in. What is the difference between these measures?

98. Two sockets in a socket wrench set have measures of $\frac{9}{16}$ in. and $\frac{3}{8}$ in. What is the difference between these two measures?

99. A piece of property has an irregular shape, with five sides, as shown in the figure. Find the total distance around the piece of property. (This distance is called the **perimeter** of the figure.)

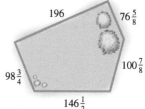

196
$76\frac{5}{8}$
$100\frac{7}{8}$
$98\frac{3}{4}$
$146\frac{1}{2}$

Measurements in feet

100. Find the perimeter of the triangle in the figure.

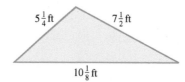

$5\frac{1}{4}$ ft $7\frac{1}{2}$ ft

$10\frac{1}{8}$ ft

101. A board is $15\frac{5}{8}$ in. long. If it must be divided into three pieces of equal length, how long must each piece be?

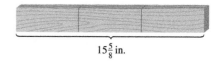

$15\frac{5}{8}$ in.

102. Paul Beaulieu's favorite recipe for barbecue sauce calls for $2\frac{1}{3}$ cups of tomato sauce. The recipe makes enough barbecue sauce to serve seven people. How much tomato sauce is needed for one serving?

103. A cake recipe calls for $1\frac{3}{4}$ cups of sugar. A caterer has $15\frac{1}{2}$ cups of sugar on hand. How many cakes can he make?

104. Kyla Williams needs $2\frac{1}{4}$ yd of fabric to cover a chair. How many chairs can she cover with $23\frac{2}{3}$ yd of fabric?

105. It takes $2\frac{3}{8}$ yd of fabric to make a costume for a school play. How much fabric would be needed for seven costumes?

106. A cookie recipe calls for $2\frac{2}{3}$ cups of sugar. How much sugar would be needed to make four batches of cookies?

107. First published in 1953, the digest-sized *TV Guide* has changed to a full-sized magazine. The full-sized magazine is 3 in. wider than the old guide. What is the difference in their heights? (*Source: TV Guide.*)

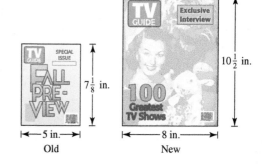

$7\frac{1}{8}$ in.
$10\frac{1}{2}$ in.
5 in.
Old
8 in.
New

108. Under existing standards, most of the holes in Swiss cheese must have diameters between $\frac{11}{16}$ and $\frac{13}{16}$ in. To accommodate new high-speed slicing machines, the U.S. Department of Agriculture wants to reduce the minimum size to $\frac{3}{8}$ in. How much smaller is $\frac{3}{8}$ in. than $\frac{11}{16}$ in.? (*Source: U.S. Department of Agriculture.*)

Approximately 38 million people living in the United States in 2006 were born in other countries. The circle graph gives the fractional number from each region of birth for these people. Use the graph to answer each question. **See Example 9.**

U.S. Foreign-Born Population By Region of Birth

Source: U.S. Census Bureau.

109. What fractional part of the foreign-born population was from other regions?

110. What fractional part of the foreign-born population was from Latin America or Asia?

111. How many people (in millions) were born in Europe?

112. At the conclusion of the Pearson Education softball league season, batting statistics for five players were as follows:

Player	At-Bats	Hits	Home Runs
Courtney Slade	36	12	3
Kari Heen	40	9	2
Adam Goldstein	11	5	1
Nathaniel Koven	16	8	0
Jonathan Wooding	20	10	2

Use the table to answer each question. Estimate as necessary.

(a) Which player got a hit in exactly $\frac{1}{3}$ of his or her at-bats?

(b) Which player got a hit in just less than $\frac{1}{2}$ of his or her at-bats?

(c) Which player got a home run in just less than $\frac{1}{10}$ of his or her at-bats?

(d) Which player got a hit in just less than $\frac{1}{4}$ of his or her at-bats?

(e) Which two players got hits in exactly the same fractional parts of their at-bats? What was the fractional part, expressed in lowest terms?

113. For each description, write a fraction in lowest terms that represents the region described.

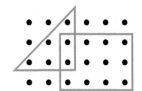

(a) The dots in the rectangle as a part of the dots in the entire figure

(b) The dots in the triangle as a part of the dots in the entire figure

(c) The dots in the overlapping region of the triangle and the rectangle as a part of the dots in the triangle alone

(d) The dots in the overlapping region of the triangle and the rectangle as a part of the dots in the rectangle alone

114. *Concept Check* Estimate the best approximation for the sum.

$$\frac{14}{26} + \frac{98}{99} + \frac{100}{51} + \frac{90}{31} + \frac{13}{27}$$

A. 6 **B.** 7 **C.** 5 **D.** 8

Reading Your Math Textbook

Take time to read each section and its examples before doing your homework. You will learn more and be better prepared to work the exercises your instructor assigns.

Approaches to Reading Your Math Textbook

Student A learns best by listening to her teacher explain things. She "gets it" when she sees the instructor work problems. She previews the section before the lecture, so she knows generally what to expect. **Student A carefully reads the section in her text *AFTER* she hears the classroom lecture on the topic.**

Student B learns best by reading on his own. He reads the section and works through the examples before coming to class. That way, he knows what the teacher is going to talk about and what questions he wants to ask. **Student B carefully reads the section in his text *BEFORE* he hears the classroom lecture on the topic.**

Which reading approach works best for you—that of Student A or Student B?

Tips for Reading Your Math Textbook

▶ **Turn off your cell phone.** You will be able to concentrate more fully on what you are reading.

▶ **Read slowly.** Read only one section—or even part of a section—at a sitting, with paper and pencil in hand.

▶ **Pay special attention to important information given in colored boxes or set in boldface type.**

▶ **Study the examples carefully.** Pay particular attention to the blue side comments and pointers.

▶ **Do the Now Try exercises in the margin on separate paper as you go.** These mirror the examples and prepare you for the exercise set. The answers are given at the bottom of the page.

▶ **Make study cards as you read.** (See **page 48.**) Make cards for new vocabulary, rules, procedures, formulas, and sample problems.

▶ **Mark anything you don't understand. *ASK QUESTIONS*** in class—everyone will benefit. Follow up with your instructor, as needed.

Select several reading tips to try this week.

1.2 Exponents, Order of Operations, and Inequality

NOW TRY
EXERCISE 1

Find the value of each exponential expression.

(a) 6^2 **(b)** $\left(\dfrac{4}{5}\right)^3$

OBJECTIVE 1 **Use exponents.** Consider the prime factored form of 81.

$$81 = 3 \cdot 3 \cdot 3 \cdot 3 \qquad \text{The factor 3 appears four times.}$$

In algebra, repeated factors are written with an *exponent*, so the product $3 \cdot 3 \cdot 3 \cdot 3$ is written as 3^4 and read as "3 to the fourth power."

$$\underbrace{3 \cdot 3 \cdot 3 \cdot 3}_{\text{4 factors of 3}} = 3^4 \quad \overset{\text{Exponent}}{\underset{\text{Base}}{}}$$

The number 4 is the **exponent,** or **power,** and 3 is the **base** in the **exponential expression** 3^4. A natural number exponent, then, tells how many times the base is used as a factor. *A number raised to the first power is simply that number.* For example,

$$5^1 = 5 \quad \text{and} \quad \left(\frac{1}{2}\right)^1 = \frac{1}{2}.$$

EXAMPLE 1 Evaluating Exponential Expressions

Find the value of each exponential expression.

(a) $5^2 = \underline{5 \cdot 5} = 25$

　　　　　 5 is used as a factor 2 times.

Read 5^2 as "5 to the second power" or, more commonly, "5 squared."

(b) $6^3 = \underline{6 \cdot 6 \cdot 6} = 216$

　　　　　 6 is used as a factor 3 times.

Read 6^3 as "6 to the third power" or, more commonly, "6 cubed."

(c) $2^5 = 2 \cdot 2 \cdot 2 \cdot 2 \cdot 2 = 32$ 　　2 is used as a factor 5 times.
Read 2^5 as "2 to the fifth power."

(d) $\left(\dfrac{2}{3}\right)^3 = \dfrac{2}{3} \cdot \dfrac{2}{3} \cdot \dfrac{2}{3} = \dfrac{8}{27}$ 　　$\frac{2}{3}$ is used as a factor 3 times.

(e) $(0.3)^2 = 0.3(0.3) = 0.09$ 　　0.3 is used as a factor 2 times. 　　*NOW TRY*

⚠ **CAUTION** *Squaring, or raising a number to the second power, is NOT the same as doubling the number.* For example,

$$\mathbf{3^2} \quad \textbf{means} \quad \mathbf{3 \cdot 3}, \quad not \quad \mathbf{2 \cdot 3}.$$

Thus $3^2 = 9$, *not* 6. Similarly, cubing, or raising a number to the third power, does *not* mean tripling the number.

OBJECTIVE 2 **Use the rules for order of operations.** When a problem involves more than one operation, we often use **grouping symbols,** such as parentheses ( ), to indicate the order in which the operations should be performed.

Consider the expression $5 + 2 \cdot 3$. To show that the multiplication should be performed before the addition, we use parentheses to group $2 \cdot 3$.

$$5 + (2 \cdot 3) \quad \text{equals} \quad 5 + 6, \quad \text{or} \quad 11.$$

NOW TRY ANSWERS
1. (a) 36 **(b)** $\frac{64}{125}$

If addition is to be performed first, the parentheses should group $5 + 2$.

$$(5 + 2) \cdot 3 \quad \text{equals} \quad 7 \cdot 3, \quad \text{or} \quad 21.$$

Other grouping symbols are brackets $[\ \ ]$, braces $\{\ \ \}$, and fraction bars. (For example, in $\frac{8 - 2}{3}$, the expression $8 - 2$ is "grouped" in the numerator.)

To work problems with more than one operation, we use the following **order of operations.** This order is used by most calculators and computers.

Order of Operations

If grouping symbols are present, simplify within them, innermost first (and above and below fraction bars separately), in the following order.

Step 1   Apply all **exponents.**

Step 2   Do any **multiplications** or **divisions** in the order in which they occur, working from left to right.

Step 3   Do any **additions** or **subtractions** in the order in which they occur, working from left to right.

If no grouping symbols are present, start with Step 1.

NOTE   In expressions such as $3(7)$ or $(-5)(-4)$, multiplication is understood.

EXAMPLE 2   Using the Rules for Order of Operations

Find the value of each expression.

(a) $4 + 5 \cdot 6$ ⟵ Be careful! Multiply first.

$= 4 + 30$ Multiply.

$= 34$ Add.

(b) $9(6 + 11)$

$= 9(17)$ Work inside parentheses.

$= 153$ Multiply.

(c) $6 \cdot 8 + 5 \cdot 2$

$= 48 + 10$ Multiply, working from left to right.

$= 58$ Add.

(d) $2(5 + 6) + 7 \cdot 3$

$= 2(11) + 7 \cdot 3$ Work inside parentheses.

$= 22 + 21$ Multiply.

$= 43$ Add.

$2^3 = 2 \cdot 2 \cdot 2$, not $2 \cdot 3$.

(e) $9 - 2^3 + 5$

$= 9 - 2 \cdot 2 \cdot 2 + 5$ Apply the exponent.

$= 9 - 8 + 5$ Multiply.

$= 1 + 5$ Subtract.

$= 6$ Add.

Write each word statement in symbols. ***See Example 5.***

85. Fifteen is equal to five plus ten.

86. Twelve is equal to twenty minus eight.

87. Nine is greater than five minus four.

88. Ten is greater than six plus one.

89. Sixteen is not equal to nineteen.

90. Three is not equal to four.

91. One-half is less than or equal to two-fourths.

92. One-third is less than or equal to three-ninths.

Write each statement with the inequality symbol reversed while keeping the same meaning. ***See Example 6.***

93. $5 < 20$ **94.** $30 > 9$ **95.** $2.5 \geq 1.3$ **96.** $4.1 \leq 5.3$

One way to measure a person's cardiofitness is to calculate how many METs, or metabolic units, he or she can reach at peak exertion. One MET is the amount of energy used when sitting quietly. To calculate ideal METs, we can use the following expressions.

$$14.7 - \text{age} \cdot 0.13 \quad \text{For women}$$
$$14.7 - \text{age} \cdot 0.11 \quad \text{For men}$$

(*Source: New England Journal of Medicine.*)

97. A 40-yr-old woman wishes to calculate her ideal MET.

(a) Write the expression, using her age.

(b) Calculate her ideal MET. (*Hint:* Use the rules for order of operations.)

(c) Researchers recommend that a person reach approximately 85% of his or her MET when exercising. Calculate 85% of the ideal MET from part (b). Then refer to the following table. What activity can the woman do that is approximately this value?

Activity	METs	Activity	METs
Golf (with cart)	2.5	Skiing (water or downhill)	6.8
Walking (3 mph)	3.3	Swimming	7.0
Mowing lawn (power mower)	4.5	Walking (5 mph)	8.0
Ballroom or square dancing	5.5	Jogging	10.2
Cycling	5.7	Skipping rope	12.0

Source: Harvard School of Public Health.

98. Repeat parts (a)–(c) of **Exercise 97** for a 55-yr-old man.

99. Repeat parts (a)–(c) of **Exercise 97** using your age.

100. The table shows the number of pupils per teacher in U.S. public schools in selected states.

(a) Which states had a figure greater than 13.9?

(b) Which states had a figure that was at most 14.7?

(c) Which states had a figure not less than 13.9?

State	Pupils per Teacher
Alaska	16.7
Texas	14.7
California	20.5
Wyoming	12.5
Maine	12.3
Idaho	17.8
Missouri	13.9

Source: National Center for Education Statistics.

Taking Lecture Notes

Study the set of sample math notes given here.

▶ **Include the date and title** of the day's lecture topic.

▶ **Include definitions,** written here in parentheses—don't trust your memory.

▶ **Skip lines and write neatly** to make reading easier.

▶ **Emphasize direction words** (like *simplify*) with their explanations.

▶ **Mark important concepts with stars, underlining, etc.**

▶ **Use two columns,** which allows an example and its explanation to be close together.

▶ **Use brackets and arrows** to clearly show steps, related material, etc.

With a partner or in a small group, compare lecture notes.

1. What are you doing to show main points in your notes (such as boxing, using stars, etc.)?

2. In what ways do you set off explanations from worked problems and subpoints (such as indenting, using arrows, circling, etc.)?

3. What new ideas did you learn by examining your class-mates' notes?

4. What new techniques will you try in your notes?

January 2

Exponents

Exponents used to show repeated multiplication.

$3 \cdot 3 \cdot 3 \cdot 3$ can be written 3^4 ← exponent (how many times it's multiplied)
base (the number being multiplied)

Read 3^2 as 3 to the 2nd power or 3 squared
3^3 as 3 to the 3rd power or 3 cubed
3^4 as 3 to the 4th power
etc.

Simplifying an expression with exponents
→ actually do the repeated multiplication

2^3 means $2 \cdot 2 \cdot 2$ and $2 \cdot 2 \cdot 2 = 8$

★Careful! 5^2 means $5 \cdot 5$ NOT $5 \cdot 2$
so $5^2 = 5 \cdot 5 = 25$ BUT $5^2 \neq 10$

Example
Simplify $2^4 \cdot 3^2$

$2 \cdot 2 \cdot 2 \cdot 2 \cdot 3 \cdot 3$

16 · 9

144

Explanation
Exponents mean multiplication.

Use 2 as a factor 4 times.
Use 3 as a factor 2 times.
$2 \cdot 2 \cdot 2 \cdot 2$ is 16
$3 \cdot 3$ is 9   } $16 \cdot 9$ is 144

Simplified result is 144 (no exponents left)

1.3 Variables, Expressions, and Equations

OBJECTIVES

1 Evaluate algebraic expressions, given values for the variables.

2 Translate word phrases to algebraic expressions.

3 Identify solutions of equations.

4 Identify solutions of equations from a set of numbers.

5 Distinguish between *expressions* and *equations*.

A **variable** is a symbol, usually a letter such as

$$x, \quad y, \quad \text{or} \quad z, \qquad \text{Variables}$$

used to represent any unknown number. An **algebraic expression** is a sequence of numbers, variables, operation symbols, and/or grouping symbols formed according to the rules of algebra.

$$x + 5, \quad 2m - 9, \quad 8p^2 + 6(p - 2) \qquad \text{Algebraic expressions}$$

$2m$ means $2 \cdot m$, the product of 2 and m.

$6(p - 2)$ means the product of 6 and $p - 2$.

OBJECTIVE 1 Evaluate algebraic expressions, given values for the variables. An algebraic expression has different numerical values for different values of the variables.

NOW TRY
EXERCISE 1
Find the value of each algebraic expression for $k = 6$.

(a) $9k$ **(b)** $4k^2$

EXAMPLE 1   Evaluating Expressions

Find the value of each algebraic expression for $x = 5$.

(a) $8x$

$= 8 \cdot x$

$= 8 \cdot 5$ Let $x = 5$.

$= 40$ Multiply.

(b) $3x^2$

$= 3 \cdot x^2$ $5^2 = 5 \cdot 5$

$= 3 \cdot 5^2$ Let $x = 5$.

$= 3 \cdot 25$ Square 5.

$= 75$ Multiply.   NOW TRY

> ⚠ **CAUTION**   In **Example 1(b)**, $3x^2$ means $3 \cdot x^2$, *not* $3x \cdot 3x$. *Unless parentheses are used, the exponent refers only to the variable or number just before it.* Use parentheses to write $3x \cdot 3x$ with exponents as $(3x)^2$.

NOW TRY
EXERCISE 2
Find the value of each expression for $x = 4$ and $y = 7$.

(a) $3x + 4y$ **(b)** $\dfrac{6x - 2y}{2y - 9}$

(c) $4x^2 - y^2$

EXAMPLE 2   Evaluating Expressions

Find the value of each expression for $x = 5$ and $y = 3$.

(a) $2x + 7y$ We could use parentheses and write $2(5) + 7(3)$.

Follow the rules for order of operations.

$= 2 \cdot 5 + 7 \cdot 3$ Let $x = 5$ and $y = 3$.

$= 10 + 21$ Multiply.

$= 31$ Add.

(b) $\dfrac{9x - 8y}{2x - y}$

$= \dfrac{9 \cdot 5 - 8 \cdot 3}{2 \cdot 5 - 3}$ Let $x = 5$ and $y = 3$.

$= \dfrac{45 - 24}{10 - 3}$ Multiply.

$= \dfrac{21}{7}$, or 3   Subtract, and then divide.

(c) $x^2 - 2y^2$ $3^2 = 3 \cdot 3$

$= 5^2 - 2 \cdot 3^2$ Let $x = 5$ and $y = 3$.

$5^2 = 5 \cdot 5$ $= 25 - 2 \cdot 9$ Apply the exponents.

$= 25 - 18$ Multiply.

$= 7$ Subtract.   NOW TRY

OBJECTIVE 2   Translate word phrases to algebraic expressions.

EXAMPLE 3   Using Variables to Write Word Phrases as Algebraic Expressions

Write each word phrase as an algebraic expression, using x as the variable.

(a) The sum of a number and 9

$x + 9$,   or $9 + x$ "Sum" is the answer to an addition problem.

(b) 7 minus a number

$7 - x$ "Minus" indicates subtraction.

$x - 7$ *is incorrect. We cannot subtract in either order and get the same result.*

NOW TRY ANSWERS
1. (a) 54   **(b)** 144
2. (a) 40   **(b)** 2   **(c)** 15

NOW TRY
EXERCISE 3
Write each word phrase as an algebraic expression, using x as the variable.

(a) The sum of a number and 10

(b) A number divided by 7

(c) The product of 3 and the difference between 9 and a number

(c) A number subtracted from 12

$$12 - x$$ ◁ Be careful with order.

Compare this result with "12 subtracted from a number," which is $x - 12$.

(d) The product of 11 and a number

$$11 \cdot x, \quad \text{or} \quad 11x$$

(e) 5 divided by a number

$$5 \div x, \quad \text{or} \quad \frac{5}{x}$$ ◁ $\frac{x}{5}$ is *not* correct here.

(f) The product of 2 and the difference between a number and 8

We are multiplying 2 times "something." This "something" is the difference between a number and 8, written $x - 8$. We use parentheses around this difference.

$$2 \cdot (x - 8), \quad \text{or} \quad 2(x - 8)$$ ◁ $8 - x$, which means the difference between 8 and a number, is not correct.

NOW TRY ↻

OBJECTIVE 3 **Identify solutions of equations.** An **equation** is a statement that two algebraic expressions are equal. *An equation always includes the equality symbol, =.*

$$x + 4 = 11, \qquad 2y = 16, \qquad 4p + 1 = 25 - p,$$
$$\frac{3}{4}x + \frac{1}{2} = 0, \qquad z^2 = 4, \qquad 4(m - 0.5) = 2m$$

Equations

To **solve** an equation means to find the values of the variable that make the equation true. Such values of the variable are called the **solutions** of the equation.

NOW TRY
EXERCISE 4
Decide whether the given number is a solution of the equation.

$$8k + 5 = 61; \quad 7$$

EXAMPLE 4 Deciding Whether a Number Is a Solution of an Equation

Decide whether the given number is a solution of the equation.

(a) $5p + 1 = 36; \quad 7$

$$5p + 1 = 36$$
$$5 \cdot 7 + 1 \overset{?}{=} 36 \qquad \text{Let } p = 7.$$
$$35 + 1 \overset{?}{=} 36 \qquad \text{Multiply.}$$
$$36 = 36 \checkmark \qquad \text{True—the left side of the equation equals the right side.}$$

Be careful! Multiply first.

The number 7 is a solution of the equation.

(b) $9m - 6 = 32; \quad 4$

$$9m - 6 = 32$$
$$9 \cdot 4 - 6 \overset{?}{=} 32 \qquad \text{Let } m = 4.$$
$$36 - 6 \overset{?}{=} 32 \qquad \text{Multiply.}$$
$$30 = 32 \qquad \text{False—the left side does } not \text{ equal the right side.}$$

The number 4 is not a solution of the equation.

NOW TRY ↻

NOW TRY ANSWERS
3. (a) $x + 10$, or $10 + x$ **(b)** $\frac{x}{7}$
(c) $3(9 - x)$
4. yes

NOW TRY
EXERCISE 1

Use an integer to express the number in boldface italics in the following statement.

At its deepest point, the floor of West Okoboji Lake sits *136* ft below the water's surface. (*Source:* www.watersafetycouncil.org)

EXAMPLE 1   Using Negative Numbers in Applications

Use an integer to express the number in boldface italics in each application.

(a) The lowest Fahrenheit temperature ever recorded was *129°* below zero at Vostok, Antarctica, on July 21, 1983. (*Source: World Almanac and Book of Facts.*)
Use -129 because "below zero" indicates a negative number.

(b) General Motors had a loss of about $*31* billion in 2008. (*Source: The Wall Street Journal.*)
Here, a loss indicates a negative "profit," -31.   NOW TRY

Fractions, introduced in **Section 1.1,** are examples of *rational numbers.*

Rational Numbers

$\{x \mid x$ is a quotient of two integers, with denominator not $0\}$ is the set of **rational numbers.**

(Read the part in the braces as "the set of all numbers x such that x is a quotient of two integers, with denominator not 0.")

NOTE   The set symbolism used in the definition of rational numbers,

$$\{x \mid x \text{ has a certain property}\},$$

is called **set-builder notation.** We use this notation when it is not possible to list all the elements of a set.

Since any number that can be written as the quotient of two integers (that is, as a fraction) is a rational number, **all integers, mixed numbers, terminating (or ending) decimals, and repeating decimals are rational.** The table gives examples.

Rational Number	Equivalent Quotient of Two Integers
-5	$\frac{-5}{1}$ (means $-5 \div 1$)
$1\frac{3}{4}$	$\frac{7}{4}$ (means $7 \div 4$)
0.23 (terminating decimal)	$\frac{23}{100}$ (means $23 \div 100$)
$0.3333\ldots$, or $0.\overline{3}$ (repeating decimal)	$\frac{1}{3}$ (means $1 \div 3$)
4.7	$\frac{47}{10}$ (means $47 \div 10$)

To **graph** a number, we place a dot on the number line at the point that corresponds to the number. The number is called the **coordinate** of the point. See **FIGURE 5.**

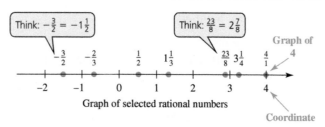

Think of the graph of a set of numbers as a picture of the set.

FIGURE 5

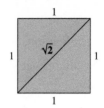

This square has diagonal of length √2. The number √2 is an irrational number.

FIGURE 6

Not all numbers are rational. For example, the square root of 2, written $\sqrt{2}$, cannot be written as a quotient of two integers. Because of this, $\sqrt{2}$ is an *irrational number*. (See **FIGURE 6**.)

Irrational Numbers

$\{x \mid x$ is a nonrational number represented by a point on the number line$\}$ is the set of **irrational numbers.**

The decimal form of an irrational number neither terminates nor repeats.

Both rational and irrational numbers can be represented by points on the number line and together form the set of *real numbers*.

Real Numbers

$\{x \mid x$ is a rational or an irrational number$\}$ is the set of **real numbers.** *

The relationships among the various sets of numbers are shown in **FIGURE 7**.

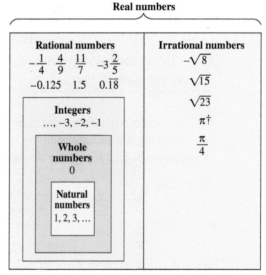

FIGURE 7

EXAMPLE 2 Determining Whether a Number Belongs to a Set

List the numbers in the following set that belong to each set of numbers.

$$\left\{ -5, -\frac{2}{3}, 0, 0.\overline{6}, \sqrt{2}, 3\frac{1}{4}, 5, 5.8 \right\}$$

(a) Natural numbers: 5

(b) Whole numbers: 0 and 5
The whole numbers consist of the natural (counting) numbers and 0.

---

*An example of a number that is not a real number is the square root of a negative number, such as $\sqrt{-5}$.

†The value of π (pi) is approximately 3.141592654. The decimal digits continue forever with no repeated pattern.

NOW TRY
EXERCISE 2

List the numbers in the following set that belong to each set of numbers.

$$\left\{-7, -\tfrac{4}{5}, 0, \sqrt{3}, 2.7, \pi, 13\right\}$$

(a) Whole numbers

(b) Integers

(c) Rational numbers

(d) Irrational numbers

(c) Integers: $-5, 0,$ and 5

(d) Rational numbers: $-5, -\tfrac{2}{3}, 0, 0.\overline{6}\left(\text{or } \tfrac{2}{3}\right), 3\tfrac{1}{4}\left(\text{or } \tfrac{13}{4}\right), 5,$ and $5.8\left(\text{or } \tfrac{58}{10}\right)$
Each of these numbers can be written as the quotient of two integers.

(e) Irrational numbers: $\sqrt{2}$

(f) Real numbers: All the numbers in the set are real numbers.   NOW TRY

OBJECTIVE 2 **Tell which of two real numbers is less than the other.** Given any two positive integers, you probably can tell which number is less than the other. Positive numbers decrease as the corresponding points on the number line go to the left. For example, $8 < 12$ because 8 is to the left of 12 on the number line. This ordering is extended to all real numbers by definition.

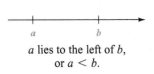

a lies to the left of b,
or $a < b$.

FIGURE 8

Ordering of Real Numbers

For any two real numbers a and b, **a is less than b** if a lies to the left of b on the number line. See **FIGURE 8**.

This means that any negative number is less than 0, and any negative number is less than any positive number. Also, 0 is less than any positive number.

NOW TRY
EXERCISE 3

Determine whether the statement is *true* or *false*.

$$-8 \le -9$$

EXAMPLE 3 **Determining the Order of Real Numbers**

Is the statement $-3 < -1$ *true* or *false*?

Locate -3 and -1 on a number line, as shown in **FIGURE 9**. Since -3 lies to the left of -1 on the number line, -3 is less than -1. The statement $-3 < -1$ is true.

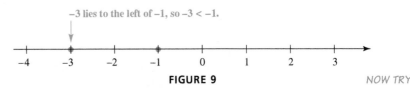

-3 lies to the left of -1, so $-3 < -1$.

FIGURE 9   NOW TRY

We can also say that, for any two real numbers a and b, **a is greater than b** if a lies to the right of b on the number line. See **FIGURE 10**.

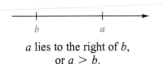

a lies to the right of b,
or $a > b$.

FIGURE 10

OBJECTIVE 3 **Find the additive inverse of a real number.** By a property of the real numbers, for any real number x (except 0), there is exactly one number on the number line the same distance from 0 as x, but on the *opposite* side of 0. See **FIGURE 11**. Such pairs of numbers are called *additive inverses,* or *opposites,* of each other.

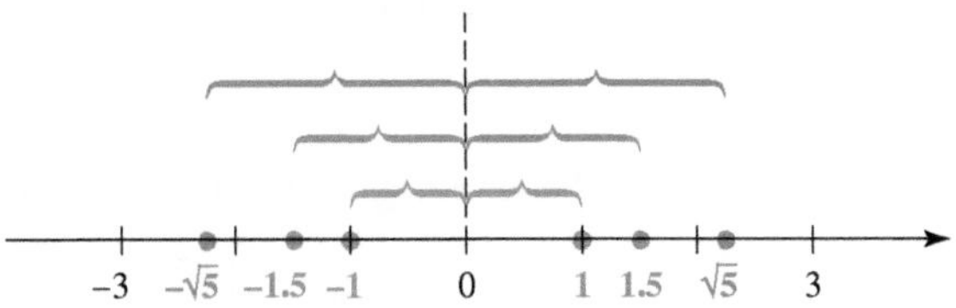

NOW TRY ANSWERS
2. **(a)** 0, 13   **(b)** $-7, 0, 13$
  (c) $-7, -\tfrac{4}{5}, 0, 2.7, 13$
  (d) $\sqrt{3}, \pi$
3. false

Pairs of additive inverses, or opposites

FIGURE 11

Additive Inverse

The **additive inverse** of a number x is the number that is the same distance from 0 on the number line as x, but on the *opposite* side of 0.

We indicate the additive inverse of a number by writing the symbol $-$ in front of the number. For example, the additive inverse of 7 is written -7. We could write the additive inverse of -3 as $-(-3)$, but we know that 3 is the additive inverse of -3. Since a number can have only one additive inverse, 3 and $-(-3)$ must represent the same number, so

$$-(-3) = 3.$$

This idea can be generalized.

Number	Additive Inverse
7	-7
-3	$-(-3)$, or 3
0	0
19	-19
$-\frac{2}{3}$	$\frac{2}{3}$
0.52	-0.52

The additive inverse of a nonzero number is found by changing the sign of the number.

Double Negative Rule

For any real number x, $\qquad -(-x) = x.$

The table in the margin shows several numbers and their additive inverses.

OBJECTIVE 4 **Find the absolute value of a real number.** Because additive inverses are the same distance from 0 on a number line, a number and its additive inverse have the same *absolute value*. The **absolute value** of a real number x, written $|x|$ and read **"the absolute value of x,"** can be defined as the distance between 0 and the number on a number line. For example,

$|2| = 2,$ The distance between 2 and 0 on a number line is 2 units.

$|-2| = 2.$ The distance between -2 and 0 on a number line is also 2 units.

Distance is a physical measurement, which is never negative. ***Therefore, the absolute value of a number is never negative.***

In symbols, the absolute value of x is defined as follows.

Absolute Value

For any real number x,

$$|x| = \begin{cases} x & \text{if } x \geq 0 \\ -x & \text{if } x < 0. \end{cases}$$

By this definition, if x is a positive number or 0, then its absolute value is x itself. For example, since 8 is a positive number,

$$|8| = 8.$$

If x is a negative number, then its absolute value is the additive inverse of x.

$$|-8| = -(-8) = 8 \qquad \text{The additive inverse of } -8 \text{ is 8.}$$

⚠ **CAUTION** The "$-x$" in the second part of the definition of absolute value does *NOT* represent a negative number. Since x is negative in the second part, $-x$ represents the opposite of a negative number—that is, a positive number. ***The absolute value of a number is never negative.***

**NOW TRY
EXERCISE 4**

Simplify by finding the absolute value.

(a) $|4|$ **(b)** $|-4|$ **(c)** $-|-4|$

EXAMPLE 4 Finding the Absolute Value

Simplify by finding the absolute value.

(a) $|0| = 0$ **(b)** $|5| = 5$ **(c)** $|-5| = -(-5) = 5$

(d) $-|5| = -(5) = -5$ **(e)** $-|-5| = -(5) = -5$

(f) $|8 - 2| = |6| = 6$ **(g)** $-|8 - 2| = -|6| = -6$

Parts (f) and (g) show that absolute value bars are grouping symbols. We perform any operations inside absolute value symbols *before* finding the absolute value.

NOW TRY

OBJECTIVE 5 Interpret the meanings of real numbers from a table of data.

**NOW TRY
EXERCISE 5**

In the table for **Example 5,** which category represents a decrease for both years?

EXAMPLE 5 Interpreting Data

The Consumer Price Index (CPI) measures the average change in prices of goods and services purchased by urban consumers in the United States.

The table shows the percent change in the Consumer Price Index for selected categories of goods and services from 2005 to 2006 and from 2006 to 2007. Use the table to answer each question.

Category	Change from 2005 to 2006	Change from 2006 to 2007
Education	6.2	5.7
Food	3.2	2.8
Gasoline	12.9	8.2
Medical care	4.0	4.4
New cars	−0.2	−1.0

Source: U.S. Bureau of Labor Statistics.

(a) What category in which year represents the greatest percent decrease?

We must find the negative number with the greatest absolute value. The number that satisfies this condition is -1.0, so the greatest percent decrease was shown by new cars from 2006 to 2007.

(b) Which category in which year represents the least change?

We must find the number (either positive, negative, or zero) with the least absolute value. From 2005 to 2006, new cars showed the least change, a decrease of 0.2%.

NOW TRY

NOW TRY ANSWERS

4. (a) 4 **(b)** 4 **(c)** −4

5. new cars

1.4 EXERCISES

MyMathLab
Math XL PRACTICE
WATCH
DOWNLOAD
READ
REVIEW

🌐 *Complete solution available on the Video Resources on DVD*

In Exercises 1–4, use an integer to express each number in boldface italics representing a change. In Exercises 5–8, use a rational number. **See Example 1.**

1. Between July 1, 2006, and July 1, 2007, the population of the United States increased by approximately **2,866,000.** (*Source:* U.S. Census Bureau.)

2. Between 2006 and 2007, the number of movie screens in the United States increased by **409.** (*Source:* Motion Picture Association of America.)

3. From 2006 to 2007, attendance at the World Series went from 225,000 to 173,000, a decrease of **52,000.** (*Source:* Major League Baseball.)

4. In 1935, there were 15,295 banks in the United States. By 2008, the number was 8441, representing a decrease of **6854** banks. (*Source:* Federal Deposit Insurance Corporation.)

5. The number of bachelor's degrees in computer and information sciences in the United States declined **11.2**% from the 2005–2006 academic year to the 2006–2007 year, while the number of bachelor's degrees in biological and biomedical sciences rose **8.6**%. (*Source:* National Center for Education Statistics.)

6. Between 2006 and 2007, print advertising revenue in the United States declined **9.4**%, while online advertising rose **18.8**%. (*Source:* Newspaper Association of America.)

7. On Tuesday, August 18, 2009, the Dow Jones Industrial Average (DJIA) closed at 9217.94. On the previous day it had closed at 9135.34. Thus, on Tuesday, it closed up **82.60** points. (*Source: The Washington Post.*)

8. On Monday, August 17, 2009, the NASDAQ closed at 1930.84. On the previous Friday, it had closed at 1985.52. Thus, on Monday, it closed down **54.68** points. (*Source: The Washington Post.*)

Concept Check   In Exercises 9–14, give a number that satisfies the given condition.

9. An integer between 3.6 and 4.6

10. A rational number between 2.8 and 2.9

11. A whole number that is not positive and is less than 1

12. A whole number greater than 3.5

13. An irrational number that is between $\sqrt{12}$ and $\sqrt{14}$

14. A real number that is neither negative nor positive

Concept Check   In Exercises 15–20, decide whether each statement is true *or* false.

15. Every natural number is positive.

16. Every whole number is positive.

17. Every integer is a rational number.

18. Every rational number is a real number.

19. Some numbers are both rational and irrational.

20. Every terminating decimal is a rational number.

Concept Check   Give three numbers between −6 *and* 6 *that satisfy each given condition.*

21. Positive real numbers but not integers

22. Real numbers but not positive numbers

23. Real numbers but not whole numbers

24. Rational numbers but not integers

25. Real numbers but not rational numbers

26. Rational numbers but not negative numbers

For Exercises 27 and 28, **see Example 2.** *List all numbers from each set that are*

(a) *natural numbers*   (b) *whole numbers*   (c) *integers*
(d) *rational numbers*   (e) *irrational numbers*   (f) *real numbers.*

27. $\left\{ -9, -\sqrt{7}, -1\frac{1}{4}, -\frac{3}{5}, 0, 0.\overline{1}, \sqrt{5}, 3, 5.9, 7 \right\}$

28. $\left\{ -5.3, -5, -\sqrt{3}, -1, -\frac{1}{9}, 0, 0.\overline{27}, 1.2, 1.8, 3, \sqrt{11} \right\}$

Graph each group of numbers on a number line. See **FIGURE 4** *and* **FIGURE 5.**

29. $0, 3, -5, -6$ **30.** $2, 6, -2, -1$ **31.** $-2, -6, -4, 3, 4$

32. $-5, -3, -2, 0, 4$ **33.** $\frac{1}{4}, 2\frac{1}{2}, -3\frac{4}{5}, -4, -1\frac{5}{8}$ **34.** $5\frac{1}{4}, 4\frac{5}{9}, -2\frac{1}{3}, 0, -3\frac{2}{5}$

35. *Concept Check*   Match each expression in Column I with its value in Column II. Choices in Column II may be used once, more than once, or not at all.

I	II
(a) $|-9|$	A. 9
(b) $-(-9)$	B. -9
(c) $-|-9|$	C. Neither A nor B
(d) $-|-(-9)|$	D. Both A and B

36. *Concept Check*   Fill in the blanks with the correct values: The opposite of -5 is _____, while the absolute value of -5 is _____. The additive inverse of -5 is _____, while the additive inverse of the absolute value of -5 is _____.

Find (a) *the opposite (or additive inverse) of each number and* (b) *the absolute value of each number. See* **Objective 3** *and* **Example 4.**

37. -7 **38.** -4 **39.** 8 **40.** 10 **41.** $-\frac{3}{4}$ **42.** $-\frac{2}{5}$

Simplify by finding the absolute value. See **Example 4.**

43. $|-6|$ **44.** $|-14|$ **45.** $-|12|$ **46.** $-|19|$

47. $-\left|-\frac{2}{3}\right|$ **48.** $-\left|-\frac{4}{5}\right|$ **49.** $|6-3|$ **50.** $-|6-3|$

51. Students often say "Absolute value is always positive." Is this true? Explain.

52. *Concept Check*   *True* or *false:*   If a is negative, then $|a| = -a$.

Select the lesser of the two given numbers. See **Examples 3 and 4.**

53. $-11, -3$ **54.** $-8, -13$ **55.** $-7, -6$

56. $-16, -17$ **57.** $4, |-5|$ **58.** $4, |-3|$

59. $|-3.5|, |-4.5|$ **60.** $|-8.9|, |-9.8|$ **61.** $-|-6|, -|-4|$

62. $-|-2|, -|-3|$ **63.** $|5-3|, |6-2|$ **64.** $|7-2|, |8-1|$

Decide whether each statement is true *or false. See* **Examples 3 and 4.**

65. $-5 < -2$ **66.** $-8 > -2$ **67.** $-4 \leq -(-5)$

68. $-6 \leq -(-3)$ **69.** $|-6| < |-9|$ **70.** $|-12| < |-20|$

71. $-|8| > |-9|$ **72.** $-|12| > |-15|$ **73.** $-|-5| \geq -|-9|$

74. $-|-12| \leq -|-15|$ **75.** $|6-5| \geq |6-2|$ **76.** $|13-8| \leq |7-4|$

The table shows the percent change in the Consumer Price Index (CPI) for selected categories of goods and services from 2004 to 2005 and from 2006 to 2007. Use the table to answer Exercises 77–80. ***See Example 5.***

77. Which category in which year represents the greatest percentage increase?

78. Which category in which year represents the greatest percentage decrease?

79. Which category in which year represents the least change?

80. Which categories represent a decrease for both years?

Category	Change from 2004 to 2005	Change from 2006 to 2007
Shelter	2.6	3.7
Apparel and upkeep	−0.7	−0.4
Fuel and other utilities	10.6	3.0
Medical care	4.0	4.4
Public transportation	3.9	1.5

Source: U.S. Bureau of Labor Statistics.

STUDY SKILLS

Tackling Your Homework

You are ready to do your homework **AFTER** you have read the corresponding textbook section and worked through the examples and Now Try exercises.

Homework Tips

▶ **Work problems neatly.** Use pencil and write legibly, so others can read your work. Skip lines between steps. Clearly separate problems from each other.

▶ **Show all your work.** It is tempting to take shortcuts. Include ALL steps.

▶ **Check your work frequently to make sure you are on the right track.** It is hard to unlearn a mistake. For all odd-numbered problems, answers are given in the back of the book.

▶ **If you have trouble with a problem, refer to the corresponding worked example in the section.** The exercise directions will often reference specific examples to review. Pay attention to every line of the worked example to see how to get from step to step.

▶ **If you are having trouble with an even-numbered problem, work the corresponding odd-numbered problem.** Check your answer in the back of the book, and apply the same steps to work the even-numbered problem.

▶ **Mark any problems you don't understand.** Ask your instructor about them.

Select several homework tips to try this week.

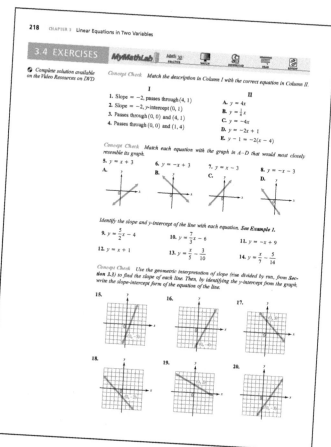

1.5 Adding and Subtracting Real Numbers

OBJECTIVE 1 **Add two numbers with the same sign.** Recall that the answer to an addition problem is called a **sum.** A number line can be used to add real numbers.

EXAMPLE 1 Adding Numbers on a Number Line

Use a number line to find each sum.

(a) $2 + 3$

Step 1 Start at 0 and draw an arrow 2 units to the *right*. See **FIGURE 12**.

Step 2 From the right end of that arrow, draw another arrow 3 units to the right.

The number below the end of this second arrow is 5, so $2 + 3 = 5$.

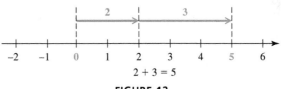

$2 + 3 = 5$

FIGURE 12

**NOW TRY
EXERCISE 1**

Use a number line to find each sum.

(a) $3 + 5$ **(b)** $-1 + (-3)$

(b) $-2 + (-4)$

(We put parentheses around -4 due to the $+$ and $-$ next to each other.)

Step 1 Start at 0 and draw an arrow 2 units to the *left*. See **FIGURE 13**.

Step 2 From the left end of the first arrow, draw a second arrow 4 units to the *left* to represent the addition of a *negative* number.

The number below the end of this second arrow is -6, so $-2 + (-4) = -6$.

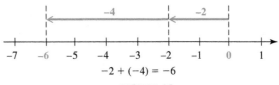

$-2 + (-4) = -6$

FIGURE 13

NOW TRY

In **Example 1(b),** the sum of the two negative numbers -2 and -4 is a negative number whose distance from 0 is the sum of the distance of -2 from 0 and the distance of -4 from 0. *That is, the sum of two negative numbers is the negative of the sum of their absolute values.*

$$-2 + (-4) = -(|-2| + |-4|) = -(2 + 4) = -6$$

NOW TRY ANSWERS

1. (a) 8 **(b)** -4

Adding Numbers with the Same Sign

To add two numbers with the *same* sign, add the absolute values of the numbers. The sum has the same sign as the numbers being added.

Example: $-4 + (-3) = -7$

NOW TRY
EXERCISE 2
Find the sum.

$$-6 + (-11)$$

EXAMPLE 2 Adding Two Negative Numbers

Find each sum.

(a) $-2 + (-9) = -(|-2| + |-9|) = -(2 + 9) = -11$

(b) $-8 + (-12) = -20$ **(c)** $-15 + (-3) = -18$ NOW TRY

OBJECTIVE 2 Add two numbers with different signs.

NOW TRY
EXERCISE 3
Use a number line to find the sum.

$$4 + (-8)$$

EXAMPLE 3 Adding Numbers with Different Signs

Use a number line to find the sum $-2 + 5$.

Step 1 Start at 0 and draw an arrow 2 units to the left. See **FIGURE 14**.

Step 2 From the left end of this arrow, draw a second arrow 5 units to the right.

The number below the end of the second arrow is 3, so $-2 + 5 = 3$.

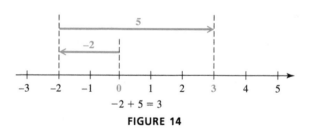

$-2 + 5 = 3$

FIGURE 14   NOW TRY

Adding Numbers with Different Signs

To add two numbers with *different* signs, find the absolute values of the numbers and subtract the lesser absolute value from the greater. Give the answer the same sign as the number having the greater absolute value.

Example: $-12 + 6 = -6$

NOW TRY
EXERCISE 4
Find the sum.

$$8 + (-17)$$

EXAMPLE 4 Adding Numbers with Different Signs

Find the sum $-12 + 5$.

    Find the absolute value of each number.

$$|-12| = 12 \quad \text{and} \quad |5| = 5$$

Then find the difference between these absolute values: $12 - 5 = 7$. The sum will be negative, since $|-12| > |5|$.

NOW TRY ANSWERS
2. -17 3. -4 4. -9

$$-12 + 5 = -7$$ NOW TRY

NOW TRY
EXERCISE 5

Check each answer.

(a) $\dfrac{2}{3} + \left(-2\dfrac{1}{9}\right) = -1\dfrac{4}{9}$

(b) $3.7 + (-5.7) = -2$

EXAMPLE 5   Adding Mentally

Check each answer by adding mentally. If necessary, use a number line.

(a) $7 + (-4) = 3$ **(b)** $-8 + 12 = 4$

(c) $-\dfrac{1}{2} + \dfrac{1}{8} = -\dfrac{4}{8} + \dfrac{1}{8} = -\dfrac{3}{8}$

   Find a common denominator.

(d) $\dfrac{5}{6} + \left(-1\dfrac{1}{3}\right) = \dfrac{5}{6} + \left(-\dfrac{4}{3}\right) = \dfrac{5}{6} + \left(-\dfrac{8}{6}\right) = -\dfrac{3}{6} = -\dfrac{1}{2}$

(e) $-4.6 + 8.1 = 3.5$ **(f)** $-16 + 16 = 0$ **(g)** $42 + (-42) = 0$

Notice in parts (f) and (g) that *when additive inverses are added, the sum is 0.*

NOW TRY

The rules for adding signed numbers are summarized as follows.

Adding Signed Numbers

Same sign   Add the absolute values of the numbers. The sum has the same sign as the given numbers being added.

Different signs   Find the absolute values of the numbers and subtract the lesser absolute value from the greater. Give the answer the same sign as the number having the greater absolute value.

OBJECTIVE 3   **Use the definition of subtraction.** Recall that the answer to a subtraction problem is called a **difference.** In the subtraction $x - y$, x is called the **minuend** and y is called the **subtrahend.**

To illustrate subtracting 4 from 7, written $7 - 4$, with a number line, we begin at 0 and draw an arrow 7 units to the right. See **FIGURE 15**. From the right end of this arrow, we draw an arrow 4 units to the *left*. The number at the end of the second arrow shows that $7 - 4 = 3$.

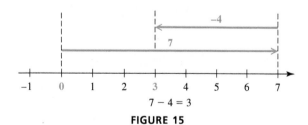

$7 - 4 = 3$

FIGURE 15

The procedure used to find the difference $7 - 4$ is exactly the same procedure that would be used to find the sum $7 + (-4)$, so

$$7 - 4 = 7 + (-4).$$

This equation suggests that *subtracting* a positive number from a greater positive number is the same as *adding* the additive inverse of the lesser number to the greater. This result leads to the definition of subtraction for all real numbers.

NOW TRY ANSWER

5. Both are correct.

Definition of Subtraction

For any real numbers x and y,

$$x - y = x + (-y).$$

To subtract y from x, add the additive inverse (or opposite) of y to x. That is, change the subtrahend to its opposite and add.

Example: $4 - 9 = 4 + (-9) = -5$

NOW TRY
EXERCISE 6

Subtract.

(a) $-5 - (-11)$

(b) $4 - 15$

(c) $-\dfrac{5}{7} - \dfrac{1}{3}$

EXAMPLE 6 Using the Definition of Subtraction

Subtract.

Change $-$ to $+$.

No change ── Additive inverse of 3

(a) $12 - 3 = 12 + (-3) = 9$

(b) $5 - 7 = 5 + (-7) = -2$ **(c)** $-6 - 9 = -6 + (-9) = -15$

Change $-$ to $+$.

No change ── Additive inverse of -5

(d) $-3 - (-5) = -3 + (5) = 2$

(e) $\dfrac{4}{3} - \left(-\dfrac{1}{2}\right) = \dfrac{4}{3} + \dfrac{1}{2} = \dfrac{8}{6} + \dfrac{3}{6} = \dfrac{11}{6}$, or $1\dfrac{5}{6}$

NOW TRY

Uses of the Symbol $-$

We use the symbol $-$ for three purposes:

1. *to represent subtraction,* as in $9 - 5 = 4$;

2. *to represent negative numbers,* such as -10, -2, and -3;

3. *to represent the opposite (or negative) of a number,* as in "the opposite (or negative) of 8 is -8."

We may see more than one use of $-$ in the same expression, such as $-6 - (-9)$, where -9 is subtracted from -6. The meaning of the $-$ symbol depends on its position in the expression.

OBJECTIVE 4 Use the rules for order of operations with real numbers.

EXAMPLE 7 Adding and Subtracting with Grouping Symbols

Perform each indicated operation.

(a) $-6 - [2 - (8 + 3)]$ Start within the innermost parentheses.

$= -6 - [2 - 11]$ Add.

$= -6 - [2 + (-11)]$ Definition of subtraction

$= -6 - [-9]$ Add.

$= -6 + (9)$ Definition of subtraction

$= 3$ Add.

NOW TRY ANSWERS
6. (a) 6 **(b)** -11
(c) $-\frac{22}{21}$, or $-1\frac{1}{21}$

NOW TRY
EXERCISE 7

Perform each indicated operation.

(a) $8 - [(-3 + 7) - (3 - 9)]$

(b) $3|6 - 9| - |4 - 12|$

(b) $5 + [(-3 - 2) - (4 - 1)]$ Work within each set of parentheses inside the brackets.

$= 5 + [(-3 + (-2)) - 3]$

$= 5 + [(-5) - 3]$

$= 5 + [(-5) + (-3)]$ Show all steps to avoid sign errors.

$= 5 + [-8]$

$= -3$

(c) $\dfrac{2}{3} - \left[\dfrac{1}{12} - \left(-\dfrac{1}{4} \right) \right]$

$= \dfrac{8}{12} - \left[\dfrac{1}{12} - \left(-\dfrac{3}{12} \right) \right]$ Find a common denominator.

$= \dfrac{8}{12} - \left[\dfrac{1}{12} + \dfrac{3}{12} \right]$ Definition of subtraction

$= \dfrac{8}{12} - \dfrac{4}{12}$ Add.

$= \dfrac{4}{12}, \ \text{ or } \ \dfrac{1}{3}$ Subtract. Write in lowest terms.

(d) $|4 - 7| + 2|6 - 3|$

$= |-3| + 2|3|$ Work within absolute value bars.

$= 3 + 2 \cdot 3$ Evaluate absolute values.

$= 3 + 6$ Multiply.

Be careful! Multiply first.

$= 9$ Add.   NOW TRY

OBJECTIVE 5 Translate words and phrases involving addition and subtraction. The table lists words and phrases that indicate addition.

Word or Phrase	Example	Numerical Expression and Simplification
Sum of	The *sum of* −3 and 4	−3 + 4, or 1
Added to	5 *added to* −8	−8 + 5, or −3
More than	12 *more than* −5	−5 + 12, or 7
Increased by	−6 *increased by* 13	−6 + 13, or 7
Plus	3 *plus* 14	3 + 14, or 17

NOW TRY
EXERCISE 8

Write a numerical expression for the phrase, and simplify the expression.

The sum of −3 and 7, increased by 10

EXAMPLE 8 Translating Words and Phrases (Addition)

Write a numerical expression for each phrase, and simplify the expression.

(a) The *sum of* −8 and 4 and 6

$-8 + 4 + 6$ simplies to $-4 + 6,$ or $2.$

Add in order from left to right.

(b) 3 *more than* −5, increased by 12

$(-5 + 3) + 12$ simplifies to $-2 + 12,$ or $10.$ NOW TRY

NOW TRY ANSWERS

7. (a) −2 **(b)** 1

8. $(-3 + 7) + 10$; 14

The table lists words and phrases that indicate subtraction in problem solving.

Word, Phrase, or Sentence	Example	Numerical Expression and Simplification
Difference between	The *difference between* −3 and −8	−3 − (−8) simplifies to −3 + 8, or 5
Subtracted from* From..., subtract....	12 *subtracted from* 18 From 12, *subtract* 8.	18 − 12, or 6 12 − 8 simplifies to 12 + (−8), or 4
Less Less than*	6 *less* 5 6 *less than* 5	6 − 5, or 1 5 − 6 simplifies to 5 + (−6), or −1
Decreased by	9 *decreased by* −4	9 − (−4) simplifies to 9 + 4, or 13
Minus	8 *minus* 5	8 − 5, or 3

*Be careful with order when translating.

⚠ CAUTION   When subtracting two numbers, be careful to write them in the correct order, because, in general,

$$x - y \neq y - x.$$

For example, $5 - 3 \neq 3 - 5$. ***Think carefully before interpreting an expression involving subtraction.***

NOW TRY
EXERCISE 9

Write a numerical expression for each phrase, and simplify the expression.

(a) The difference between 5 and −8, decreased by 4

(b) 7 less than −2

EXAMPLE 9   Translating Words and Phrases (Subtraction)

Write a numerical expression for each phrase, and simplify the expression.

(a) The difference between −8 and 5
When "difference between" is used, write the numbers in the order given.*

$$-8 - 5 \quad \text{simplifies to} \quad -8 + (-5), \quad \text{or} \quad -13.$$

(b) 4 subtracted from the sum of 8 and −3
First, add 8 and −3. Next, subtract 4 from this sum.

$$[8 + (-3)] - 4 \quad \text{simplifies to} \quad 5 - 4, \quad \text{or} \quad 1.$$

(c) 4 less than −6
Here, 4 must be taken *from* −6, so write −6 first.

Be careful with order. $-6 - 4$ simplifies to $-6 + (-4)$,   or -10.

Notice that "4 less than −6" differs from "4 *is less than* −6." The second of these is symbolized $4 < -6$ (which is a false statement).

(d) 8, decreased by 5 less than 12
First, write "5 less than 12" as $12 - 5$. Next, subtract $12 - 5$ from 8.

$$8 - (12 - 5) \quad \text{simplifies to} \quad 8 - 7, \quad \text{or} \quad 1. \qquad \text{NOW TRY}$$

NOW TRY ANSWERS
9. (a) [5 − (−8)] − 4; 9
   (b) −2 − 7; −9

*In some cases, people interpret "the difference between" (at least for two positive numbers) to represent the larger minus the smaller. However, we will not do so in this book.

NOW TRY
EXERCISE 10

Find the difference between a gain of 226 yd on the football field by the Chesterfield Bears and a loss of 7 yd by the New London Wildcats.

EXAMPLE 10 Solving a Problem Involving Subtraction

The record-high temperature in the United States is 134°F, recorded at Death Valley, California, in 1913. The record low is −80°F, at Prospect Creek, Alaska, in 1971. See **FIGURE 16**. What is the difference between these highest and lowest temperatures? (*Source: National Climatic Data Center.*)

We must subtract the lowest temperature from the highest temperature.

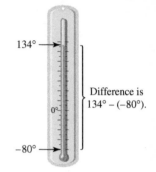

> Order of numbers matters in subtraction.

$$134 - (-80)$$
$$= 134 + 80 \quad \text{Definition of subtraction}$$
$$= 214 \quad \text{Add.}$$

The difference between the two temperatures is 214°F.

134° →
Difference is 134° − (−80°).
0° →
−80° →

FIGURE 16

NOW TRY

OBJECTIVE 6 Use signed numbers to interpret data.

NOW TRY
EXERCISE 11

Refer to **FIGURE 17** and use a signed number to represent the change in the CPI from 2003 to 2004.

EXAMPLE 11 Using a Signed Number to Interpret Data

The bar graph in **FIGURE 17** gives the Consumer Price Index (CPI) for footwear between 2002 and 2007.

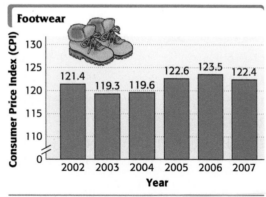

Footwear

Consumer Price Index (CPI)

130 — 121.4 — 119.3 — 119.6 — 122.6 — 123.5 — 122.4

2002 2003 2004 2005 2006 2007
Year

Source: U.S. Bureau of Labor Statistics.
FIGURE 17

(a) Use a signed number to represent the change in the CPI from 2005 to 2006.
Start with the index number for 2006. Subtract from it the index number for 2005.

$$\underbrace{123.5}_{\text{2006 index}} - \underbrace{122.6}_{\text{2005 index}} = \underbrace{+0.9}_{\substack{\text{A positive number} \\ \text{indicates an increase.}}}$$

(b) Use a signed number to represent the change in the CPI from 2006 to 2007.

$$\underbrace{122.4}_{\text{2007 index}} - \underbrace{123.5}_{\text{2006 index}} = 122.4 + (-123.5) = \underbrace{-1.1}_{\substack{\text{A negative number} \\ \text{indicates a decrease.}}}$$

NOW TRY

NOW TRY ANSWERS
10. 233 yd
11. 0.3

1.5 EXERCISES

MyMathLab Math XL PRACTICE WATCH DOWNLOAD READ REVIEW

◉ *Complete solution available on the Video Resources on DVD*

Concept Check Fill in each blank with the correct response.

◉ **1.** The sum of two negative numbers will always be a _____ number.
(positive/negative)

Give a number-line illustration using the sum −2 + (−3).

2. The sum of a number and its opposite will always be _____.

◉ **3.** When adding a positive number and a negative number, where the negative number has the greater absolute value, the sum will be a _____ number. Give
(positive/negative)

a number-line illustration using the sum −4 + 2.

4. To simplify the expression 8 + [−2 + (−3 + 5)], one should begin by adding _____ and _____, according to the rule for order of operations.

5. By the definition of subtraction, in order to perform the subtraction −6 − (−8), we must add the opposite of _____ to _____ to get _____.

6. "The difference between 7 and 12" translates as _____, while "the difference between 12 and 7" translates as _____.

Concept Check In Exercises 7–10, suppose that *x* represents a positive number and *y* represents a negative number. Determine whether the given expression must represent a positive number or a negative number.

7. $x - y$ **8.** $y - x$ **9.** $y - |x|$ **10.** $x + |y|$

Find each sum. **See Examples 1–7.**

◉ **11.** $-6 + (-2)$ **12.** $-9 + (-2)$ **13.** $-5 + (-7)$

14. $-11 + (-5)$ **15.** $6 + (-4)$ **16.** $11 + (-8)$

17. $4 + (-6)$ **18.** $3 + (-7)$ **19.** $-3.5 + 12.4$

20. $-12.5 + 21.3$ **21.** $4 + [13 + (-5)]$ **22.** $6 + [2 + (-13)]$

23. $8 + [-2 + (-1)]$ **24.** $12 + [-3 + (-4)]$ **25.** $-2 + [5 + (-1)]$

26. $-8 + [9 + (-2)]$ **27.** $-6 + [6 + (-9)]$ **28.** $-3 + [3 + (-8)]$

29. $[(-9) + (-3)] + 12$ **30.** $[(-8) + (-6)] + 14$ ◉ **31.** $-\dfrac{1}{6} + \dfrac{2}{3}$

32. $-\dfrac{6}{25} + \dfrac{19}{20}$ **33.** $\dfrac{5}{8} + \left(-\dfrac{17}{12}\right)$ **34.** $\dfrac{9}{10} + \left(-\dfrac{3}{5}\right)$

35. $2\dfrac{1}{2} + \left(-3\dfrac{1}{4}\right)$ **36.** $-4\dfrac{3}{8} + 6\dfrac{1}{2}$

37. $-6.1 + [3.2 + (-4.8)]$ **38.** $-9.4 + [-5.8 + (-1.4)]$

39. $[-3 + (-4)] + [5 + (-6)]$ **40.** $[-8 + (-3)] + [-7 + (-6)]$

41. $[-4 + (-3)] + [8 + (-1)]$ **42.** $[-5 + (-9)] + [16 + (-21)]$

43. $[-4 + (-6)] + [(-3) + (-8)] + [12 + (-11)]$

44. $[-2 + (-11)] + [12 + (-2)] + [18 + (-6)]$

Find each difference. **See Examples 1–7.**

45. $4 - 7$ **46.** $8 - 13$ ◉ **47.** $5 - 9$ **48.** $6 - 11$

49. $-7 - 1$ **50.** $-9 - 4$ **51.** $-8 - 6$ **52.** $-9 - 5$

53. $7 - (-2)$ **54.** $9 - (-2)$ **55.** $-6 - (-2)$ **56.** $-7 - (-5)$

57. $2 - (3 - 5)$

58. $-3 - (4 - 11)$

59. $\dfrac{1}{2} - \left(-\dfrac{1}{4}\right)$

60. $\dfrac{1}{3} - \left(-\dfrac{4}{3}\right)$

61. $-\dfrac{3}{4} - \dfrac{5}{8}$

62. $-\dfrac{5}{6} - \dfrac{1}{2}$

63. $\dfrac{5}{8} - \left(-\dfrac{1}{2} - \dfrac{3}{4}\right)$

64. $\dfrac{9}{10} - \left(\dfrac{1}{8} - \dfrac{3}{10}\right)$

65. $3.4 - (-8.2)$

66. $5.7 - (-11.6)$

67. $-6.4 - 3.5$

68. $-4.4 - 8.6$

*Perform each indicated operation. **See Examples 1–7.***

69. $(4 - 6) + 12$

70. $(3 - 7) + 4$

71. $(8 - 1) - 12$

72. $(9 - 3) - 15$

73. $6 - (-8 + 3)$

74. $8 - (-9 + 5)$

75. $2 + (-4 - 8)$

76. $6 + (-9 - 2)$

77. $|-5 - 6| + |9 + 2|$

78. $|-4 + 8| + |6 - 1|$

79. $|-8 - 2| - |-9 - 3|$

80. $|-4 - 2| - |-8 - 1|$

81. $\left(-\dfrac{3}{4} - \dfrac{5}{2}\right) - \left(-\dfrac{1}{8} - 1\right)$

82. $\left(-\dfrac{3}{8} - \dfrac{2}{3}\right) - \left(-\dfrac{9}{8} - 3\right)$

83. $\left(-\dfrac{1}{2} + 0.25\right) - \left(-\dfrac{3}{4} + 0.75\right)$

84. $\left(-\dfrac{3}{2} - 0.75\right) - \left(0.5 - \dfrac{1}{2}\right)$

85. $-9 + [(3 - 2) - (-4 + 2)]$

86. $-8 - [(-4 - 1) + (9 - 2)]$

87. $-3 + [(-5 - 8) - (-6 + 2)]$

88. $-4 + [(-12 + 1) - (-1 - 9)]$

89. $-9.1237 + [(-4.8099 - 3.2516) + 11.27903]$

90. $-7.6247 - [(-3.9928 + 1.42773) - (-2.80981)]$

*Write a numerical expression for each phrase and simplify. **See Examples 8 and 9.***

91. The sum of -5 and 12 and 6

92. The sum of -3 and 5 and -12

93. 14 added to the sum of -19 and -4

94. -2 added to the sum of -18 and 11

95. The sum of -4 and -10, increased by 12

96. The sum of -7 and -13, increased by 14

97. $\dfrac{2}{7}$ more than the sum of $\dfrac{5}{7}$ and $-\dfrac{9}{7}$

98. 1.85 more than the sum of -1.25 and -4.75

99. The difference between 4 and -8

100. The difference between 7 and -14

101. 8 less than -2

102. 9 less than -13

103. The sum of 9 and -4, decreased by 7

104. The sum of 12 and -7, decreased by 14

105. 12 less than the difference between 8 and -5

106. 19 less than the difference between 9 and -2

*Solve each problem. **See Example 10.***

107. Based on 2020 population projections, New York will lose 5 seats in the U.S. House of Representatives, Pennsylvania will lose 4 seats, and Ohio will lose 3. Write a signed number that represents the total number of seats these three states are projected to lose. (*Source:* Population Reference Bureau.)

108. Michigan is projected to lose 3 seats in the U.S. House of Representatives and Illinois 2 in 2020. The states projected to gain the most seats are California with 9, Texas with 5, Florida with 3, Georgia with 2, and Arizona with 2. Write a signed number that represents the algebraic sum of these changes. (*Source:* Population Reference Bureau.)

109. The largest change in temperature ever recorded within a 24-hr period occurred in Montana, on January 23–24, 1916. The temperature fell 100°F from a starting temperature of 44°F. What was the low temperature during this period? (*Source: Guinness World Records.*)

110. The lowest temperature ever recorded in Tennessee was −32°F. The highest temperature ever recorded there was 145°F more than the lowest. What was this highest temperature? (*Source:* National Climatic Data Center.)

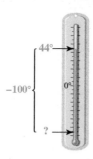

111. The lowest temperature ever recorded in Illinois was −36°F on January 5, 1999. The lowest temperature ever recorded in Utah was on February 1, 1985, and was 33°F lower than Illinois's record low. What is the record low temperature for Utah? (*Source:* National Climatic Data Center.)

112. The top of Mt. Whitney, visible from Death Valley, has an altitude of 14,494 ft above sea level. The bottom of Death Valley is 282 ft below sea level. Using 0 as sea level, find the difference between these two elevations. (*Source: World Almanac and Book of Facts.*)

113. The surface, or rim, of a canyon is at altitude 0. On a hike down into the canyon, a party of hikers stops for a rest at 130 m below the surface. The hikers then descend another 54 m. Write the new altitude as a signed number.

114. A pilot announces to the passengers that the current altitude of their plane is 34,000 ft. Because of turbulence, the pilot is forced to descend 2100 ft. Write the new altitude as a signed number.

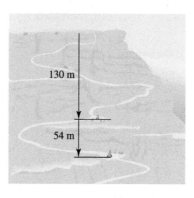

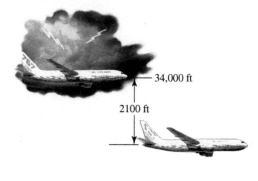

115. In 2005, Americans saved −0.5% of their after-tax incomes. In May 2009, they saved 6.9%. (*Source:* U.S. Bureau of Economic Analysis.)

  (a) Find the difference between the 2009 and the 2005 amounts.

  (b) How could Americans have a negative personal savings rate in 2005?

116. In 2000, the U.S. federal budget had a surplus of $236 billion. In 2008, the federal budget had a deficit of $455 billion. Find the difference between the 2008 and the 2000 amounts. (*Source:* U.S. Treasury Department.)

117. In 1998, undergraduate college students had an average (mean) credit card balance of $1879. The average balance increased $869 by 2000, then dropped $579 by 2004, and then increased $1004 by 2008. What was the average credit card balance of undergraduate college students in 2008? (*Source:* Sallie Mae.)

118. Among entertainment expenditures, the average annual spending per U.S. household on fees and admissions was $526 in 2001. This amount decreased $32 by 2003 and then increased $112 by 2006. What was the average household expenditure for fees and admissions in 2006? (*Source:* U.S. Bureau of Labor Statistics.)

119. Nadine Blackwood enjoys playing Triominoes every Wednesday night. Last Wednesday, on four successive turns, her scores were −19, 28, −5, and 13. What was her final score for the four turns?

120. Bruce Buit also enjoys playing Triominoes. On five successive turns, his scores were −13, 15, −12, 24, and 14. What was his total score for the five turns?

121. In August, Susan Goodman began with a checking account balance of $904.89. Her checks and deposits for August are as follows:

Checks	Deposits
$35.84	$85.00
$26.14	$120.76
$3.12	

Assuming no other transactions, what was her account balance at the end of August?

122. In September, Jeffery Cooper began with a checking account balance of $904.89. His checks and deposits for September are as follows:

Checks	Deposits
$41.29	$80.59
$13.66	$276.13
$84.40	

Assuming no other transactions, what was his account balance at the end of September?

123. Linda Des Jardines owes $870.00 on her MasterCard account. She returns two items costing $35.90 and $150.00 and receives credit for these on the account. Next, she makes a purchase of $82.50 and then two more purchases of $10.00 each. She makes a payment of $500.00. She then incurs a finance charge of $37.23. How much does she still owe?

124. Marcial Echenique owes $679.00 on his Visa account. He returns three items costing $36.89, $29.40, and $113.55 and receives credit for these on the account. Next, he makes purchases of $135.78 and $412.88 and two purchases of $20.00 each. He makes a payment of $400. He then incurs a finance charge of $24.57. How much does he still owe?

The bar graph shows federal budget outlays for the U.S. Department of Homeland Security for the years 2005 through 2008. In Exercises 125–128, use a signed number to represent the change in outlay for each period. ***See Example 11.***

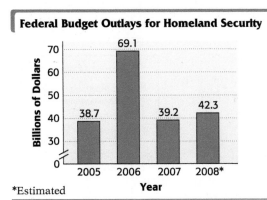

Federal Budget Outlays for Homeland Security

*Estimated

Year

Source: U.S. Department of Management and Budget.

125. 2005 to 2006

126. 2006 to 2007

127. 2007 to 2008

128. 2005 to 2008

The two tables show the heights of some selected mountains and the depths of some selected trenches. Use the information given to answer Exercises 129–134.

Mountain	Height (in feet)
Foraker	17,400
Wilson	14,246
Pikes Peak	14,110

Trench	Depth (in feet, as a negative number)
Philippine	−32,995
Cayman	−24,721
Java	−23,376

Source: World Almanac and Book of Facts.

129. What is the difference between the height of Mt. Foraker and the depth of the Philippine Trench?

130. What is the difference between the height of Pikes Peak and the depth of the Java Trench?

131. How much deeper is the Cayman Trench than the Java Trench?

132. How much deeper is the Philippine Trench than the Cayman Trench?

133. How much higher is Mt. Wilson than Pikes Peak?

134. If Mt. Wilson and Pikes Peak were stacked one on top of the other, how much higher would they be than Mt. Foraker?

STUDY SKILLS

Using Study Cards

You may have used "flash cards" in other classes. In math, "study cards" can help you remember terms and definitions, procedures, and concepts. Use study cards to

▶ Quickly review when you have a few minutes;

▶ Review before a quiz or test.

One of the advantages of study cards is that you learn while you are making them.

Vocabulary Cards

Put the word and a page reference on the front of the card. On the back, write the definition, an example, any related words, and a sample problem (if appropriate).

Procedure ("Steps") Cards

Write the name of the procedure on the front of the card. Then write each step in words. On the back of the card, put an example showing each step.

Make a vocabulary card and a procedure card for material you are learning now.

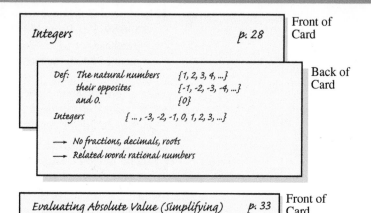

Front of Card

Back of Card

Front of Card

Back of Card

1.6 Multiplying and Dividing Real Numbers

OBJECTIVES

1 Find the product of a positive number and a negative number.

2 Find the product of two negative numbers.

3 Identify factors of integers.

4 Use the reciprocal of a number to apply the definition of division.

5 Use the rules for order of operations when multiplying and dividing signed numbers.

6 Evaluate expressions involving variables.

7 Translate words and phrases involving multiplication and division.

8 Translate simple sentences into equations.

The result of multiplication is called the **product.** We know that the product of two positive numbers is positive. We also know that the product of 0 and any positive number is 0, so we extend that property to all real numbers.

Multiplication by Zero

For any real number x, $x \cdot 0 = 0.$

OBJECTIVE 1 Find the product of a positive number and a negative number. Look at the following pattern.

$$3 \cdot 5 = 15$$
$$3 \cdot 4 = 12$$
$$3 \cdot 3 = 9$$
$$3 \cdot 2 = 6 \quad \text{The products decrease by 3.}$$
$$3 \cdot 1 = 3$$
$$3 \cdot 0 = 0$$
$$3 \cdot (-1) = ?$$

What should $3(-1)$ equal? The product $3(-1)$ represents the sum

$$-1 + (-1) + (-1) = -3,$$

so the product should be -3. Also,

$$3(-2) = -2 + (-2) + (-2) = -6$$

and $\qquad\qquad 3(-3) = -3 + (-3) + (-3) = -9.$

These results maintain the pattern in the list, which suggests the following rule.

Multiplying Numbers with Different Signs

For any positive real numbers x and y,

$$x(-y) = -(xy) \qquad \text{and} \qquad (-x)y = -(xy).$$

That is, the product of two numbers with opposite signs is negative.

Examples: $6(-3) = -18$ and $(-6)3 = -18$

NOW TRY EXERCISE 1

Find each product.

(a) $-11(9)$ **(b)** $3.1(-2.5)$

EXAMPLE 1 Multiplying a Positive Number and a Negative Number

Find each product, using the multiplication rule given in the box.

(a) $8(-5) = -(8 \cdot 5) = -40$ **(b)** $(-5)4 = -(5 \cdot 4) = -20$

(c) $-9\left(\dfrac{1}{3}\right) = -\left(9 \cdot \dfrac{1}{3}\right) = -3$ **(d)** $6.2(-4.1) = -(6.2 \cdot 4.1) = -25.42$

NOW TRY

NOW TRY ANSWERS

1. (a) -99 **(b)** -7.75

OBJECTIVE 2 Find the product of two negative numbers. Look at another pattern.

$$-5(4) = -20$$
$$-5(3) = -15$$
$$-5(2) = -10$$ The products increase by 5.
$$-5(1) = -5$$
$$-5(0) = 0$$
$$-5(-1) = ?$$

The numbers in color on the left of the equals symbol decrease by 1 for each step down the list. The products on the right increase by 5 for each step down the list. To maintain this pattern, $-5(-1)$ should be 5 more than $-5(0)$, or 5 more than 0, so

$$-5(-1) = 5.$$

The pattern continues with

$$-5(-2) = 10$$
$$-5(-3) = 15$$
$$-5(-4) = 20$$
$$-5(-5) = 25,$$

and so on, which suggests the next rule.

Multiplying Two Negative Numbers

For any positive real numbers x and y,

$$-x(-y) = xy.$$

That is, the product of two negative numbers is positive.

Example: $-5(-4) = 20$

EXAMPLE 2 Multiplying Two Negative Numbers

Find each product, using the multiplication rule given in the box.

(a) $-9(-2) = 9 \cdot 2 = 18$ **(b)** $-6(-12) = 6 \cdot 12 = 72$

(c) $-8(-1) = 8 \cdot 1 = 8$ **(d)** $-\dfrac{2}{3}\left(-\dfrac{3}{2}\right) = \dfrac{2}{3} \cdot \dfrac{3}{2} = 1$ NOW TRY

The following box summarizes multiplying signed numbers.

Multiplying Signed Numbers

The product of two numbers having the *same* sign is *positive*.

The product of two numbers having *different* signs is *negative*.

OBJECTIVE 3 Identify factors of integers. The definition of **factor** from **Section 1.1** can be extended to integers. If the product of two integers is a third integer, then each of the two integers is a *factor* of the third. The table on the next page shows examples.

NOW TRY
EXERCISE 2
Find the product.

$$-\dfrac{1}{7}\left(-\dfrac{5}{2}\right)$$

NOW TRY ANSWER

2. $\dfrac{5}{14}$

Integer	18	20	15	7	1
Pairs of factors	1, 18	1, 20	1, 15	1, 7	1, 1
	2, 9	2, 10	3, 5	−1, −7	−1, −1
	3, 6	4, 5	−1, −15		
	−1, −18	−1, −20	−3, −5		
	−2, −9	−2, −10			
	−3, −6	−4, −5			

Number	Multiplicative Inverse (Reciprocal)
4	$\frac{1}{4}$
0.3, or $\frac{3}{10}$	$\frac{10}{3}$
−5	$\frac{1}{-5}$, or $-\frac{1}{5}$
$-\frac{5}{8}$	$-\frac{8}{5}$

A number and its multiplicative inverse have a product of **1.** For example,

$$4 \cdot \tfrac{1}{4} = \tfrac{4}{4} = 1.$$

OBJECTIVE 4 **Use the reciprocal of a number to apply the definition of division.** Recall that the result of division is called the **quotient.** The quotient of two numbers is found by multiplying by the *reciprocal,* or *multiplicative inverse,* of the second number.

Reciprocal or Multiplicative Inverse

Pairs of numbers whose product is 1 are called **reciprocals,** or **multiplicative inverses,** of each other.

The table in the margin shows several numbers and their multiplicative inverses.

Definition of Division

For any real numbers x and y, with $y \neq 0$, $\dfrac{x}{y} = x \cdot \dfrac{1}{y}.$

That is, to divide two numbers, multiply the first by the reciprocal, or multiplicative inverse, of the second.

Example: $\dfrac{-8}{4} = -8 \cdot \dfrac{1}{4} = 2$

NOTE Recall that an equivalent form of $\frac{x}{y}$ is $x \div y$, where x is called the **dividend** and y is called the **divisor.** For example, $\frac{-8}{4} = -8 \div 4.$

Since division is defined in terms of multiplication, all the rules for multiplying signed numbers also apply to dividing them.

NOW TRY EXERCISE 3
Find each quotient, using the definition of division.

(a) $\dfrac{15}{-3}$ (b) $\dfrac{9.81}{-0.9}$

(c) $-\dfrac{5}{6} \div \dfrac{17}{9}$

EXAMPLE 3 Using the Definition of Division

Find each quotient, using the definition of division.

(a) $\dfrac{12}{3} = 12 \cdot \dfrac{1}{3} = 4$ $\frac{x}{y} = x \cdot \frac{1}{y}$ (b) $\dfrac{-10}{2} = -10 \cdot \dfrac{1}{2} = -5$

> Remember to write in lowest terms.

(c) $\dfrac{-1.47}{-7} = -1.47\left(-\dfrac{1}{7}\right) = 0.21$ (d) $-\dfrac{2}{3} \div \left(-\dfrac{4}{5}\right) = -\dfrac{2}{3} \cdot \left(-\dfrac{5}{4}\right) = \dfrac{5}{6}$

NOW TRY ANSWERS
3. **(a)** −5 **(b)** −10.9 **(c)** $-\frac{15}{34}$

NOW TRY

We can use multiplication to check a division problem. Consider **Example 3(a).**

$$\frac{12}{3} = 4, \quad \text{since} \quad 4 \cdot 3 = 12.$$

[Multiply to check a division problem.]

This relationship between multiplication and division allows us to investigate division by 0. Consider the quotient $\frac{0}{3}$.

$$\frac{0}{3} = 0, \quad \text{since} \quad 0 \cdot 3 = 0.$$

Now consider $\frac{3}{0}$.

$$\frac{3}{0} = ?$$

We need to find a number that when multiplied by 0 will equal 3, that is, $? \cdot 0 = 3$. *No* real number satisfies this equation, since the product of any real number and 0 must be 0. Thus,

$\frac{x}{0}$ **is not a number, and** *division by 0 is undefined.* **If a division problem involves division by 0, write "undefined."**

Division Involving 0

For any real number x, with $x \neq 0$,

$$\frac{0}{x} = 0 \quad \text{and} \quad \frac{x}{0} \text{ is undefined.}$$

Examples: $\quad \dfrac{0}{-10} = 0 \quad \text{and} \quad \dfrac{-10}{0} \text{ is undefined.}$

When dividing fractions, multiplying by the reciprocal works well. However, using the definition of division directly with integers may be awkward. It is easier to divide in the usual way and then determine the sign of the answer.

Dividing Signed Numbers

The quotient of two numbers having the *same* sign is *positive*.

The quotient of two numbers having *different* signs is *negative*.

Examples: $\quad \dfrac{15}{5} = 3, \quad \dfrac{-15}{-5} = 3, \quad \dfrac{15}{-5} = -3, \quad \text{and} \quad \dfrac{-15}{5} = -3$

NOW TRY EXERCISE 4

Find each quotient.

(a) $\dfrac{-10}{5}$ (b) $\dfrac{-1.44}{-0.12}$

(c) $-\dfrac{3}{8} \div \dfrac{7}{10}$

EXAMPLE 4 Dividing Signed Numbers

Find each quotient.

(a) $\dfrac{8}{-2} = -4$ (b) $\dfrac{-100}{5} = -20$ (c) $\dfrac{-4.5}{-0.09} = 50$

(d) $-\dfrac{1}{8} \div \left(-\dfrac{3}{4}\right) = -\dfrac{1}{8} \cdot \left(-\dfrac{4}{3}\right) = \dfrac{1}{6}$ [Remember to write in lowest terms.]

NOW TRY ANSWERS

4. (a) -2 (b) 12 (c) $-\frac{15}{28}$

NOW TRY

From the definitions of multiplication and division of real numbers,

$$\frac{-40}{8} = -40 \cdot \frac{1}{8} = -5 \quad \text{and} \quad \frac{40}{-8} = 40\left(\frac{1}{-8}\right) = -5, \quad \text{so} \quad \frac{-40}{8} = \frac{40}{-8}.$$

Based on this example, the quotient of a positive and a negative number can be expressed in any of the following three forms.

Equivalent Forms

For any positive real numbers x and y, $\dfrac{-x}{y} = \dfrac{x}{-y} = -\dfrac{x}{y}.$

Similarly, the quotient of two negative numbers can be expressed as a quotient of two positive numbers.

Equivalent Forms

For any positive real numbers x and y, $\dfrac{-x}{-y} = \dfrac{x}{y}.$

OBJECTIVE 5 Use the rules for order of operations when multiplying and dividing signed numbers.

∩ NOW TRY
  EXERCISE 5

Perform each indicated operation.

(a) $-4(6) - (-5)(5)$

(b) $\dfrac{12(-4) - 6(-3)}{-4(7 - 16)}$

EXAMPLE 5 Using the Rules for Order of Operations

Perform each indicated operation.

(a) $-9(2) - (-3)(2)$

$\quad = -18 - (-6)$ Multiply.

$\quad = -18 + 6$ Definition of subtraction

$\quad = -12$ Add.

(b) $-5(-2 - 3)$

$\quad = -5(-5)$ Work inside the parentheses.

$\quad = 25$ Multiply.

(c) $-6 + 2(3 - 5)$ ◀ Begin inside the parentheses.

Do *not* add first.

$\quad = -6 + 2(-2)$ Subtract inside the parentheses.

$\quad = -6 + (-4)$ Multiply.

$\quad = -10$ Add.

(d) $\dfrac{5(-2) - 3(4)}{2(1 - 6)}$

$\quad = \dfrac{-10 - 12}{2(-5)}$ Simplify the numerator and denominator separately.

$\quad = \dfrac{-22}{-10}, \quad \text{or} \quad \dfrac{11}{5}$ Subtract in the numerator. Multiply in the denominator. Write in lowest terms.

NOW TRY ↻

NOW TRY ANSWERS
5. **(a)** 1 **(b)** $-\frac{5}{6}$

OBJECTIVE 6 Evaluate expressions involving variables.

NOW TRY
EXERCISE 6

Evaluate $\dfrac{3x^2 - 12}{y}$ for $x = -4$ and $y = -3$.

EXAMPLE 6 Evaluating Expressions for Numerical Values

Evaluate each expression for $x = -1$, $y = -2$, and $m = -3$.

(a) $(3x + 4y)(-2m)$

> Use parentheses around substituted negative values to avoid errors.

$= [3(-1) + 4(-2)][-2(-3)]$ Substitute the given values for the variables.

$= [-3 + (-8)][6]$ Multiply.

$= [-11]6$ Add inside the brackets.

$= -66$ Multiply.

(b) $2x^2 - 3y^2$

> Think: $(-2)^2 = -2(-2) = 4$

$= 2(-1)^2 - 3(-2)^2$ Substitute.

> Think: $(-1)^2 = -1(-1) = 1$

$= 2(1) - 3(4)$ Apply the exponents.

$= 2 - 12$ Multiply.

$= -10$ Subtract.

(c) $\dfrac{4y^2 + x}{m}$

$= \dfrac{4(-2)^2 + (-1)}{-3}$ Substitute.

$= \dfrac{4(4) + (-1)}{-3}$ Apply the exponent.

$= \dfrac{16 + (-1)}{-3}$ Multiply.

$= \dfrac{15}{-3}$, or -5 Add, and then divide.   NOW TRY

OBJECTIVE 7 Translate words and phrases involving multiplication and division. The table gives words and phrases that indicate multiplication.

Word or Phrase	Example	Numerical Expression and Simplification
Product of	The *product of* −5 and −2	−5(−2), or 10
Times	13 *times* −4	13(−4), or −52
Twice (meaning "2 times")	*Twice* 6	2(6), or 12
Of (used with fractions)	$\frac{1}{2}$ *of* 10	$\frac{1}{2}$(10), or 5
Percent of	12% *of* −16	0.12(−16), or −1.92
As much as	$\frac{2}{3}$ *as much as* 30	$\frac{2}{3}$(30), or 20

EXAMPLE 7 Translating Words and Phrases (Multiplication)

Write a numerical expression for each phrase, and simplify the expression.

(a) The product of 12 and the sum of 3 and −6

$12[3 + (-6)]$ simplifies to $12[-3]$, or -36.

(b) Twice the difference between 8 and −4

$2[8 - (-4)]$ simplifies to $2[12]$, or   24.

NOW TRY ANSWER
6. −12

NOW TRY
EXERCISE 7

Write a numerical expression for each phrase, and simplify the expression.

(a) Twice the sum of -10 and 7

(b) 40% of the difference between 45 and 15

(c) Two-thirds of the sum of -5 and -3

$$\frac{2}{3}[-5 + (-3)] \quad \text{simplifies to} \quad \frac{2}{3}[-8], \quad \text{or} \quad -\frac{16}{3}.$$

(d) 15% of the difference between 14 and -2

Remember that 15% = 0.15.

$$0.15[14 - (-2)] \quad \text{simplifies to} \quad 0.15[16], \quad \text{or} \quad 2.4.$$

(e) Double the product of 3 and 4

$$2 \cdot (3 \cdot 4) \quad \text{simplifies to} \quad 2(12), \quad \text{or} \quad 24. \qquad \text{NOW TRY}$$

In algebra, quotients are usually represented with a fraction bar. The symbol $\div$ is seldom used. The table gives some phrases associated with division.

Phrase	Example	Numerical Expression and Simplification
Quotient of	The *quotient of* -24 and 3	$\frac{-24}{3}$, or -8
Divided by	-16 *divided by* -4	$\frac{-16}{-4}$, or 4
Ratio of	The *ratio of* 2 to 3	$\frac{2}{3}$

When translating a phrase involving division, we write the first number named as the numerator and the second as the denominator.

NOW TRY
EXERCISE 8

Write a numerical expression for the phrase, and simplify the expression.

The quotient of 21 and the sum of 10 and -7

EXAMPLE 8 Interpreting Words and Phrases Involving Division

Write a numerical expression for each phrase, and simplify the expression.

(a) The *quotient of* 14 and the sum of -9 and 2

"Quotient" indicates division.

$$\frac{14}{-9 + 2} \quad \text{simplifies to} \quad \frac{14}{-7}, \quad \text{or} \quad -2.$$

(b) The product of 5 and -6, *divided by* the difference between -7 and 8

$$\frac{5(-6)}{-7 - 8} \quad \text{simplifies to} \quad \frac{-30}{-15}, \quad \text{or} \quad 2. \qquad \text{NOW TRY}$$

OBJECTIVE 8 Translate simple sentences into equations.

EXAMPLE 9 Translating Sentences into Equations

Write each sentence as an equation, using x as the variable. Then find the solution from the list of integers between -12 and 12, inclusive.

(a) Three *times* a number *is* -18.

The word *times* indicates multiplication.   The word *is* translates as =.

$$3 \cdot x = -18, \quad \text{or} \quad 3x = -18 \qquad 3 \cdot x = 3x$$

The integer between -12 and 12, inclusive, that makes this statement true is -6, since $3(-6) = -18$. The solution of the equation is -6.

NOW TRY ANSWERS
7. **(a)** $2(-10 + 7)$; -6
  (b) $0.40(45 - 15)$; 12
8. $\frac{21}{10 + (-7)}$; 7

NOW TRY
EXERCISE 9

Write each sentence as an equation, using x as the variable. Then find the solution from the list of integers between -12 and 12, inclusive.

(a) The sum of a number and -4 is 7.

(b) The difference between -8 and a number is -11.

(b) The sum of a number and 9 is 12.

$$x + 9 = 12$$

Since $3 + 9 = 12$, the solution of this equation is 3.

(c) The difference between a number and 5 is 0.

$$x - 5 = 0$$

Since $5 - 5 = 0$, the solution of this equation is 5.

(d) The quotient of 24 and a number is -2.

$$\frac{24}{x} = -2$$

Here, x must be a negative number, since the numerator is positive and the quotient is negative. Since $\frac{24}{-12} = -2$, the solution is -12.

NOW TRY

⚠ **CAUTION** In **Examples 7 and 8,** the *phrases* translate as *expressions,* while in **Example 9,** the *sentences* translate as *equations.* ***An expression is a phrase. An equation is a sentence with something on the left side, an $=$ symbol, and something on the right side.***

$$\frac{5(-6)}{-7 - 8} \qquad 3x = -18$$

      Expression   Equation

NOW TRY ANSWERS
9. **(a)** $x + (-4) = 7$; 11
   (b) $-8 - x = -11$; 3

1.6 EXERCISES

MyMathLab   Math XL PRACTICE   WATCH   DOWNLOAD   READ   REVIEW

🌐 *Complete solution available on the Video Resources on DVD*

Concept Check   Fill in each blank with one of the following: greater than 0, less than 0, equal to 0.

1. The product or the quotient of two numbers with the same sign is _____.

2. The product or the quotient of two numbers with different signs is _____.

3. If three negative numbers are multiplied, the product is _____.

4. If two negative numbers are multiplied and then their product is divided by a negative number, the result is _____.

5. If a negative number is squared and the result is added to a positive number, the result is _____.

6. The reciprocal of a negative number is _____.

7. If three positive numbers, five negative numbers, and zero are multiplied, the product is _____.

8. The cube of a negative number is _____.

🌐 9. *Concept Check* Complete this statement: The quotient formed by any nonzero number divided by 0 is _____, and the quotient formed by 0 divided by any nonzero number is _____. Give an example of each quotient.

10. *Concept Check* Which expression is undefined?

   A. $\dfrac{4 + 4}{4 + 4}$ **B.** $\dfrac{4 - 4}{4 + 4}$ **C.** $\dfrac{4 - 4}{4 - 4}$ **D.** $\dfrac{4 - 4}{4}$

NOW TRY
EXERCISE 1

Use a commutative property
to complete each statement.

(a) $7 + (-3) = -3 +$ _____

(b) $(-5)4 = 4 \cdot$ _____

EXAMPLE 1 Using the Commutative Properties

Use a commutative property to complete each statement.

(a) $-8 + 5 = 5 +$ _?_   Notice that the "order" changed.

$\qquad -8 + 5 = 5 + (-8)$ Commutative property of addition

(b) $(-2)7 = \underline{\ ?\ } (-2)$

$\qquad -2(7) = 7(-2)$ Commutative property of multiplication

NOW TRY

OBJECTIVE 2 **Use the associative properties.** When we *associate* one object with another, we think of those objects as being grouped together.

The **associative properties** say that when we add or multiply three numbers, we can group the first two together or the last two together and get the same answer.

Associative Properties

$$(a + b) + c = a + (b + c) \qquad \text{Addition}$$
$$(ab)c = a(bc) \qquad \text{Multiplication}$$

NOW TRY
EXERCISE 2

Use an associative property to
complete each statement.

(a) $-9 + (3 + 7) =$ _____

(b) $5[(-4) \cdot 9] =$ _____

EXAMPLE 2 Using the Associative Properties

Use an associative property to complete each statement.

(a) $-8 + (1 + 4) = (-8 + \underline{\ ?\ }) + 4$ The "order" is the same. The "grouping" changed.

$\qquad -8 + (1 + 4) = (-8 + 1) + 4$ Associative property of addition

(b) $[2 \cdot (-7)] \cdot 6 = 2 \cdot \underline{\ ?\ }$

$\qquad [2 \cdot (-7)] \cdot 6 = 2 \cdot [(-7) \cdot 6]$ Associative property of multiplication

NOW TRY

By the associative property, the sum (or product) of three numbers will be the same no matter how the numbers are "associated" in groups. Parentheses can be left out if a problem contains only addition (or multiplication). For example,

$$(-1 + 2) + 3 \quad \text{and} \quad -1 + (2 + 3) \quad \text{can be written as} \quad -1 + 2 + 3.$$

EXAMPLE 3 Distinguishing Between Properties

Is each statement an example of the associative or the commutative property?

(a) $(2 + 4) + 5 = 2 + (4 + 5)$

The order of the three numbers is the same on both sides of the equals symbol. The only change is in the *grouping,* or association, of the numbers. This is an example of the associative property.

(b) $6 \cdot (3 \cdot 10) = 6 \cdot (10 \cdot 3)$

The same numbers, 3 and 10, are grouped on each side. On the left, the 3 appears first, but on the right, the 10 appears first. Since the only change involves the *order* of the numbers, this is an example of the commutative property.

NOW TRY ANSWERS
1. **(a)** 7 **(b)** -5
2. **(a)** $(-9 + 3) + 7$
   (b) $[5 \cdot (-4)] \cdot 9$

NOW TRY
EXERCISE 3
Is $5 + (7 + 6) = 5 + (6 + 7)$ an example of the associative property or the commutative property?

(c) $(8 + 1) + 7 = 8 + (7 + 1)$

Both the order and the grouping are changed. On the left, the order of the three numbers is 8, 1, and 7. On the right, it is 8, 7, and 1. On the left, the 8 and 1 are grouped. On the right, the 7 and 1 are grouped. Therefore, *both* properties are used.

NOW TRY

NOW TRY
EXERCISE 4
Find each sum or product.
(a) $8 + 54 + 7 + 6 + 32$
(b) $5(37)(20)$

EXAMPLE 4 Using the Commutative and Associative Properties

Find each sum or product.

(a) $23 + 41 + 2 + 9 + 25$

$= (41 + 9) + (23 + 2) + 25$

$= 50 + 25 + 25$

$= 100$

Use the commutative and associative properties.

(b) $25(69)(4)$

$= 25(4)(69)$

$= 100(69)$

$= 6900$

NOW TRY

OBJECTIVE 3 **Use the identity properties.** If a child wears a costume on Halloween, the child's appearance is changed, but his or her *identity* is unchanged. The identity of a real number is left unchanged when identity properties are applied.

The **identity properties** say that the sum of 0 and any number equals that number, and the product of 1 and any number equals that number.

Identity Properties

$a + 0 = a$	and	$0 + a = a$	Addition
$a \cdot 1 = a$	and	$1 \cdot a = a$	Multiplication

The number 0 leaves the identity, or value, of any real number unchanged by addition, so 0 is called the **identity element for addition,** or the **additive identity.** Since multiplication by 1 leaves any real number unchanged, 1 is the **identity element for multiplication,** or the **multiplicative identity.**

NOW TRY
EXERCISE 5
Use an identity property to complete each statement.

(a) $\dfrac{2}{5} \cdot \underline{\hspace{1cm}} = \dfrac{2}{5}$

(b) $8 + \underline{\hspace{1cm}} = 8$

EXAMPLE 5 Using the Identity Properties

Use an identity property to complete each statement.

(a) $-3 + \underline{0} = -3$

$-3 + \ 0 \ = -3$

Identity property of addition

(b) $\underline{?} \cdot \dfrac{1}{2} = \dfrac{1}{2}$

$1 \ \cdot \dfrac{1}{2} = \dfrac{1}{2}$

Identity property of multiplication

NOW TRY

NOW TRY ANSWERS
3. commutative
4. (a) 107 (b) 3700
5. (a) 1 (b) 0

NOW TRY
EXERCISE 6
Simplify.

(a) $\dfrac{16}{20}$ (b) $\dfrac{2}{5} + \dfrac{3}{20}$

EXAMPLE 6   Using the Identity Property to Simplify Expressions

Simplify.

(a) $\dfrac{49}{35}$

$= \dfrac{7 \cdot 7}{5 \cdot 7}$ Factor.

$= \dfrac{7}{5} \cdot \dfrac{7}{7}$ Write as a product.

$= \dfrac{7}{5} \cdot 1$ Divide.

$= \dfrac{7}{5}$ Identity property

(b) $\dfrac{3}{4} + \dfrac{5}{24}$

$= \dfrac{3}{4} \cdot 1 + \dfrac{5}{24}$ Identity property

$= \dfrac{3}{4} \cdot \dfrac{6}{6} + \dfrac{5}{24}$ Use $1 = \frac{6}{6}$ to get a common denominator.

$= \dfrac{18}{24} + \dfrac{5}{24}$ Multiply.

$= \dfrac{23}{24}$ Add.

NOW TRY

OBJECTIVE 4   **Use the inverse properties.**   Each day before you go to work or school, you probably put on your shoes. Before you go to sleep at night, you probably take them off, and this leads to the same situation that existed before you put them on. These operations from everyday life are examples of *inverse* operations.

The **inverse properties** of addition and multiplication lead to the additive and multiplicative identities, respectively. Recall that $-a$ is the **additive inverse,** or **opposite,** of a and $\frac{1}{a}$ is the **multiplicative inverse,** or **reciprocal,** of the nonzero number a. The sum of the numbers a and $-a$ is 0, and the product of the nonzero numbers a and $\frac{1}{a}$ is 1.

Inverse Properties

$a + (-a) = 0$ and $-a + a = 0$ Addition

$a \cdot \dfrac{1}{a} = 1$ and $\dfrac{1}{a} \cdot a = 1$ $(a \neq 0)$ Multiplication

NOW TRY
EXERCISE 7
Use an inverse property to complete each statement.

(a) $10 + \underline{\hspace{1cm}} = 0$

(b) $-9 \cdot \underline{\hspace{1cm}} = 1$

EXAMPLE 7   Using the Inverse Properties

Use an inverse property to complete each statement.

(a) $-\dfrac{1}{2} + \dfrac{1}{2} = 0$

$-\dfrac{1}{2} + \dfrac{1}{2} = 0$

(b) $4 + (-4) = 0$

$4 + (-4) = 0$

(c) $-0.75 + \dfrac{3}{4} = 0$

$-0.75 + \dfrac{3}{4} = 0$

The inverse property of addition is used in parts (a)–(c).

(d) $\dfrac{2}{5} \cdot \dfrac{5}{2} = 1$

$\dfrac{2}{5} \cdot \dfrac{5}{2} = 1$

(e) $-5\left(-\dfrac{1}{5}\right) = 1$

$-5\left(-\dfrac{1}{5}\right) = 1$

(f) $4(0.25) = 1$

$4(0.25) = 1$

The inverse property of multiplication is used in parts (d)–(f).   *NOW TRY*

NOW TRY ANSWERS
6. (a) $\frac{4}{5}$ (b) $\frac{11}{20}$
7. (a) -10 (b) $-\frac{1}{9}$

**NOW TRY
EXERCISE 8**

Simplify.

$$-\frac{1}{3}x + 7 + \frac{1}{3}x$$

EXAMPLE 8 Using Properties to Simplify an Expression

Simplify.

$$-2x + 10 + 2x$$
$$= (-2x + 10) + 2x \qquad \text{Order of operations}$$
$$= [10 + (-2x)] + 2x \qquad \text{Commutative property}$$
$$= 10 + [(-2x) + 2x] \qquad \text{Associative property}$$
$$= 10 + 0 \qquad \text{Inverse property}$$
$$= 10 \qquad \text{Identity property} \qquad \text{NOW TRY}$$

> For *any* value of x, $-2x$ and $2x$ are additive inverses.

NOTE The steps of **Example 8** may be skipped when we actually do the simplification.

OBJECTIVE 5 Use the distributive property. The word *distribute* means "to give out from one to several." Look at the value of the following expressions:

$$2(5 + 8), \quad \text{which equals} \quad 2(13), \quad \text{or} \quad 26$$
$$2(5) + 2(8), \quad \text{which equals} \quad 10 + 16, \quad \text{or} \quad 26.$$

Since both expressions equal 26,

$$2(5 + 8) = 2(5) + 2(8).$$

This result is an example of the *distributive property of multiplication with respect to addition,* the only property involving *both* addition and multiplication. With this property, a product can be changed to a sum or difference. This idea is illustrated in **FIGURE 18**.

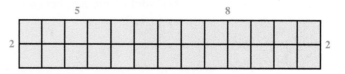

The area of the left part is $2(5) = 10$.
The area of the right part is $2(8) = 16$.
The total area is $2(5 + 8) = 2(13) = 26$,
or the total area is $2(5) + 2(8) = 10 + 16 = 26$.
Thus, $2(5 + 8) = 2(5) + 2(8)$.

FIGURE 18

The **distributive property** says that multiplying a number a by a sum of numbers $b + c$ gives the same result as multiplying a by b and a by c and then adding the two products.

Distributive Property

$$a(b + c) = ab + ac \qquad \text{and} \qquad (b + c)a = ba + ca$$

As the arrows show, the a outside the parentheses is "distributed" over the b and c inside. The distributive property is also valid for multiplication over subtraction.

$$a(b - c) = ab - ac \qquad \text{and} \qquad (b - c)a = ba - ca$$

The distributive property can be extended to more than two numbers.

$$a(b + c + d) = ab + ac + ad$$

The distributive property can also be used "in reverse."

$$ac + bc = (a + b)c$$

NOW TRY ANSWER
8. 7

NOW TRY
EXERCISE 9

Use the distributive property to rewrite each expression.

(a) $-5(4x + 1)$

(b) $6(2r + t - 5z)$

(c) $5x - 5y$

EXAMPLE 9 Using the Distributive Property

Use the distributive property to rewrite each expression.

(a) $5(9 + 6)$

$= 5 \cdot 9 + 5 \cdot 6$ Distributive property

$= 45 + 30$ Multiply.

Multiply first. $= 75$ Add.

(b) $4(x + 5 + y)$

$= 4x + 4 \cdot 5 + 4y$ Distributive property

$= 4x + 20 + 4y$ Multiply.

(c) $-\dfrac{1}{2}(4x + 3)$ Think: $-\frac{1}{2}(4x) = \left(-\frac{1}{2} \cdot 4\right)x = \left(-\frac{1}{2} \cdot \frac{4}{1}\right)x$

$= -\dfrac{1}{2}(4x) + \left(-\dfrac{1}{2}\right)(3)$ Distributive property

$= -2x - \dfrac{3}{2}$ Multiply.

(d) $3(k - 9)$

$= 3[k + (-9)]$ Definition of subtraction

$= 3k + 3(-9)$ Distributive property

$= 3k - 27$ Multiply.

(e) $8(3r + 11t + 5z)$

$= 8(3r) + 8(11t) + 8(5z)$ Distributive property

$= (8 \cdot 3)r + (8 \cdot 11)t + (8 \cdot 5)z$ Associative property

$= 24r + 88t + 40z$ Multiply.

(f) $6 \cdot 8 + 6 \cdot 2$

$= 6(8 + 2)$ Distributive property in reverse

$= 6(10)$ Add.

$= 60$ Multiply.

(g) $4x - 4m$

$= 4(x - m)$ Distributive property in reverse

(h) $6x - 12$

$= 6 \cdot x - 6 \cdot 2$

$= 6(x - 2)$ Distributive property in reverse   NOW TRY

⚠ **CAUTION** In practice, we often omit the first step in **Example 9(d)**, where we rewrote the subtraction as addition of the additive inverse.

$3(k - 9)$

$= 3k - 3(9)$ Be careful not to make a sign error.

$= 3k - 27$ Multiply.

NOW TRY ANSWERS
9. (a) $-20x - 5$
  (b) $12r + 6t - 30z$
  (c) $5(x - y)$

NOW TRY
EXERCISE 10

Write each expression without parentheses.

(a) $-(2 - r)$

(b) $-(2x - 5y - 7)$

The symbol $-a$ may be interpreted as $-1 \cdot a$. Using this result and the distributive property, we can remove (or clear) parentheses from some expressions.

EXAMPLE 10 Using the Distributive Property to Remove (Clear) Parentheses

Write each expression without parentheses.

(a) $-(2y + 3)$

> The $-$ symbol indicates a factor of -1.

$= -1 \cdot (2y + 3)$ $-a = -1 \cdot a$

$= -1 \cdot 2y + (-1) \cdot 3$ Distributive property

$= -2y - 3$ Multiply.

(b) $-(-9w - 2)$

$= -1(-9w - 2)$

$= -1(-9w) - 1(-2)$

$= 9w + 2$

> We can also interpret the negative sign in front of the parentheses to mean the *opposite* of each of the terms within the parentheses.

(c) $-(-x - 3y + 6z)$

$= -1(-1x - 3y + 6z)$

> Be careful with signs.

$= -1(-1x) - 1(-3y) - 1(6z)$

$= x + 3y - 6z$ $-1(-1x) = 1x = x$ NOW TRY

Here is a summary of the properties of real numbers discussed in this section.

Properties of Addition and Multiplication

For any real numbers a, b, and c, the following properties hold.

Commutative Properties $a + b = b + a$ $ab = ba$

Associative Properties $(a + b) + c = a + (b + c)$

$(ab)c = a(bc)$

Identity Properties   There is a real number 0 such that

$$a + 0 = a \quad \text{and} \quad 0 + a = a.$$

There is a real number 1 such that

$$a \cdot 1 = a \quad \text{and} \quad 1 \cdot a = a.$$

Inverse Properties   For each real number a, there is a single real number $-a$ such that

$$a + (-a) = 0 \quad \text{and} \quad (-a) + a = 0.$$

For each nonzero real number a, there is a single real number $\frac{1}{a}$ such that

$$a \cdot \frac{1}{a} = 1 \quad \text{and} \quad \frac{1}{a} \cdot a = 1.$$

Distributive Properties $a(b + c) = ab + ac$ $(b + c)a = ba + ca$

NOW TRY ANSWERS
10. (a) $-2 + r$
(b) $-2x + 5y + 7$

1.7 EXERCISES

Complete solution available on the Video Resources on DVD

1. *Concept Check*   Match each item in Column I with the correct choice(s) from Column II. Choices may be used once, more than once, or not at all.

I

(a) Identity element for addition
(b) Identity element for multiplication
(c) Additive inverse of *a*
(d) Multiplicative inverse, or reciprocal, of the nonzero number *a*
(e) The number that is its own additive inverse
(f) The two numbers that are their own multiplicative inverses
(g) The only number that has no multiplicative inverse
(h) An example of the associative property
(i) An example of the commutative property
(j) An example of the distributive property

II

A. $(5 \cdot 4) \cdot 3 = 5 \cdot (4 \cdot 3)$
B. 0
C. $-a$
D. -1
E. $5 \cdot 4 \cdot 3 = 60$
F. 1
G. $(5 \cdot 4) \cdot 3 = 3 \cdot (5 \cdot 4)$
H. $5(4 + 3) = 5 \cdot 4 + 5 \cdot 3$
I. $\dfrac{1}{a}$

2. *Concept Check*   Fill in the blanks: The commutative property allows us to change the _____ of the terms in a sum or the factors in a product. The associative property allows us to change the _____ of the terms in a sum or the factors in a product.

Concept Check   *Tell whether or not the following everyday activities are commutative.*

3. Washing your face and brushing your teeth

4. Putting on your left sock and putting on your right sock

5. Preparing a meal and eating a meal

6. Starting a car and driving away in a car

7. Putting on your socks and putting on your shoes

8. Getting undressed and taking a shower

9. *Concept Check*   Use parentheses to show how the associative property can be used to give two different meanings to the phrase "foreign sales clerk."

10. *Concept Check*   Use parentheses to show how the associative property can be used to give two different meanings to the phrase "defective merchandise counter."

Use the commutative or the associative property to complete each statement. State which property is used. ***See Examples 1 and 2.***

11. $-15 + 9 = 9 + $ _____

12. $6 + (-2) = -2 + $ _____

13. $-8 \cdot 3 = $ _____ $\cdot (-8)$

14. $-12 \cdot 4 = 4 \cdot $ _____

15. $(3 + 6) + 7 = 3 + ($ _____ $+ 7)$

16. $(-2 + 3) + 6 = -2 + ($ _____ $+ 6)$

17. $7 \cdot (2 \cdot 5) = ($ _____ $\cdot 2) \cdot 5$

18. $8 \cdot (6 \cdot 4) = (8 \cdot $ _____ $) \cdot 4$

19. *Concept Check*   Evaluate $25 - (6 - 2)$ and evaluate $(25 - 6) - 2$. Do you think subtraction is associative?

20. *Concept Check*   Evaluate $180 \div (15 \div 3)$ and evaluate $(180 \div 15) \div 3$. Do you think division is associative?

21. *Concept Check*   Complete the table and the statement beside it.

Number	Additive Inverse	Multiplicative Inverse
5		
-10		
$-\frac{1}{2}$		
$\frac{3}{8}$		
x		$(x \neq 0)$
$-y$		$(y \neq 0)$

In general, a number and its additive inverse have _____ signs.
(the same/opposite)

A number and its multiplicative inverse have _____ signs.
(the same/opposite)

22. *Concept Check*   The following conversation actually took place between one of the authors of this book and his son, Jack, when Jack was 4 years old:

DADDY: "Jack, what is 3 + 0?"
JACK: "3."
DADDY: "Jack, what is 4 + 0?"
JACK: "4. And Daddy, *string* plus zero equals *string*!"

What property of addition did Jack recognize?

Decide whether each statement is an example of the commutative, associative, identity, inverse, *or* distributive property. ***See Examples 1, 2, 3, 5, 6, 7, and 9.***

23. $4 + 15 = 15 + 4$

24. $3 + 12 = 12 + 3$

25. $5 \cdot (13 \cdot 7) = (5 \cdot 13) \cdot 7$

26. $-4 \cdot (2 \cdot 6) = (-4 \cdot 2) \cdot 6$

27. $-6 + (12 + 7) = (-6 + 12) + 7$

28. $(-8 + 13) + 2 = -8 + (13 + 2)$

29. $-9 + 9 = 0$

30. $1 + (-1) = 0$

31. $\frac{2}{3}\left(\frac{3}{2}\right) = 1$

32. $\frac{5}{8}\left(\frac{8}{5}\right) = 1$

33. $1.75 + 0 = 1.75$

34. $-8.45 + 0 = -8.45$

35. $(4 + 17) + 3 = 3 + (4 + 17)$

36. $(-8 + 4) + 12 = 12 + (-8 + 4)$

37. $2(x + y) = 2x + 2y$

38. $9(t + s) = 9t + 9s$

39. $-\frac{5}{9} = -\frac{5}{9} \cdot \frac{3}{3} = -\frac{15}{27}$

40. $-\frac{7}{12} = -\frac{7}{12} \cdot \frac{7}{7} = -\frac{49}{84}$

41. $4(2x) + 4(3y) = 4(2x + 3y)$

42. $6(5t) - 6(7r) = 6(5t - 7r)$

Find each sum or product. ***See Example 4.***

43. $97 + 13 + 3 + 37$

44. $49 + 199 + 1 + 1$

45. $1999 + 2 + 1 + 8$

46. $2998 + 3 + 2 + 17$

47. $159 + 12 + 141 + 88$

48. $106 + 8 + (-6) + (-8)$

49. $843 + 627 + (-43) + (-27)$

50. $1846 + 1293 + (-46) + (-93)$

51. $5(47)(2)$

52. $2(79)5$

53. $-4 \cdot 5 \cdot 93 \cdot 5$

54. $2 \cdot 25 \cdot 67 \cdot (-2)$

Simplify each expression. ***See Examples 7 and 8.***

55. $6t + 8 - 6t + 3$

56. $9r + 12 - 9r + 1$

57. $\frac{2}{3}x - 11 + 11 - \frac{2}{3}x$

58. $\frac{1}{5}y + 4 - 4 - \frac{1}{5}y$

59. $\left(\frac{9}{7}\right)(-0.38)\left(\frac{7}{9}\right)$

60. $\left(\frac{4}{5}\right)(-0.73)\left(\frac{5}{4}\right)$

61. $t + (-t) + \frac{1}{2}(2)$

62. $w + (-w) + \frac{1}{4}(4)$

63. *Concept Check*   Suppose that a student simplifies the expression $-3(4 - 6)$ as shown.

$$-3(4 - 6)$$
$$= -3(4) - 3(6)$$
$$= -12 - 18$$
$$= -30$$

WHAT WENT WRONG? Work the problem correctly.

64. Explain how the procedure of changing $\frac{3}{4}$ to $\frac{9}{12}$ requires the use of the multiplicative identity element, 1.

Use the distributive property to rewrite each expression. Simplify if possible. **See Example 9.**

65. $5(9 + 8)$ **66.** $6(11 + 8)$ **67.** $4(t + 3)$

68. $5(w + 4)$ **69.** $7(z - 8)$ **70.** $8(x - 6)$

71. $-8(r + 3)$ **72.** $-11(x + 4)$ **73.** $-\dfrac{1}{4}(8x + 3)$

74. $-\dfrac{1}{3}(9x + 5)$ **75.** $-5(y - 4)$ **76.** $-9(g - 4)$

77. $-\dfrac{4}{3}(12y + 15z)$ **78.** $-\dfrac{2}{5}(10b + 20a)$ **79.** $8z + 8w$

80. $4s + 4r$ **81.** $7(2v) + 7(5r)$ **82.** $13(5w) + 13(4p)$

83. $8(3r + 4s - 5y)$ **84.** $2(5u - 3v + 7w)$ **85.** $-3(8x + 3y + 4z)$

86. $-5(2x - 5y + 6z)$ **87.** $5x + 15$ **88.** $9p + 18$

Write each expression without parentheses. **See Example 10.**

89. $-(4t + 3m)$ **90.** $-(9x + 12y)$ **91.** $-(-5c - 4d)$

92. $-(-13x - 15y)$ **93.** $-(-q + 5r - 8s)$ **94.** $-(-z + 5w - 9y)$

1.8   Simplifying Expressions

OBJECTIVES

1 Simplify expressions.
2 Identify terms and numerical coefficients.
3 Identify like terms.
4 Combine like terms.
5 Simplify expressions from word phrases.

OBJECTIVE 1   **Simplify expressions.** We use the properties of **Section 1.7** to do this.

EXAMPLE 1 Simplifying Expressions

Simplify each expression.

(a) $4x + 8 + 9$ simplifies to $4x + 17$.

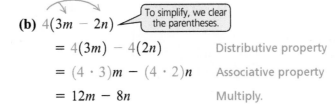

(b) $4(3m - 2n)$ ← To simplify, we clear the parentheses.

$$= 4(3m) - 4(2n)$$ Distributive property

$$= (4 \cdot 3)m - (4 \cdot 2)n$$ Associative property

$$= 12m - 8n$$ Multiply.

NOW TRY
EXERCISE 1
Simplify each expression.
(a) $3(2x - 4y)$
(b) $-4 - (-3y + 5)$

(c) $6 + 3(4k + 5)$

$= 6 + 3(4k) + 3(5)$ — Distributive property

Don't start by adding!

$= 6 + (3 \cdot 4)k + 3(5)$ — Associative property

$= 6 + 12k + 15$ — Multiply.

$= 6 + 15 + 12k$ — Commutative property

$= 21 + 12k$ — Add.

(d) $5 - (2y - 8)$

$= 5 - 1(2y - 8)$ — $-a = -1 \cdot a$

$= 5 - 1(2y) - 1(-8)$ — Distributive property

Be careful with signs. $= 5 - 2y + 8$ — Multiply.

$= 5 + 8 - 2y$ — Commutative property

$= 13 - 2y$ — Add. NOW TRY

NOTE The steps using the commutative and associative properties will not be shown in the rest of the examples. However, be aware that they are usually involved.

Term	Numerical Coefficient
8	8
$-7y$	-7
$34r^3$	34
$-26x^5yz^4$	-26
$-k$, or $-1k$	-1
r, or $1r$	1
$\frac{3x}{8} = \frac{3}{8}x$	$\frac{3}{8}$
$\frac{x}{3} = \frac{1x}{3} = \frac{1}{3}x$	$\frac{1}{3}$

OBJECTIVE 2 **Identify terms and numerical coefficients.** A **term** is a number, a variable, or a product or quotient of numbers and variables raised to powers, such as

$$9x, \quad 15y^2, \quad -3, \quad -8m^2n, \quad \frac{2}{p}, \quad \text{and} \quad k. \quad \text{Terms}$$

In the term $9x$, the **numerical coefficient**, or simply **coefficient**, of the variable x is 9. Additional examples are shown in the table in the margin.

⚠ **CAUTION** It is important to be able to distinguish between *terms* and *factors*. Consider the following expressions.

$8x^3 + 12x^2$ — This expression has **two terms**, $8x^3$ and $12x^2$. Terms are separated by a + or − symbol.

$(8x^3)(12x^2)$ — This is a **one-term** expression. The factors $8x^3$ and $12x^2$ are multiplied.

OBJECTIVE 3 **Identify like terms.** Terms with exactly the same variables that have the same exponents are **like terms.** Here are some examples.

Like Terms		**Unlike Terms**		
$9t$ and $4t$		$4y$ and $7t$		Different variables
$6x^2$ and $-5x^2$		$17x$ and $-8x^2$		Different exponents
$-2pq$ and $11pq$		$4xy^2$ and $4xy$		Different exponents
$3x^2y$ and $5x^2y$		$-7wz^3$ and $2xz^3$		Different variables

NOW TRY ANSWERS
1. **(a)** $6x - 12y$ **(b)** $3y - 9$

OBJECTIVE 4 **Combine like terms.** Recall that the distributive property

$$a(b + c) = ab + ac \quad \text{can be written "in reverse" as} \quad ab + ac = a(b + c).$$

This last form, which may be used to find the sum or difference of like terms, provides justification for **combining like terms.**

⌒ *NOW TRY*
  EXERCISE 2

Combine like terms in each expression.

(a) $4x + 6x - 7x$ **(b)** $z + z$

(c) $4p^2 - 3p^2$

EXAMPLE 2 **Combining Like Terms**

Combine like terms in each expression.

(a) $-9m + 5m$

$= (-9 + 5)m$

$= -4m$

(b) $6r + 3r + 2r$

$= (6 + 3 + 2)r$

$= 11r$

(c) $4x + x$

$= 4x + 1x \qquad x = 1x$

$= (4 + 1)x$

$= 5x$

(d) $16y^2 - 9y^2$

$= (16 - 9)y^2$

$= 7y^2$

(e) $32y + 10y^2$ These unlike terms cannot be combined. *NOW TRY* ⤸

⚠ CAUTION *Remember that only like terms may be combined.*

EXAMPLE 3 **Simplifying Expressions Involving Like Terms**

Simplify each expression.

(a) $14y + 2(6 + 3y)$

$= 14y + 2(6) + 2(3y)$ Distributive property

$= 14y + 12 + 6y$ Multiply.

$= 20y + 12$ Combine like terms.

(b) $\qquad 9k - 6 - 3(2 - 5k)$ ⟨Be careful with signs.⟩

$= 9k - 6 - 3(2) - 3(-5k)$ Distributive property

$= 9k - 6 - 6 + 15k$ Multiply.

$= 24k - 12$ Combine like terms.

(c) $\qquad -(2 - r) + 10r$

$= -1(2 - r) + 10r$ $-a = -1 \cdot a$

$= -1(2) - 1(-r) + 10r$ Distributive property

⟨Be careful with signs.⟩ $= -2 + 1r + 10r$ Multiply.

$= -2 + 11r$ Combine like terms.

(d) $100[0.03(x + 4)]$

$= [(100)(0.03)](x + 4)$ Associative property

$= 3(x + 4)$ Multiply.

$= 3x + 12$ Distributive property

NOW TRY ANSWERS

2. (a) $3x$ **(b)** $2z$ **(c)** p^2

NOW TRY
EXERCISE 3

Simplify each expression.

(a) $5k - 6 - (3 - 4k)$

(b) $\dfrac{1}{4}x - \dfrac{2}{3}(x - 9)$

(e) $5(2a - 6) - 3(4a - 9)$

$\qquad = 10a - 30 - 12a + 27$ Distributive property

$\qquad = -2a - 3$ Combine like terms.

(f) $-\dfrac{2}{3}(x - 6) - \dfrac{1}{6}x$

$\qquad = -\dfrac{2}{3}x - \dfrac{2}{3}(-6) - \dfrac{1}{6}x$ Distributive property

$\qquad = -\dfrac{2}{3}x + 4 - \dfrac{1}{6}x$ Multiply.

$\qquad = -\dfrac{4}{6}x + 4 - \dfrac{1}{6}x$ Get a common denominator.

$\qquad = -\dfrac{5}{6}x + 4$ Combine like terms.   *NOW TRY*

NOTE **Examples 2 and 3** suggest that like terms may be combined by adding or subtracting the coefficients of the terms and keeping the same variable factors.

OBJECTIVE 5   **Simplify expressions from word phrases.**

NOW TRY
EXERCISE 4

Translate the phrase into a mathematical expression and simplify.

Twice a number, subtracted from the sum of the number and 5

EXAMPLE 4   **Translating Words into a Mathematical Expression**

Translate the phrase into a mathematical expression and simplify.

The sum of 9, five times a number,
four times the number, and
six times the number

The word "sum" indicates that the terms should be added. Use x for the number.

$\qquad 9 + 5x + 4x + 6x$ simplifies to $9 + 15x$.   Combine like terms.

> This is an expression to be simplified, *not* an equation to be solved.

   NOW TRY

NOW TRY ANSWERS

3. (a) $9k - 9$ **(b)** $-\dfrac{5}{12}x + 6$

4. $(x + 5) - 2x; -x + 5$

1.8 EXERCISES

MyMathLab   Math XL PRACTICE   WATCH   DOWNLOAD   READ   REVIEW

🔘 *Complete solution available on the Video Resources on DVD*

Concept Check   In Exercises 1–4, choose the letter of the correct response.

1. Which expression is a simplified form of $-(6x - 3)$?

   A. $-6x - 3$ **B.** $-6x + 3$ **C.** $6x - 3$ **D.** $6x + 3$

2. Which is an example of a term with numerical coefficient 5?

   A. $5x^3y^7$ **B.** x^5 **C.** $\dfrac{x}{5}$ **D.** 5^2xy^3

5. An **integer** is
 A. a positive or negative number
 B. a natural number, its opposite, or zero
 C. any number that can be graphed on a number line
 D. the quotient of two numbers.
6. The **absolute value** of a number is
 A. the graph of the number
 B. the reciprocal of the number

C. the opposite of the number
D. the distance between 0 and the number on a number line.
7. A **term** is
 A. a numerical factor
 B. a number, a variable, or a product or quotient of numbers and variables raised to powers
 C. one of several variables with the same exponents

D. a sum of numbers and variables raised to powers.
8. A **numerical coefficient** is
 A. the numerical factor of the variable(s) in a term
 B. the number of terms in an expression
 C. a variable raised to a power
 D. the variable factor in a term.

ANSWERS

1. D; *Example:* Since $2 \times 5 = 10$, the numbers 2 and 5 are factors of 10. Other factors of 10 are $-10, -5, -2, -1, 1$, and 10.   **2.** C; *Examples:* 2, 3, 11, 41, 53   **3.** C; *Example:* In 2^3, the number 3 is the exponent (or power), so 2 is a factor three times, and $2^3 = 2 \cdot 2 \cdot 2 = 8$.   **4.** A; *Examples:* a, b, c **5.** B; *Examples:* $-9, 0, 6$ **6.** D; *Examples:* $|2| = 2$ and $|-2| = 2$ **7.** B; *Examples:* $6, \frac{x}{2}, -4ab^2$ **8.** A; *Examples:* The term 3 has numerical coefficient 3, $8z$ has numerical coefficient 8, and $-10x^4y$ has numerical coefficient -10.

QUICK REVIEW

CONCEPTS	EXAMPLES

1.1 Fractions

Operations with Fractions

Addition/Subtraction

1. *Same denominator:* Add/subtract the numerators and keep the same denominator.
2. *Different denominators:* Find the LCD, and write each fraction with this LCD. Then follow the procedure above.

Multiplication: Multiply numerators and multiply denominators.

Division: Multiply the first fraction by the reciprocal of the second fraction.

Perform each operation.

$$\frac{2}{5} + \frac{7}{5} = \frac{2 + 7}{5} = \frac{9}{5}, \quad \text{or} \quad 1\frac{4}{5}$$

$$\frac{2}{3} - \frac{1}{2} = \frac{4}{6} - \frac{3}{6} \qquad \text{6 is the LCD.}$$

$$= \frac{4 - 3}{6} = \frac{1}{6}$$

$$\frac{4}{3} \cdot \frac{5}{6} = \frac{20}{18} = \frac{10}{9}, \quad \text{or} \quad 1\frac{1}{9}$$

$$\frac{6}{5} \div \frac{1}{4} = \frac{6}{5} \cdot \frac{4}{1} = \frac{24}{5}, \quad \text{or} \quad 4\frac{4}{5}$$

1.2 Exponents, Order of Operations, and Inequality

Order of Operations

Simplify within any parentheses or brackets and above and below fraction bars first. Always follow this order.

Step 1 Apply all exponents.

Step 2 Do any multiplications or divisions from left to right.

Step 3 Do any additions or subtractions from left to right.

Simplify $36 - 4(2^2 + 3)$.

$$36 - 4(2^2 + 3)$$
$$= 36 - 4(4 + 3) \qquad \text{Apply the exponent.}$$
$$= 36 - 4(7) \qquad \text{Add inside the parentheses.}$$
$$= 36 - 28 \qquad \text{Multiply.}$$
$$= 8 \qquad \text{Subtract.}$$

1.3 Variables, Expressions, and Equations

Evaluate an expression with a variable by substituting a given number for the variable.

Evaluate $2x + y^2$ for $x = 3$ and $y = -4$.

$$2x + y^2$$
$$= 2(3) + (-4)^2 \qquad \text{Substitute.}$$
$$= 6 + 16 \qquad \text{Multiply. Apply the exponent.}$$
$$= 22 \qquad \text{Add.}$$

(continued)

CONCEPTS	EXAMPLES
Values of a variable that make an equation true are solutions of the equation.	Is 2 a solution of $5x + 3 = 18$? $5(2) + 3 \stackrel{?}{=} 18$ Let $x = 2$. $13 = 18$ False 2 is not a solution.

1.4 Real Numbers and the Number Line

Ordering Real Numbers
a is less than b if a is to the left of b on the number line.

The additive inverse of x is $-x$.

The absolute value of x, written $|x|$, is the distance between x and 0 on the number line.

Graph -2, 0, and 3.

$$-2 < 3 \qquad 3 > 0 \qquad 0 < 3$$

$$-(5) = -5 \qquad -(-7) = 7 \qquad -0 = 0$$

$$|13| = 13 \qquad |0| = 0 \qquad |-5| = 5$$

1.5 Adding and Subtracting Real Numbers

Adding Two Signed Numbers
Same sign   Add their absolute values. The sum has that same sign.

Different signs   Subtract their absolute values. The sum has the sign of the number with greater absolute value.

Definition of Subtraction
$$x - y = x + (-y)$$

Add.
$$9 + 4 = 13$$
$$-8 + (-5) = -13$$
$$7 + (-12) = -5$$
$$-5 + 13 = 8$$

Subtract.
$$-3 - 4 = -3 + (-4) = -7$$
$$-2 - (-6) = -2 + 6 = 4$$
$$13 - (-8) = 13 + 8 = 21$$

1.6 Multiplying and Dividing Real Numbers

Multiplying and Dividing Two Signed Numbers
Same sign   The product (or quotient) is *positive*.
Different signs   The product (or quotient) is *negative*.

Definition of Division
$$\frac{x}{y} = x \cdot \frac{1}{y}, \quad y \neq 0$$

0 divided by a nonzero number equals 0.
Division by 0 is undefined.

Multiply or divide.

$$6 \cdot 5 = 30 \qquad -7(-8) = 56 \qquad \frac{20}{4} = 5$$

$$\frac{-24}{-6} = 4 \qquad -6(5) = -30 \qquad 6(-5) = -30$$

$$\frac{-18}{9} = -2 \qquad \frac{49}{-7} = -7$$

$$\frac{10}{2} = 10 \cdot \frac{1}{2} = 5$$

$$\frac{0}{5} = 0 \qquad \frac{5}{0} \text{ is undefined.}$$

1.7 Properties of Real Numbers

Commutative Properties
$$a + b = b + a$$
$$ab = ba$$

Associative Properties
$$(a + b) + c = a + (b + c)$$
$$(ab)c = a(bc)$$

Identity Properties
$$a + 0 = a \qquad 0 + a = a$$
$$a \cdot 1 = a \qquad 1 \cdot a = a$$

$$7 + (-1) = -1 + 7$$
$$5(-3) = (-3)5$$

$$(3 + 4) + 8 = 3 + (4 + 8)$$
$$[-2(6)]4 = -2[(6)4]$$

$$-7 + 0 = -7 \qquad 0 + (-7) = -7$$
$$9 \cdot 1 = 9 \qquad 1 \cdot 9 = 9$$

(continued)

CONCEPTS	EXAMPLES
Inverse Properties $$a + (-a) = 0 \qquad -a + a = 0$$ $$a \cdot \frac{1}{a} = 1 \qquad \frac{1}{a} \cdot a = 1 \quad (a \neq 0)$$	$$7 + (-7) = 0 \qquad -7 + 7 = 0$$ $$-2\left(-\frac{1}{2}\right) = 1 \qquad -\frac{1}{2}(-2) = 1$$
Distributive Properties $$a(b + c) = ab + ac$$ $$(b + c)a = ba + ca$$ $$a(b - c) = ab - ac$$	$$5(4 + 2) = 5(4) + 5(2)$$ $$(4 + 2)5 = 4(5) + 2(5)$$ $$9(5 - 4) = 9(5) - 9(4)$$
1.8 Simplifying Expressions ***Only like terms may be combined.*** We use the distributive property to combine like terms.	$-3y^2 + 6y^2 + 14y^2$ $\quad = (-3 + 6 + 14)y^2$ $\quad = 17y^2$ $\qquad$ $4(3 + 2x) - 6(5 - x)$ $\qquad = 4(3) + 4(2x) - 6(5) - 6(-x)$ $\qquad = 12 + 8x - 30 + 6x$ $\qquad = 14x - 18$

CHAPTER ① REVIEW EXERCISES

1.1 *Perform each indicated operation.*

1. $\dfrac{8}{5} \div \dfrac{32}{15}$ $\qquad$ **2.** $2\dfrac{4}{5} \cdot 1\dfrac{1}{4}$ $\qquad$ **3.** $\dfrac{5}{8} - \dfrac{1}{6}$ $\qquad$ **4.** $\dfrac{3}{8} + 3\dfrac{1}{2} - \dfrac{3}{16}$

The circle graph indicates the fraction of cars in different size categories sold in the United States in 2007. There were approximately 7618 thousand cars sold that year.

5. About how many luxury cars, to the nearest thousand, were sold?

6. To the nearest thousand, how many of the cars sold were *not* small cars?

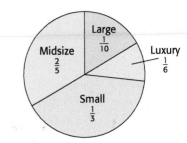

U.S. Car Sales by Size, 2007

Source: World Almanac and Book of Facts.

1.2 *Find the value of each exponential expression.*

7. 5^4 $\qquad$ **8.** $\left(\dfrac{3}{5}\right)^3$ $\qquad$ **9.** $(0.02)^2$ $\qquad$ **10.** $(0.1)^3$

Find the value of each expression.

11. $8 \cdot 5 - 13$ $\qquad$ **12.** $16 + 12 \div 4 - 2$ $\qquad$ **13.** $20 - 2(5 + 3)$

14. $7[3 + 6(3^2)]$ $\qquad$ **15.** $\dfrac{9(4^2 - 3)}{4 \cdot 5 - 17}$ $\qquad$ **16.** $\dfrac{6(5 - 4) + 2(4 - 2)}{3^2 - (4 + 3)}$

Tell whether each statement is true *or* false.

17. $12 \cdot 3 - 6 \cdot 6 \leq 0$ **18.** $3[5(2) - 3] > 20$ **19.** $9 \leq 4^2 - 8$

Write each word statement in symbols.

20. Thirteen is less than seventeen.   **21.** Five plus two is not equal to ten.

22. Two-thirds is greater than or equal to four-sixths.

1.3   *Evaluate each expression for x = 6 and y = 3.*

23. $2x + 6y$ **24.** $4(3x - y)$ **25.** $\dfrac{x}{3} + 4y$ **26.** $\dfrac{x^2 + 3}{3y - x}$

Write each word phrase as an algebraic expression, using x as the variable.

27. Six added to a number   **28.** A number subtracted from eight

29. Nine subtracted from six times a number   **30.** Three-fifths of a number added to 12

Decide whether the given number is a solution of the given equation.

31. $5x + 3(x + 2) = 22;$ 2   **32.** $\dfrac{t + 5}{3t} = 1;$ 6

Write each word statement as an equation. Use x as the variable. Then find the solution from the set $\{0, 2, 4, 6, 8, 10\}$.

33. Six less than twice a number is 10.   **34.** The product of a number and 4 is 8.

1.4   *Graph each group of numbers on a number line.*

35. $-4, -\dfrac{1}{2}, 0, 2.5, 5$ **36.** $-2, |-3|, -3, |-1|$

Classify each number, using the sets natural numbers, whole numbers, integers, rational numbers, irrational numbers, *and* real numbers.

37. $\dfrac{4}{3}$ **38.** $0.\overline{63}$ **39.** 19   **40.** $\sqrt{6}$

Select the lesser number in each pair.

41. $-10, 5$ **42.** $-8, -9$ **43.** $-\dfrac{2}{3}, -\dfrac{3}{4}$ **44.** $0, -|23|$

Decide whether each statement is true *or* false.

45. $12 > -13$ **46.** $0 > -5$ **47.** $-9 < -7$ **48.** $-13 \geq -13$

For each number, (a) find the opposite of the number and (b) find the absolute value of the number.

49. -9 **50.** 0   **51.** 6   **52.** $-\dfrac{5}{7}$

Simplify.

53. $|-12|$ **54.** $-|3|$ **55.** $-|-19|$ **56.** $-|9 - 2|$

1.5   *Perform each indicated operation.*

57. $-10 + 4$ **58.** $14 + (-18)$ **59.** $-8 + (-9)$

60. $\dfrac{4}{9} + \left(-\dfrac{5}{4}\right)$ **61.** $-13.5 + (-8.3)$ **62.** $(-10 + 7) + (-11)$

63. $[-6 + (-8) + 8] + [9 + (-13)]$ **64.** $(-4 + 7) + (-11 + 3) + (-15 + 1)$

65. $-7 - 4$

66. $-12 - (-11)$

67. $5 - (-2)$

68. $-\dfrac{3}{7} - \dfrac{4}{5}$

69. $2.56 - (-7.75)$

70. $(-10 - 4) - (-2)$

71. $(-3 + 4) - (-1)$

72. $-(-5 + 6) - 2$

Write a numerical expression for each phrase, and simplify the expression.

73. 19 added to the sum of -31 and 12

74. 13 more than the sum of -4 and -8

75. The difference between -4 and -6

76. Five less than the sum of 4 and -8

Find the solution of each equation from the set $\{-3, -2, -1, 0, 1, 2, 3\}$.

77. $x + (-2) = -4$

78. $12 + x = 11$

Solve each problem.

79. George Fagley found that his checkbook balance was $-\$23.75$, so he deposited $\$50.00$. What is his new balance?

80. The low temperature in Yellowknife, in the Canadian Northwest Territories, one January day was $-26°F$. It rose $16°$ that day. What was the high temperature?

81. Reginald Fulwood owed a friend $\$28$. He repaid $\$13$, but then borrowed another $\$14$. What positive or negative amount represents his present financial status?

82. If the temperature drops $7°$ below its previous level of $-3°$, what is the new temperature?

83. Mark Sanchez of the New York Jets passed for a gain of 8 yd, was sacked for a loss of 12 yd, and then threw a 42 yd touchdown pass. What positive or negative number represents the total net yardage for the plays?

84. On Monday, August 31, 2009, the Dow Jones Industrial Average closed at 9496.28, down 47.92 from the previous Friday. What was the closing value the previous Friday? (*Source: The Washington Post.*)

1.6 *Perform each indicated operation.*

85. $(-12)(-3)$

86. $15(-7)$

87. $-\dfrac{4}{3}\left(-\dfrac{3}{8}\right)$

88. $(-4.8)(-2.1)$

89. $5(8 - 12)$

90. $(5 - 7)(8 - 3)$

91. $2(-6) - (-4)(-3)$

92. $3(-10) - 5$

93. $\dfrac{-36}{-9}$

94. $\dfrac{220}{-11}$

95. $-\dfrac{1}{2} \div \dfrac{2}{3}$

96. $-33.9 \div (-3)$

97. $\dfrac{-5(3) - 1}{8 - 4(-2)}$

98. $\dfrac{5(-2) - 3(4)}{-2[3 - (-2)] - 1}$

99. $\dfrac{10^2 - 5^2}{8^2 + 3^2 - (-2)}$

100. $\dfrac{(0.6)^2 + (0.8)^2}{(-1.2)^2 - (-0.56)}$

Evaluate each expression if $x = -5$, $y = 4$, *and* $z = -3$.

101. $6x - 4z$

102. $5x + y - z$

103. $5x^2$

104. $z^2(3x - 8y)$

Write a numerical expression for each phrase, and simplify the expression.

105. Nine less than the product of -4 and 5

106. Five-sixths of the sum of 12 and -6

107. The quotient of 12 and the sum of 8 and -4

108. The product of -20 and 12, divided by the difference between 15 and -15

Write each sentence in symbols, using x as the variable, and find the solution from the list of integers between −12 and 12.

109. 8 times a number is −24.

110. The quotient of a number and 3 is −2.

Find the average of each group of numbers.

111. 26, 38, 40, 20, 4, 14, 96, 18

112. −12, 28, −36, 0, 12, −10

1.7 *Decide whether each statement is an example of the* commutative, associative, identity, inverse, *or* distributive *property.*

113. $6 + 0 = 6$

114. $5 \cdot 1 = 5$

115. $-\dfrac{2}{3}\left(-\dfrac{3}{2}\right) = 1$

116. $17 + (-17) = 0$

117. $5 + (-9 + 2) = [5 + (-9)] + 2$

118. $w(xy) = (wx)y$

119. $3x + 3y = 3(x + y)$

120. $(1 + 2) + 3 = 3 + (1 + 2)$

Use the distributive property to rewrite each expression. Simplify if possible.

121. $7y + 14$

122. $-12(4 - t)$

123. $3(2s) + 3(5y)$

124. $-(-4r + 5s)$

1.8 *Combine like terms whenever possible.*

125. $2m + 9m$

126. $15p^2 - 7p^2 + 8p^2$

127. $5p^2 - 4p + 6p + 11p^2$

128. $-2(3k - 5) + 2(k + 1)$

129. $7(2m + 3) - 2(8m - 4)$

130. $-(2k + 8) - (3k - 7)$

Translate each phrase into a mathematical expression. Use x to represent the number, and combine like terms when possible.

131. Seven times a number, subtracted from the product of −2 and three times the number

132. A number multiplied by 8, added to the sum of 5 and four times the number

MIXED REVIEW EXERCISES*

Perform each indicated operation.

133. $\dfrac{6(-4) + 2(-12)}{5(-3) + (-3)}$

134. $\dfrac{3}{8} - \dfrac{5}{12}$

135. $\dfrac{8^2 + 6^2}{7^2 + 1^2}$

136. $-\dfrac{12}{5} \div \dfrac{9}{7}$

137. $2\dfrac{5}{6} - 4\dfrac{1}{3}$

138. $\left(-\dfrac{5}{6}\right)^2$

139. $[(-2) + 7 - (-5)] + [-4 - (-10)]$

140. $-16(-3.5) - 7.2(-3)$

141. $-8 + [(-4 + 17) - (-3 - 3)]$

142. $-4(2t + 1) - 8(-3t + 4)$

143. $5x^2 - 12y^2 + 3x^2 - 9y^2$

144. $(-8 - 3) - 5(2 - 9)$

145. Write a sentence or two explaining the special considerations involving 0 in division.

146. The highest temperature ever recorded in Iowa was 118°F at Keokuk on July 20, 1934. The lowest temperature ever recorded in the state was at Elkader on February 3, 1996, and was 165° lower than the highest temperature. What is the record low temperature for Iowa? (*Source:* National Climatic Data Center.)

---

*The order of exercises in this final group does not correspond to the order in which topics occur in the chapter. This random ordering should help you prepare for the chapter test in yet another way.

(continued)

The bar graph shows public high school (grades 9–12) enrollment in millions for selected years from 1980 to 2005 in the United States. Use a signed number to represent the change in enrollment for each period.

147. 1980 to 1985

148. 1985 to 1990

149. 1995 to 2000

150. 2000 to 2005

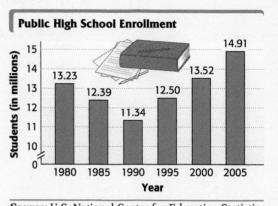

Public High School Enrollment

Source: U.S. National Center for Education Statistics.

CHAPTER (**1**)

TEST

CHAPTER
Test Prep
VIDEOS
Step-by-step test solutions are found on the Chapter Test Prep Videos available via the Video Resources on DVD, in *MyMathLab*, or on You Tube (search "LialCombinedAlgebra").

View the complete solutions to all Chapter Test exercises on the Video Resources on DVD.

1. Write $\frac{63}{99}$ in lowest terms.   **2.** Add: $\frac{5}{8} + \frac{11}{12} + \frac{7}{15}$.   **3.** Divide: $\frac{19}{15} \div \frac{6}{5}$.

4. *True* or *false?* $4[-20 + 7(-2)] \le 135$

5. Graph the group of numbers $-1, -3, |-4|, |-1|$ on a number line.

6. To which of the following sets does $-\frac{2}{3}$ belong: natural numbers, whole numbers, integers, rational numbers, irrational numbers, real numbers?

7. Explain how a number line can be used to show that -8 is less than -1.

8. Write in symbols: The quotient of -6 and the sum of 2 and -8. Simplify the expression.

Perform each indicated operation.

9. $-2 - (5 - 17) + (-6)$

10. $-5\frac{1}{2} + 2\frac{2}{3}$

11. $-6 - [-7 + (2 - 3)]$

12. $4^2 + (-8) - (2^3 - 6)$

13. $(-5)(-12) + 4(-4) + (-8)^2$

14. $\dfrac{30(-1 - 2)}{-9[3 - (-2)] - 12(-2)}$

Find the solution of each equation from the set $\{-6, -4, -2, 0, 2, 4, 6\}$.

15. $-x + 3 = -3$

16. $-3x = -12$

Evaluate each expression, given $x = -2$ and $y = 4$.

17. $3x - 4y^2$

18. $\dfrac{5x + 7y}{3(x + y)}$

Solve each problem.

19. The highest elevation in Argentina is Mt. Aconcagua, which is 6960 m above sea level. The lowest point in Argentina is the Valdés Peninsula, 40 m below sea level. Find the difference between the highest and lowest elevations.

20. For a certain system of rating relief pitchers, 3 points are awarded for a save, 3 points are awarded for a win, 2 points are subtracted for a loss, and 2 points are subtracted for a blown save. If Brad Lidge of the Philadelphia Phillies has 4 saves, 3 wins, 2 losses, and 1 blown save, how many points does he have?

21. For 2009, the U.S. federal government collected $2.10 trillion in revenues, but spent $3.52 trillion. Write the federal budget deficit as a signed number. (*Source: The Gazette.*)

Match each property in Column I with the example of it in Column II.

I	II
22. Commutative property	**A.** $3x + 0 = 3x$
23. Associative property	**B.** $(5 + 2) + 8 = 8 + (5 + 2)$
24. Inverse property	**C.** $-3(x + y) = -3x + (-3y)$
25. Identity property	**D.** $-5 + (3 + 2) = (-5 + 3) + 2$
26. Distributive property	**E.** $-\dfrac{5}{3}\left(-\dfrac{3}{5}\right) = 1$

27. What property is used to clear parentheses and write $3(x + 1)$ as $3x + 3$?

28. Consider the expression $-6[5 + (-2)]$.

   (a) Evaluate it by first working within the brackets.

   (b) Evaluate it by using the distributive property.

   (c) Why must the answers in parts (a) and (b) be the same?

Simplify by combining like terms.

29. $8x + 4x - 6x + x + 14x$

30. $5(2x - 1) - (x - 12) + 2(3x - 5)$

Linear Equations and Inequalities in One Variable

In 1924, 258 competitors gathered in Chamonix, France, for the 16 events of the first Olympic Winter Games. This small, mainly European, sports competition has become the world's largest global sporting event. The XXI Olympic Winter Games, hosted in 2010 by Vancouver, British Columbia, attracted 2500 athletes, who competed in 86 events. First introduced at the 1920 Games in Antwerp, Belgium, the five interlocking rings on the Olympic flag symbolize unity among the nations of Africa, the Americas, Asia, Australia, and Europe. (*Source:* www.olympic.org)

Throughout this chapter we use *linear equations* to solve applications about the Olympics.

2.1 The Addition Property of Equality

OBJECTIVES

1 Identify linear equations.

2 Use the addition property of equality.

3 Simplify, and then use the addition property of equality.

An **equation** is a statement asserting that two algebraic expressions are equal.

⚠ CAUTION *Remember that an equation includes an equals symbol.*

Equation (to solve)   Expression (to simplify or evaluate)

$$x - 5 = 2$$ $$x - 5$$

Left side   Right side

OBJECTIVE 1 **Identify linear equations.** The simplest type of equation is a *linear equation.*

Linear Equation in One Variable

A **linear equation in one variable** can be written in the form

$$Ax + B = C,$$

where A, B, and C are real numbers, and $A \neq 0$.

$$4x + 9 = 0, \quad 2x - 3 = 5, \quad \text{and} \quad x = 7 \qquad \text{Linear equations}$$

$$x^2 + 2x = 5, \quad \frac{1}{x} = 6, \quad \text{and} \quad |2x + 6| = 0 \qquad \textit{Non}\text{linear equations}$$

A **solution** of an equation is a number that makes the equation true when it replaces the variable. An equation is solved by finding its **solution set,** the set of all solutions. Equations with exactly the same solution sets are **equivalent equations.**

A linear equation in x is solved by using a series of steps to produce a simpler equivalent equation of the form

$$x = \text{a number} \qquad \text{or} \qquad \text{a number} = x.$$

OBJECTIVE 2 **Use the addition property of equality.** In the linear equation $x - 5 = 2$, both $x - 5$ and 2 represent the same number because that is the meaning of the equals symbol. To solve the equation, we change the left side from $x - 5$ to just x, as follows.

$x - 5 = 2$	Given equation
$x - 5 + 5 = 2 + 5$	Add 5 to *each* side to keep them equal.
$x + 0 = 7$	Additive inverse property
$x = 7$	Additive identity property

Add 5. It is the opposite (additive inverse) of −5, and −5 + 5 = 0.

The solution is 7. We check by replacing x with 7 in the original equation.

CHECK		
	$x - 5 = 2$	Original equation
	$7 - 5 \overset{?}{=} 2$	Let $x = 7$.
	$2 = 2 \checkmark$	True

The left side equals the right side.

Since the final equation is true, 7 checks as the solution and $\{7\}$ is the solution set.

To solve the equation $x - 5 = 2$, we used the **addition property of equality.**

> ### Addition Property of Equality
>
> If A, B, and C represent real numbers, then the equations
>
> $$A = B \quad \text{and} \quad A + C = B + C$$
>
> are equivalent equations.
>
> That is, we can add the same number to each side of an equation without changing the solution.

FIGURE 1

In this property, C represents a real number. Any quantity that represents a real number can be added to each side of an equation to obtain an equivalent equation.

NOTE Equations can be thought of in terms of a balance. Thus, adding the same quantity to each side does not affect the balance. See **FIGURE 1**.

NOW TRY
EXERCISE 1
Solve $x - 13 = 4$.

EXAMPLE 1 Applying the Addition Property of Equality

Solve $x - 16 = 7$.

Our goal is to get an equivalent equation of the form $x = $ a number.

$$x - 16 = 7$$
$$x - 16 + 16 = 7 + 16 \qquad \text{Add 16 to each side.}$$
$$x = 23 \qquad \text{Combine like terms.}$$

CHECK Substitute 23 for x in the *original* equation.

$$x - 16 = 7 \qquad \text{Original equation}$$
$$23 - 16 \stackrel{?}{=} 7 \qquad \text{Let } x = 23.$$

7 is *not the* solution.

$$7 = 7 \checkmark \qquad \text{True}$$

Since a true statement results, 23 is the solution and $\{23\}$ is the solution set.

NOW TRY

⚠ CAUTION *The final line of the check does* **not** *give the solution to the problem,* only a confirmation that the solution found is correct.

NOW TRY
EXERCISE 2
Solve $t - 5.7 = -7.2$.

EXAMPLE 2 Applying the Addition Property of Equality

Solve $x - 2.9 = -6.4$.

Our goal is to isolate x.

$$x - 2.9 = -6.4$$
$$x - 2.9 + 2.9 = -6.4 + 2.9 \qquad \text{Add 2.9 to each side.}$$
$$x = -3.5$$

CHECK
$$x - 2.9 = -6.4 \qquad \text{Original equation}$$
$$-3.5 - 2.9 \stackrel{?}{=} -6.4 \qquad \text{Let } x = -3.5.$$
$$-6.4 = -6.4 \checkmark \qquad \text{True}$$

NOW TRY ANSWERS
1. $\{17\}$ **2.** $\{-1.5\}$

Since a true statement results, the solution set is $\{-3.5\}$. NOW TRY

The addition property of equality says that the same number may be *added* to each side of an equation. In **Section 1.5,** subtraction was defined as addition of the opposite. Thus, we can also use the following rule when solving an equation.

> **The same number may be *subtracted* from each side of an equation without changing the solution.**

**NOW TRY
EXERCISE 3**

Solve $-15 = x + 12$.

EXAMPLE 3 Applying the Addition Property of Equality

Solve $-7 = x + 22$.

Here, the variable x is on the right side of the equation.

$$-7 = x + 22 \quad \boxed{\text{The variable can be isolated on } \textit{either} \text{ side.}}$$

$$-7 - 22 = x + 22 - 22 \qquad \text{Subtract 22 from each side.}$$

$$-29 = x, \quad \text{or} \quad x = -29 \qquad \begin{array}{l}\text{Rewrite; a number } = x,\\ \text{or } x = \text{a number.}\end{array}$$

CHECK
$$-7 = x + 22 \qquad \text{Original equation}$$
$$-7 \stackrel{?}{=} -29 + 22 \qquad \text{Let } x = -29.$$
$$-7 = -7 \checkmark \qquad \text{True}$$

The check confirms that the solution set is $\{-29\}$.

NOW TRY

NOTE In **Example 3,** what happens if we subtract $-7 - 22$ incorrectly, obtaining $x = -15$, instead of $x = -29$, as the last line of the solution? A check should indicate an error.

CHECK
$$-7 = x + 22 \qquad \text{Original equation from } \textbf{Example 3}$$
$$\boxed{\begin{array}{l}\text{The left side does}\\ \textit{not} \text{ equal the}\\ \text{right side.}\end{array}} \quad -7 \stackrel{?}{=} -15 + 22 \qquad \text{Let } x = -15.$$
$$-7 = 7 \qquad \text{False}$$

The false statement indicates that -15 is *not* a solution of the equation. If this happens, rework the problem.

**NOW TRY
EXERCISE 4**

Solve $\frac{2}{3}x - 4 = \frac{5}{3}x$.

EXAMPLE 4 Subtracting a Variable Expression

Solve $\frac{3}{5}x + 17 = \frac{8}{5}x$.

$$\frac{3}{5}x + 17 = \frac{8}{5}x \qquad \text{Original equation}$$

$$\frac{3}{5}x + 17 - \frac{3}{5}x = \frac{8}{5}x - \frac{3}{5}x \qquad \text{Subtract } \tfrac{3}{5}x \text{ from each side.}$$

$$\boxed{\begin{array}{l}\text{From now on we}\\ \text{will skip this step.}\end{array}} \quad 17 = 1x \qquad \tfrac{3}{5}x - \tfrac{3}{5}x = 0;\ \tfrac{8}{5}x - \tfrac{3}{5}x = \tfrac{5}{5}x = 1x$$

$$17 = x \qquad \text{Multiplicative identity property}$$

Check by replacing x with 17 in the original equation. The solution set is $\{17\}$.

NOW TRY ANSWERS
3. $\{-27\}$ 4. $\{-4\}$

NOW TRY

66. $-5x + 4x - 8x = 0$ **67.** $8w - 4w + w = -3$ **68.** $9x - 3x + x = -4$

69. $\dfrac{1}{3}x - \dfrac{1}{4}x + \dfrac{1}{12}x = 3$ **70.** $\dfrac{2}{5}x + \dfrac{1}{10}x - \dfrac{1}{20}x = 18$

71. *Concept Check* Write an equation that requires the use of the multiplication property of equality, where each side must be multiplied by $\frac{2}{3}$ and the solution is a negative number.

72. *Concept Check* Write an equation that requires the use of the multiplication property of equality, where each side must be divided by 100 and the solution is not an integer.

Write an equation using the information given in the problem. Use x as the variable. Then solve the equation.

73. When a number is multiplied by 4, the result is 6. Find the number.

74. When a number is multiplied by -4, the result is 10. Find the number.

75. When a number is divided by -5, the result is 2. Find the number.

76. If twice a number is divided by 5, the result is 4. Find the number.

PREVIEW EXERCISES

Simplify each expression. **See Section 1.8.**

77. $-(3m + 5)$ **78.** $-4(-1 + 6x)$

79. $4(-5 + 2p) - 3(p - 4)$ **80.** $2(4k - 7) - 4(-k + 3)$

Solve each equation. **See Section 2.1.**

81. $4x + 5 + 2x = 7x$ **82.** $2x + 5x - 3x + 4 = 3x + 2$

2.3 More on Solving Linear Equations

OBJECTIVES

1. Learn and use the four steps for solving a linear equation.
2. Solve equations with fractions or decimals as coefficients.
3. Solve equations with no solution or infinitely many solutions.
4. Write expressions for two related unknown quantities.

OBJECTIVE 1 **Learn and use the four steps for solving a linear equation.**
We now apply *both* properties of equality to solve linear equations.

Solving a Linear Equation

Step 1 **Simplify each side separately.** Clear (eliminate) parentheses, fractions, and decimals, using the distributive property as needed, and combine like terms.

Step 2 **Isolate the variable term on one side.** Use the addition property if necessary so that the variable term is on one side of the equation and a number is on the other.

Step 3 **Isolate the variable.** Use the multiplication property if necessary to get the equation in the form $x =$ a number, or a number $= x$. (Other letters may be used for variables.)

Step 4 **Check.** Substitute the proposed solution into the *original* equation to see if a true statement results. If not, rework the problem.

Remember that when we solve an equation, our primary goal is to isolate the variable on one side of the equation.

**NOW TRY
EXERCISE 1**
Solve $7 + 2m = -3$.

EXAMPLE 1 Applying Both Properties of Equality to Solve an Equation

Solve $-6x + 5 = 17$.

Step 1 There are no parentheses, fractions, or decimals in this equation, so this step is not necessary.

Our goal is to isolate x.

$$-6x + 5 = 17$$

Step 2
$$-6x + 5 - 5 = 17 - 5 \qquad \text{Subtract 5 from each side.}$$
$$-6x = 12 \qquad \text{Combine like terms.}$$

Step 3
$$\frac{-6x}{-6} = \frac{12}{-6} \qquad \text{Divide each side by } -6.$$
$$x = -2$$

Step 4 Check by substituting -2 for x in the original equation.

CHECK
$$-6x + 5 = 17 \qquad \text{Original equation}$$
$$-6(-2) + 5 \stackrel{?}{=} 17 \qquad \text{Let } x = -2.$$
$$12 + 5 \stackrel{?}{=} 17 \qquad \text{Multiply.}$$
$$17 = 17 \ \checkmark \qquad \text{True}$$

The solution, -2, checks, so the solution set is $\{-2\}$. **NOW TRY**

**NOW TRY
EXERCISE 2**
Solve $2q + 3 = 4q - 9$.

EXAMPLE 2 Applying Both Properties of Equality to Solve an Equation

Solve $3x + 2 = 5x - 8$.

Step 1 There are no parentheses, fractions, or decimals in the equation.

Our goal is to isolate x.

$$3x + 2 = 5x - 8$$

Step 2
$$3x + 2 - 5x = 5x - 8 - 5x \qquad \text{Subtract } 5x \text{ from each side.}$$
$$-2x + 2 = -8 \qquad \text{Combine like terms.}$$
$$-2x + 2 - 2 = -8 - 2 \qquad \text{Subtract 2 from each side.}$$
$$-2x = -10 \qquad \text{Combine like terms.}$$

Step 3
$$\frac{-2x}{-2} = \frac{-10}{-2} \qquad \text{Divide each side by } -2.$$
$$x = 5$$

Step 4 Check by substituting 5 for x in the original equation.

CHECK
$$3x + 2 = 5x - 8 \qquad \text{Original equation}$$
$$3(5) + 2 \stackrel{?}{=} 5(5) - 8 \qquad \text{Let } x = 5.$$
$$15 + 2 \stackrel{?}{=} 25 - 8 \qquad \text{Multiply.}$$
$$17 = 17 \ \checkmark \qquad \text{True}$$

The solution, 5, checks, so the solution set is $\{5\}$. **NOW TRY**

NOW TRY ANSWERS
1. $\{-5\}$ **2.** $\{6\}$

NOTE *Remember that the variable can be isolated on either side of the equation.* In **Example 2,** x will be isolated on the right if we begin by subtracting $3x$.

$$3x + 2 = 5x - 8 \qquad \text{Equation from \textbf{Example 2}}$$
$$3x + 2 - 3x = 5x - 8 - 3x \qquad \text{Subtract } 3x \text{ from each side.}$$
$$2 = 2x - 8 \qquad \text{Combine like terms.}$$
$$2 + 8 = 2x - 8 + 8 \qquad \text{Add 8 to each side.}$$
$$10 = 2x \qquad \text{Combine like terms.}$$
$$\frac{10}{2} = \frac{2x}{2} \qquad \text{Divide each side by 2.}$$
$$5 = x \qquad \text{The same solution results.}$$

There are often several equally correct ways to solve an equation.

NOW TRY
EXERCISE 3

Solve.

$$3(z - 6) - 5z = -7z + 7$$

EXAMPLE 3   Using the Four Steps to Solve an Equation

Solve $4(k - 3) - k = k - 6$.

Step 1   Clear parentheses using the distributive property.

$$4(k - 3) - k = k - 6$$
$$4(k) + 4(-3) - k = k - 6 \qquad \text{Distributive property}$$
$$4k - 12 - k = k - 6 \qquad \text{Multiply.}$$
$$3k - 12 = k - 6 \qquad \text{Combine like terms.}$$

Step 2
$$3k - 12 - k = k - 6 - k \qquad \text{Subtract } k.$$
$$2k - 12 = -6 \qquad \text{Combine like terms.}$$
$$2k - 12 + 12 = -6 + 12 \qquad \text{Add 12.}$$
$$2k = 6 \qquad \text{Combine like terms.}$$

Step 3
$$\frac{2k}{2} = \frac{6}{2} \qquad \text{Divide by 2.}$$
$$k = 3$$

Step 4   CHECK
$$4(k - 3) - k = k - 6 \qquad \text{Original equation}$$
$$4(3 - 3) - 3 \overset{?}{=} 3 - 6 \qquad \text{Let } k = 3.$$
$$4(0) - 3 \overset{?}{=} 3 - 6 \qquad \text{Work inside the parentheses.}$$
$$-3 = -3 \ \checkmark \qquad \text{True}$$

The solution set of the equation is $\{3\}$.   *NOW TRY*

EXAMPLE 4   Using the Four Steps to Solve an Equation

Solve $8z - (3 + 2z) = 3z + 1$.

Step 1
$$8z - (3 + 2z) = 3z + 1$$
$$8z - 1(3 + 2z) = 3z + 1 \qquad \text{Multiplicative identity property}$$
$$8z - 3 - 2z = 3z + 1 \qquad \text{Distributive property}$$

Be careful with signs.

$$6z - 3 = 3z + 1 \qquad \text{Combine like terms.}$$

NOW TRY ANSWER
3. $\{5\}$

NOW TRY
EXERCISE 4

Solve.

$5x - (x + 9) = x - 4$

Step 2 $6z - 3 - 3z = 3z + 1 - 3z$ Subtract 3z.

$3z - 3 = 1$ Combine like terms.

$3z - 3 + 3 = 1 + 3$ Add 3.

$3z = 4$ Combine like terms.

Step 3 $\dfrac{3z}{3} = \dfrac{4}{3}$ Divide by 3.

$z = \dfrac{4}{3}$

Step 4   Check that $\left\{\dfrac{4}{3}\right\}$ is the solution set.   NOW TRY

⚠ **CAUTION**   In an expression such as $8z - (3 + 2z)$ in **Example 4,** the $-$ sign acts like a factor of -1 and affects the sign of *every* term within the parentheses.

$$8z - (3 + 2z)$$
$$= 8z - 1(3 + 2z)$$
$$= 8z + (-1)(3 + 2z)$$
$$= 8z - 3 - 2z$$

Change to $-$ in *both* terms.

NOW TRY
EXERCISE 5

Solve.

$24 - 4(7 - 2t) = 4(t - 1)$

EXAMPLE 5   Using the Four Steps to Solve an Equation

Solve $4(4 - 3x) = 32 - 8(x + 2)$.

Step 1 $4(4 - 3x) = 32 - 8(x + 2)$ Be careful with signs.

$16 - 12x = 32 - 8x - 16$ Distributive property

$16 - 12x = 16 - 8x$ Combine like terms.

Step 2 $16 - 12x + 8x = 16 - 8x + 8x$ Add 8x.

$16 - 4x = 16$ Combine like terms.

$16 - 4x - 16 = 16 - 16$ Subtract 16.

$-4x = 0$ Combine like terms.

Step 3 $\dfrac{-4x}{-4} = \dfrac{0}{-4}$ Divide by -4.

$x = 0$

Step 4   CHECK $4(4 - 3x) = 32 - 8(x + 2)$ Original equation

$4[4 - 3(0)] \overset{?}{=} 32 - 8(0 + 2)$ Let x = 0.

$4(4 - 0) \overset{?}{=} 32 - 8(2)$ Multiply and add.

$4(4) \overset{?}{=} 32 - 16$ Subtract and multiply.

$16 = 16 \checkmark$ True

Since the solution 0 checks, the solution set is $\{0\}$.   NOW TRY

OBJECTIVE 2   Solve equations with fractions or decimals as coefficients.

To avoid messy computations, we clear an equation of fractions by multiplying each side by the least common denominator (LCD) of all the fractions in the equation.

NOW TRY ANSWERS

4. $\left\{\dfrac{5}{3}\right\}$ **5.** $\{0\}$

⚠️ **CAUTION** *When clearing an equation of fractions, be sure to multiply every term on each side of the equation by the LCD.*

NOW TRY
EXERCISE 6
Solve.

$$\frac{1}{2}x + \frac{5}{8}x = \frac{3}{4}x - 6$$

EXAMPLE 6 Solving an Equation with Fractions as Coefficients

Solve $\frac{2}{3}x - \frac{1}{2}x = -\frac{1}{6}x - 2$.

Step 1 The LCD of all the fractions in the equation is 6.

$$\frac{2}{3}x - \frac{1}{2}x = -\frac{1}{6}x - 2$$

> Pay particular attention here.

$$6\left(\frac{2}{3}x - \frac{1}{2}x\right) = 6\left(-\frac{1}{6}x - 2\right)$$

Multiply each side by 6, the LCD.

$$6\left(\frac{2}{3}x\right) + 6\left(-\frac{1}{2}x\right) = 6\left(-\frac{1}{6}x\right) + 6(-2)$$

Distributive property; multiply *each* term inside the parentheses by 6.

> The fractions have been cleared.

$$4x - 3x = -x - 12$$ Multiply.

$$x = -x - 12$$ Combine like terms.

Step 2 $$x + x = -x - 12 + x$$ Add *x*.

$$2x = -12$$ Combine like terms.

Step 3 $$\frac{2x}{2} = \frac{-12}{2}$$ Divide by 2.

$$x = -6$$

Step 4 CHECK $$\frac{2}{3}x - \frac{1}{2}x = -\frac{1}{6}x - 2$$ Original equation

$$\frac{2}{3}(-6) - \frac{1}{2}(-6) \overset{?}{=} -\frac{1}{6}(-6) - 2$$ Let $x = -6$.

$$-4 + 3 \overset{?}{=} 1 - 2$$ Multiply.

$$-1 = -1 \ \checkmark$$ True

The solution, -6, checks, so the solution set is $\{-6\}$.   NOW TRY

EXAMPLE 7 Solving an Equation with Fractions as Coefficients

Solve $\frac{1}{3}(x + 5) - \frac{3}{5}(x + 2) = 1$.

Step 1 $$\frac{1}{3}(x + 5) - \frac{3}{5}(x + 2) = 1$$

$$15\left[\frac{1}{3}(x + 5) - \frac{3}{5}(x + 2)\right] = 15(1)$$

Clear the fractions. Multiply by 15, the LCD.

$$15\left[\frac{1}{3}(x + 5)\right] + 15\left[-\frac{3}{5}(x + 2)\right] = 15(1)$$

Distributive property

$$5(x + 5) - 9(x + 2) = 15$$ Multiply.

$$\boxed{\begin{array}{l}15[\frac{1}{3}(x + 5)] \\ = 15 \cdot \frac{1}{3} \cdot (x + 5) \\ = 5(x + 5)\end{array}}$$

$$5x + 25 - 9x - 18 = 15$$ Distributive property

$$-4x + 7 = 15$$ Combine like terms.

NOW TRY ANSWER
6. $\{-16\}$

NOW TRY
EXERCISE 7
Solve.

$$\frac{2}{3}(x + 2) - \frac{1}{2}(3x + 4) = -4$$

Step 2

$$-4x + 7 - 7 = 15 - 7 \quad \text{Subtract 7.}$$

$$-4x = 8 \quad \text{Combine like terms.}$$

Step 3

$$\frac{-4x}{-4} = \frac{8}{-4} \quad \text{Divide by } -4.$$

$$x = -2$$

Step 4 Check to confirm that $\{-2\}$ is the solution set.

NOW TRY

> ⚠ **CAUTION** Be sure you understand how to multiply by the LCD to clear an equation of fractions. *Study Step 1 in Examples 6 and 7 carefully.*

NOW TRY
EXERCISE 8
Solve.

$$0.05(13 - t) - 0.2t = 0.08(30)$$

EXAMPLE 8 Solving an Equation with Decimals as Coefficients

Solve $0.1t + 0.05(20 - t) = 0.09(20)$.

Step 1 The decimals here are expressed as tenths (0.1) and hundredths $(0.05$ and $0.09)$. We choose the least exponent on 10 needed to eliminate the decimals. Here, we use $10^2 = 100$.

$$0.1t + 0.05(20 - t) = 0.09(20)$$

$$0.10t + 0.05(20 - t) = 0.09(20) \quad 0.1 = 0.10$$

$$100[0.10t + 0.05(20 - t)] = 100[0.09(20)] \quad \text{Multiply by 100.}$$

$$100(0.10t) + 100[0.05(20 - t)] = 100[0.09(20)] \quad \text{Distributive property}$$

$$10t + 5(20 - t) = 9(20) \quad \text{Multiply.}$$

$$10t + 5(20) + 5(-t) = 180 \quad \text{Distributive property}$$

$$10t + 100 - 5t = 180 \quad \text{Multiply.}$$

$$5t + 100 = 180 \quad \text{Combine like terms.}$$

Step 2

$$5t + 100 - 100 = 180 - 100 \quad \text{Subtract 100.}$$

$$5t = 80 \quad \text{Combine like terms.}$$

Step 3

$$\frac{5t}{5} = \frac{80}{5} \quad \text{Divide by 5.}$$

$$t = 16$$

Step 4 Check to confirm that $\{16\}$ is the solution set.

NOW TRY

> **NOTE** In **Example 8**, multiplying by 100 is the same as moving the decimal point two places to the right.
>
> $$0.10t + 0.05(20 - t) = 0.09(20)$$
>
> $$10t + 5(20 - t) = 9(20) \quad \text{Multiply by 100.}$$

OBJECTIVE 3 Solve equations with no solution or infinitely many solutions. Each equation so far has had exactly one solution. An equation with exactly one solution is a **conditional equation** because it is only true under certain conditions. Some equations may have no solution or infinitely many solutions.

NOW TRY ANSWERS
7. $\{4\}$ 8. $\{-7\}$

NOW TRY
EXERCISE 9

Solve.

$-3(x - 7) = 2x - 5x + 21$

EXAMPLE 9   Solving an Equation That Has Infinitely Many Solutions

Solve $5x - 15 = 5(x - 3)$.

$$5x - 15 = 5(x - 3)$$

$$5x - 15 = 5x - 15 \qquad \text{Distributive property}$$

$$5x - 15 - 5x = 5x - 15 - 5x \qquad \text{Subtract } 5x.$$

Notice that the variable "disappeared."

$$-15 = -15 \qquad \text{Combine like terms.}$$

$$-15 + 15 = -15 + 15 \qquad \text{Add 15.}$$

$$0 = 0 \qquad \text{True}$$

Solution set: {all real numbers}

Since the last statement $(0 = 0)$ is true, *any* real number is a solution. We could have predicted this from the second line in the solution,

$$5x - 15 = 5x - 15. \leftarrow \text{This is true for } any \text{ value of } x.$$

Try several values for x in the original equation to see that they all satisfy it.

An equation with both sides exactly the same, like $0 = 0$, is called an **identity.** An identity is true for all replacements of the variables. As shown above, we write the solution set as **{all real numbers}.**   NOW TRY

⚠ CAUTION   In **Example 9,** do not write $\{0\}$ as the solution set. While 0 is a solution, there are infinitely many other solutions. *For* $\{0\}$ *to be the solution set, the last line must include a variable, such as x, and read* $x = 0$, *not* $0 = 0$.

NOW TRY
EXERCISE 10

Solve.

$-4x + 12 = 3 - 4(x - 3)$

EXAMPLE 10   Solving an Equation That Has No Solution

Solve $2x + 3(x + 1) = 5x + 4$.

$$2x + 3(x + 1) = 5x + 4$$

$$2x + 3x + 3 = 5x + 4 \qquad \text{Distributive property}$$

$$5x + 3 = 5x + 4 \qquad \text{Combine like terms.}$$

$$5x + 3 - 5x = 5x + 4 - 5x \qquad \text{Subtract } 5x.$$

Again, the variable "disappeared."

$$3 = 4 \qquad \text{False}$$

There is no solution.   Solution set: ∅

A false statement $(3 = 4)$ results. The original equation, called a **contradiction,** has no solution. Its solution set is the **empty set,** or **null set,** symbolized **∅.**   NOW TRY

⚠ CAUTION   **DO NOT** write $\{\emptyset\}$ to represent the empty set.

The table summarizes the solution sets of the equations in this section.

Type of Equation	Final Equation in Solution	Number of Solutions	Solution Set
Conditional (See Examples 1–8.)	x = a number	One	{a number}
Identity (See Example 9.)	A true statement with no variable, such as $0 = 0$	Infinite	{all real numbers}
Contradiction (See Example 10.)	A false statement with no variable, such as $3 = 4$	None	∅

NOW TRY ANSWERS
9. {all real numbers}   10. ∅

OBJECTIVE 4 Write expressions for two related unknown quantities.

NOW TRY
EXERCISE 11
Two numbers have a sum of 18. If one of the numbers is represented by m, find an expression for the other number.

EXAMPLE 11 Translating a Phrase into an Algebraic Expression

Perform each translation.

(a) Two numbers have a sum of 23. If one of the numbers is represented by x, find an expression for the other number.

First, suppose that the sum of two numbers is 23, and one of the numbers is 10. How would you find the other number? You would subtract 10 from 23.

$$23 - 10 \leftarrow \text{This gives 13 as the other number.}$$

Instead of using 10 as one of the numbers, use x. The other number would be obtained in the same way—by subtracting x from 23.

$$23 - x. \quad \leftarrow \boxed{x - 23 \text{ is not correct.}}$$

To check, find the sum of the two numbers:

$$x + (23 - x) = 23, \quad \text{as required.}$$

(b) Two numbers have a product of 24. If one of the numbers is represented by x, find an expression for the other number.

Suppose that one of the numbers is 4. To find the other number, we would divide 24 by 4.

$$\frac{24}{4} \leftarrow \begin{array}{l} \text{This gives 6 as the other number.} \\ \text{The product } 6 \cdot 4 \text{ is 24.} \end{array}$$

In the same way, if x is one of the numbers, then we divide 24 by x to find the other number.

NOW TRY ANSWER
11. $18 - m$

$$\frac{24}{x} \leftarrow \text{The other number} \qquad \text{NOW TRY}$$

2.3 EXERCISES

MyMathLab   Math XL PRACTICE   WATCH   DOWNLOAD   READ   REVIEW

🌐 *Complete solution available on the Video Resources on DVD*

✎ *Using the methods of this section, what should we do first when solving each equation? Do not actually solve.*

1. $7x + 8 = 1$

2. $7x - 5x + 15 = 8 + x$

3. $3(2t - 4) = 20 - 2t$

4. $\frac{3}{4}z = -15$

5. $\frac{2}{3}x - \frac{1}{6} = \frac{3}{2}x + 1$

6. $0.9x + 0.3(x + 12) = 6$

7. *Concept Check* Which equation does *not* have {all real numbers} as its solution set?

   A. $5x = 4x + x$ **B.** $2(x + 6) = 2x + 12$ **C.** $\frac{1}{2}x = 0.5x$ **D.** $3x = 2x$

8. *Concept Check* The expression $100[0.03(x - 10)]$ is equivalent to which of the following?

   A. $0.03x - 0.3$ **B.** $3x - 3$ **C.** $3x - 10$ **D.** $3x - 30$

Solve each equation, and check your solution. See Examples 1–5, 9, and 10.

9. $3x + 2 = 14$

10. $4x + 3 = 27$

11. $-5z - 4 = 21$

12. $-7w - 4 = 10$

13. $4p - 5 = 2p$

14. $6q - 2 = 3q$

15. $2x + 9 = 4x + 11$ **16.** $7p + 8 = 9p - 2$ **17.** $5m + 8 = 7 + 3m$

18. $4r + 2 = r - 6$ **19.** $-12x - 5 = 10 - 7x$ **20.** $-16w - 3 = 13 - 8w$

21. $12h - 5 = 11h + 5 - h$ **22.** $-4x - 1 = -5x + 1 + 3x$

23. $7r - 5r + 2 = 5r + 2 - r$ **24.** $9p - 4p + 6 = 7p + 6 - 3p$

25. $3(4x + 2) + 5x = 30 - x$ **26.** $5(2m + 3) - 4m = 2m + 25$

27. $-2p + 7 = 3 - (5p + 1)$ **28.** $4x + 9 = 3 - (x - 2)$

29. $6(3w + 5) = 2(10w + 10)$ **30.** $4(2x - 1) = -6(x + 3)$

31. $-(4x + 2) - (-3x - 5) = 3$ **32.** $-(6k - 5) - (-5k + 8) = -3$

33. $6(4x - 1) = 12(2x + 3)$ **34.** $6(2x + 8) = 4(3x - 6)$

35. $3(2x - 4) = 6(x - 2)$ **36.** $3(6 - 4x) = 2(-6x + 9)$

37. $11x - 5(x + 2) = 6x + 5$ **38.** $6x - 4(x + 1) = 2x + 4$

Solve each equation, and check your solution. **See Examples 6–8.**

39. $\dfrac{3}{5}t - \dfrac{1}{10}t = t - \dfrac{5}{2}$ **40.** $-\dfrac{2}{7}r + 2r = \dfrac{1}{2}r + \dfrac{17}{2}$

41. $\dfrac{3}{4}x - \dfrac{1}{3}x + 5 = \dfrac{5}{6}x$ **42.** $\dfrac{1}{5}x - \dfrac{2}{3}x - 2 = -\dfrac{2}{5}x$

43. $\dfrac{1}{7}(3x + 2) - \dfrac{1}{5}(x + 4) = 2$ **44.** $\dfrac{1}{4}(3x - 1) + \dfrac{1}{6}(x + 3) = 3$

45. $-\dfrac{1}{4}(x - 12) + \dfrac{1}{2}(x + 2) = x + 4$ **46.** $\dfrac{1}{9}(p + 18) + \dfrac{1}{3}(2p + 3) = p + 3$

47. $\dfrac{2}{3}k - \left(k - \dfrac{1}{2}\right) = \dfrac{1}{6}(k - 51)$ **48.** $-\dfrac{5}{6}q - (q - 1) = \dfrac{1}{4}(-q + 80)$

49. $0.2(60) + 0.05x = 0.1(60 + x)$ **50.** $0.3(30) + 0.15x = 0.2(30 + x)$

51. $1.00x + 0.05(12 - x) = 0.10(63)$ **52.** $0.92x + 0.98(12 - x) = 0.96(12)$

53. $0.6(10{,}000) + 0.8x = 0.72(10{,}000 + x)$ **54.** $0.2(5000) + 0.3x = 0.25(5000 + x)$

Solve each equation, and check your solution. **See Examples 1–10.**

55. $10(2x - 1) = 8(2x + 1) + 14$ **56.** $9(3k - 5) = 12(3k - 1) - 51$

57. $\dfrac{1}{2}(x + 2) + \dfrac{3}{4}(x + 4) = x + 5$ **58.** $\dfrac{1}{3}(x + 3) + \dfrac{1}{6}(x - 6) = x + 3$

59. $0.1(x + 80) + 0.2x = 14$ **60.** $0.3(x + 15) + 0.4(x + 25) = 25$

61. $4(x + 8) = 2(2x + 6) + 20$ **62.** $4(x + 3) = 2(2x + 8) - 4$

63. $9(v + 1) - 3v = 2(3v + 1) - 8$ **64.** $8(t - 3) + 4t = 6(2t + 1) - 10$

Write the answer to each problem in terms of the variable. **See Example 11.**

65. Two numbers have a sum of 11. One of the numbers is q. What expression represents the other number?

66. Two numbers have a sum of 34. One of the numbers is r. What expression represents the other number?

67. The product of two numbers is 9. One of the numbers is x. What expression represents the other number?

68. The product of two numbers is -6. One of the numbers is m. What expression represents the other number?

69. A football player gained x yards rushing. On the next down, he gained 9 yd. What expression represents the number of yards he gained altogether?

70. A football player gained y yards on a punt return. On the next return, he gained 6 yd. What expression represents the number of yards he gained altogether?

71. A baseball player got 65 hits one season. He got h of the hits in one game. What expression represents the number of hits he got in the rest of the games?

72. A hockey player scored 42 goals in one season. He scored n goals in one game. What expression represents the number of goals he scored in the rest of the games?

73. Monica is x years old. What expression represents her age 15 yr from now? 5 yr ago?

74. Chandler is y years old. What expression represents his age 4 yr ago? 11 yr from now?

75. Cliff has r quarters. Express the value of the quarters in cents.

76. Claire has y dimes. Express the value of the dimes in cents.

77. A bank teller has t dollars, all in $5 bills. What expression represents the number of $5 bills the teller has?

78. A clerk has v dollars, all in $10 bills. What expression represents the number of $10 bills the clerk has?

79. A plane ticket costs x dollars for an adult and y dollars for a child. Find an expression that represents the total cost for 3 adults and 2 children.

80. A concert ticket costs p dollars for an adult and q dollars for a child. Find an expression that represents the total cost for 4 adults and 6 children.

PREVIEW EXERCISES

Write each phrase as a mathematical expression using x as the variable. ***See Sections 1.3, 1.5, 1.6, and 1.8.***

81. A number added to -6

82. A number decreased by 9

83. The difference between -5 and a number

84. The quotient of -6 and a nonzero number

85. The product of 12 and the difference between a number and 9

86. The quotient of 9 more than a number and 6 less than the number

---

SUMMARY EXERCISES on Solving Linear Equations

This section provides practice in solving all the types of linear equations introduced in ***Sections 2.1–2.3.***

Solve each equation, and check your solution.

1. $x + 2 = -3$

2. $2m + 8 = 16$

3. $12.5x = -63.75$

4. $-x = -12$

5. $\dfrac{4}{5}x = -20$

6. $7m - 5m = -12$

7. $5x - 9 = 3(x - 3)$

8. $\dfrac{x}{-2} = 8$

9. $-x = 6$

10. $\dfrac{2}{3}x + 8 = \dfrac{1}{4}x$

11. $4x + 2(3 - 2x) = 6$

12. $-6z = -14$

13. $-3(m - 4) + 2(5 + 2m) = 29$

14. $-0.3x + 2.1(x - 4) = -6.6$

15. $0.08x + 0.06(x + 9) = 1.24$

16. $x - 16.2 = 7.5$

17. $7m - (2m - 9) = 39$

18. $7(p - 2) + p = 2(p + 2)$

19. $-2t + 5t - 9 = 3(t - 4) - 5$

20. $3(m + 5) - 1 + 2m = 5(m + 2)$

21. $0.2(50) + 0.8r = 0.4(50 + r)$

22. $2.3x + 13.7 = 1.3x + 2.9$

23. $2(3 + 7x) - (1 + 15x) = 2$

24. $6q - 9 = 12 + 3q$

25. $2(4 + 3r) = 3(r + 1) + 11$

26. $r + 9 + 7r = 4(3 + 2r) - 3$

27. $\frac{1}{4}x - 4 = \frac{3}{2}x + \frac{3}{4}x$

28. $0.6(100 - x) + 0.4x = 0.5(92)$

29. $\frac{3}{4}(z - 2) - \frac{1}{3}(5 - 2z) = -2$

30. $2 - (m + 4) = 3m - 2$

STUDY SKILLS

Using Study Cards Revisited

We introduced study cards on **page 48.** Another type of study card follows.

Practice Quiz Cards

Write a problem with direction words (like *solve, simplify*) on the front of the card, and work the problem on the back. Make one for each type of problem you learn.

Solve $4(3x - 4) = 2(6x - 9) + 2.$ p. 103   Front of Card

Back of Card

$$4(3x - 4) = 2(6x - 9) + 2$$

$12x - 16 = 12x - 18 + 2$ Distributive property

$12x - 16 = 12x - 16$ Combine like terms.

$12x - 16 + 16 = 12x - 16 + 16$ Add 16.

$12x = 12x$ Combine like terms.

$12x - 12x = 12x - 12x$ Subtract 12x.

$0 = 0$ True

When both sides of an equation are the same, it is called an identity.

<u>Any</u> real number will work, so the solution set is {<u>all real numbers</u>} (not just {0}).

Make a practice quiz card for material you are learning now.

2.4 An Introduction to Applications of Linear Equations

OBJECTIVE 1 **Learn the six steps for solving applied problems.** To solve applied problems, the following six-step method is often applicable.

Solving an Applied Problem

Step 1 **Read** the problem carefully. What information is given? What are you asked to find?

Step 2 **Assign a variable** to represent the unknown value. Use a sketch, diagram, or table, as needed. If necessary, express any other unknown values in terms of the variable.

Step 3 **Write an equation** using the variable expression(s).

Step 4 **Solve** the equation.

Step 5 **State the answer.** Label it appropriately. Does it seem reasonable?

Step 6 **Check** the answer in the words of the *original* problem.

OBJECTIVE 2 **Solve problems involving unknown numbers.**

EXAMPLE 1 Finding the Value of an Unknown Number

If 4 is multiplied by a number decreased by 7, the product is 100. Find the number.

Step 1 **Read** the problem carefully. We are asked to find a number.

Step 2 **Assign a variable** to represent the unknown quantity.

$$\text{Let } x = \text{the number.}$$

Step 3 **Write an equation.**

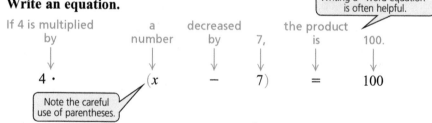

Step 4 **Solve** the equation.

$$4(x - 7) = 100 \qquad \text{Equation from Step 3}$$
$$4x - 28 = 100 \qquad \text{Distributive property}$$
$$4x - 28 + 28 = 100 + 28 \qquad \text{Add 28.}$$
$$4x = 128 \qquad \text{Combine like terms.}$$
$$\frac{4x}{4} = \frac{128}{4} \qquad \text{Divide by 4.}$$
$$x = 32$$

Step 5 **State the answer.** The number is 32.

Step 6 **Check.** When 32 is decreased by 7, we get $32 - 7 = 25$. If 4 is multiplied by 25, we get 100, as required. The answer, 32, is correct.   *NOW TRY*

NOW TRY
EXERCISE 1

If 5 is added to a number, the result is 7 less than 3 times the number. Find the number.

NOW TRY ANSWER
1. 6

OBJECTIVE 3 Solve problems involving sums of quantities.

> **PROBLEM-SOLVING HINT**
>
> To solve problems involving sums of quantities, choose a variable to represent one of the unknowns. *Then represent the other quantity in terms of the same variable.* (See **Example 11** in **Section 2.3**.)

NOW TRY
EXERCISE 2

In the 2006 Winter Olympics in Torino, Italy, Russia won 7 fewer medals than Germany. The two countries won a total of 51 medals. How many medals did each country win? (*Source:* U.S. Olympic Committee.)

EXAMPLE 2   Finding Numbers of Olympic Medals

In the 2006 Winter Olympics in Torino, Italy, the United States won 11 more medals than Sweden. The two countries won a total of 39 medals. How many medals did each country win? (*Source:* U.S. Olympic Committee.)

Step 1   **Read** the problem carefully. We are given information about the total number of medals and asked to find the number each country won.

Step 2   **Assign a variable.**

Let x = the number of medals Sweden won.

Then $x + 11$ = the number of medals the United States won.

Step 3   **Write an equation.**

$$39 = x + (x + 11)$$

Step 4   **Solve the equation.**

$$39 = 2x + 11 \qquad \text{Combine like terms.}$$
$$39 - 11 = 2x + 11 - 11 \qquad \text{Subtract 11.}$$
$$28 = 2x \qquad \text{Combine like terms.}$$
$$\frac{28}{2} = \frac{2x}{2} \qquad \text{Divide by 2.}$$
$$14 = x, \quad \text{or} \quad x = 14$$

Step 5   **State the answer.** The variable x represents the number of medals Sweden won, so Sweden won 14 medals. The number of medals the United States won is

$$x + 11 = 14 + 11 = 25.$$

Step 6   **Check.** Since the United States won 25 medals and Sweden won 14, the total number of medals was $25 + 14 = 39$. Because $25 - 14 = 11$, the United States won 11 more medals than Sweden. This information agrees with what is given in the problem, so the answer checks.   *NOW TRY*

NOW TRY ANSWER
2. Germany: 29 medals;
    Russia: 22 medals

> **NOTE** The problem in **Example 2** could also be solved by letting x represent the number of medals the United States won. Then $x - 11$ would represent the number of medals Sweden won. The equation would be different.
>
> $$39 = x + (x - 11)$$
>
> The solution of this equation is 25, which is the number of U.S. medals. The number of Swedish medals would be $25 - 11 = 14$. *The answers are the same,* whichever approach is used, even though the equation and its solution are different.

◠ NOW TRY
↳ EXERCISE 3

In one week, the owner of Carly's Coffeehouse found that the number of orders for bagels was $\frac{2}{3}$ the number of orders for chocolate scones. If the total number of orders for the two items was 525, how many orders were placed for bagels?

EXAMPLE 3 Finding the Number of Orders for Tea

The owner of Terry's Coffeehouse found that on one day the number of orders for tea was $\frac{1}{3}$ the number of orders for coffee. If the total number of orders for the two drinks was 76, how many orders were placed for tea?

Step 1 **Read** the problem. It asks for the number of orders for tea.

Step 2 **Assign a variable.** Because of the way the problem is stated, let the variable represent the number of orders for coffee.

Let $x =$ the number of orders for coffee.

Then $\frac{1}{3}x =$ the number of orders for tea.

Step 3 **Write an equation.** Use the fact that the total number of orders was 76.

The total	is	orders for coffee	plus	orders for tea.
↓	↓	↓	↓	↓
76	$=$	x	$+$	$\frac{1}{3}x$

Step 4 **Solve.**

$$76 = \frac{4}{3}x \qquad \begin{array}{l}x = 1x = \frac{3}{3}x; \\ \text{Combine like terms.}\end{array}$$

$$\frac{3}{4}(76) = \frac{3}{4}\left(\frac{4}{3}x\right) \qquad \text{Multiply by } \frac{3}{4}.$$

> Be careful! This is *not* the answer.

$$57 = x$$

Step 5 **State the answer.** In this problem, *x does not represent the quantity that we are asked to find.* The number of orders for tea was $\frac{1}{3}x$. So $\frac{1}{3}(57) = 19$ is the number of orders for tea.

Step 6 **Check.** The number of orders for tea, 19, is one-third the number of orders for coffee, 57, and $19 + 57 = 76$. Since this agrees with the information given in the problem, the answer is correct.

NOW TRY ⤸

PROBLEM-SOLVING HINT

In **Example 3**, it was easier to let the variable represent the quantity that was *not* specified. This required extra work in Step 5 to find the number of orders for tea. In some cases, this approach is easier than letting the variable represent the quantity that we are asked to find.

NOW TRY ANSWER
3. 210 bagel orders

NOW TRY
EXERCISE 4

At the Sherwood Estates pool party, each resident brought four guests. If a total of 175 people visited the pool that day, how many were residents and how many were guests?

EXAMPLE 4   Analyzing a Gasoline-Oil Mixture

A lawn trimmer uses a mixture of gasoline and oil. The mixture contains 16 oz of gasoline for each 1 ounce of oil. If the tank holds 68 oz of the mixture, how many ounces of oil and how many ounces of gasoline does it require when it is full?

Step 1   **Read** the problem. We must find how many ounces of oil and gasoline are needed to fill the tank.

Step 2   **Assign a variable.**

Let x = the number of ounces of oil required.

Then $16x$ = the number of ounces of gasoline required.

A diagram like the following is sometimes helpful.

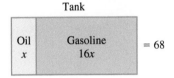

Step 3   **Write an equation.**

Amount of gasoline   plus   amount of oil   is   total amount in tank.

$$16x \quad + \quad x \quad = \quad 68$$

Step 4   **Solve.** $17x = 68$ Combine like terms.

$$\frac{17x}{17} = \frac{68}{17}$$ Divide by 17.

$$x = 4$$

Step 5   **State the answer.** The lawn trimmer requires 4 oz of oil, and $16(4) = 64$ oz of gasoline when full.

Step 6   **Check.** Since $4 + 64 = 68$, and 64 is 16 times 4, the answer checks.

NOW TRY

PROBLEM-SOLVING HINT

Sometimes we must find three unknown quantities. When the three unknowns are compared in *pairs*, **let the variable represent the unknown found in both pairs.**

EXAMPLE 5   Dividing a Board into Pieces

A project calls for three pieces of wood. The longest piece must be twice the length of the middle-sized piece. The shortest piece must be 10 in. shorter than the middle-sized piece. If a board 70 in. long is to be used, how long can each piece be?

Step 1   **Read** the problem. There will be three answers.

Step 2   **Assign a variable.** Since the middle-sized piece appears in both pairs of comparisons, let x represent the length, in inches, of the middle-sized piece.

Let x = the length of the middle-sized piece.

Then $2x$ = the length of the longest piece,

and $x - 10$ = the length of the shortest piece.

NOW TRY ANSWER
4. 35 residents; 140 guests

NOW TRY
EXERCISE 5

A basketball player spent 6 hr watching game films, practicing free throws, and lifting weights. He spent twice as much time lifting weights as practicing free throws and 2 hr longer watching game films than practicing free throws. How many hours did he spend on each task?

A sketch is helpful here. See **FIGURE 2**.

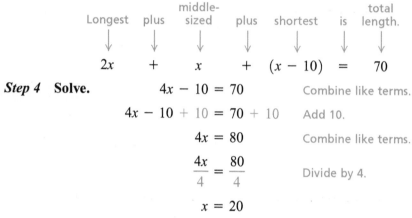

FIGURE 2

Step 3 **Write an equation.**

Longest	plus	middle-sized	plus	shortest	is	total length.
↓	↓	↓	↓	↓	↓	↓
$2x$	$+$	x	$+$	$(x - 10)$	$=$	70

Step 4 **Solve.**

$$4x - 10 = 70 \qquad \text{Combine like terms.}$$

$$4x - 10 + 10 = 70 + 10 \qquad \text{Add 10.}$$

$$4x = 80 \qquad \text{Combine like terms.}$$

$$\frac{4x}{4} = \frac{80}{4} \qquad \text{Divide by 4.}$$

$$x = 20$$

Step 5 **State the answer.** The middle-sized piece is 20 in. long, the longest piece is $2(20) = 40$ in. long, and the shortest piece is $20 - 10 = 10$ in. long.

Step 6 **Check.** The lengths sum to 70 in. All problem conditions are satisfied.

NOW TRY

Consecutive integers

FIGURE 3

OBJECTIVE 4 **Solve problems involving consecutive integers.** Two integers that differ by 1 are called **consecutive integers.** For example, 3 and 4, 6 and 7, and -2 and -1 are pairs of consecutive integers. See **FIGURE 3**.

In general, if x represents an integer, x + 1 represents the next greater consecutive integer.

EXAMPLE 6 Finding Consecutive Integers

Two pages that face each other in this book have 225 as the sum of their page numbers. What are the page numbers?

Step 1 **Read** the problem. Because the two pages face each other, they must have page numbers that are consecutive integers.

Step 2 **Assign a variable.**

Let $x =$ the lesser page number.

Then $x + 1 =$ the greater page number.

Step 3 **Write an equation.** The sum of the page numbers is 225.

$$x + (x + 1) = 225$$

Step 4 **Solve.**

$$2x + 1 = 225 \qquad \text{Combine like terms.}$$

$$2x = 224 \qquad \text{Subtract 1.}$$

$$x = 112 \qquad \text{Divide by 2.}$$

NOW TRY ANSWER

5. practicing free throws: 1 hr;
lifting weights: 2 hr;
watching game films: 3 hr

**NOW TRY
EXERCISE 6**

Two pages that face each other have 593 as the sum of their page numbers. What are the page numbers?

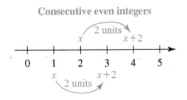

Consecutive even integers

Consecutive odd integers

FIGURE 4

Step 5 **State the answer.** The lesser page number is 112, and the greater page number is 112 + 1 = 113. (Your book is opened to these two pages.)

Step 6 **Check.** The sum of 112 and 113 is 225. The answer is correct.

NOW TRY

Consecutive *even* integers, such as 8 and 10, differ by 2. Similarly, **consecutive** *odd* integers, such as 9 and 11, also differ by 2. See **FIGURE 4**.

In general, if x represents an even or odd integer, x + 2 represents the next greater consecutive even or odd integer, respectively.

In this book, we list consecutive integers in increasing order.

PROBLEM-SOLVING HINT

If x = the lesser integer, then, for any

two consecutive integers, use	$x,\ x + 1;$
two consecutive *even* integers, use	$x,\ x + 2;$
two consecutive *odd* integers, use	$x,\ x + 2.$

**NOW TRY
EXERCISE 7**

Find two consecutive odd integers such that the sum of twice the lesser and three times the greater is 191.

EXAMPLE 7 Finding Consecutive Odd Integers

If the lesser of two consecutive odd integers is doubled, the result is 7 more than the greater of the two integers. Find the two integers.

Let x be the lesser integer. Since the two numbers are consecutive *odd* integers, then $x + 2$ is the greater. Now we write an equation.

| If the lesser is doubled, | the result is | 7 | more than | the greater. |
| $2x$ | $=$ | 7 | $+$ | $(x + 2)$ |

$$2x = 9 + x \qquad \text{Combine like terms.}$$
$$x = 9 \qquad \text{Subtract } x.$$

The lesser integer is 9 and the greater is 9 + 2 = 11. As a check, when 9 is doubled, we get 18, which is 7 more than the greater odd integer, 11. The answers are correct.

NOW TRY

OBJECTIVE 5 **Solve problems involving supplementary and complementary angles.** An angle can be measured by a unit called the **degree** (°), which is $\frac{1}{360}$ of a complete rotation. Two angles whose sum is 90° are said to be **complementary,** or *complements* of each other. An angle that measures 90° is a **right angle.** Two angles whose sum is 180° are said to be **supplementary,** or *supplements* of each other. One angle *supplements* the other to form a **straight angle** of 180°. See **FIGURE 5**.

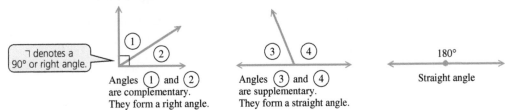

FIGURE 5

NOW TRY ANSWERS
6. 296, 297 **7.** 37, 39

> **PROBLEM-SOLVING HINT**
>
> If *x* represents the degree measure of an angle, then
>
> **90 − *x*** represents the degree measure of its complement.
>
> **180 − *x*** represents the degree measure of its supplement.

**NOW TRY
EXERCISE 8**

Find the measure of an angle whose complement is twice its measure.

EXAMPLE 8 Finding the Measure of an Angle

Find the measure of an angle whose complement is five times its measure.

Step 1 **Read** the problem. We must find the measure of an angle, given information about the measure of its complement.

Step 2 **Assign a variable.**

Let x = the degree measure of the angle.

Then $90 - x$ = the degree measure of its complement.

Step 3 **Write an equation.**

Measure of the complement	is	5 times the measure of the angle.
↓	↓	↓
$90 - x$	$=$	$5x$

Step 4 **Solve.**

$$90 - x + x = 5x + x \qquad \text{Add } x.$$

$$90 = 6x \qquad \text{Combine like terms.}$$

$$\frac{90}{6} = \frac{6x}{6} \qquad \text{Divide by 6.}$$

$$15 = x, \quad \text{or} \quad x = 15$$

Step 5 **State the answer.** The measure of the angle is 15°.

Step 6 **Check.** If the angle measures 15°, then its complement measures 90° − 15° = 75°, which is equal to five times 15°, as required.

NOW TRY

EXAMPLE 9 Finding the Measure of an Angle

Find the measure of an angle whose supplement is 10° more than twice its complement.

Step 1 **Read** the problem. We are to find the measure of an angle, given information about its complement and its supplement.

Step 2 **Assign a variable.**

Let x = the degree measure of the angle.

Then $90 - x$ = the degree measure of its complement,

and $180 - x$ = the degree measure of its supplement.

We can visualize this information using a sketch. See **FIGURE 6**.

NOW TRY ANSWER
8. 30°

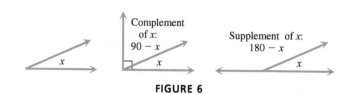

FIGURE 6

NOW TRY
EXERCISE 9

Find the measure of an angle whose supplement is 46° less than three times its complement.

Step 3 **Write an equation.**

Supplement   is   10   more than   twice   its complement.

$$180 - x = 10 + 2 \cdot (90 - x)$$

> Be sure to use parentheses here.

Step 4 **Solve.** $180 - x = 10 + 180 - 2x$ Distributive property

$180 - x = 190 - 2x$ Combine like terms.

$180 - x + 2x = 190 - 2x + 2x$ Add $2x$.

$180 + x = 190$ Combine like terms.

$180 + x - 180 = 190 - 180$ Subtract 180.

$x = 10$

Step 5 **State the answer.** The measure of the angle is 10°.

Step 6 **Check.** The complement of 10° is 80° and the supplement of 10° is 170°. 170° is equal to 10° more than twice 80° (that is, $170 = 10 + 2(80)$ is true). Therefore, the answer is correct.   NOW TRY

NOW TRY ANSWER
9. 22°

2.4 EXERCISES

MyMathLab Math XL PRACTICE WATCH DOWNLOAD READ REVIEW

1. *Concept Check* A problem requires finding the number of cars on a dealer's lot. Which would *not* be a reasonable answer? Justify your response.

  A. 0   **B.** 45   **C.** 1   **D.** $6\frac{1}{2}$

2. *Concept Check* A problem requires finding the number of hours a lightbulb is on during a day. Which would *not* be a reasonable answer? Justify your response.

  A. 0   **B.** 4.5   **C.** 13   **D.** 25

3. *Concept Check* A problem requires finding the distance traveled in miles. Which would *not* be a reasonable answer? Justify your response.

  A. −10   **B.** 1.8   **C.** $10\frac{1}{2}$ **D.** 50

4. *Concept Check* A problem requires finding the time in minutes. Which would *not* be a reasonable answer? Justify your response.

  A. 0   **B.** 10.5   **C.** −5   **D.** 90

Solve each problem. ***See Example 1.***

5. The product of 8, and a number increased by 6, is 104. What is the number?

6. The product of 5, and 3 more than twice a number, is 85. What is the number?

7. If 2 is added to five times a number, the result is equal to 5 more than four times the number. Find the number.

8. If four times a number is added to 8, the result is three times the number, added to 5. Find the number.

9. If 2 is subtracted from a number and this difference is tripled, the result is 6 more than the number. Find the number.

10. If 3 is added to a number and this sum is doubled, the result is 2 more than the number. Find the number.

11. The sum of three times a number and 7 more than the number is the same as the difference between −11 and twice the number. What is the number?

12. If 4 is added to twice a number and this sum is multiplied by 2, the result is the same as if the number is multiplied by 3 and 4 is added to the product. What is the number?

Solve each problem. ***See Example 2.***

13. Pennsylvania and Ohio were the states with the most remaining drive-in movie screens in the United States in 2007. Pennsylvania had 2 more screens than Ohio, and there were 68 screens total in the two states. How many drive-in movie screens remained in each state? (*Source:* www.drive-ins.com)

14. As of 2008, the two most highly watched episodes in the history of television were the final episode of *M*A*S*H* and the final episode of *Cheers*. The number of viewers for these original broadcasts in 1983 was about 92 million, with 8 million more people watching the *M*A*S*H* episode than the *Cheers* episode. How many people watched each show? (*Source:* Nielsen Media Research.)

15. In August 2009, the U.S. Senate had a total of 98 Democrats and Republicans. There were 18 more Democrats than Republicans. How many members of each party were there? (*Source:* www.thegreenpapers.com)

16. In August 2009, the total number of Democrats and Republicans in the U.S. House of Representatives was 434. There were 78 more Democrats than Republicans. How many members of each party were there? (*Source:* www.thegreenpapers.com)

17. Bon Jovi and Bruce Springsteen had the two top-grossing North American concert tours for 2008, together generating $415.3 million in ticket sales. If Bruce Springsteen took in $6.1 million less than Bon Jovi, how much did each tour generate? (*Source:* www.billboard.com)

18. The Toyota Camry was the top-selling passenger car in the United States in 2007, followed by the Honda Accord. Accord sales were 81 thousand less than Camry sales, and 865 thousand of the two types of cars were sold. How many of each make of car were sold? (*Source:* *World Almanac and Book of Facts.*)

19. In the 2008–2009 NBA regular season, the Boston Celtics won two more than three times as many games as they lost. The Celtics played 82 games. How many wins and losses did the team have? (*Source:* www.NBA.com)

20. In the 2008 regular baseball season, the Tampa Bay Rays won 33 fewer than twice as many games as they lost. They played 162 regular-season games. How many wins and losses did the team have? (*Source:* www.MLB.com)

21. A one-cup serving of orange juice contains 3 mg less than four times the amount of vitamin C as a one-cup serving of pineapple juice. Servings of the two juices contain a total of 122 mg of vitamin C. How many milligrams of vitamin C are in a serving of each type of juice? (*Source:* U.S. Agriculture Department.)

22. A one-cup serving of pineapple juice has 9 more than three times as many calories as a one-cup serving of tomato juice. Servings of the two juices contain a total of 173 calories. How many calories are in a serving of each type of juice? (*Source:* U.S. Agriculture Department.)

Solve each problem. **See Examples 3 and 4.**

23. In one day, a store sold $\frac{8}{5}$ as many DVDs as CDs. The total number of DVDs and CDs sold that day was 273. How many DVDs were sold?

24. A workout that combines weight training and aerobics burns a total of 374 calories. If doing aerobics burns $\frac{12}{5}$ as many calories as weight training, how many calories does each activity burn?

25. The world's largest taco contained approximately 1 kg of onion for every 6.6 kg of grilled steak. The total weight of these two ingredients was 617.6 kg. To the nearest tenth of a kilogram, how many kilograms of each ingredient were used to make the taco? (*Source: Guinness World Records.*)

26. As of 2005, the combined population of China and India was estimated at 2.4 billion. If there were about 0.8 as many people living in India as China, what was the population of each country, to the nearest tenth of a billion? (*Source:* U.S. Census Bureau.)

27. The value of a "Mint State-63" (uncirculated) 1950 Jefferson nickel minted at Denver is twice the value of a 1945 nickel in similar condition minted at Philadelphia. Together, the total value of the two coins is $24.00. What is the value of each coin? (*Source:* Yeoman, R., *A Guide Book of United States Coins,* 62nd edition, 2009.)

28. U.S. five-cent coins are made from a combination of two metals: nickel and copper. For every 1 pound of nickel, 3 lb of copper are used. How many pounds of copper would be needed to make 560 lb of five-cent coins? (*Source:* The United States Mint.)

29. A recipe for whole-grain bread calls for 1 oz of rye flour for every 4 oz of whole-wheat flour. How many ounces of each kind of flour should be used to make a loaf of bread weighing 32 oz?

30. A medication contains 9 mg of active ingredients for every 1 mg of inert ingredients. How much of each kind of ingredient would be contained in a single 250-mg caplet?

Solve each problem. **See Example 5.**

31. An office manager booked 55 airline tickets, divided among three airlines. He booked 7 more tickets on American Airlines than United Airlines. On Southwest Airlines, he booked 4 more than twice as many tickets as on United. How many tickets did he book on each airline?

32. A mathematics textbook editor spent 7.5 hr making telephone calls, writing e-mails, and attending meetings. She spent twice as much time attending meetings as making telephone calls and 0.5 hr longer writing e-mails than making telephone calls. How many hours did she spend on each task?

33. A party-length submarine sandwich that is 59 in. long is cut into three pieces. The middle piece is 5 in. longer than the shortest piece, and the shortest piece is 9 in. shorter than the longest piece. How long is each piece?

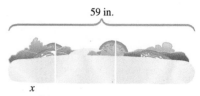

59 in.

x

34. China earned a total of 100 medals at the 2008 Beijing Summer Olympics. The number of gold medals earned was 23 more than the number of bronze medals. The number of bronze medals earned was 7 more than the number of silver medals. How many of each kind of medal did China earn? (*Source: World Almanac and Book of Facts.*)

35. Venus is 31.2 million mi farther from the sun than Mercury, while Earth is 57 million mi farther from the sun than Mercury. If the total of the distances from these three planets to the sun is 196.2 million mi, how far away from the sun is Mercury? (All distances given here are *mean* (*average*) distances.) (*Source: The New York Times Almanac.*)

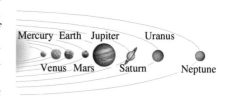

Mercury Earth Jupiter Uranus

Venus Mars Saturn Neptune

36. Together, Saturn, Jupiter, and Uranus have a total of 137 known satellites (moons). Jupiter has 16 more satellites than Saturn, and Uranus has 20 fewer satellites than Saturn. How many known satellites does Uranus have? (*Source: The New York Times Almanac.*)

37. The sum of the measures of the angles of any triangle is 180°. In triangle *ABC*, angles *A* and *B* have the same measure, while the measure of angle *C* is 60° greater than each of *A* and *B*. What are the measures of the three angles?

38. In triangle *ABC*, the measure of angle *A* is 141° more than the measure of angle *B*. The measure of angle *B* is the same as the measure of angle *C*. Find the measure of each angle. (*Hint:* **See Exercise 37.**)

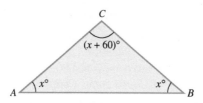

C

$(x + 60)°$

$x°$

A

$x°$

B

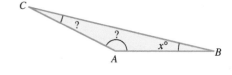

C

?

?

A

$x°$

B

Solve each problem. ***See Examples 6 and 7.***

39. The numbers on two consecutively numbered gym lockers have a sum of 137. What are the locker numbers?

40. The numbers on two consecutive checkbook checks have a sum of 357. What are the numbers?

x $x + 1$

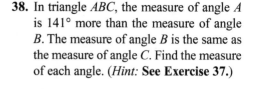

$x + 1$

x

41. Two pages that are back-to-back in this book have 203 as the sum of their page numbers. What are the page numbers?

42. Two apartments have numbers that are consecutive integers. The sum of the numbers is 59. What are the two apartment numbers?

43. Find two consecutive even integers such that the lesser added to three times the greater gives a sum of 46.

44. Find two consecutive odd integers such that twice the greater is 17 more than the lesser.

45. When the lesser of two consecutive integers is added to three times the greater, the result is 43. Find the integers.

46. If five times the lesser of two consecutive integers is added to three times the greater, the result is 59. Find the integers.

Brain Busters   *Solve each problem.*

47. If the sum of three consecutive even integers is 60, what is the first of the three even integers? (*Hint:* If x and $x + 2$ represent the first two consecutive even integers, how would you represent the third consecutive even integer?)

48. If the sum of three consecutive odd integers is 69, what is the third of the three odd integers?

49. If 6 is subtracted from the third of three consecutive odd integers and the result is multiplied by 2, the answer is 23 less than the sum of the first and twice the second of the integers. Find the integers.

50. If the first and third of three consecutive even integers are added, the result is 22 less than three times the second integer. Find the integers.

Solve each problem. **See Examples 8 and 9.**

51. Find the measure of an angle whose complement is four times its measure.

52. Find the measure of an angle whose complement is five times its measure.

53. Find the measure of an angle whose supplement is eight times its measure.

54. Find the measure of an angle whose supplement is three times its measure.

55. Find the measure of an angle whose supplement measures 39° more than twice its complement.

56. Find the measure of an angle whose supplement measures 38° less than three times its complement.

57. Find the measure of an angle such that the difference between the measures of its supplement and three times its complement is 10°.

58. Find the measure of an angle such that the sum of the measures of its complement and its supplement is 160°.

PREVIEW EXERCISES

Use the given values to evaluate each expression. **See Section 1.3.**

59. LW; $L = 6, W = 4$ **60.** rt; $r = 25, t = 4.5$

61. $2L + 2W$; $L = 8, W = 2$ **62.** $\dfrac{1}{2}h(b + B)$; $h = 10, b = 4, B = 12$

2.5 Formulas and Additional Applications from Geometry

OBJECTIVES

1 Solve a formula for one variable, given values of the other variables.
2 Use a formula to solve an applied problem.
3 Solve problems involving vertical angles and straight angles.
4 Solve a formula for a specified variable.

NOW TRY EXERCISE 1

Find the value of the remaining variable.

$$P = 2a + 2b;$$
$$P = 78, a = 12$$

A **formula** is an equation in which variables are used to describe a relationship. For example, formulas exist for finding perimeters and areas of geometric figures, calculating money earned on bank savings, and converting among measurements.

$$P = 4s, \quad \mathcal{A} = \pi r^2, \quad I = prt, \quad F = \frac{9}{5}C + 32 \qquad \text{Formulas}$$

Many of the formulas used in this book are given on the inside covers.

OBJECTIVE 1 Solve a formula for one variable, given values of the other variables. In **Example 1**, we use the idea of *area*. The **area** of a plane (two-dimensional) geometric figure is a measure of the surface covered by the figure.

EXAMPLE 1 Using Formulas to Evaluate Variables

Find the value of the remaining variable in each formula.

(a) $\mathcal{A} = LW; \quad \mathcal{A} = 64, L = 10$

As shown in **FIGURE 7**, this formula gives the area $\mathcal{A}$ of a rectangle with length L and width W. Substitute the given values into the formula.

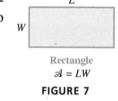

Rectangle
$\mathcal{A} = LW$
FIGURE 7

$$\mathcal{A} = LW \qquad \text{In this book, } \mathcal{A} \text{ denotes area.}$$
$$64 = 10W \qquad \text{Let } \mathcal{A} = 64 \text{ and } L = 10. \quad \text{(Solve for } W.)$$
$$\frac{64}{10} = \frac{10W}{10} \qquad \text{Divide by 10.}$$
$$6.4 = W$$

The width is 6.4. Since $10(6.4) = 64$, the given area, the answer checks.

(b) $\mathcal{A} = \frac{1}{2}h(b + B); \quad \mathcal{A} = 210, B = 27, h = 10$

This formula gives the area of a trapezoid. See **FIGURE 8**.

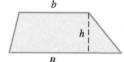

Trapezoid
$\mathcal{A} = \frac{1}{2}h(b + B)$
FIGURE 8

$$\mathcal{A} = \frac{1}{2}h(b + B)$$
$$210 = \frac{1}{2}(10)(b + 27) \qquad \text{Let } \mathcal{A} = 210, h = 10, B = 27. \quad \text{(Solve for } b.)$$
$$210 = 5(b + 27) \qquad \text{Multiply.}$$
$$210 = 5b + 135 \qquad \text{Distributive property}$$
$$210 - 135 = 5b + 135 - 135 \qquad \text{Subtract 135.}$$
$$75 = 5b \qquad \text{Combine like terms.}$$
$$\frac{75}{5} = \frac{5b}{5} \qquad \text{Divide by 5.}$$
$$15 = b$$

The length of the shorter parallel side, b, is 15. This answer checks, since

$$\frac{1}{2}(10)(15 + 27) = 210, \quad \text{as required.} \qquad \text{NOW TRY}$$

NOW TRY ANSWER
1. $b = 27$

A supermarket charges the following prices for a certain brand of liquid detergent.

Size	Price
150 oz	$19.97
100 oz	$13.97
75 oz	$ 8.94

Which size is the best buy? What is the unit cost for that size?

To find the best buy, write ratios comparing the price for each size of jar to the number of units (ounces) per jar. Then divide to obtain the price per unit (ounce).

Size	Unit Cost (dollars per ounce)
18 oz	$\dfrac{\$1.78}{18} = \$0.099$ ← The best buy
28 oz	$\dfrac{\$2.97}{28} = \$0.106$
40 oz	$\dfrac{\$3.98}{40} = \$0.100$

(Results are rounded to the nearest thousandth.)

Because the 18-oz size produces the lowest unit cost, it is the best buy. This example shows that buying the largest size does not always provide the best buy.

NOW TRY

OBJECTIVE 2 Solve proportions. A ratio is used to compare two numbers or amounts. A **proportion** says that two ratios are equal. For example, the proportion

$$\frac{3}{4} = \frac{15}{20}$$

A proportion is a special type of equation.

says that the ratios $\frac{3}{4}$ and $\frac{15}{20}$ are equal. In the proportion

$$\frac{a}{b} = \frac{c}{d} \quad (\text{where } b, d \neq 0),$$

a, b, c, and d are the **terms** of the proportion. The terms a and d are called the **extremes**, and the terms b and c are called the **means.** We read the proportion $\frac{a}{b} = \frac{c}{d}$ as **"a is to b as c is to d."** Multiplying each side of this proportion by the common denominator, bd, gives the following.

$$bd \cdot \frac{a}{b} = bd \cdot \frac{c}{d} \qquad \text{Multiply each side by } bd.$$

$$\frac{b}{b}(d \cdot a) = \frac{d}{d}(b \cdot c) \qquad \text{Associative and commutative properties}$$

$$ad = bc \qquad \text{Commutative and identity properties}$$

We can also find the products ad and bc by multiplying diagonally.

$$ad = bc$$

$$\frac{a}{b} = \frac{c}{d}$$

For this reason, ad and bc are called **cross products.**

Cross Products

If $\frac{a}{b} = \frac{c}{d}$, then the cross products ad and bc are equal—that is, ***the product of the extremes equals the product of the means.***

Also, if $ad = bc$, then $\frac{a}{b} = \frac{c}{d}$ (where $b, d \neq 0$).

NOW TRY ANSWER
2. 75 oz; $0.119 per oz

NOTE If $\frac{a}{c} = \frac{b}{d}$, then $ad = cb$, or $ad = bc$. This means that the two proportions are equivalent, and the proportion

$$\frac{a}{b} = \frac{c}{d} \quad \text{can also be written as} \quad \frac{a}{c} = \frac{b}{d} \quad (\text{where } c, d \neq 0).$$

Sometimes one form is more convenient to work with than the other.

NOW TRY
EXERCISE 3

Decide whether each proportion is *true* or *false*.

(a) $\frac{1}{3} = \frac{33}{100}$ (b) $\frac{4}{13} = \frac{16}{52}$

EXAMPLE 3 Deciding Whether Proportions Are True

Decide whether each proportion is *true* or *false*.

(a) $\frac{3}{4} = \frac{15}{20}$

Check to see whether the cross products are equal.

$$3 \cdot 20 = 60 \qquad 4 \cdot 15 = 60$$

$$\frac{3}{4} = \frac{15}{20}$$

The cross products are equal, so the proportion is true.

(b) $\frac{6}{7} = \frac{30}{32}$

The cross products, $6 \cdot 32 = 192$ and $7 \cdot 30 = 210$, are not equal, so the proportion is false.

NOW TRY

Four numbers are used in a proportion. If any three of these numbers are known, the fourth can be found.

NOW TRY
EXERCISE 4

Solve the proportion.

$$\frac{9}{7} = \frac{x}{56}$$

EXAMPLE 4 Finding an Unknown in a Proportion

Solve the proportion $\frac{5}{9} = \frac{x}{63}$.

$$\frac{5}{9} = \frac{x}{63} \quad \boxed{\text{Solve for } x.}$$

$$5 \cdot 63 = 9 \cdot x \qquad \text{Cross products must be equal.}$$

$$315 = 9x \qquad \text{Multiply.}$$

$$\frac{315}{9} = \frac{9x}{9} \qquad \text{Divide by 9.}$$

$$35 = x$$

Check by substituting 35 for x in the proportion. The solution set is $\{35\}$.

NOW TRY

NOW TRY ANSWERS
3. (a) false (b) true
4. $\{72\}$

⚠ **CAUTION** *The cross-product method cannot be used directly if there is more than one term on either side of the equals symbol.*

45. Eight quarts of oil cost $14.00. How much do 5 qt of oil cost?

46. Four tires cost $398.00. How much do 7 tires cost?

47. If 9 pairs of jeans cost $121.50, find the cost of 5 pairs.

48. If 7 shirts cost $87.50, find the cost of 11 shirts.

49. If 6 gal of premium unleaded gasoline costs $19.56, how much would it cost to completely fill a 15-gal tank?

50. If sales tax on a $16.00 DVD is $1.32, find the sales tax on a $120.00 DVD player.

51. The distance between Kansas City, Missouri, and Denver is 600 mi. On a certain wall map, this is represented by a length of 2.4 ft. On the map, how many feet would there be between Memphis and Philadelphia, two cities that are actually 1000 mi apart?

52. The distance between Singapore and Tokyo is 3300 mi. On a certain wall map, this distance is represented by 11 in. The actual distance between Mexico City and Cairo is 7700 mi. How far apart are they on the same map?

53. A wall map of the United States has a distance of 8.5 in. between Memphis and Denver, two cities that are actually 1040 mi apart. The actual distance between St. Louis and Des Moines is 333 mi. How far apart are St. Louis and Des Moines on the map?

54. A wall map of the United States has a distance of 8.0 in. between New Orleans and Chicago, two cities that are actually 912 mi apart. The actual distance between Milwaukee and Seattle is 1940 mi. How far apart are Milwaukee and Seattle on the map?

55. On a world globe, the distance between Capetown and Bangkok, two cities that are actually 10,080 km apart, is 12.4 in. The actual distance between Moscow and Berlin is 1610 km. How far apart are Moscow and Berlin on this globe?

56. On a world globe, the distance between Rio de Janeiro and Hong Kong, two cities that are actually 17,615 km apart, is 21.5 in. The actual distance between Paris and Stockholm is 1605 km. How far apart are Paris and Stockholm on this globe?

57. According to the directions on a bottle of Armstrong® Concentrated Floor Cleaner, for routine cleaning, $\frac{1}{4}$ cup of cleaner should be mixed with 1 gal of warm water. How much cleaner should be mixed with $10\frac{1}{2}$ gal of water?

58. The directions on the bottle mentioned in **Exercise 57** also specify that, for extra-strength cleaning, $\frac{1}{2}$ cup of cleaner should be used for each gallon of water. For extra-strength cleaning, how much cleaner should be mixed with $15\frac{1}{2}$ gal of water?

59. The euro is the common currency used by most European countries, including Italy. On August 15, 2009, the exchange rate between euros and U.S. dollars was 1 euro to $1.4294. Ashley went to Rome and exchanged her U.S. currency for euros, receiving 300 euros. How much in U.S. dollars did she exchange? (*Source:* www.xe.com/ucc)

60. If 8 U.S. dollars can be exchanged for 103.0 Mexican pesos, how many pesos can be obtained for $65? (Round to the nearest tenth.)

61. Biologists tagged 500 fish in North Bay on August 20. At a later date, they found 7 tagged fish in a sample of 700. Estimate the total number of fish in North Bay to the nearest hundred.

62. On June 13, researchers at West Okoboji Lake tagged 840 fish. A few weeks later, a sample of 1000 fish contained 18 that were tagged. Approximate the fish population to the nearest hundred.

Two triangles are **similar** if they have the same shape (but not necessarily the same size). Similar triangles have sides that are proportional. The figure shows two similar triangles. Notice that the ratios of the corresponding sides all equal $\frac{3}{2}$:

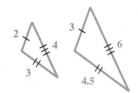

$$\frac{3}{2} = \frac{3}{2}, \qquad \frac{4.5}{3} = \frac{3}{2}, \qquad \frac{6}{4} = \frac{3}{2}.$$

If we know that two triangles are similar, we can set up a proportion to solve for the length of an unknown side.

Use a proportion to find the lengths x and y in each pair of similar triangles.

63.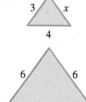

64.

65.

66.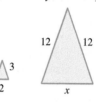

67.

68.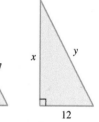

For Exercises 69 and 70, **(a)** draw a sketch consisting of two right triangles depicting the situation described, and **(b)** solve the problem. (Source: Guinness World Records.)

69. An enlarged version of the chair used by George Washington at the Constitutional Convention casts a shadow 18 ft long at the same time a vertical pole 12 ft high casts a shadow 4 ft long. How tall is the chair?

70. One of the tallest candles ever constructed was exhibited at the 1897 Stockholm Exhibition. If it cast a shadow 5 ft long at the same time a vertical pole 32 ft high cast a shadow 2 ft long, how tall was the candle?

The Consumer Price Index (CPI) provides a means of determining the purchasing power of the U.S. dollar from one year to the next. Using the period from 1982 to 1984 as a measure of 100.0, the CPI for selected years from 1995 through 2007 is shown in the table. To use the CPI to predict a price in a particular year, we set up a proportion and compare it with a known price in another year:

$$\frac{\text{price in year } A}{\text{index in year } A} = \frac{\text{price in year } B}{\text{index in year } B}.$$

Year	Consumer Price Index
1995	152.4
1997	160.5
1999	166.6
2001	177.1
2003	184.0
2005	195.3
2007	207.3

Source: Bureau of Labor Statistics.

Use the CPI figures in the table to find the amount that would be charged for using the same amount of electricity that cost $225 in 1995. Give your answer to the nearest dollar.

71. in 1997   **72.** in 1999   **73.** in 2003   **74.** in 2007

Convert each percent to a decimal. **See Examples 7(a) and 7(b).**

75. 53%   **76.** 38%   **77.** 96%   **78.** 11%

79. 9%   **80.** 7%   **81.** 129%   **82.** 174%

NOW TRY
EXERCISE 7

Two cars leave a parking lot at the same time, one traveling east and the other traveling west. The westbound car travels 6 mph faster than the eastbound car. In $\frac{1}{4}$ hr, they are 35 mi apart. What are their rates?

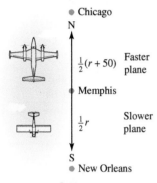

FIGURE 17

NOW TRY ANSWER
7. 67 mph; 73 mph

EXAMPLE 7 Solving a Motion Problem

Two planes leave Memphis at the same time. One heads south to New Orleans. The other heads north to Chicago. The Chicago plane flies 50 mph faster than the New Orleans plane. In $\frac{1}{2}$ hr, the planes are 275 mi apart. What are their rates?

Step 1 **Read** the problem carefully.

Step 2 **Assign a variable.**

Let r = the rate of the slower plane.

Then $r + 50$ = the rate of the faster plane.

	Rate	Time	Distance
Slower plane	r	$\frac{1}{2}$	$\frac{1}{2}r$
Faster plane	$r + 50$	$\frac{1}{2}$	$\frac{1}{2}(r + 50)$

Sum is 275 mi.

Step 3 **Write an equation.** As **FIGURE 17** shows, the planes are headed in *opposite* directions. The *sum* of their distances equals 275 mi.

$$\frac{1}{2}r + \frac{1}{2}(r + 50) = 275$$

Step 4 **Solve.**

$r + (r + 50) = 550$ Multiply by 2.

$2r + 50 = 550$ Combine like terms.

$2r = 500$ Subtract 50.

$r = 250$ Divide by 2.

Step 5 **State the answer.** The slower plane (headed south) has a rate of 250 mph. The rate of the faster plane is $250 + 50 = 300$ mph.

Step 6 **Check.** Verify that $\frac{1}{2}(250) + \frac{1}{2}(300) = 275$ mi.

NOW TRY

2.7 EXERCISES

MyMathLab   Math XL PRACTICE   WATCH   DOWNLOAD   READ   REVIEW

Complete solution available on the Video Resources on DVD

Answer each question. **See Example 1 and the Problem-Solving Hint preceding Example 4.**

1. How much pure alcohol is in 150 L of a 30% alcohol solution?

2. How much pure acid is in 250 mL of a 14% acid solution?

3. If $25,000 is invested for 1 yr at 3% simple interest, how much interest is earned?

4. If $10,000 is invested for 1 yr at 3.5% simple interest, how much interest is earned?

5. What is the monetary value of 35 half-dollars?

6. What is the monetary value of 283 nickels?

Concept Check Solve each percent problem. Remember that base × rate = percentage.

7. The population of New Mexico in 2007 was about 1,917,000, with 44.4% Hispanic. What is the best estimate of the Hispanic population in New Mexico? (*Source:* U.S. Census Bureau.)

     A. 850,000   **B.** 85,000   **C.** 650,000   **D.** 44,000

8. The population of Alabama in 2007 was about 4,628,000, with 26.5% represented by African-Americans. What is the best estimate of the African-American population in Alabama? (*Source:* U.S. Census Bureau.)

   A. 600,000   **B.** 750,000   **C.** 1,200,000   **D.** 1,500,000

9. The graph shows the breakdown, by approximate percents, of the colors chosen for new 2007 model-year full-size and intermediate cars sold in the United States. If approximately 3.8 million of these cars were sold, about how many were each color? (*Source:* Ward's Communications.)

   (a) White   **(b)** Silver   **(c)** Red

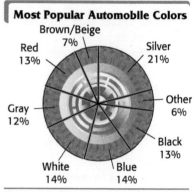

Most Popular Automobile Colors

Source: DuPont Automotive Products.

10. An average middle-income family will spend $221,190 to raise a child born in 2008 from birth to age 18. The graph shows the breakdown, by approximate percents, for various expense categories. To the nearest dollar, about how much will be spent to provide the following?

    (a) Housing
    (b) Food
    (c) Health care

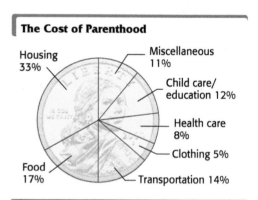

The Cost of Parenthood

Source: U.S. Department of Agriculture.

Concept Check   Answer each question.

11. Suppose that a chemist is mixing two acid solutions, one of 20% concentration and the other of 30% concentration. Which concentration could *not* be obtained?

    A. 22%   **B.** 24%   **C.** 28%   **D.** 32%

12. Suppose that pure alcohol is added to a 24% alcohol mixture. Which concentration could *not* be obtained?

    A. 22%   **B.** 26%   **C.** 28%   **D.** 30%

Work each mixture problem. **See Example 2.**

13. How many liters of 25% acid solution must a chemist add to 80 L of 40% acid solution to obtain a solution that is 30% acid?

Liters of Solution	Rate	Liters of Acid
x	0.25	$0.25x$
80	0.40	$0.40(80)$
$x + 80$	0.30	$0.30(x + 80)$

14. How many gallons of 50% antifreeze must be mixed with 80 gal of 20% antifreeze to obtain a mixture that is 40% antifreeze?

Gallons of Mixture	Rate	Gallons of Antifreeze
x	0.50	$0.50x$
80	0.20	$0.20(80)$
$x + 80$	0.40	$0.40(x + 80)$

15. A pharmacist has 20 L of a 10% drug solution. How many liters of 5% solution must be added to get a mixture that is 8%?

Liters of Solution	Rate	Liters of Pure Drug
20		20(0.10)
	0.05	
	0.08	

16. A certain metal is 20% tin. How many kilograms of this metal must be mixed with 80 kg of a metal that is 70% tin to get a metal that is 50% tin?

Kilograms of Metal	Rate	Kilograms of Pure Tin
x	0.20	
	0.70	
	0.50	

17. In a chemistry class, 12 L of a 12% alcohol solution must be mixed with a 20% solution to get a 14% solution. How many liters of the 20% solution are needed?

18. How many liters of a 10% alcohol solution must be mixed with 40 L of a 50% solution to get a 40% solution?

19. Minoxidil is a drug that has recently proven to be effective in treating male pattern baldness. Water must be added to 20 mL of a 4% minoxidil solution to dilute it to a 2% solution. How many milliliters of water should be used? (*Hint:* Water is 0% minoxidil.)

20. A pharmacist wishes to mix a solution that is 2% minoxidil. She has on hand 50 mL of a 1% solution, and she wishes to add some 4% solution to it to obtain the desired 2% solution. How much 4% solution should she add?

21. How many liters of a 60% acid solution must be mixed with a 75% acid solution to get 20 L of a 72% solution?

22. How many gallons of a 12% indicator solution must be mixed with a 20% indicator solution to get 10 gal of a 14% solution?

Work each investment problem using simple interest. ***See Example 3.***

23. Arlene Frank is saving money for her college education. She deposited some money in a savings account paying 5% and $1200 less than that amount in a second account paying 4%. The two accounts produced a total of $141 interest in 1 yr. How much did she invest at each rate?

24. Margaret Fennell won a prize for her work. She invested part of the money in a certificate of deposit at 4% and $3000 more than that amount in a bond paying 6%. Her annual interest income was $780. How much did Margaret invest at each rate?

25. An artist invests in a tax-free bond paying 6%, and $6000 more than three times as much in mutual funds paying 5%. Her total annual interest income from the investments is $825. How much does she invest at each rate?

26. With income earned by selling the rights to his life story, an actor invests some of the money at 3% and $30,000 more than twice as much at 4%. The total annual interest earned from the investments is $5600. How much is invested at each rate?

Work each problem involving monetary values. ***See Example 4.***

27. A coin collector has $1.70 in dimes and nickels. She has two more dimes than nickels. How many nickels does she have?

Number of Coins	Denomination	Total Value
x	0.05	0.05x
	0.10	

28. A bank teller has $725 in $5 bills and $20 bills. The teller has five more twenties than fives. How many $5 bills does the teller have?

Number of Bills	Denomination	Total Value
x	5	
x + 5	20	

29. In May 2009, U.S. first-class mail rates increased to 44 cents for the first ounce, plus 17 cents for each additional ounce. If Sabrina spent $14.40 for a total of 45 stamps of these two denominations, how many stamps of each denomination did she buy? (*Source:* U.S. Postal Service.)

30. A movie theater has two ticket prices: $8 for adults and $5 for children. If the box office took in $4116 from the sale of 600 tickets, how many tickets of each kind were sold?

31. Harriet Amato operates a coffee shop. One of her customers wants to buy two kinds of beans: Arabian Mocha and Colombian Decaf. If she wants twice as much Mocha as Colombian Decaf, how much of each can she buy for a total of $87.50? (Prices are listed on the sign.)

```
Arabian Mocha ........ $8.50/lb
Chocolate Mint ....... $10.50/lb
Colombian Decaf ...... $8.00/lb
French Roast ......... $7.50/lb
Guatemalan Spice ..... $9.50/lb
Hazelnut Decaf ....... $10.00/lb
Italian Espresso ..... $9.00/lb
Kona Deluxe .......... $11.50/lb
```

32. Harriet's Special Blend contains a combination of French Roast and Kona Deluxe beans. How many pounds of Kona Deluxe should she mix with 12 lb of French Roast to get a blend to be sold for $10 a pound?

Solve each problem involving distance, rate, and time. ***See Example 5.***

33. *Concept Check* Which choice is the best estimate for the average rate of a bus trip of 405 mi that lasted 8.2 hr?

A. 50 mph   **B.** 30 mph   **C.** 60 mph   **D.** 40 mph

34. Suppose that an automobile averages 45 mph and travels for 30 min. Is the distance traveled $45 \times 30 = 1350$ mi? If not, explain why not, and give the correct distance.

35. A driver averaged 53 mph and took 10 hr to travel from Memphis to Chicago. What is the distance between Memphis and Chicago?

36. A small plane traveled from Warsaw to Rome, averaging 164 mph. The trip took 2 hr. What is the distance from Warsaw to Rome?

37. The winner of the 2008 Indianapolis 500 (mile) race was Scott Dixon, who drove his Dellara-Honda to victory at a rate of 143.567 mph. What was his time (to the nearest thousandth of an hour)? (*Source: World Almanac and Book of Facts.*)

38. In 2008, Jimmie Johnson drove his Chevrolet to victory in the Brickyard 400 (mile) race at a rate of 115.117 mph. What was his time (to the nearest thousandth of an hour)? (*Source: World Almanac and Book of Facts.*)

In Exercises 39–42, find the rate on the basis of the information provided. Use a calculator and round your answers to the nearest hundredth. All events were at the 2008 Olympics. (Source: World Almanac and Book of Facts.)

	Event	Participant	Distance	Time
39.	100-m hurdles, women	Dawn Harper, USA	100 m	12.54 sec
40.	400-m hurdles, women	Melanie Walker, Jamaica	400 m	52.64 sec
41.	400-m hurdles, men	Angelo Taylor, USA	400 m	47.25 sec
42.	400-m run, men	LaShawn Merritt, USA	400 m	43.75 sec

Solve each motion problem. **See Examples 6 and 7.**

43. Atlanta and Cincinnati are 440 mi apart. John leaves Cincinnati, driving toward Atlanta at an average rate of 60 mph. Pat leaves Atlanta at the same time, driving toward Cincinnati in her antique auto, averaging 28 mph. How long will it take them to meet?

	r	t	d
John	60	t	$60t$
Pat	28	t	$28t$

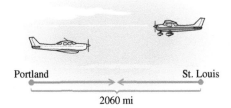

44. St. Louis and Portland are 2060 mi apart. A small plane leaves Portland, traveling toward St. Louis at an average rate of 90 mph. Another plane leaves St. Louis at the same time, traveling toward Portland and averaging 116 mph. How long will it take them to meet?

	r	t	d
Plane Leaving Portland	90	t	$90t$
Plane Leaving St. Louis	116	t	$116t$

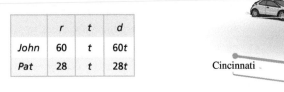

45. A train leaves Kansas City, Kansas, and travels north at 85 km per hr. Another train leaves at the same time and travels south at 95 km per hour. How long will it take before they are 315 km apart?

46. Two steamers leave a port on a river at the same time, traveling in opposite directions. Each is traveling at 22 mph. How long will it take for them to be 110 mi apart?

🌐 **47.** From a point on a straight road, Marco and Celeste ride bicycles in the same direction. Marco rides at 10 mph and Celeste rides at 12 mph. In how many hours will they be 15 mi apart?

48. At a given hour, two steamboats leave a city in the same direction on a straight canal. One travels at 18 mph and the other travels at 24 mph. In how many hours will the boats be 9 mi apart?

🌐 **49.** Two planes leave an airport at the same time, one flying east, the other flying west. The eastbound plane travels 150 mph slower. They are 2250 mi apart after 3 hr. Find the rate of each plane.

	r	t	d
Eastbound	$x - 150$	3	
Westbound	x	3	

50. Two trains leave a city at the same time. One travels north, and the other travels south 20 mph faster. In 2 hr, the trains are 280 mi apart. Find their rates.

	r	t	d
Northbound	x	2	
Southbound	$x + 20$	2	

51. Two cars start from towns 400 mi apart and travel toward each other. They meet after 4 hr. Find the rate of each car if one travels 20 mph faster than the other.

52. Two cars leave towns 230 km apart at the same time, traveling directly toward one another. One car travels 15 km per hr slower than the other. They pass one another 2 hr later. What are their rates?

Brains Busters   *Solve each problem.*

53. Kevin is three times as old as Bob. Three years ago the sum of their ages was 22 yr. How old is each now? (*Hint:* Write an expression first for the age of each now and then for the age of each three years ago.)

54. A store has 39 qt of milk, some in pint cartons and some in quart cartons. There are six times as many quart cartons as pint cartons. How many quart cartons are there? (*Hint:* 1 qt = 2 pt)

55. A table is three times as long as it is wide. If it were 3 ft shorter and 3 ft wider, it would be square (with all sides equal). How long and how wide is the table?

56. Elena works for $6 an hour. A total of 25% of her salary is deducted for taxes and insurance. How many hours must she work to take home $450?

57. Paula received a paycheck for $585 for her weekly wages less 10% deductions. How much was she paid before the deductions were made?

58. At the end of a day, the owner of a gift shop had $2394 in the cash register. This amount included sales tax of 5% on all sales. Find the amount of the sales.

PREVIEW EXERCISES

Decide whether each statement is true *or* false. ***See Section 1.4.***

59. $6 > 6$ **60.** $10 \leq 10$ **61.** $-4 \leq -3$ **62.** $-11 > -9$ **63.** $0 > -\dfrac{1}{2}$

64. Graph the numbers $-3, -\frac{2}{3}, 0, 2, \frac{7}{2}$ on a number line. **See Section 1.4.**

2.8 Solving Linear Inequalities

An **inequality** is an algebraic expression related by

$<$ "is less than," $\leq$ "is less than or equal to,"

$>$ "is greater than," or $\geq$ "is greater than or equal to."

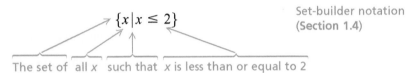

Linear Inequality in One Variable

A **linear inequality in one variable** can be written in the form

$$Ax + B < C, \quad Ax + B \leq C, \quad Ax + B > C, \quad \text{or} \quad Ax + B \geq C,$$

where A, B, and C represent real numbers, and $A \neq 0$.

Some examples of linear inequalities in one variable follow.

$$x + 5 < 2, \quad z - \frac{3}{4} \geq 5, \quad \text{and} \quad 2k + 5 \leq 10 \qquad \text{Linear inequalities}$$

We solve a linear inequality by finding all real number solutions of it. For example, the solution set

$$\{x \mid x \leq 2\} \qquad \text{Set-builder notation (Section 1.4)}$$

The set of all x such that x is less than or equal to 2

includes *all real numbers* that are less than or equal to 2, not just the *integers* less than or equal to 2.

OBJECTIVE 1 **Graph intervals on a number line.** Graphing is a good way to show the solution set of an inequality. To graph all real numbers belonging to the set $\{x \mid x \leq 2\}$, we place a square bracket at 2 on a number line and draw an arrow extending from the bracket to the left (since all numbers *less than* 2 are also part of the graph). See **FIGURE 18**.

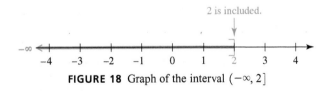

FIGURE 18 Graph of the interval $(-\infty, 2]$

The set of numbers less than or equal to 2 is an example of an **interval** on the number line. We can write this interval using **interval notation.**

$$(-\infty, 2] \qquad \text{Interval notation}$$

The **negative infinity** symbol $-\infty$ does not indicate a number, but shows that the interval includes *all* real numbers less than 2. Again, the square bracket indicates that 2 is part of the solution.

NOW TRY
EXERCISE 1

Write each inequality in interval notation, and graph the interval.

(a) $x < -1$ **(b)** $-2 \leq x$

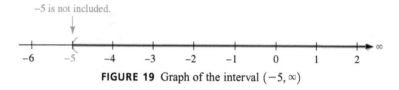

Graphing Intervals on a Number Line

Write each inequality in interval notation, and graph the interval.

(a) $x > -5$

The statement $x > -5$ says that x can represent any number greater than -5 but cannot equal -5. The interval is written $(-5, \infty)$. We graph this interval by placing a parenthesis at -5 and drawing an arrow to the right, as in **FIGURE 19**. The parenthesis at -5 indicates that -5 is *not* part of the graph.

−5 is not included.

FIGURE 19 Graph of the interval $(-5, \infty)$

(b) $3 > x$

The statement $3 > x$ means the same as $x < 3$. ***The inequality symbol continues to point toward the lesser number.*** The graph of $x < 3$, written in interval notation as $(-\infty, 3)$, is shown in **FIGURE 20**.

FIGURE 20 Graph of the interval $(-\infty, 3)$

NOW TRY

Keep the following important concepts regarding interval notation in mind:

1. A parenthesis indicates that an endpoint is *not included* in a solution set.

2. A bracket indicates that an endpoint is *included* in a solution set.

3. A parenthesis is *always* used next to an infinity symbol, $-\infty$ or ∞.

4. The set of all real numbers is written in interval notation as $(-\infty, \infty)$.

NOTE Some texts use a solid circle ● rather than a square bracket to indicate that an endpoint is included in a number line graph. An open circle ○ is used to indicate noninclusion, rather than a parenthesis.

The table summarizes methods of expressing solution sets of linear inequalities.

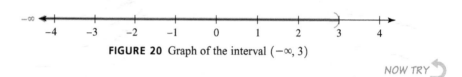

Set-Builder Notation	Interval Notation	Graph
$\{x \mid x < a\}$	$(-\infty, a)$	
$\{x \mid x \leq a\}$	$(-\infty, a]$	
$\{x \mid x > a\}$	(a, ∞)	
$\{x \mid x \geq a\}$	$[a, \infty)$	
$\{x \mid x \text{ is a real number}\}$	$(-\infty, \infty)$	

NOW TRY ANSWERS
1. (a) $(-\infty, -1)$

(b) $[-2, \infty)$

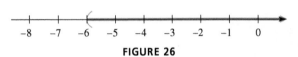

NOW TRY
EXERCISE 6

Solve and graph the solution set.

$$\frac{3}{4}(x - 2) + \frac{1}{2} > \frac{1}{5}(x - 8)$$

	$6\left[-\dfrac{2}{3}(x - 3)\right] - 6\left(\dfrac{1}{2}\right) < 6\left[\dfrac{1}{2}(5 - x)\right]$	Distributive property
	$-4(x - 3) - 3 < 3(5 - x)$	Multiply.
Step 1	$-4x + 12 - 3 < 15 - 3x$	Distributive property
	$-4x + 9 < 15 - 3x$	
Step 2	$-4x + 9 + 3x < 15 - 3x + 3x$	Add $3x$.
	$-x + 9 < 15$	
	$-x + 9 - 9 < 15 - 9$	Subtract 9.
	$-x < 6$	
Step 3	$-1(-x) > -1(6)$	Multiply by -1. Change $<$ to $>$.

Be careful here.

Reverse the inequality symbol when multiplying by a *negative* number.

$$x > -6$$

Check that the solution set is $(-6, \infty)$. See the graph in **FIGURE 26**.

$$\overset{\longleftarrow \qquad \qquad \qquad \qquad \qquad \qquad \qquad \longrightarrow}{\underset{-8 \quad -7 \quad -6 \quad -5 \quad -4 \quad -3 \quad -2 \quad -1 \quad \ 0}{|\quad\ \ |\quad\ \ (\quad\ \ |\quad\ \ |\quad\ \ |\quad\ \ |\quad\ \ |\quad\ \ |}}$$

FIGURE 26

NOW TRY

OBJECTIVE 5 Solve applied problems by using inequalities.

The table gives some common phrases that suggest inequality.

Phrase/Word	Example	Inequality
Is more than	A number *is more than* 4	$x > 4$
Is less than	A number *is less than* -12	$x < -12$
Exceeds	A number *exceeds* 3.5	$x > 3.5$
Is at least	A number *is at least* 6	$x \geq 6$
Is at most	A number *is at most* 8	$x \leq 8$

NOW TRY
EXERCISE 7

A local health club charges a $40 one-time enrollment fee, plus $35 per month for a membership. Sara can spend no more than $355 on this exercise expense. What is the *maximum* number of months that Sara can belong to this health club?

EXAMPLE 7 Using a Linear Inequality to Solve a Rental Problem

A rental company charges $15 to rent a chain saw, plus $2 per hr. Tom Ruhberg can spend no more than $35 to clear some logs from his yard. What is the *maximum amount* of time he can use the rented saw?

Step 1 **Read** the problem again.

Step 2 **Assign a variable.** Let x = the number of hours he can rent the saw.

Step 3 **Write an inequality.** He must pay $15, plus $2x$, to rent the saw for x hours, and this amount must be *no more than* $35.

Cost of renting	is no more than	35 dollars.	
$15 + 2x$	$\leq$	35	Since "is more than" translates as $>$, "is *no* more than" translates as $\leq$.

Step 4 **Solve.**

$$2x \leq 20 \qquad \text{Subtract 15.}$$
$$x \leq 10 \qquad \text{Divide by 2.}$$

Step 5 **State the answer.** He can use the saw for a maximum of 10 hr. (Of course, he may use it for less time, as indicated by the inequality $x \leq 10$.)

Step 6 **Check.** If Tom uses the saw for 10 hr, he will spend $15 + 2(10) = 35$ dollars, the maximum amount.

NOW TRY

NOW TRY ANSWERS

6. $\left(-\frac{12}{11}, \infty\right)$

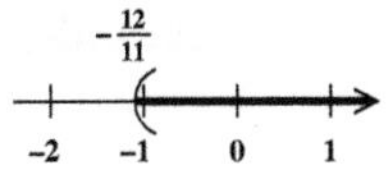

$$\overset{\qquad -\frac{12}{11}}{\underset{-2 \quad -1 \quad\ 0 \quad\ 1}{\longleftarrow\ |\ \ (\ |\ \ |\ \ |\ \longrightarrow}}$$

7. 9 months

NOTE In **Example 7,** we used the six problem-solving steps from **Section 2.4,** changing Step 3 from

"Write an equation"   to   "Write an inequality."

The next example uses the idea of finding the average of a number of scores. *In general, to find the average of n numbers, add the numbers and divide by n.*

NOW TRY
EXERCISE 8

Kristine has grades of 98 and 85 on her first two tests in algebra. If she wants an average of at least 90 after her third test, what score must she make on that test?

EXAMPLE 8   Finding an Average Test Score

John Baker has grades of 86, 88, and 78 on his first three tests in geometry. If he wants an average of at least 80 after his fourth test, what are the possible scores he can make on that test?

Step 1   **Read** the problem again.

Step 2   **Assign a variable.** Let x = John's score on his fourth test.

Step 3   **Write an inequality.**

$$\underset{\text{Average}}{\underbrace{\frac{86 + 88 + 78 + x}{4}}} \underset{\substack{\text{is at} \\ \text{least 80.}}}{\geq} 80 \qquad \text{To find his average after four tests,} \\ \text{add the test scores and divide by 4.}$$

Step 4   **Solve.**

$$\frac{252 + x}{4} \geq 80 \qquad \text{Add in the numerator.}$$

$$4\left(\frac{252 + x}{4}\right) \geq 4(80) \qquad \text{Multiply by 4.}$$

$$252 + x \geq 320$$

$$252 + x - 252 \geq 320 - 252 \qquad \text{Subtract 252.}$$

$$x \geq 68 \qquad \text{Combine like terms.}$$

Step 5   **State the answer.** He must score 68 or more on the fourth test to have an average of *at least* 80.

Step 6   **Check.**

$$\frac{86 + 88 + 78 + 68}{4} = \frac{320}{4} = 80$$

(Also show that a score greater than 68 gives an average greater than 80.)

NOW TRY

⚠ CAUTION   In applied problems, remember that

| | at least | translates as | is greater than or equal to |
| and | at most | translates as | is less than or equal to. |

OBJECTIVE 6 **Solve linear inequalities with three parts.** Inequalities that say that one number is *between* two other numbers are **three-part inequalities.** For example,

NOW TRY ANSWER
8. 87 or more

$$-3 < 5 < 7 \qquad \text{says that 5 is } \textit{between } -3 \text{ and } 7.$$

NOW TRY
EXERCISE 9

Write the inequality in interval notation, and graph the interval.

$$0 \le x < 2$$

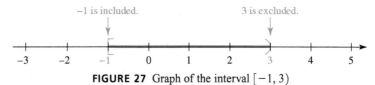

EXAMPLE 9 Graphing a Three-Part Inequality

Write the inequality in interval notation, and graph the interval.

$$-1 \le x < 3$$

The statement is read "-1 is less than or equal to x *and x is less than 3*." We want the set of numbers *between* -1 and 3, with -1 included and 3 excluded. In interval notation, we write $[-1, 3)$, using a square bracket at -1 because -1 is part of the graph and a parenthesis at 3 because 3 is not part of the graph. See **FIGURE 27**.

-1 is included.   3 is excluded.

-3   -2   -1   0   1   2   3   4   5

FIGURE 27 Graph of the interval $[-1, 3)$

NOW TRY

The three-part inequality

$$3 < x + 2 < 8 \qquad \text{says that } x + 2 \text{ is } between \text{ 3 and 8.}$$

We solve this inequality as follows.

$$3 - 2 < x + 2 - 2 < 8 - 2 \qquad \text{Subtract 2 from each part.}$$
$$1 < \quad x \quad < 6$$

The idea is to get the inequality in the form

$$\text{a number} < x < \text{another number.}$$

⚠ **CAUTION** *Three-part inequalities are written so that the symbols point in the same direction and both point toward the lesser number.* It would be *wrong* to write an inequality as $8 < x + 2 < 3$, since this would imply that $8 < 3$, a false statement.

EXAMPLE 10 Solving Three-Part Inequalities

Solve each inequality, and graph the solution set.

(a)
$$4 < \quad 3x - 5 \quad \le 10$$
$$4 + 5 < 3x - 5 + 5 \le 10 + 5 \qquad \text{Add 5 to each part.}$$
$$9 < \quad 3x \quad \le 15$$

Remember to divide all *three* parts by 3.
$$\frac{9}{3} < \quad \frac{3x}{3} \quad \le \frac{15}{3} \qquad \text{Divide each part by 3.}$$
$$3 < \quad x \quad \le 5$$

The solution set is $(3, 5]$. Its graph is shown in **FIGURE 28**.

NOW TRY ANSWER
9. $[0, 2)$

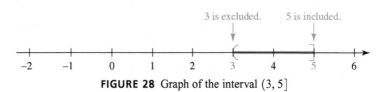

3 is excluded.   5 is included.

-2   -1   0   1   2   3   4   5   6

FIGURE 28 Graph of the interval $(3, 5]$

NOW TRY
EXERCISE 10

Solve the inequality, and graph the solution set.

$$-4 \le \frac{3}{2}x - 1 \le 0$$

(b)

$$-4 \le \frac{2}{3}m - 1 < 8$$

$$3(-4) \le 3\left(\frac{2}{3}m - 1\right) < 3(8) \qquad \text{Multiply each part by 3 to clear the fraction.}$$

$$-12 \le 2m - 3 < 24 \qquad \text{Distributive property}$$

$$-12 + 3 \le 2m - 3 + 3 < 24 + 3 \qquad \text{Add 3 to each part.}$$

$$-9 \le 2m < 27$$

$$\frac{-9}{2} \le \frac{2m}{2} < \frac{27}{2} \qquad \text{Divide each part by 2.}$$

$$-\frac{9}{2} \le m < \frac{27}{2}$$

The solution set is $\left[-\frac{9}{2}, \frac{27}{2}\right)$. Its graph is shown in **FIGURE 29**.

Think: $-\frac{9}{2} = -4\frac{1}{2}$

Think: $\frac{27}{2} = 13\frac{1}{2}$

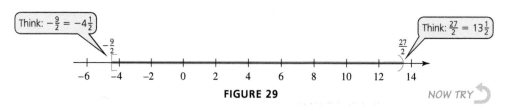

FIGURE 29

NOW TRY

NOTE The inequality in **Example 10(b)**, $-4 \le \frac{2}{3}m - 1 < 8$, can also be solved by first adding 1 to each part and then multiplying each part by $\frac{3}{2}$. Try this.

The table summarizes methods of expressing solution sets of three-part inequalities.

Set-Builder Notation	Interval Notation	Graph
$\{x \mid a < x < b\}$	(a, b)	
$\{x \mid a < x \le b\}$	$(a, b]$	
$\{x \mid a \le x < b\}$	$[a, b)$	
$\{x \mid a \le x \le b\}$	$[a, b]$	

NOW TRY ANSWER

10. $\left[-2, \frac{2}{3}\right]$

⬤ *Complete solution available on the Video Resources on DVD*

Concept Check *Work each problem.*

1. When graphing an inequality, use a parenthesis if the inequality symbol is _____ or _____ . Use a square bracket if the inequality symbol is _____ or _____ .

2. *True* or *false*? In interval notation, a square bracket is sometimes used next to an infinity symbol.

3. In interval notation, the set $\{x \mid x > 0\}$ is written _____ .

4. How does the graph of $x \ge -7$ differ from the graph of $x > -7$?

Concept Check   *Write an inequality involving the variable x that describes each set of numbers graphed.*

5.
```
   -4 -3 -2 -1  0  1  2  3
```

6.
```
   -4 -3 -2 -1  0  1  2  3  4
```

7.
```
   -2 -1  0  1  2  3  4  5
```

8.
```
   -2 -1  0  1  2  3  4  5
```

*Write each inequality in interval notation, and graph the interval. **See Example 1.***

9. $k \le 4$ **10.** $x \le 3$ **11.** $x < -3$ **12.** $r < -11$ **13.** $t > 4$

14. $m > 5$ **15.** $0 \ge x$ **16.** $1 \ge x$ **17.** $-\dfrac{1}{2} \le x$ **18.** $-\dfrac{3}{4} \le x$

*Solve each inequality. Write the solution set in interval notation, and graph it. **See Example 2.***

19. $z - 8 \ge -7$ **20.** $p - 3 \ge -11$ **21.** $2k + 3 \ge k + 8$

22. $3x + 7 \ge 2x + 11$ **23.** $3n + 5 < 2n - 6$ **24.** $5x - 2 < 4x - 5$

*Solve each inequality. Write the solution set in interval notation, and graph it. **See Example 3.***

25. $3x < 18$ **26.** $5x < 35$ **27.** $2y \ge -20$

28. $6m \ge -24$ **29.** $-8t > 24$ **30.** $-7x > 49$

31. $-x \ge 0$ **32.** $-k < 0$ **33.** $-\dfrac{3}{4}r < -15$

34. $-\dfrac{7}{8}t < -14$ **35.** $-0.02x \le 0.06$ **36.** $-0.03v \ge -0.12$

*Solve each inequality. Write the solution set in interval notation, and graph it. **See Examples 4–6.***

37. $8x + 9 \le -15$

38. $6x + 7 \le -17$

39. $-4x - 3 < 1$

40. $-5x - 4 < 6$

41. $5r + 1 \ge 3r - 9$

42. $6t + 3 < 3t + 12$

43. $6x + 3 + x < 2 + 4x + 4$

44. $-4w + 12 + 9w \ge w + 9 + w$

45. $-x + 4 + 7x \le -2 + 3x + 6$

46. $14y - 6 + 7y > 4 + 10y - 10$

47. $5(t - 1) > 3(t - 2)$

48. $7(m - 2) < 4(m - 4)$

49. $5(x + 3) - 6x \le 3(2x + 1) - 4x$

50. $2(x - 5) + 3x < 4(x - 6) + 1$

51. $4x - (6x + 1) \le 8x + 2(x - 3)$

52. $2y - (4y + 3) > 6y + 3(y + 4)$

53. $\dfrac{2}{3}(p + 3) > \dfrac{5}{6}(p - 4)$

54. $\dfrac{7}{9}(y - 4) \le \dfrac{4}{3}(y + 5)$

55. $\dfrac{2}{3}(3x - 1) \ge \dfrac{3}{2}(2x - 3)$

56. $\dfrac{7}{5}(10x - 1) < \dfrac{2}{3}(6x + 5)$

57. $-\dfrac{1}{4}(p + 6) + \dfrac{3}{2}(2p - 5) < 10$

58. $\dfrac{3}{5}(t - 2) - \dfrac{1}{4}(2t - 7) \le 3$

FOR INDIVIDUAL OR GROUP WORK

Work Exercises 59–62 in order, to see how the solutions of an inequality are closely connected to the solution of the corresponding equation.

59. Solve the equation $3x + 2 = 14$, and graph the solution set on a number line.

60. Solve the inequality $3x + 2 > 14$, and graph the solution set on a number line.

61. Solve the inequality $3x + 2 < 14$, and graph the solution set on a number line.

62. If we were to graph all the solution sets from **Exercises 59–61** on the same number line, describe the graph. (This is called the **union** of all the solution sets.)

Concept Check *Translate each statement into an inequality. Use x as the variable.*

63. You must be at least 18 yr old to vote.

64. Less than 1 in. of rain fell.

65. Chicago received more than 5 in. of snow.

66. A full-time student must take at least 12 credits.

67. Tracy could spend at most $20 on a gift.

68. The car's speed exceeded 60 mph.

Solve each problem. **See Examples 7 and 8.**

69. Christy Heinrich has scores of 76 and 81 on her first two algebra tests. If she wants an average of at least 80 after her third test, what possible scores can she make on that test?

70. Joseph Despagne has scores of 96 and 86 on his first two geometry tests. What possible scores can he make on his third test so that his average is at least 90?

71. When 2 is added to the difference between six times a number and 5, the result is greater than 13 added to five times the number. Find all such numbers.

72. When 8 is subtracted from the sum of three times a number and 6, the result is less than 4 more than the number. Find all such numbers.

73. The formula for converting Fahrenheit temperature to Celsius is

$$C = \frac{5}{9}(F - 32).$$

If the Celsius temperature on a certain winter day in Minneapolis is never less than $-25°$, how would you describe the corresponding Fahrenheit temperatures? (*Source:* National Climatic Data Center.)

74. The formula for converting Celsius temperature to Fahrenheit is

$$F = \frac{9}{5}C + 32.$$

The Fahrenheit temperature of Phoenix has never exceeded $122°$. How would you describe this using Celsius temperature? (*Source:* National Climatic Data Center.)

75. For what values of x would the rectangle have a perimeter of at least 400?

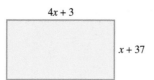

76. For what values of x would the triangle have a perimeter of at least 72?

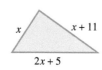

77. For a certain provider, an international phone call costs $2.00 for the first 3 min, plus $0.30 per minute for each minute or fractional part of a minute after the first 3 min. If x represents the number of minutes of the length of the call after the first 3 min, then $2 + 0.30x$ represents the cost of the call. If Alan Lebovitz has $5.60 to spend on a call, what is the maximum total time he can use the phone?

78. At the Speedy Gas'n Go, a car wash costs $4.50 and gasoline is selling for $3.20 per gallon. Carla Arriola has $38.10 to spend, and her car is so dirty that she must have it washed. What is the maximum number of gallons of gasoline that she can purchase?

A company that produces DVDs has found that revenue from the sales of the DVDs is $5 per DVD, less sales costs of $100. Production costs are $125, plus $4 per DVD. Profit (P) is given by revenue (R) less cost (C), so the company must find the production level x that makes

$$P > 0, \quad \text{that is,} \quad R - C > 0. \qquad P = R - C$$

79. Write an expression for revenue R, letting x represent the production level (number of DVDs to be produced).

80. Write an expression for production costs C in terms of x.

81. Write an expression for profit P, and then solve the inequality $P > 0$.

82. Describe the solution in terms of the problem.

Concept Check Write a three-part inequality involving the variable x that describes each set of numbers graphed.

83.

84.

85.

86.

Write each inequality in interval notation, and graph the interval. **See Example 9.**

87. $8 \le x \le 10$

88. $3 \le x \le 5$

89. $0 < y \le 10$

90. $-3 \le x < 0$

91. $4 > x > -3$

92. $6 \ge x \ge -4$

Solve each inequality. Write the solution set in interval notation, and graph it. **See Example 10.**

93. $-5 \le 2x - 3 \le 9$

94. $-7 \le 3x - 4 \le 8$

95. $5 < 1 - 6m < 12$

96. $-1 \le 1 - 5q \le 16$

97. $10 < 7p + 3 < 24$

98. $-8 \le 3r - 1 \le -1$

99. $-12 \le \frac{1}{2}z + 1 \le 4$

100. $-6 \le 3 + \frac{1}{3}x \le 5$

101. $1 \le 3 + \frac{2}{3}p \le 7$

102. $2 < 6 + \frac{3}{4}x < 12$

103. $-7 \le \frac{5}{4}r - 1 \le -1$

104. $-12 \le \frac{3}{7}x + 2 \le -4$

PREVIEW EXERCISES

*Find the value of y when (**a**) x = −2 and (**b**) x = 4. **See Sections 1.3 and 2.3.***

105. $y = 5x + 3$

106. $y = 4 - 3x$

107. $6x - 2 = y$

108. $4x + 7y = 11$

109. $2x - 5y = 10$

110. $y + 3x = 8$

STUDY SKILLS

Taking Math Tests

Techniques To Improve Your Test Score	Comments
Come prepared with a pencil, eraser, paper, and calculator, if allowed.	Working in pencil lets you erase, keeping your work neat and readable.
Scan the entire test, note the point values of different problems, and plan your time accordingly.	To do 20 problems in 50 minutes, allow $50 \div 20 = 2.5$ minutes per problem. Spend less time on the easier problems.
Do a "knowledge dump" when you get the test. Write important notes to yourself in a corner of the test, such as formulas.	Writing down tips and things that you've memorized at the beginning allows you to relax later.
Read directions carefully, and circle any significant words. When you finish a problem, read the directions again to make sure you did what was asked.	Pay attention to announcements written on the board or made by your instructor. Ask if you don't understand.
Show all your work. Many teachers give partial credit if some steps are correct, even if the final answer is wrong. **Write neatly.**	If your teacher can't read your writing, you won't get credit for it. If you need more space to work, ask to use extra paper.
Write down anything that might help solve a problem: a formula, a diagram, etc. If you can't get it, circle the problem and come back to it later. Do *not* erase anything you wrote down.	If you know even a little bit about the problem, write it down. The answer may come to you as you work on it, or you may get partial credit. Don't spend too long on any one problem.
If you can't solve a problem, make a guess. Do not change it unless you find an obvious mistake.	Have a good reason for changing an answer. Your first guess is usually your best bet.
Check that the answer to an application problem is reasonable and makes sense. Read the problem again to make sure you've answered the question.	Use common sense. Can the father really be seven years old? Would a month's rent be $32,140? Label your answer: $, years, inches, etc.
Check for careless errors. Rework the problem without looking at your previous work. Compare the two answers.	Reworking the problem from the beginning forces you to rethink it. If possible, use a different method to solve the problem.

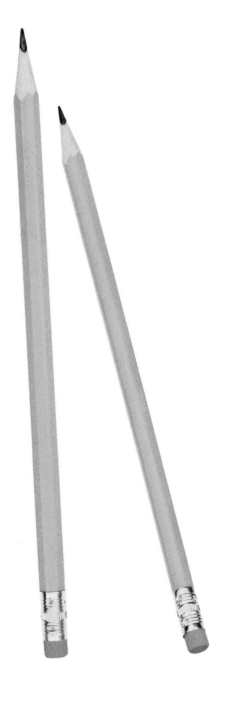

Select several tips to try when you take your next math test.

CHAPTER (2) SUMMARY

KEY TERMS

2.1
equation
linear equation in one
  variable
solution
solution set
equivalent equations

2.3
conditional equation
identity

contradiction
empty (null) set

2.4
consecutive integers
degree
complementary angles
right angle
supplementary angles
straight angle

2.5
formula
area
perimeter
vertical angles
volume

2.6
ratio
proportion
terms of a proportion

extremes
means
cross products

2.8
inequality
linear inequality in one
  variable
interval on a number line
interval notation
three-part inequality

NEW SYMBOLS

$\emptyset$ empty set
$1°$ one degree

a to b, $a{:}b$, or $\dfrac{a}{b}$
  the ratio of a to b

∞ infinity
$-\infty$ negative infinity
$(-\infty, \infty)$ set of all real
  numbers

(a, b) interval notation for
  $a < x < b$
$[a, b]$ interval notation for
  $a \le x \le b$

TEST YOUR WORD POWER

See how well you have learned the vocabulary in this chapter.

1. A **solution set** is the set of numbers that
   A. make an expression undefined
   B. make an equation false
   C. make an equation true
   D. make an expression equal to 0.

2. **Complementary angles** are angles
   A. formed by two parallel lines
   B. whose sum is 90°
   C. whose sum is 180°
   D. formed by perpendicular lines.

3. **Supplementary angles** are angles
   A. formed by two parallel lines
   B. whose sum is 90°
   C. whose sum is 180°
   D. formed by perpendicular lines.

4. A **ratio**
   A. compares two quantities using a quotient
   B. says that two quotients are equal
   C. is a product of two quantities
   D. is a difference between two quantities.

5. A **proportion**
   A. compares two quantities using a quotient
   B. says that two quotients are equal
   C. is a product of two quantities
   D. is a difference between two quantities.

6. An **inequality** is
   A. a statement that two algebraic expressions are equal
   B. a point on a number line
   C. an equation with no solutions
   D. a statement with algebraic expressions related by $<$, $\le$, $>$, or $\ge$.

7. **Interval notation** is
   A. a portion of a number line
   B. a special notation for describing a point on a number line
   C. a way to use symbols to describe an interval on a number line
   D. a notation to describe unequal quantities.

ANSWERS

1. C; *Example:* {8} is the solution set of $2x + 5 = 21$.   2. B; *Example:* Angles with measures 35° and 55° are complementary angles.
3. C; *Example:* Angles with measures 112° and 68° are supplementary angles.   4. A; *Example:* $\frac{7 \text{ in.}}{12 \text{ in.}}$, or $\frac{7}{12}$ 5. B; *Example:* $\frac{2}{3} = \frac{8}{12}$
6. D; *Examples:* $x < 5, 7 + 2y \ge 11, -5 < 2z - 1 \le 3$ 7. C; *Examples:* $(-\infty, 5], (1, \infty), [-3, 13), (-\infty, \infty)$

QUICK REVIEW

CONCEPTS	EXAMPLES

2.1 The Addition Property of Equality

The same number may be added to (or subtracted from) each side of an equation without changing the solution.

Solve. $\quad x - 6 = 12$

$\qquad x - 6 + 6 = 12 + 6 \qquad$ Add 6.

$\qquad\qquad\qquad x = 18 \qquad$ Combine like terms.

Solution set: $\{18\}$

2.2 The Multiplication Property of Equality

Each side of an equation may be multiplied (or divided) by the same nonzero number without changing the solution.

Solve. $\qquad \dfrac{3}{4}x = -9$

$\dfrac{4}{3} \cdot \left(\dfrac{3}{4}x \right) = \dfrac{4}{3}(-9) \qquad$ Multiply by $\frac{4}{3}$.

$\qquad\qquad\quad x = -12$

Solution set: $\{-12\}$

2.3 More on Solving Linear Equations

Step 1 Simplify each side separately.

Solve.

$$2x + 2(x + 1) = 14 + x$$

$$2x + 2x + 2 = 14 + x \qquad \text{Distributive property}$$

$$4x + 2 = 14 + x \qquad \text{Combine like terms.}$$

Step 2 Isolate the variable term on one side.

$$4x + 2 - x - 2 = 14 + x - x - 2 \qquad \text{Subtract } x. \text{ Subtract 2.}$$

$$3x = 12 \qquad \text{Combine like terms.}$$

Step 3 Isolate the variable.

$$\frac{3x}{3} = \frac{12}{3} \qquad \text{Divide by 3.}$$

$$x = 4$$

Step 4 Check.

CHECK $\quad 2(4) + 2(4 + 1) \overset{?}{=} 14 + 4 \qquad$ Let $x = 4$.

$$18 = 18 \checkmark \qquad \text{True}$$

Solution set: $\{4\}$

2.4 An Introduction to Applications of Linear Equations

Step 1 Read.

One number is five more than another. Their sum is 21. What are the numbers?

Step 2 Assign a variable.

Let $\qquad x =$ the lesser number.

Then $\quad x + 5 =$ the greater number.

Step 3 Write an equation.

$$x + (x + 5) = 21$$

Step 4 Solve the equation.

$$2x + 5 = 21 \qquad \text{Combine like terms.}$$

$$2x = 16 \qquad \text{Subtract 5.}$$

$$x = 8 \qquad \text{Divide by 2.}$$

Step 5 State the answer.

The numbers are 8 and 13.

Step 6 Check.

13 is five more than 8, and $8 + 13 = 21$. It checks.

(continued)

CONCEPTS	EXAMPLES
2.5 Formulas and Additional Applications from Geometry	
To find the value of one of the variables in a formula, given values for the others, substitute the known values into the formula.	Find L if $\mathcal{A} = LW$, given that $\mathcal{A} = 24$ and $W = 3$. $$24 = L \cdot 3 \quad \mathcal{A} = 24, W = 3$$ $$\frac{24}{3} = \frac{L \cdot 3}{3} \quad \text{Divide by 3.}$$ $$8 = L$$
To solve a formula for one of the variables, isolate that variable by treating the other variables as numbers and using the steps for solving equations.	Solve $P = 2a + 2b$ for b. $$P - 2a = 2a + 2b - 2a \qquad \text{Subtract } 2a.$$ $$P - 2a = 2b \qquad\qquad \text{Combine like terms.}$$ $$\frac{P - 2a}{2} = \frac{2b}{2} \qquad\qquad \text{Divide by 2.}$$ $$\frac{P - 2a}{2} = b, \quad \text{or} \quad b = \frac{P - 2a}{2}$$
2.6 Ratio, Proportion, and Percent	
To write a ratio, express quantities in the same units.	4 ft to 8 in. $= 48$ in. to 8 in. $= \dfrac{48}{8} = \dfrac{6}{1}$
To solve a proportion, use the method of cross products.	Solve. $\dfrac{x}{12} = \dfrac{35}{60}$ $$60x = 12 \cdot 35 \qquad \text{Cross products}$$ $$60x = 420 \qquad\quad \text{Multiply.}$$ $$x = 7 \qquad\qquad \text{Divide by 60.}$$ Solution set: $\{7\}$
To solve a percent problem, use the percent equation. **amount = percent (as a decimal) · base**	65 is what percent of 325? $$65 = p \cdot 325$$ $$\frac{65}{325} = p$$ $$0.2 = p, \quad \text{or} \quad 20\% = p$$ 65 is 20% of 325.
2.7 Further Applications of Linear Equations	
Step 1 Read.	Two cars leave from the same point, traveling in opposite directions. One travels at 45 mph and the other at 60 mph. How long will it take them to be 210 mi apart?
Step 2 Assign a variable. Make a table and/or draw a sketch to help solve the problem. The three forms of the formula relating distance, rate, and time are $$d = rt, \quad r = \frac{d}{t}, \quad \text{and} \quad t = \frac{d}{r}.$$	Let t = time it takes for them to be 210 mi apart. 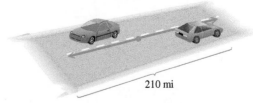 210 mi

(continued)

CONCEPTS	EXAMPLES

EXAMPLES

	Rate	Time	Distance
One Car	45	t	$45t$
Other Car	60	t	$60t$

The sum of the distances is 210 mi.

Step 3 Write an equation.

$$45t + 60t = 210$$

Step 4 Solve the equation.

$$105t = 210 \quad \text{Combine like terms.}$$
$$t = 2 \quad \text{Divide by 105.}$$

Steps 5 and 6 State the answer and check the solution.

It will take them 2 hr to be 210 mi apart.

2.8 Solving Linear Inequalities

Step 1 Simplify each side separately.

Solve the inequality, and graph the solution set.
$$3(1 - x) + 5 - 2x > 9 - 6$$
$$3 - 3x + 5 - 2x > 9 - 6 \quad \text{Clear parentheses.}$$
$$8 - 5x > 3 \quad \text{Combine like terms.}$$

Step 2 Isolate the variable term on one side.

$$8 - 5x - 8 > 3 - 8 \quad \text{Subtract 8.}$$
$$-5x > -5 \quad \text{Combine like terms.}$$

Step 3 Isolate the variable.

$$\frac{-5x}{-5} < \frac{-5}{-5} \quad \begin{array}{l}\text{Divide by } -5.\\ \text{Change} > \text{to} <.\end{array}$$

Be sure to reverse the direction of the inequality symbol when multiplying or dividing by a negative number.

$$x < 1$$

Solution set: $(-\infty, 1)$

To solve a three-part inequality such as
$$4 < 2x + 6 < 8,$$
work with all three expressions at the same time.

Solve.
$$4 < 2x + 6 < 8$$
$$4 - 6 < 2x + 6 - 6 < 8 - 6 \quad \text{Subtract 6.}$$
$$-2 < 2x < 2$$
$$\frac{-2}{2} < \frac{2x}{2} < \frac{2}{2} \quad \text{Divide by 2.}$$
$$-1 < x < 1$$

Solution set: $(-1, 1)$

CHAPTER ② REVIEW EXERCISES

2.1–2.3 *Solve each equation.*

1. $x - 5 = 1$

2. $x + 8 = -4$

3. $3t + 1 = 2t + 8$

4. $5z = 4z + \dfrac{2}{3}$

5. $(4r - 2) - (3r + 1) = 8$

6. $3(2x - 5) = 2 + 5x$

7. $7x = 35$

8. $12r = -48$

9. $2p - 7p + 8p = 15$

10. $\dfrac{x}{12} = -1$

11. $\dfrac{5}{8}q = 8$

12. $12m + 11 = 59$

13. $3(2x + 6) - 5(x + 8) = x - 22$

14. $5x + 9 - (2x - 3) = 2x - 7$

15. $\dfrac{1}{2}r - \dfrac{r}{3} = \dfrac{r}{6}$

16. $0.1(x + 80) + 0.2x = 14$

17. $3x - (-2x + 6) = 4(x - 4) + x$

18. $\dfrac{1}{2}(x + 3) - \dfrac{2}{3}(x - 2) = 3$

> **2.4** *Solve each problem.*

19. If 7 is added to five times a number, the result is equal to three times the number. Find the number.

20. In 2009, Illinois had 118 members in its House of Representatives, consisting of only Democrats and Republicans. There were 22 more Democrats than Republicans. How many representatives from each party were there? (*Source:* www.ilga.gov)

21. The land area of Hawaii is 5213 mi² greater than the area of Rhode Island. Together, the areas total 7637 mi². What is the area of each of the two states?

22. The height of Seven Falls in Colorado is $\frac{5}{2}$ the height of Twin Falls in Idaho. The sum of the heights is 420 ft. Find the height of each. (*Source: World Almanac and Book of Facts.*)

23. The supplement of an angle measures 10 times the measure of its complement. What is the measure of the angle?

24. Find two consecutive odd integers such that when the lesser is added to twice the greater, the result is 24 more than the greater integer.

> **2.5** *A formula is given along with the values for all but one of the variables. Find the value of the variable that is not given. Use 3.14 as an approximation for π.*

25. $\mathcal{A} = \dfrac{1}{2}bh;$ $\mathcal{A} = 44, b = 8$

26. $\mathcal{A} = \dfrac{1}{2}h(b + B);$ $h = 8, b = 3, B = 4$

27. $C = 2\pi r;$ $C = 29.83$

28. $V = \dfrac{4}{3}\pi r^3;$ $r = 6$

Solve each formula for the specified variable.

29. $\mathcal{A} = bh$ for h

30. $\mathcal{A} = \dfrac{1}{2}h(b + B)$ for h

Find the measure of each marked angle.

31.

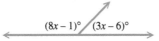

$(8x - 1)°$ $(3x - 6)°$

32.

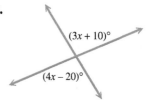

$(3x + 10)°$

$(4x - 20)°$

Solve each problem.

33. The perimeter of a certain rectangle is 16 times the width. The length is 12 cm more than the width. Find the width of the rectangle.

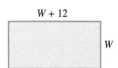

$W + 12$

W

34. The Ziegfield Room in Reno, Nevada, has a circular turntable on which its showgirls dance. The circumference of the table is 62.5 ft. What is the diameter? What is the radius? What is the area? (Use $\pi = 3.14$.) (*Source: Guinness World Records.*)

35. A baseball diamond is a square with a side of 90 ft. The pitcher's mound is located 60.5 ft from home plate, as shown in the figure. Find the measures of the angles marked in the figure. (*Hint:* Recall that the sum of the measures of the angles of any triangle is 180°.)

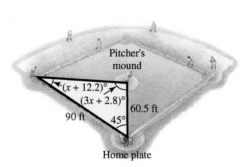

2.6 *Give a ratio for each word phrase, writing fractions in lowest terms.*

36. 60 cm to 40 cm   **37.** 5 days to 2 weeks   **38.** 90 in. to 10 ft

Solve each equation.

39. $\dfrac{p}{21} = \dfrac{5}{30}$

40. $\dfrac{5 + x}{3} = \dfrac{2 - x}{6}$

Solve each problem.

41. The tax on a $24.00 item is $2.04. How much tax would be paid on a $36.00 item?

42. The distance between two cities on a road map is 32 cm. The two cities are actually 150 km apart. The distance on the map between two other cities is 80 cm. How far apart are these cities?

43. In the 2008 Olympics in Beijing, China, Japanese athletes earned 25 medals. Two of every 5 medals were bronze. How many bronze medals did Japan earn? (*Source: World Almanac and Book of Facts.*)

44. Find the best buy. Give the unit price to the nearest thousandth for that size. (*Source:* Cub Foods.)

CEREAL

Size	Price
15 oz	$2.69
20 oz	$3.29
25.5 oz	$3.49

45. What is 8% of 75?

46. What percent of 12 is 21?

47. 36% of what number is 900?

2.7 *Solve each problem.*

48. A nurse must mix 15 L of a 10% solution of a drug with some 60% solution to obtain a 20% mixture. How many liters of the 60% solution will be needed?

49. Robert Kay invested $10,000, from which he earns an annual income of $550 per year. He invested part of the $10,000 at 5% annual interest and the remainder in bonds paying 6% interest. How much did he invest at each rate?

50. In 1846, the vessel *Yorkshire* traveled from Liverpool to New York, a distance of 3150 mi, in 384 hr. What was the *Yorkshire's* average rate? Round your answer to the nearest tenth.

51. Janet Hartnett drove from Louisville to Dallas, a distance of 819 mi, averaging 63 mph. What was her driving time?

52. Two planes leave St. Louis at the same time. One flies north at 350 mph and the other flies south at 420 mph. In how many hours will they be 1925 mi apart?

2.8 *Write each inequality in interval notation, and graph it.*

53. $x \geq -4$ **54.** $x < 7$ **55.** $-5 \leq x < 6$

56. *Concept Check* Which inequality requires reversing the inequality symbol when it is solved?

    A. $4x \geq -36$ **B.** $-4x \leq 36$ **C.** $4x < 36$ **D.** $4x > 36$

Solve each inequality. Write the solution set in interval notation, and graph it.

57. $x + 6 \geq 3$ **58.** $5x < 4x + 2$

59. $-6x \leq -18$ **60.** $8(x - 5) - (2 + 7x) \geq 4$

61. $4x - 3x > 10 - 4x + 7x$ **62.** $3(2x + 5) + 4(8 + 3x) < 5(3x + 7)$

63. $-3 \leq 2x + 1 \leq 4$ **64.** $9 < 3x + 5 \leq 20$

Solve each problem.

65. Awilda Delgado has grades of 94 and 88 on her first two calculus tests. What possible scores on a third test will give her an average of at least 90?

66. If nine times a number is added to 6, the result is at most 3. Find all such numbers.

MIXED REVIEW EXERCISES

Solve.

67. $\dfrac{x}{7} = \dfrac{x - 5}{2}$ **68.** $I = prt$ for r

69. $-2x > -4$ **70.** $2k - 5 = 4k + 13$

71. $0.05x + 0.02x = 4.9$ **72.** $2 - 3(x - 5) = 4 + x$

73. $9x - (7x + 2) = 3x + (2 - x)$ **74.** $\dfrac{1}{3}s + \dfrac{1}{2}s + 7 = \dfrac{5}{6}s + 5 + 2$

75. A family of four with a monthly income of \$3800 plans to spend 8% of this amount on entertainment. How much will be spent on entertainment?

76. Athletes in vigorous training programs can eat 50 calories per day for every 2.2 lb of body weight. To the nearest hundred, how many calories can a 175-lb athlete consume per day? (*Source: The Gazette.*)

77. The Golden Gate Bridge in San Francisco is 2604 ft longer than the Brooklyn Bridge. Together, their spans total 5796 ft. How long is each bridge? (*Source: World Almanac and Book of Facts.*)

78. Find the best buy. Give the unit price to the nearest thousandth for that size. (*Source:* Cub Foods.)

LAUNDRY DETERGENT

Size	Price
50 oz	$ 4.69
100 oz	$ 5.98
200 oz	$13.68

79. If 1 qt of oil must be mixed with 24 qt of gasoline, how much oil would be needed for 192 qt of gasoline?

80. Two trains are 390 mi apart. They start at the same time and travel toward one another, meeting 3 hr later. If the rate of one train is 30 mph more than the rate of the other train, find the rate of each train.

81. The perimeter of a triangle is 96 m. One side is twice as long as another, and the third side is 30 m long. What is the length of the longest side?

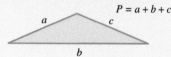

82. The perimeter of a certain square cannot be greater than 200 m. Find the possible values for the length of a side.

CHAPTER 2 TEST

View the complete solutions to all Chapter Test exercises on the Video Resources on DVD.

Solve each equation.

1. $5x + 9 = 7x + 21$

2. $-\frac{4}{7}x = -12$

3. $7 - (x - 4) = -3x + 2(x + 1)$

4. $0.6(x + 20) + 0.8(x - 10) = 46$

5. $-8(2x + 4) = -4(4x + 8)$

Solve each problem.

6. In the 2008 baseball season, the Los Angeles Angels of Anaheim won the most games of any major league team. The Angels won 24 less than twice as many games as they lost. They played 162 regular-season games. How many wins and losses did the Angels have? (*Source:* www.MLB.com)

7. Three islands in the Hawaiian island chain are Hawaii (the Big Island), Maui, and Kauai. Together, their areas total 5300 mi². The island of Hawaii is 3293 mi² larger than the island of Maui, and Maui is 177 mi² larger than Kauai. What is the area of each island?

8. Find the measure of an angle if its supplement measures 10° more than three times its complement.

9. The formula for the perimeter of a rectangle is $P = 2L + 2W$.

  (a) Solve for W.

  (b) If $P = 116$ and $L = 40$, find the value of W.

10. Find the measure of each marked angle.

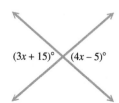

Solve each equation.

11. $\dfrac{z}{8} = \dfrac{12}{16}$

12. $\dfrac{x + 5}{3} = \dfrac{x - 3}{4}$

Solve each problem.

13. Find the best buy. Give the unit price to the nearest thousandth for that size.

PROCESSED
CHEESE SLICES

Size	Price
8 oz	$2.79
16 oz	$4.99
32 oz	$7.99

14. The distance between Milwaukee and Boston is 1050 mi. On a certain map, this distance is represented by 42 in. On the same map, Seattle and Cincinnati are 92 in. apart. What is the actual distance between Seattle and Cincinnati?

15. Carlos Periu invested some money at 3% simple interest and $6000 more than that amount at 4.5% simple interest. After 1 yr, his total interest from the two accounts was $870. How much did he invest at each rate?

16. Two cars leave from the same point, traveling in opposite directions. One travels at a constant rate of 50 mph, while the other travels at a constant rate of 65 mph. How long will it take for them to be 460 mi apart?

Solve each inequality. Write the solution set in interval notation, and graph it.

17. $-4x + 2(x - 3) \geq 4x - (3 + 5x) - 7$ **18.** $-10 < 3x - 4 \leq 14$

19. Susan Jacobson has grades of 76 and 81 on her first two algebra tests. If she wants an average of at least 80 after her third test, what score must she make on that test?

20. Write a short explanation of the additional (extra) rule that must be remembered when solving an inequality (as opposed to solving an equation).

CHAPTERS (1–2) CUMULATIVE REVIEW EXERCISES

Perform each indicated operation.

1. $\dfrac{5}{6} + \dfrac{1}{4} - \dfrac{7}{15}$

2. $\dfrac{9}{8} \cdot \dfrac{16}{3} \div \dfrac{5}{8}$

Translate from words to symbols. Use x as the variable.

3. The difference between half a number and 18

4. The quotient of 6 and 12 more than a number is 2.

5. *True* or *false?* $\dfrac{8(7) - 5(6 + 2)}{3 \cdot 5 + 1} \geq 1$

Perform each indicated operation.

6. $\dfrac{-4(9)(-2)}{-3^2}$

7. $(-7 - 1)(-4) + (-4)$

8. Find the value of $\dfrac{3x^2 - y^3}{-4z}$ when $x = -2, y = -4$, and $z = 3$.

Name each property illustrated.

9. $7(p + q) = 7p + 7q$

10. $3 + (5 + 2) = 3 + (2 + 5)$

Solve each equation, and check the solution.

11. $2r - 6 = 8r$

12. $4 - 5(s + 2) = 3(s + 1) - 1$

13. $\frac{2}{3}x + \frac{3}{4}x = -17$

14. $\frac{2x + 3}{5} = \frac{x - 4}{2}$

15. Solve $3x + 4y = 24$ for y.

Solve each inequality. Write the solution set in interval notation, and graph it.

16. $6(r - 1) + 2(3r - 5) \leq -4$

17. $-18 \leq -9z < 9$

Solve each problem.

18. A 40-cm piece of yarn must be cut into three pieces. The longest piece is to be three times as long as the middle-sized piece, and the shortest piece is to be 5 cm shorter than the middle-sized piece. Find the length of each piece.

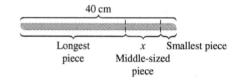

19. A fully inflated professional basketball has a circumference of 78 cm. What is the radius of a circular cross section through the center of the ball? (Use 3.14 as the approximation for π.) Round your answer to the nearest hundredth.

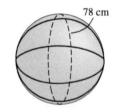

20. Two cars are 400 mi apart. Both start at the same time and travel toward one another. They meet 4 hr later. If the rate of one car is 20 mph faster than the other, what is the rate of each car?

Linear Equations in Two Variables

In recent years, college students, like U.S. consumers as a whole, have increased their dependency on credit cards. In 2008, 84% of undergraduates had at least one credit card, up from 76% in 2004. The average (mean) outstanding balance for undergraduates grew from $946 in 2004 to a record-high $3173 in 2008, with 92% of these students using credit cards to pay direct education expenses. (*Source:* Sallie Mae.)

In **Example 7** of **Section 3.2,** we examine a *linear equation in two variables* that models credit card debt in the United States.

3.1 Linear Equations in Two Variables; The Rectangular Coordinate System

OBJECTIVE 1 Interpret graphs. A line graph is used to show changes or trends in data over time. To form a **line graph,** we connect a series of points representing data with line segments.

EXAMPLE 1 Interpreting a Line Graph

The line graph in **FIGURE 1** shows average prices of a gallon of regular unleaded gasoline in the United States for the years 2001 through 2008.

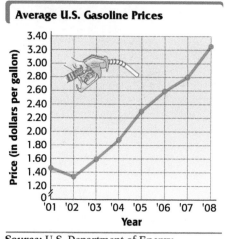

Source: U.S. Department of Energy.

FIGURE 1

NOW TRY
EXERCISE 1

Refer to the line graph in **FIGURE 1.**

(a) Estimate the average price of a gallon of gasoline in 2006.

(b) About how much did the average price of a gallon of gasoline increase from 2006 to 2008?

(a) Between which years did the average price of a gallon of gasoline decrease?

The line between 2001 and 2002 falls, so the average price of a gallon of gasoline decreased from 2001 to 2002.

(b) What was the general trend in the average price of a gallon of gasoline from 2002 through 2008?

The line graph rises from 2002 to 2008, so the average price of a gallon of gasoline increased over those years.

(c) Estimate the average price of a gallon of gasoline in 2002 and 2008. About how much did the price increase between 2002 and 2008?

Move up from 2002 on the horizontal scale to the point plotted for 2002. Looking across at the vertical scale, this point is about three-fourths of the way between the lines on the vertical scale for $1.20 and $1.40. Halfway between the lines for $1.20 and $1.40 would be $1.30. So, it cost about $1.35 for a gallon of gasoline in 2002.

Similarly, move up from 2008 on the horizontal scale to the point plotted for 2008. Then move across to the vertical scale. The price for a gallon of gasoline in 2008 was about $3.25.

Between 2002 and 2008, the average price of a gallon of gasoline increased by about

$$\$3.25 - \$1.35 = \$1.90. \qquad \textit{NOW TRY} $$

NOW TRY ANSWERS
1. **(a)** about $2.60
   (b) about $0.65

Year	Average Price (in dollars per gallon)
2001	1.46
2002	1.36
2003	1.59
2004	1.88
2005	2.30
2006	2.59
2007	2.80
2008	3.25

Actual Data Source: U.S. Department of Energy.

The line graph in **FIGURE 1** relates years to average prices for a gallon of gasoline. We can also represent these two related quantities using a table of data, as shown in the margin. In table form, we can see more precise data rather than estimating it. Trends in the data are easier to see from the graph, which gives a "picture" of the data.

We can extend these ideas to the subject of this chapter, *linear equations in **two** variables.* A linear equation in two variables, one for each of the quantities being related, can be used to represent the data in the table or graph. ***The graph of a linear equation in two variables is a line.***

Linear Equation in Two Variables

A **linear equation in two variables** is an equation that can be written in the form

$$Ax + By = C,$$

where A, B, and C are real numbers and A and B are not both 0.

Some examples of linear equations in two variables in this form, called *standard form,* are

$$3x + 4y = 9, \quad x - y = 0, \quad \text{and} \quad x + 2y = -8. \qquad \text{Linear equations in two variables}$$

NOTE   Other linear equations in two variables, such as

$$y = 4x + 5 \quad \text{and} \quad 3x = 7 - 2y,$$

are not written in standard form, but could be algebraically rewritten in this form. We discuss the forms of linear equations in more detail in **Section 3.4.**

OBJECTIVE 2   **Write a solution as an ordered pair.**   Recall from **Section 1.3** that a *solution* of an equation is a number that makes the equation true when it replaces the variable. For example, the linear equation in *one* variable

$$x - 2 = 5$$

has solution 7, since replacing x with 7 gives a true statement.

A solution of a linear equation in* two *variables requires* two *numbers, one for each variable. For example, a true statement results when we replace x with 2 and y with 13 in the equation $y = 4x + 5$, since

$$13 = 4(2) + 5. \qquad \text{Let } x = 2 \text{ and } y = 13.$$

The pair of numbers $x = 2$ and $y = 13$ gives a solution of the equation $y = 4x + 5$. The phrase "$x = 2$ and $y = 13$" is abbreviated

$$\underset{\text{Ordered pair}}{\underbrace{(\overset{\displaystyle x\text{-value}}{2}, \overset{\displaystyle y\text{-value}}{13})}}$$

with the x-value, 2, and the y-value, 13, given as a pair of numbers written inside parentheses. ***The x-value is always given first.*** A pair of numbers such as (2, 13) is called an **ordered pair.**

⚠️ **CAUTION** The ordered pairs $(2, 13)$ and $(13, 2)$ are *not* the same. In the first pair, $x = 2$ and $y = 13$. In the second pair, $x = 13$ and $y = 2$. ***The order in which the numbers are written in an ordered pair is important.***

OBJECTIVE 3 Decide whether a given ordered pair is a solution of a given equation. We substitute the x- and y-values of an ordered pair into a linear equation in two variables to see whether the ordered pair is a solution. An ordered pair that is a solution of an equation is said to *satisfy* the equation.

NOW TRY
EXERCISE 2

Decide whether each ordered pair is a solution of the equation.

$$3x - 7y = 19$$

(a) $(3, 4)$ **(b)** $(-3, -4)$

EXAMPLE 2 Deciding Whether Ordered Pairs Are Solutions of an Equation

Decide whether each ordered pair is a solution of the equation $2x + 3y = 12$.

(a) $(3, 2)$

Substitute 3 for x and 2 for y in the equation.

$$2x + 3y = 12$$
$$2(3) + 3(2) \stackrel{?}{=} 12 \qquad \text{Let } x = 3 \text{ and } y = 2.$$
$$6 + 6 \stackrel{?}{=} 12 \qquad \text{Multiply.}$$
$$12 = 12 \checkmark \quad \text{True}$$

This result is true, so $(3, 2)$ is a solution of $2x + 3y = 12$.

(b) $(-2, -7)$

$$2x + 3y = 12$$
$$2(-2) + 3(-7) \stackrel{?}{=} 12 \qquad \text{Let } x = -2 \text{ and } y = -7.$$
$$-4 + (-21) \stackrel{?}{=} 12 \qquad \text{Multiply.}$$
$$-25 = 12 \qquad \text{False}$$

Use parentheses to avoid errors.

This result is false, so $(-2, -7)$ is *not* a solution of $2x + 3y = 12$. NOW TRY

OBJECTIVE 4 Complete ordered pairs for a given equation. Substituting a number for one variable in a linear equation makes it possible to find the value of the other variable.

EXAMPLE 3 Completing Ordered Pairs

Complete each ordered pair for the equation $y = 4x + 5$.

(a) $(7, \underline{})$ The x-value always comes first.

In this ordered pair, $x = 7$. To find the corresponding value of y, replace x with 7 in the equation.

$$y = 4x + 5$$
$$y = 4(7) + 5 \qquad \text{Let } x = 7.$$
$$y = 28 + 5 \qquad \text{Multiply.}$$
$$y = 33 \qquad \text{Add.}$$

NOW TRY ANSWERS
2. **(a)** no **(b)** yes

The ordered pair is $(7, 33)$.

*NOW TRY
EXERCISE 3*
Complete each ordered pair for the equation.

$$y = 3x - 12$$

(a) $(4, \_\_)$ **(b)** $(\_\_, 3)$

(b) $(\_\_, -3)$

In this ordered pair, $y = -3$. Find the corresponding value of x by replacing y with -3 in the equation.

$$y = 4x + 5$$
$$-3 = 4x + 5 \qquad \text{Let } y = -3.$$
$$-8 = 4x \qquad \text{Subtract 5 from each side.}$$
$$-2 = x \qquad \text{Divide each side by 4.}$$

The ordered pair is $(-2, -3)$.

NOW TRY

OBJECTIVE 5   **Complete a table of values.** Ordered pairs are often displayed in a **table of values.** Although we usually write tables of values vertically, they may be written horizontally.

EXAMPLE 4   **Completing Tables of Values**

Complete the table of values for each equation. Write the results as ordered pairs.

(a) $x - 2y = 8$

x	y
2	
10	
	0
	-2

To complete the first two ordered pairs, let $x = 2$ and $x = 10$, respectively, in the equation.

	If	$x = 2,$		If	$x = 10,$
	then	$x - 2y = 8$		then	$x - 2y = 8$
	becomes	$2 - 2y = 8$		becomes	$10 - 2y = 8$
		$-2y = 6$			$-2y = -2$
		$y = -3.$			$y = 1.$

The first two ordered pairs are $(2, -3)$ and $(10, 1)$. Complete the last two ordered pairs by letting $y = 0$ and $y = -2$, respectively.

	If	$y = 0,$		If	$y = -2,$
	then	$x - 2y = 8$		then	$x - 2y = 8$
	becomes	$x - 2(0) = 8$		becomes	$x - 2(-2) = 8$
		$x - 0 = 8$			$x + 4 = 8$
		$x = 8.$			$x = 4.$

The last two ordered pairs are $(8, 0)$ and $(4, -2)$. The completed table of values and corresponding ordered pairs follow.

x	y	Ordered Pairs
2	-3	⟶ (2, -3)
10	1	⟶ (10, 1)
8	0	⟶ (8, 0)
4	-2	⟶ (4, -2)

NOW TRY ANSWERS
3. (a) $(4, 0)$ **(b)** $(5, 3)$

Each ordered pair is a solution of the given equation $x - 2y = 8$.

NOW TRY
EXERCISE 4

Complete the table of values for the equation. Write the results as ordered pairs.

$$5x - 4y = 20$$

x	y
0	
	0
2	

(b) $x = 5$

x	y
	-2
	6
	3

The given equation is $x = 5$. No matter which value of y is chosen, the value of x is always 5.

x	y		Ordered Pairs
5	-2	⟶	(5, -2)
5	6	⟶	(5, 6)
5	3	⟶	(5, 3)

NOW TRY

NOTE We can think of $x = 5$ in **Example 4(b)** as an equation in two variables by rewriting $x = 5$ as $x + 0y = 5$. This form of the equation shows that, for any value of y, the value of x is 5. Similarly, $y = 4$ can be written $0x + y = 4$.

OBJECTIVE 6 **Plot ordered pairs.** In **Section 2.3,** we saw that linear equations in *one* variable had either one, zero, or an infinite number of real number solutions. These solutions could be graphed on *one* number line. For example, the linear equation in one variable $x - 2 = 5$ has solution 7, which is graphed on the number line in **FIGURE 2**.

FIGURE 2

Every linear equation in *two* variables has an infinite number of ordered pairs (x, y) as solutions. To graph these solutions, we need *two* number lines, one for each variable, drawn at right angles as in **FIGURE 3**. The horizontal number line is called the **x-axis,** and the vertical line is called the **y-axis.** The point at which the x-axis and y-axis intersect is called the **origin.** Together, the x-axis and y-axis form a **rectangular coordinate system.**

The rectangular coordinate system is divided into four regions, called **quadrants.** These quadrants are numbered counterclockwise, as shown in **FIGURE 3**.

René Descartes   (1596–1650)
The rectangular coordinate system is also called the **Cartesian coordinate system,** in honor of René Descartes, the French mathematician credited with its invention.

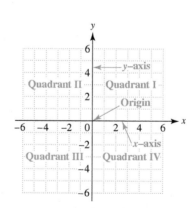

FIGURE 3 Rectangular Coordinate System

The x-axis and y-axis determine a **plane**—a flat surface illustrated by a sheet of paper. By referring to the two axes, we can associate every point in the plane with an ordered pair. The numbers in the ordered pair are called the **coordinates** of the point.

NOW TRY ANSWER

4.

x	y
0	-5
4	0
2	$-\frac{5}{2}$

$(0, -5), (4, 0), \left(2, -\frac{5}{2}\right)$

NOTE In a plane, *both* numbers in the ordered pair are needed to locate a point. The ordered pair is a name for the point.

⌒ *NOW TRY*
↘ *EXERCISE 5*

Plot the given points in a co-ordinate system.

$(-3, 1), (2, -4), (0, -1),$
$\left(\frac{5}{2}, 3\right), (-4, -3), (-4, 0)$

EXAMPLE 5   Plotting Ordered Pairs

Plot the given points in a coordinate system.

(a) $(2, 3)$ **(b)** $(-1, -4)$ **(c)** $(-2, 3)$ **(d)** $(3, -2)$ **(e)** $\left(\frac{3}{2}, 2\right)$

(f) $(4, -3.75)$ **(g)** $(5, 0)$ **(h)** $(0, -3)$ **(i)** $(0, 0)$

The point $(2, 3)$ from part (a) is **plotted** (graphed) in **FIGURE 4**. The other points are plotted in **FIGURE 5**.

In each case, begin at the origin. Move right or left the number of units that corresponds to the *x*-coordinate in the ordered pair—*right if the x-coordinate is positive or left if it is negative.* Then turn and move up or down the number of units that corresponds to the *y*-coordinate—*up if the y-coordinate is positive or down if it is negative.*

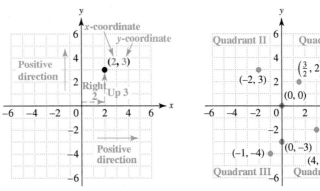

FIGURE 4   **FIGURE 5**

Notice the difference in the locations of the points $(-2, 3)$ and $(3, -2)$ in parts (c) and (d). The point $(-2, 3)$ is in quadrant II, whereas the point $(3, -2)$ is in quadrant IV. *The order of the coordinates is important. The x-coordinate is always given first in an ordered pair.*

To plot the point $\left(\frac{3}{2}, 2\right)$ in part (e), think of the improper fraction $\frac{3}{2}$ as the mixed number $1\frac{1}{2}$ and move $\frac{3}{2}$ $\left(\text{or } 1\frac{1}{2}\right)$ units to the right along the *x*-axis. Then turn and go 2 units up, parallel to the *y*-axis. The point $(4, -3.75)$ in part (f) is plotted similarly, by approximating the location of the decimal *y*-coordinate.

In part (g), the point $(5, 0)$ lies on the *x*-axis since the *y*-coordinate is 0. In part (h), the point $(0, -3)$ lies on the *y*-axis since the *x*-coordinate is 0. In part (i), the point $(0, 0)$ is at the origin. *Points on the axes themselves are not in any quadrant.*

NOW TRY ⤴

NOW TRY ANSWER
5.

Sometimes we can use a linear equation to mathematically describe, or *model,* a real-life situation, as shown in the next example.

NOW TRY
EXERCISE 6
Use the linear equation in
Example 6 to estimate the
number of twin births in
2004. Interpret the results.

EXAMPLE 6 Completing Ordered Pairs to Estimate the Number
of Twin Births

The annual number of twin births in the United States from 2001 through 2006 can
be closely approximated by the linear equation

Number of twin births ⟶ ⟵ Year

$$y = 3.049x - 5979.0,$$

which relates x, the year, and y, the number of twin births in thousands. (*Source:
Department of Health and Human Services.*)

(a) Complete the table of values for the given linear equation.

x (Year)	y (Number of Twin Births, in thousands)
2001	
2003	
2006	

To find y when $x = 2001$, we substitute into the equation.

$\approx$ means "is
approximately equal to."

$$y = 3.049(2001) - 5979.0 \qquad \text{Let } x = 2001.$$
$$y \approx 122 \qquad \text{Use a calculator.}$$

This means that in 2001, there were about 122 thousand (or 122,000) twin births.
We substitute the years 2003 and 2006 in the same way to complete the table.

x (Year)	y (Number of Twin Births, in thousands)	Ordered Pairs (x, y)
2001	122	⟶ (2001, 122)
2003	128	⟶ (2003, 128)
2006	137	⟶ (2006, 137)

Here each year x is paired
with the number of twin
births y (in thousands).

(b) Graph the ordered pairs found in part (a).

The ordered pairs are graphed in **FIGURE 6**. This graph of ordered pairs of data is
called a **scatter diagram.**

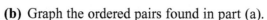

NUMBER OF TWIN BIRTHS

Notice the axes labels and scales.
Each square represents 1 unit in the
horizontal direction and 5 units in
the vertical direction. Because the
numbers in the first ordered pair
are large, we show a break in the
axes near the origin.

FIGURE 6

NOW TRY ANSWER
6. $y \approx 131$; There were
approximately 131 thousand
(or 131,000) twin births in the
U.S. in 2004.

A scatter diagram enables us to tell whether two quantities are related to each
other. In **FIGURE 6**, the plotted points could be connected to approximate a straight ***line,***
so the variables x (year) and y (number of twin births) have a ***line***ar relationship. The
increase in the number of twin births is also reflected. *NOW TRY*

⚠ **CAUTION** The equation in **Example 6** is valid only for the years 2001 through 2006, because it was based on data for those years. *Do not assume that this equation would provide reliable data for other years, since the data for those years may not follow the same pattern.*

3.1 EXERCISES

MyMathLab Math XL PRACTICE WATCH DOWNLOAD READ REVIEW

🌐 *Complete solution available on the Video Resources on DVD*

The line graph shows the overall unemployment rate in the U.S. civilian labor force in August of the years 2003 through 2009. Use the graph to work Exercises 1–4. ***See Example 1.***

1. Between which pairs of consecutive years did the unemployment rate decrease?

2. What was the general trend in the unemployment rate between 2007 and 2009?

3. Estimate the overall unemployment rate in 2003 and 2004. About how much did the unemployment rate decline between 2003 and 2004?

4. During which year(s)

   (a) was the unemployment rate greater than 6%, but less than 7%?

   (b) did the unemployment rate stay the same?

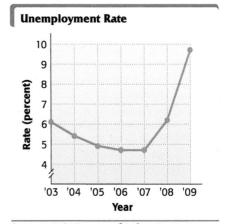

Unemployment Rate

Source: U.S. Bureau of Labor Statistics.

Concept Check   Fill in each blank with the correct response.

5. The symbol (x, y) _____ represent an ordered pair, while the symbols $[x, y]$ and
   (does/does not)
   $\{x, y\}$ _____ represent ordered pairs.
   (do/do not)

6. The ordered pair $(3, 2)$ is a solution of the equation $2x - 5y =$ _____.

7. The point whose graph has coordinates $(-4, 2)$ is in quadrant _____.

8. The point whose graph has coordinates $(0, 5)$ lies on the _____-axis.

9. The ordered pair $(4, \_)$ is a solution of the equation $y = 3$.

10. The ordered pair $(\_, -2)$ is a solution of the equation $x = 6$.

Decide whether the given ordered pair is a solution of the given equation. ***See Example 2.***

🌐 11. $x + y = 8$; $(0, 8)$ 12. $x + y = 9$; $(0, 9)$ 13. $2x + y = 5$; $(3, -1)$

14. $2x - y = 6$; $(4, 2)$ 🌐 15. $5x - 3y = 15$; $(5, 2)$ 16. $4x - 3y = 6$; $(2, 1)$

17. $x = -4y$; $(-8, 2)$ 18. $y = 3x$; $(2, 6)$ 19. $y = 2$; $(4, 2)$

20. $x = -6$; $(-6, 5)$ 21. $x - 6 = 0$; $(4, 2)$ 22. $x + 4 = 0$; $(-6, 2)$

Complete each ordered pair for the equation $y = 2x + 7$. ***See Example 3.***

🌐 23. $(5, \_)$ 24. $(2, \_)$ 25. $(\_, -3)$ 26. $(\_, 0)$

Complete each ordered pair for the equation $y = -4x - 4$. ***See Example 3.***

27. $(\_, 0)$ 28. $(0, \_)$ 29. $(\_, 24)$ 30. $(\_, 16)$

*Complete each table of values. Write the results as ordered pairs. **See Example 4.***

🌐 **31.** $4x + 3y = 24$

x	y
0	
	0
	4

32. $2x + 3y = 12$

x	y
0	
	0
	8

33. $4x - 9y = -36$

x	y
	0
0	
	8

34. $3x - 5y = -15$

x	y
0	
	0
	-6

35. $x = 12$

x	y
	3
	8
	0

36. $x = -9$

x	y
	6
	2
	-3

37. $y = -10$

x	y
4	
0	
-4	

38. $y = -6$

x	y
8	
4	
-2	

39. $y + 2 = 0$

x	y
9	
2	
0	

40. $y + 6 = 0$

x	y
6	
3	
0	

41. $x - 4 = 0$

x	y
	4
	0
	-4

42. $x - 8 = 0$

x	y
	8
	3
	0

📝 **43.** Do $(3, 4)$ and $(4, 3)$ correspond to the same point in the plane? Explain.

📝 **44.** Do $(4, -1)$ and $(-1, 4)$ represent the same ordered pair? Explain.

45. Give the ordered pairs for the points labeled A–F in the figure. (All coordinates are integers.) Tell the quadrant in which each point is located. **See Example 5.**

46. *Concept Check* The origin is represented by the ordered pair _____ .

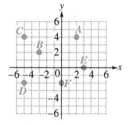

*Plot and label each point in a rectangular coordinate system. **See Example 5.***

47. $(6, 2)$ **48.** $(5, 3)$ **49.** $(-4, 2)$ **50.** $(-3, 5)$

51. $\left(-\dfrac{4}{5}, -1\right)$ **52.** $\left(-\dfrac{3}{2}, -4\right)$ **53.** $(3, -1.75)$ **54.** $(5, -4.25)$

55. $(0, 4)$ **56.** $(0, -3)$ **57.** $(4, 0)$ **58.** $(-3, 0)$

Concept Check Fill in each blank with the word *positive* or the word *negative*.

The point with coordinates (x, y) is in

59. quadrant III if x is _____ and y is _____ .

60. quadrant II if x is _____ and y is _____ .

61. quadrant IV if x is _____ and y is _____ .

62. quadrant I if x is _____ and y is _____ .

📝 **63.** A point (x, y) has the property that $xy < 0$. In which quadrant(s) must the point lie? Explain.

📝 **64.** A point (x, y) has the property that $xy > 0$. In which quadrant(s) must the point lie? Explain.

*Complete each table of values. Then plot and label the ordered pairs. **See Examples 4 and 5.***

65. $x - 2y = 6$

x	y
0	
	0
2	
	-1

66. $2x - y = 4$

x	y
0	
	0
1	
	-6

67. $3x - 4y = 12$

x	y
0	
	0
-4	
	-4

NOW TRY
EXERCISE 1
Graph $2x - 4y = 8$.

Write each x-value first.

The ordered pairs are $(0, -4)$ and $(5, 0)$. We find a third ordered pair (as a check) by choosing some other number for x or y. We choose $y = 2$.

$$4x - 5y = 20$$
$$4x - 5(2) = 20 \qquad \text{Let } y = 2.$$
$$4x - 10 = 20 \qquad \text{Multiply.}$$
$$4x = 30 \qquad \text{Add 10.}$$
$$x = \frac{30}{4}, \quad \text{or} \quad \frac{15}{2} \qquad \text{Divide by 4. Write in lowest terms.}$$

This gives the ordered pair $\left(\frac{15}{2}, 2\right)$, or $\left(7\frac{1}{2}, 2\right)$. We plot the three ordered pairs $(0, -4)$, $(5, 0)$, and $\left(7\frac{1}{2}, 2\right)$, and draw a line through them, as shown in **FIGURE 9**.

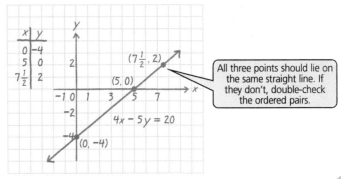

All three points should lie on the same straight line. If they don't, double-check the ordered pairs.

FIGURE 9

NOW TRY

EXAMPLE 2 Graphing a Linear Equation

Graph $y = -\frac{3}{2}x + 3$.

Although this linear equation is not in standard form ($Ax + By = C$), it *could* be written in that form. To find two different points on the graph, we first let $x = 0$ and then let $y = 0$.

$$y = -\frac{3}{2}x + 3 \qquad\qquad y = -\frac{3}{2}x + 3$$
$$y = -\frac{3}{2}(0) + 3 \quad \text{Let } x = 0. \qquad 0 = -\frac{3}{2}x + 3 \quad \text{Let } y = 0.$$
$$y = 0 + 3 \quad \text{Multiply.} \qquad \frac{3}{2}x = 3 \quad \text{Add } \frac{3}{2}x.$$
$$y = 3 \quad \text{Add.} \qquad x = 2 \quad \text{Multiply by } \frac{2}{3}.$$

This gives the ordered pairs $(0, 3)$ and $(2, 0)$. To find a third point, we let $x = -2$.

$$y = -\frac{3}{2}x + 3$$

Choosing a multiple of 2 makes multiplying by $-\frac{3}{2}$ easier.

$$y = -\frac{3}{2}(-2) + 3 \quad \text{Let } x = -2.$$
$$y = 3 + 3 \quad \text{Multiply.}$$
$$y = 6 \quad \text{Add.}$$

NOW TRY ANSWER
1.

NOW TRY
EXERCISE 2

Graph $y = \frac{1}{3}x + 1$.

This gives the ordered pair $(-2, 6)$. We plot the three ordered pairs and draw a line through them, as shown in **FIGURE 10**.

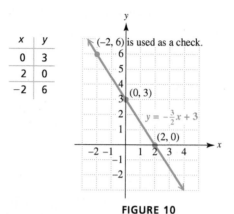

x	y
0	3
2	0
-2	6

FIGURE 10

NOW TRY

OBJECTIVE 2 **Find intercepts.** In **FIGURE 10**, the graph intersects (crosses) the y-axis at $(0, 3)$ and the x-axis at $(2, 0)$. For this reason, $(0, 3)$ is called the **y-intercept** and $(2, 0)$ is called the **x-intercept** of the graph. The intercepts are particularly useful for graphing linear equations.

Finding Intercepts

To find the x-intercept, let $y = 0$ in the given equation and solve for x. Then $(x, 0)$ is the x-intercept.

To find the y-intercept, let $x = 0$ in the given equation and solve for y. Then $(0, y)$ is the y-intercept.

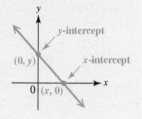

EXAMPLE 3 **Finding Intercepts**

Find the intercepts for the graph of $2x + y = 4$. Then draw the graph.

To find the y-intercept, let $x = 0$.

$$2x + y = 4$$
$$2(0) + y = 4 \quad \text{Let } x = 0.$$
$$0 + y = 4$$
$$y = 4 \quad \text{y-intercept is } (0, 4).$$

To find the x-intercept, let $y = 0$.

$$2x + y = 4$$
$$2x + 0 = 4 \quad \text{Let } y = 0.$$
$$2x = 4$$
$$x = 2 \quad \text{x-intercept is } (2, 0).$$

The intercepts are $(0, 4)$ and $(2, 0)$. To find a third point, we let $x = 4$.

$$2x + y = 4$$
$$2(4) + y = 4 \quad \text{Let } x = 4.$$
$$8 + y = 4 \quad \text{Multiply.}$$
$$y = -4 \quad \text{Subtract 8.}$$

NOW TRY ANSWER

2.

This gives the ordered pair $(4, -4)$. The graph, with the two intercepts in red, is shown in **FIGURE 11** on the next page.

NOW TRY
EXERCISE 3
Find the intercepts for the
graph of $x + 2y = 2$. Then
draw the graph.

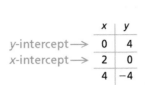

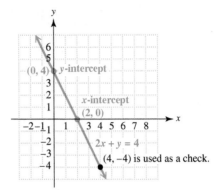

FIGURE 11

NOW TRY

⚠ **CAUTION**   *When choosing x- or y-values to find ordered pairs to plot, be careful to choose so that the resulting points are not too close together.* For example, using $(-1, -1)$, $(0, 0)$, and $(1, 1)$ to graph $x - y = 0$ may result in an inaccurate line. It is better to choose points whose x-values differ by at least 2.

OBJECTIVE 3   Graph linear equations of the form $Ax + By = 0$.

NOW TRY
EXERCISE 4
Graph $2x + y = 0$.

EXAMPLE 4   Graphing an Equation with x- and y-Intercepts $(0, 0)$

Graph $x - 3y = 0$.

To find the y-intercept, let $x = 0$.

$x - 3y = 0$
$0 - 3y = 0$ Let $x = 0$.
$-3y = 0$
$y = 0$ y-intercept is $(0, 0)$.

To find the x-intercept, let $y = 0$.

$x - 3y = 0$
$x - 3(0) = 0$ Let $y = 0$.
$x - 0 = 0$
$x = 0$ x-intercept is $(0, 0)$.

The x- and y-intercepts are the *same* point, $(0, 0)$. We must select *two other values* for x or y to find two other points on the graph. We choose $x = 6$ and $x = -6$.

$x - 3y = 0$
$6 - 3y = 0$ Let $x = 6$.
$-3y = -6$
$y = 2$ Gives $(6, 2)$

$x - 3y = 0$
$-6 - 3y = 0$ Let $x = -6$.
$-3y = 6$
$y = -2$ Gives $(-6, -2)$

We use the ordered pairs $(-6, -2)$, $(0, 0)$, and $(6, 2)$ to draw the graph in **FIGURE 12**.

NOW TRY ANSWERS
3. x-intercept: $(2, 0)$;
   y-intercept: $(0, 1)$

4.

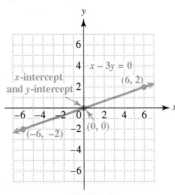

FIGURE 12

NOW TRY

Line through the Origin

If A and B are nonzero real numbers, the graph of a linear equation of the form

$$Ax + By = 0$$

passes through the origin $(0, 0)$.

OBJECTIVE 4 Graph linear equations of the form $y = b$ or $x = a$. Consider the following linear equations:

$y = -4$, which can be written $0x + y = -4$;

$x = 3$, which can be written $x + 0y = 3$.

When the coefficient of x or y is 0, the graph of the linear equation is a horizontal or vertical line.

NOW TRY
EXERCISE 5

Graph $y = 2$.

EXAMPLE 5 Graphing an Equation of the Form $y = b$ (Horizontal Line)

Graph $y = -4$.

For any value of x, y is always equal to -4. Three ordered pairs that satisfy the equation are shown in the table of values. Drawing a line through these points gives the **horizontal line** shown in **FIGURE 13**. The y-intercept is $(0, -4)$. There is no x-intercept.

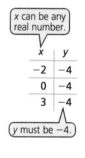

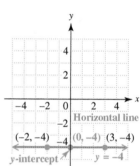

FIGURE 13

NOW TRY

Horizontal Line

The graph of the linear equation $y = b$, where b is a real number, is the horizontal line with y-intercept $(0, b)$. There is no x-intercept (unless the horizontal line is the x-axis itself).

NOW TRY
EXERCISE 6

Graph $x + 4 = 0$.

NOW TRY ANSWERS

5.

6.

EXAMPLE 6 Graphing an Equation of the Form $x = a$ (Vertical Line)

Graph $x - 3 = 0$.

First we add 3 to each side of the equation $x - 3 = 0$ to get $x = 3$. All ordered-pair solutions of this equation have x-coordinate 3. Any number can be used for y. We show three ordered pairs that satisfy the equation in the table of values. The graph is the **vertical line** shown in **FIGURE 14**. The x-intercept is $(3, 0)$. There is no y-intercept.

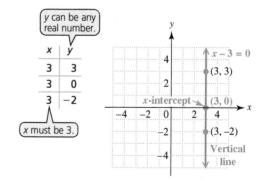

FIGURE 14

NOW TRY

> ## Vertical Line
>
> The graph of the linear equation $x = a$, where a is a real number, is the vertical line with x-intercept $(a, 0)$. There is no y-intercept (unless the vertical line is the y-axis itself).

The equation of the x-axis is the horizontal line $y = 0$, and the equation of the y-axis is the vertical line $x = 0$.

⚠ CAUTION   The equations of horizontal and vertical lines are often confused with each other. Remember that the graph of $y = b$ is parallel to the x-axis and the graph of $x = a$ is parallel to the y-axis (for $a \neq 0$ and $b \neq 0$).

A summary of the forms of linear equations from this section follows.

Graphing a Linear Equation		
Equation	**To Graph**	**Example**
$y = b$	Draw a horizontal line, through $(0, b)$.	$y = -2$
$x = a$	Draw a vertical line, through $(a, 0)$.	$x = 4$
$Ax + By = 0$	The graph passes through $(0, 0)$. To find additional points that lie on the graph, choose any value for x or y, except 0.	$x = 2y$
$Ax + By = C$ **(but not of the types above)**	Find any two points on the line. A good choice is to find the intercepts. Let $x = 0$, and find the corresponding value of y. Then let $y = 0$, and find x. As a check, get a third point by choosing a value for x or y that has not yet been used.	$(4, 3)$ $(2, 0)$ $3x - 2y = 6$ $(0, -3)$

OBJECTIVE 5 Use a linear equation to model data.

NOW TRY
EXERCISE 7
Use (a) the graph and (b) the equation in **Example 7** to approximate credit card debt in 2006.

EXAMPLE 7 Using a Linear Equation to Model Credit Card Debt·

Credit card debt in the United States increased steadily from 2000 through 2008. The amount of debt y in billions of dollars can be modeled by the linear equation

$$y = 32.0x + 684,$$

where $x = 0$ represents 2000, $x = 1$ represents 2001, and so on. (*Source: The Nilson Report.*)

(a) Use the equation to approximate credit card debt in the years 2000, 2004, and 2008.

For 2000: $y = 32.0(0) + 684$ Replace x with 0.
          $y = 684$ billion dollars

For 2004: $y = 32.0(4) + 684$ $2004 - 2000 = 4$
          $y = 812$ billion dollars   Replace x with 4.

For 2008: $y = 32.0(8) + 684$ $2008 - 2000 = 8$
          $y = 940$ billion dollars   Replace x with 8.

(b) Write the information from part (a) as three ordered pairs, and use them to graph the given linear equation.

Since x represents the year and y represents the debt, the ordered pairs are

$$(0, 684), \quad (4, 812), \quad \text{and} \quad (8, 940).$$

See **FIGURE 15**. (Arrowheads are not included with the graphed line, since the data are for the years 2000 to 2008 only—that is, from $x = 0$ to $x = 8$.)

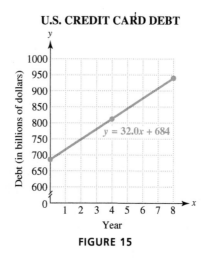

U.S. CREDIT CARD DEBT

$y = 32.0x + 684$

Year

FIGURE 15

(c) Use the graph and then the equation to approximate credit card debt in 2002.

For 2002, $x = 2$. On the graph, find 2 on the horizontal axis, move up to the graphed line and then across to the vertical axis. It appears that credit card debt in 2002 was about 750 billion dollars. To use the equation, substitute 2 for x.

$y = 32.0x + 684$ Given linear equation

$y = 32.0(2) + 684$ Let $x = 2$.

$y = 748$ billion dollars   Multiply, and then add.

NOW TRY ANSWERS
7. (a) about 875 billion dollars
   (b) 876 billion dollars

This result for 2002 is close to our estimate of 750 billion dollars from the graph.

NOW TRY

Among the basic features of graphing calculators is their ability to graph equations. We must solve the equation for y in order to enter it into the calculator. Also, we must select a "window" for the graph, determined by the minimum and maximum values of x and y. The *standard window* is from $x = -10$ to $x = 10$ and from $y = -10$ to $y = 10$, written $[-10, 10]$, $[-10, 10]$, with the x-interval first.

To graph $2x + y = 4$, discussed in **Example 3,** we first solve for y.

$$y = -2x + 4 \qquad \text{Subtract } 2x.$$

We enter this equation into the calculator and choose the standard window to get the graph in **FIGURE 16**. The line intersects the x-axis at $(2, 0)$, indicating that 2 is the solution of the equation

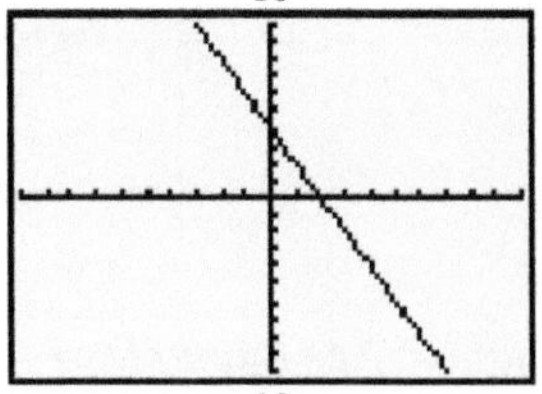

$$-2x + 4 = 0.$$

FIGURE 16

For Discussion or Writing

Rewrite each equation with the left side equal to 0, the form required for a graphing calculator. (It is not necessary to clear parentheses or combine like terms.)

1. $3x + 4 - 2x - 7 = 4x + 3$ **2.** $5x - 15 = 3(x - 2)$

3.2 EXERCISES

MyMathLab   Math XL PRACTICE   WATCH   DOWNLOAD   READ   REVIEW

Complete solution available on the Video Resources on DVD

*Use the given equation to complete the given ordered pairs. Then graph each equation by plotting the points and drawing a line through them. **See Examples 1 and 2.***

1. $x + y = 5$
$(0, \underline{}), (\underline{}, 0), (2, \underline{})$

2. $x - y = 2$
$(0, \underline{}), (\underline{}, 0), (5, \underline{})$

3. $y = \dfrac{2}{3}x + 1$
$(0, \underline{}), (3, \underline{}), (-3, \underline{})$

4. $y = -\dfrac{3}{4}x + 2$
$(0, \underline{}), (4, \underline{}), (-4, \underline{})$

5. $3x = -y - 6$
$(0, \underline{}), (\underline{}, 0), \left(-\dfrac{1}{3}, \underline{}\right)$

6. $x = 2y + 3$
$(\underline{}, 0), (0, \underline{}), \left(\underline{}, \dfrac{1}{2}\right)$

7. *Concept Check* Match the information about each graph in Column I with the correct linear equation in Column II.

I	**II**
(a) The graph of the equation has y-intercept $(0, -4)$.	**A.** $3x + y = -4$
(b) The graph of the equation has $(0, 0)$ as x-intercept and y-intercept.	**B.** $x - 4 = 0$
	C. $y = 4x$
(c) The graph of the equation does not have an x-intercept.	**D.** $y = 4$
(d) The graph of the equation has x-intercept $(4, 0)$.	

8. *Concept Check* Which of these equations have a graph with only one intercept?

A. $x + 8 = 0$ **B.** $x - y = 3$ **C.** $x + y = 0$ **D.** $y = 4$

Concept Check *Find the intercepts of each graph. (All coordinates are integers.)*

9.
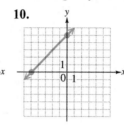

10.
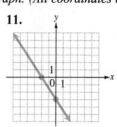

11.
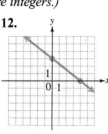

12.

Find the x-intercept and the y-intercept for the graph of each equation. ***See Examples 1–6.***

13. $x - y = 8$ **14.** $x - y = 7$ **15.** $5x - 2y = 20$ **16.** $-3x + 2y = 12$

17. $x + 6y = 0$ **18.** $3x + y = 0$ **19.** $y = -2x + 4$ **20.** $y = 3x + 6$

21. $y = \dfrac{1}{3}x - 2$ **22.** $y = \dfrac{1}{4}x - 1$ **23.** $2x - 3y = 0$ **24.** $4x - 5y = 0$

25. $x - 4 = 0$ **26.** $x - 5 = 0$ **27.** $y = 2.5$ **28.** $y = -1.5$

29. *Concept Check*   Match each equation in (a)–(d) with its graph in A–D.

(a) $x = -2$ **(b)** $y = -2$ **(c)** $x = 2$ **(d)** $y = 2$

A.
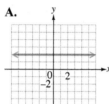

B.
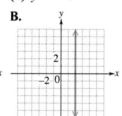

C.
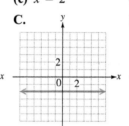

D.
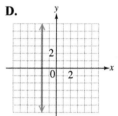

30. *Concept Check*   What is the equation of the *x*-axis? What is the equation of the *y*-axis?

Graph each linear equation. ***See Examples 1–6.***

31. $x = y + 2$ **32.** $x = -y + 6$ **33.** $x - y = 4$

34. $x - y = 5$ **35.** $2x + y = 6$ **36.** $-3x + y = -6$

37. $y = 2x - 5$ **38.** $y = 4x + 3$ **39.** $3x + 7y = 14$

40. $6x - 5y = 18$ **41.** $y = -\dfrac{3}{4}x + 3$ **42.** $y = -\dfrac{2}{3}x - 2$

43. $y - 2x = 0$ **44.** $y + 3x = 0$ **45.** $y = -6x$

46. $y = 4x$ **47.** $y = -1$ **48.** $y = 3$

49. $x + 2 = 0$ **50.** $x - 4 = 0$ **51.** $-3y = 15$

52. $-2y = 12$ **53.** $x + 2 = 8$ **54.** $x - 1 = -4$

Concept Check   In Exercises 55–62, describe what the graph of each linear equation will look like in the coordinate plane. (Hint: *Rewrite the equation if necessary so that it is in a more recognizable form.*)

55. $3x = y - 9$ **56.** $2x = y - 4$ **57.** $x - 10 = 1$ **58.** $x + 4 = 3$

59. $3y = -6$ **60.** $5y = -15$ **61.** $2x = 4y$ **62.** $3x = 9y$

Concept Check   Plot each set of points, and draw a line through them. Then give the equation of the line.

63. $(3, 5), (3, 0),$ and $(3, -3)$ **64.** $(1, 3), (1, 0),$ and $(1, -1)$

65. $(-3, -3), (0, -3),$ and $(4, -3)$ **66.** $(-5, 5), (0, 5),$ and $(3, 5)$

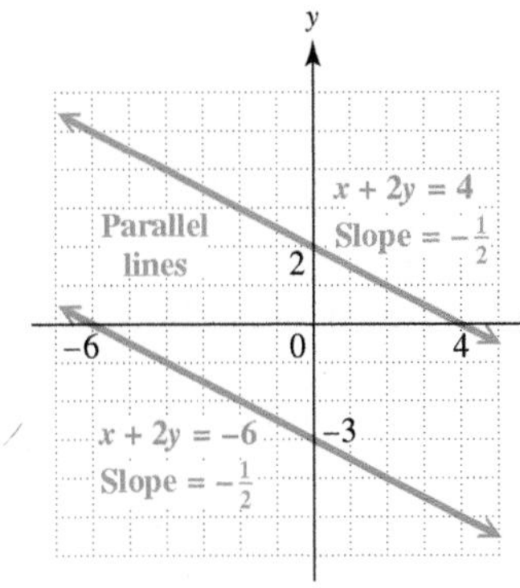

FIGURE 27

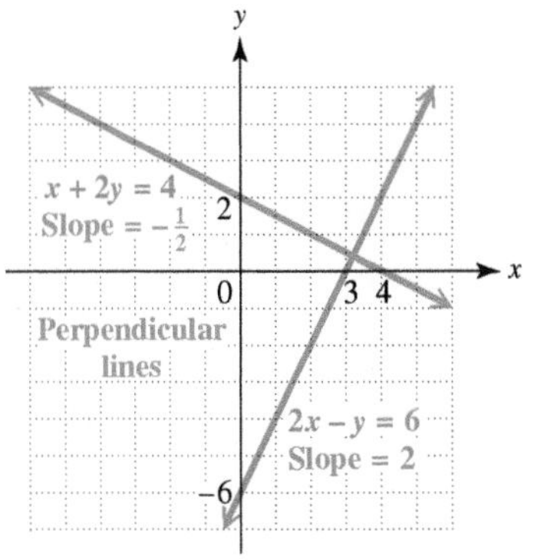

FIGURE 28

FIGURE 28 shows the graphs of $x + 2y = 4$ and $2x - y = 6$. These lines appear to be **perpendicular** (that is, they intersect at a 90° angle). As shown earlier, solving $x + 2y = 4$ for y gives $y = -\frac{1}{2}x + 2$, with slope $-\frac{1}{2}$. We must solve $2x - y = 6$ for y.

$$2x - y = 6$$

$$-y = -2x + 6 \qquad \text{Subtract } 2x.$$

$$y = 2x - 6 \qquad \text{Multiply by } -1.$$

$$\uparrow$$
$$\text{Slope}$$

The product of the two slopes $-\frac{1}{2}$ and 2 is

$$-\frac{1}{2}(2) = -1.$$

The product of the slopes of two perpendicular lines, neither of which is vertical, is always -1. This means that the slopes of perpendicular lines are negative (or opposite) reciprocals—if one slope is the nonzero number a, the other is $-\frac{1}{a}$. The table in the margin shows several examples.

Number	Negative Reciprocal
$\frac{3}{4}$	$-\frac{4}{3}$
$\frac{1}{2}$	$-\frac{2}{1}$, or -2
-6, or $-\frac{6}{1}$	$\frac{1}{6}$
-0.4, or $-\frac{4}{10}$	$\frac{10}{4}$, or 2.5

The product of each number and its negative reciprocal is -1.

Slopes of Parallel and Perpendicular Lines

Two lines with the same slope are parallel.

Two lines whose slopes have a product of -1 are perpendicular.

EXAMPLE 6 Deciding Whether Two Lines Are Parallel or Perpendicular

Decide whether each pair of lines is *parallel, perpendicular,* or *neither.*

(a) $\quad x + 3y = 7$

$\quad -3x + \quad y = 3$

Find the slope of each line by first solving each equation for y.

$x + 3y = 7$

$3y = -x + 7 \qquad \text{Subtract } x.$

$y = -\frac{1}{3}x + \frac{7}{3} \qquad \text{Divide by 3.}$

Slope is $-\frac{1}{3}$.

$-3x + y = 3$

$y = 3x + 3 \qquad \text{Add } 3x.$

Slope is 3.

NOW TRY
EXERCISE 6
Decide whether the
pair of lines is *parallel,
perpendicular,* or *neither.*

$$2x - 3y = 1$$
$$4x + 6y = 5$$

Since the slopes $-\frac{1}{3}$ and 3 are not equal, the lines are not parallel. Check the product of the slopes.

$$-\frac{1}{3}(3) = -1 \qquad \text{The slopes are negative reciprocals.}$$

The two lines are perpendicular because the product of their slopes is -1.

(b) $4x - y = 4 \xrightarrow{\text{Solve for } y.} y = 4x - 4$

$ 8x - 2y = -12 \xrightarrow{\phantom{\text{Solve for } y.}} y = 4x + 6$

Both lines have slope 4, so the lines are parallel.

(c) $4x + 3y = 6 \xrightarrow{\text{Solve for } y.} y = -\frac{4}{3}x + 2$

$ 2x - y = 5 \xrightarrow{\phantom{\text{Solve for } y.}} y = 2x - 5$

Here the slopes are $-\frac{4}{3}$ and 2. These lines are neither parallel nor perpendicular, because $-\frac{4}{3} \neq 2$ and $-\frac{4}{3} \cdot 2 \neq -1$.

(d) $6x - y = 1 \xrightarrow{\text{Solve for } y.} y = 6x - 1$

$ x - 6y = -12 \xrightarrow{\phantom{\text{Solve for } y.}} y = \frac{1}{6}x + 2$

NOW TRY ANSWER
6. neither

The slopes are 6 and $\frac{1}{6}$. The lines are not parallel, nor are they perpendicular. $\left(\textit{Be careful! } 6\left(\frac{1}{6}\right) = 1, \textit{not } -1.\right)$

NOW TRY

3.3 EXERCISES

MyMathLab Math XL PRACTICE   WATCH   DOWNLOAD   READ   REVIEW

🌐 *Complete solution available
on the Video Resources on DVD*

Use the indicated points to find the slope of each line. ***See Example 1.***

🌐 **1.**
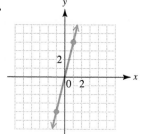

2.
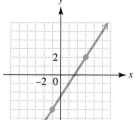

3.
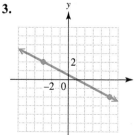

4.
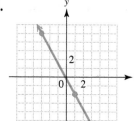

5.
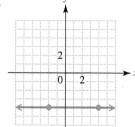

6.
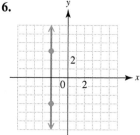

📝 **7.** In the context of the graph of a straight line, what is meant by "rise"? What is meant by "run"?

📝 **8.** Explain in your own words what is meant by *slope* of a line.

9. *Concept Check* Match the graph of each line in (a)–(d) with its slope in A–D.

(a) 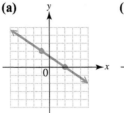   **(b)** 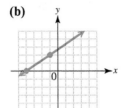   **(c)** 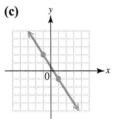   **(d)**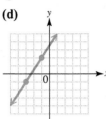

A. $\dfrac{2}{3}$ **B.** $\dfrac{3}{2}$ **C.** $-\dfrac{2}{3}$ **D.** $-\dfrac{3}{2}$

10. *Concept Check* Decide whether the line with the given slope rises from left to right, falls from left to right, is horizontal, or is vertical.

  (a) $m = -4$ **(b)** $m = 0$ **(c)** m is undefined.   **(d)** $m = \dfrac{3}{7}$

Concept Check On a pair of axes similar to the one shown, sketch the graph of a straight line having the indicated slope.

11. Negative

12. Positive

13. Undefined

14. Zero

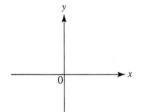

Concept Check The figure at the right shows a line that has a positive slope (because it rises from left to right) and a positive y-value for the y-intercept (because it intersects the y-axis above the origin).

*For each line in Exercises 15–20, decide whether **(a)** the slope is positive, negative, or zero and **(b)** the y-value of the y-intercept is positive, negative, or zero.*

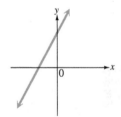

15. 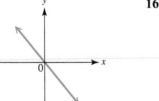   **16.** 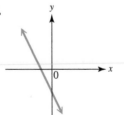   **17.**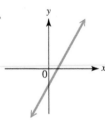

18. 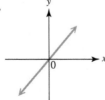   **19.** 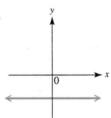   **20.**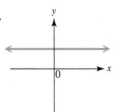

21. *Concept Check* What is the slope (or grade) of this hill?

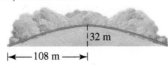

132 m
108 m

22. *Concept Check* What is the slope (or pitch) of this roof?

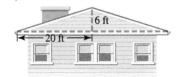

6 ft
20 ft

23. *Concept Check* What is the slope of the slide? (*Hint:* The slide *drops* 8 ft vertically as it extends 12 ft horizontally.)

24. *Concept Check* What is the slope (or grade) of this ski slope? (*Hint:* The ski slope drops 25 ft vertically for every 100 horizontal feet.)

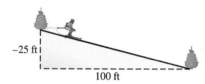

25. *Concept Check* A student was asked to find the slope of the line through the points $(2, 5)$ and $(-1, 3)$. His answer, $-\frac{2}{3}$, was incorrect. He showed his work as

$$\frac{3 - 5}{2 - (-1)} = \frac{-2}{3} = -\frac{2}{3}.$$

WHAT WENT WRONG? Give the correct slope.

26. *Concept Check* A student was asked to find the slope of the line through the points $(-2, 4)$ and $(6, -1)$. Her answer, $-\frac{8}{5}$, was incorrect. She showed her work as

$$\frac{6 - (-2)}{-1 - 4} = \frac{8}{-5} = -\frac{8}{5}.$$

WHAT WENT WRONG? Give the correct slope.

*Find the slope of the line through each pair of points. **See Examples 2–4.***

27. $(1, -2)$ and $(-3, -7)$ **28.** $(4, -1)$ and $(-2, -8)$ **29.** $(0, 3)$ and $(-2, 0)$

30. $(8, 0)$ and $(0, -5)$ **31.** $(4, 3)$ and $(-6, 3)$ **32.** $(6, 5)$ and $(-12, 5)$

33. $(-2, 4)$ and $(-3, 7)$ **34.** $(-4, 5)$ and $(-5, 8)$

35. $(-12, 3)$ and $(-12, -7)$ **36.** $(-8, 6)$ and $(-8, -1)$

37. $(4.8, 2.5)$ and $(3.6, 2.2)$ **38.** $(3.1, 2.6)$ and $(1.6, 2.1)$

39. $\left(-\frac{7}{5}, \frac{3}{10}\right)$ and $\left(\frac{1}{5}, -\frac{1}{2}\right)$ **40.** $\left(-\frac{4}{3}, \frac{1}{2}\right)$ and $\left(\frac{1}{3}, -\frac{5}{6}\right)$

*Find the slope of each line. **See Example 5.***

41. $y = 5x + 12$ **42.** $y = 2x + 3$ **43.** $4y = x + 1$

44. $2y = x + 4$ **45.** $3x - 2y = 3$ **46.** $6x - 4y = 4$

47. $-3x + 2y = 5$ **48.** $-2x + 4y = 5$ **49.** $y = -5$

50. $y = 4$ **51.** $x = 6$ **52.** $x = -2$

53. *Concept Check* What is the slope of a line whose graph is parallel to the graph of $3x + y = 7$? Perpendicular to the graph of $3x + y = 7$?

54. *Concept Check* What is the slope of a line whose graph is parallel to the graph of $-5x + y = -3$? Perpendicular to the graph of $-5x + y = -3$?

55. *Concept Check* If two lines are both vertical or both horizontal, which of the following are they?

     A. Parallel   **B.** Perpendicular   **C.** Neither parallel nor perpendicular

56. *Concept Check* If a line is vertical, what is true of any line that is perpendicular to it?

For each pair of equations, give the slopes of the lines and then determine whether the two lines are parallel, perpendicular, *or* neither. *See Example 6.*

57. $2x + 5y = 4$
$4x + 10y = 1$

58. $-4x + 3y = 4$
$-8x + 6y = 0$

59. $8x - 9y = 6$
$8x + 6y = -5$

60. $5x - 3y = -2$
$3x - 5y = -8$

61. $3x - 2y = 6$
$2x + 3y = 3$

62. $3x - 5y = -1$
$5x + 3y = 2$

63. $5x - y = 1$
$x - 5y = -10$

64. $3x - 4y = 12$
$4x + 3y = 12$

RELATING CONCEPTS   EXERCISES 65–70

FOR INDIVIDUAL OR GROUP WORK

FIGURE A *gives public school enrollment (in thousands) in grades 9–12 in the United States.* **FIGURE B** *gives the (average) number of public school students per computer.*

Public School Enrollment Grades 9–12

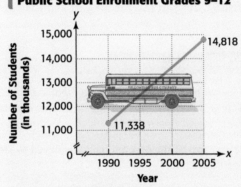

Source: U.S. Department of Education.

FIGURE A

Students Per Computer

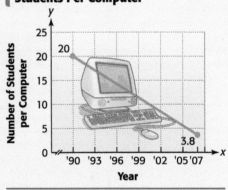

Source: Quality Education Data, Inc.

FIGURE B

Work Exercises 65–70 in order.

65. Use the ordered pairs (1990, 11,338) and (2005, 14,818) to find the slope of the line in **FIGURE A**.

66. The slope of the line in **FIGURE A** is _____. This means that
(positive/negative)
during the period represented, enrollment _____.
(increased/decreased)

67. The slope of a line represents the *rate of change of the line*. On the basis of **FIGURE A**, what was the increase in students *per year* during the period shown?

68. Use the given information to find the slope, to the nearest hundredth, of the line in **FIGURE B**.

69. The slope of the line in **FIGURE B** is _____. This means that
(positive/negative)
the number of students per computer _____ during the period
represented.   (increased/decreased)

70. On the basis of **FIGURE B**, what was the decrease in students per computer *per year* during the period shown?

The graph shows album sales (which include CD, vinyl, cassette, and digital albums) and music purchases (which include digital tracks, albums, singles, and music videos) in millions of units from 2004 through 2008. Use the graph to work Exercises 71 and 72.

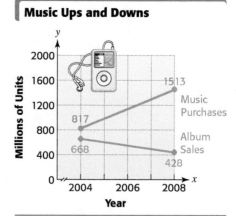

Music Ups and Downs

71. Locate the line on the graph that represents music purchases.

  (a) Write two ordered pairs (x, y), where x is the year and y is purchases in millions of units, to represent the data for the years 2004 and 2008.

  (b) Use the ordered pairs from part (a) to find the slope of the line.

  ✍ (c) Interpret the meaning of the slope in the context of this problem.

Source: Nielsen SoundScan.

72. Locate the line on the graph that represents album sales. Repeat parts (a)–(c) of **Exercise 71.** For part (a), x is the year and y is sales in millions of units.

TECHNOLOGY INSIGHTS   EXERCISES 73–76

Some graphing calculators have the capability of displaying a table of points for a graph. The table shown here gives several points that lie on a line designated Y_1.

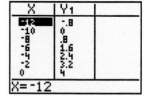

73. Use any two of the ordered pairs displayed to find the slope of the line.

74. What is the x-intercept of the line?

75. What is the y-intercept of the line?

76. Which one of the two lines shown is the graph of Y_1?

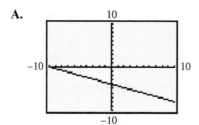

A.

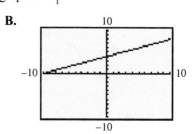

B.

PREVIEW EXERCISES

Solve each equation for y. See Section 2.5.

77. $2x + 5y = 15$ **78.** $-4x + 3y = 8$ **79.** $10x = 30 + 3y$

80. $8x = 8 - 2y$ **81.** $y - (-8) = 2(x - 4)$ **82.** $y - 3 = 4[x - (-6)]$

Writing and Graphing Equations of Lines

OBJECTIVES

1 Use the slope-intercept form of the equation of a line.

2 Graph a line by using its slope and a point on the line.

3 Write an equation of a line by using its slope and any point on the line.

4 Write an equation of a line by using two points on the line.

5 Write an equation of a line that fits a data set.

OBJECTIVE 1 **Use the slope-intercept form of the equation of a line.** In **Section 3.3,** we found the slope (steepness) of a line by solving the equation of the line for y. In that form, the slope is the coefficient of x. For example, the slope of the line with equation $y = 2x + 3$ is 2. What does the number 3 represent?

To find out, suppose a line has slope m and y-intercept $(0, b)$. We can find an equation of this line by choosing another point (x, y) on the line, as shown in **FIGURE 29.** Then we use the slope formula.

$$m = \frac{y - b}{x - 0} \quad \leftarrow \text{Change in } y\text{-values}$$
$$\phantom{m = \frac{y - b}{x - 0}} \quad \leftarrow \text{Change in } x\text{-values}$$

$$m = \frac{y - b}{x} \quad \text{Subtract in the denominator.}$$

$$mx = y - b \quad \text{Multiply by } x.$$

$$mx + b = y \quad \text{Add } b.$$

$$y = mx + b \quad \text{Rewrite.}$$

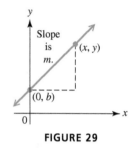

FIGURE 29

This result is the *slope-intercept form* of the equation of a line, because both the slope and the y-intercept of the line can be read directly from the equation. For the line with equation $y = 2x + 3$, the number 3 gives the y-intercept $(0, 3)$.

Slope-Intercept Form

The **slope-intercept form** of the equation of a line with slope m and y-intercept $(0, b)$ is

$$y = mx + b.$$

Slope ↗   ↖ $(0, b)$ is the y-intercept.

Remember: The intercept given by slope-intercept form is the y-intercept.

⟲ *NOW TRY*
  EXERCISE 1

Identify the slope and y-intercept of the line with each equation.

(a) $y = -\dfrac{3}{5}x - 9$

(b) $y = -\dfrac{x}{3} + \dfrac{7}{3}$

EXAMPLE 1 Identifying Slopes and y-Intercepts

Identify the slope and y-intercept of the line with each equation.

(a) $y = -4x + 1$
  Slope ↗   ↖ y-intercept $(0, 1)$

(b) $y = x - 8$ can be written as $y = 1x + (-8)$.
          Slope ↗   ↖ y-intercept $(0, -8)$

(c) $y = 6x$ can be written as $y = 6x + 0$.
              Slope ↗   ↖ y-intercept $(0, 0)$

(d) $y = \frac{x}{4} - \frac{3}{4}$ can be written as $y = \frac{1}{4}x + \left(-\frac{3}{4}\right)$.
            Slope ↗   ↖ y-intercept $\left(0, -\frac{3}{4}\right)$

NOW TRY ⟳

NOW TRY ANSWERS

1. (a) slope: $-\frac{3}{5}$; y-intercept: $(0, -9)$

(b) slope: $-\frac{1}{3}$; y-intercept: $\left(0, \frac{7}{3}\right)$

Given the slope and y-intercept of a line, we can write an equation of the line.

NOW TRY
EXERCISE 2

Write an equation of the line with slope -4 and y-intercept $(0, 2)$.

EXAMPLE 2 Writing an Equation of a Line

Write an equation of the line with slope $\frac{2}{3}$ and y-intercept $(0, -1)$.

Here, $m = \frac{2}{3}$ and $b = -1$, so the equation is

Slope → 　　 ← y-intercept is $(0, b)$.

$$y = mx + b \qquad \text{Slope-intercept form}$$

$$y = \frac{2}{3}x + (-1), \quad \text{or} \quad y = \frac{2}{3}x - 1. \qquad \text{NOW TRY}$$

OBJECTIVE 2 Graph a line by using its slope and a point on the line. We can use the slope and y-intercept to graph a line.

Graphing a Line by Using the Slope and y-Intercept

Step 1 Write the equation in slope-intercept form, if necessary, by solving for y.

Step 2 Identify the y-intercept. Graph the point $(0, b)$.

Step 3 Identify slope m of the line. Use the geometric interpretation of slope ("rise over run") to find another point on the graph by counting from the y-intercept.

Step 4 Join the two points with a line to obtain the graph. (If desired, obtain a third point, such as the x-intercept, as a check.)

EXAMPLE 3 Graphing Lines by Using Slopes and y-intercepts

Graph the equation of each line by using the slope and y-intercept.

(a) $y = \frac{2}{3}x - 1$

Step 1 The equation is in slope-intercept form.

$$y = \frac{2}{3}x - 1$$

↑　　　↑
Slope　　Value of b in y-intercept $(0, b)$

Step 2 The y-intercept is $(0, -1)$. Graph this point. See **FIGURE 30**.

Step 3 The slope is $\frac{2}{3}$. By the definition of slope,

$$m = \frac{\text{change in } y \text{ (rise)}}{\text{change in } x \text{ (run)}} = \frac{2}{3}.$$

From the y-intercept, count up 2 units and to the right 3 units to obtain the point $(3, 1)$.

Step 4 Draw the line through the points $(0, -1)$ and $(3, 1)$ to obtain the graph in **FIGURE 30**.

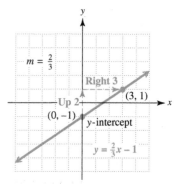

FIGURE 30

NOW TRY ANSWER
2. $y = -4x + 2$

NOW TRY
EXERCISE 3

Graph $3x + 2y = 8$ by using the slope and y-intercept.

(b) $3x + 4y = 8$

Step 1 Solve for y to write the equation in slope-intercept form.

$$3x + 4y = 8$$

Isolate y on one side. $\quad 4y = -3x + 8 \qquad$ Subtract $3x$.

Slope-intercept form → $y = -\dfrac{3}{4}x + 2 \qquad$ Divide by 4.

Step 2 The y-intercept is $(0, 2)$. Graph this point. See **FIGURE 31**.

Step 3 The slope is $-\dfrac{3}{4}$, which can be written as either $\dfrac{-3}{4}$ or $\dfrac{3}{-4}$. We use $\dfrac{-3}{4}$ here.

$$m = \frac{\text{change in } y \text{ (rise)}}{\text{change in } x \text{ (run)}} = \frac{-3}{4}$$

From the y-intercept, count *down* 3 units (because of the negative sign) and to the right 4 units, to obtain the point $(4, -1)$.

Step 4 Draw the line through the two points $(0, 2)$ and $(4, -1)$ to obtain the graph in **FIGURE 31**.

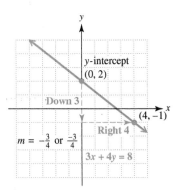

FIGURE 31

NOW TRY

NOTE In Step 3 of **Example 3(b)**, we could use $\dfrac{3}{-4}$ for the slope. From the y-intercept, count up 3 units and to the *left* 4 units (because of the negative sign) to obtain the point $(-4, 5)$. Confirm that this produces the same line.

NOW TRY
EXERCISE 4

Graph the line through $(-3, -4)$ with slope $\dfrac{5}{2}$.

EXAMPLE 4 Graphing a Line by Using the Slope and a Point

Graph the line through $(-2, 3)$ with slope -4.

First, locate the point $(-2, 3)$. Write the slope as

$$m = \frac{\text{change in } y \text{ (rise)}}{\text{change in } x \text{ (run)}} = -4 = \frac{-4}{1}.$$

Locate another point on the line by counting *down* 4 units and then to the right 1 unit. Finally, draw the line through this new point P and the given point $(-2, 3)$. See **FIGURE 32**.

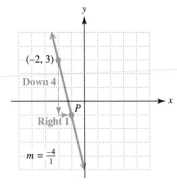

FIGURE 32

NOW TRY

NOW TRY ANSWERS

3.

4.

NOTE In **Example 4**, we could have written the slope as $\dfrac{4}{-1}$ instead. Verify that this produces the same line.

OBJECTIVE 3 Write an equation of a line by using its slope and any point on the line. We can use the slope-intercept form to write the equation of a line if we know the slope and any point on the line.

Write an equation, in slope-intercept form, of the line having slope 3 and passing through the point $(-2, 1)$.

EXAMPLE 5 Using the Slope-Intercept Form to Write an Equation

Write an equation, in slope-intercept form, of the line having slope 4 passing through the point $(2, 5)$.

Since the line passes through the point $(2, 5)$, we can substitute $x = 2, y = 5$, and the given slope $m = 4$ into $y = mx + b$ and solve for b.

$$y = mx + b \qquad \text{Slope-intercept form}$$
$$5 = 4(2) + b \qquad \text{Let } x = 2, y = 5, \text{ and } m = 4.$$
$$5 = 8 + b \qquad \text{Multiply.}$$
$$-3 = b \qquad \text{Subtract 8.}$$

$(0, b)$ is the y-intercept. Don't stop here.

Now substitute the values of m and b into slope-intercept form.

$$y = mx + b \qquad \text{Slope-intercept form}$$
$$y = 4x - 3 \qquad m = 4 \text{ and } b = -3 \qquad \text{NOW TRY}$$

There is another form that can be used to write the equation of a line. To develop this form, let m represent the slope of a line and let (x_1, y_1) represent a given point on the line. Let (x, y) represent any other point on the line. See **FIGURE 33**. Then,

$$m = \frac{y - y_1}{x - x_1} \qquad \text{Definition of slope}$$
$$m(x - x_1) = y - y_1 \qquad \text{Multiply each side by } x - x_1.$$
$$y - y_1 = m(x - x_1). \qquad \text{Rewrite.}$$

This result is the *point-slope form* of the equation of a line.

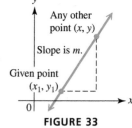

FIGURE 33

Point-Slope Form

The **point-slope form** of the equation of a line with slope m passing through the point (x_1, y_1) is

$$y - y_1 = m(x - x_1).$$

Slope ↓ ... ↑ Given point ↑

EXAMPLE 6 Using the Point-Slope Form to Write Equations

Write an equation of each line. Give the final answer in slope-intercept form.

(a) Through $(-2, 4)$, with slope -3

The given point is $(-2, 4)$ so $x_1 = -2$ and $y_1 = 4$. Also, $m = -3$.

$$y - y_1 = m(x - x_1) \qquad \text{Point-slope form}$$
$$y - 4 = -3[x - (-2)] \qquad \text{Let } y_1 = 4, m = -3, x_1 = -2.$$
$$y - 4 = -3(x + 2) \qquad \text{Definition of subtraction}$$
$$y - 4 = -3x - 6 \qquad \text{Distributive property}$$
$$y = -3x - 2 \qquad \text{Add 4.}$$

Only y_1, m, and x_1 are replaced with numbers.

NOW TRY
EXERCISE 6

Write an equation of the line through $(3, -1)$, with slope $-\frac{2}{5}$. Give the final answer in slope-intercept form.

(b) Through $(4, 2)$, with slope $\frac{3}{5}$

$$y - y_1 = m(x - x_1) \qquad \text{Point-slope form}$$

$$y - 2 = \frac{3}{5}(x - 4) \qquad \text{Let } y_1 = 2,\, m = \tfrac{3}{5},\, x_1 = 4.$$

$$y - 2 = \frac{3}{5}x - \frac{12}{5} \qquad \text{Distributive property}$$

$$y = \frac{3}{5}x - \frac{12}{5} + \frac{10}{5} \qquad \text{Add } 2 = \tfrac{10}{5} \text{ to each side.}$$

$$y = \frac{3}{5}x - \frac{2}{5} \qquad \text{Combine like terms.} \qquad \text{NOW TRY}$$

OBJECTIVE 4 **Write an equation of a line by using two points on the line.** Many of the linear equations in **Sections 3.1–3.3** were given in the form

$$Ax + By = C, \qquad \text{Standard form}$$

called **standard form**, where A, B, and C are real numbers and A and B are not both 0. In most cases, A, B, and C are rational numbers. For consistency in this book, we give answers so that A, B, and C are integers with greatest common factor 1 and $A \geq 0$.

NOTE The definition of standard form is not the same in all texts. A linear equation can be written in many different, equally correct, ways. For example,

$$3x + 4y = 12, \quad 6x + 8y = 24, \quad \text{and} \quad -9x - 12y = -36$$

all represent the same set of ordered pairs. When giving answers in standard form, let us agree that $3x + 4y = 12$ is preferable to the other forms because the greatest common factor of 3, 4, and 12 is 1 and $A \geq 0$.

NOW TRY
EXERCISE 7

Write an equation of the line through the points $(4, 1)$ and $(6, -2)$. Give the final answer in

(a) slope-intercept form and

(b) standard form.

EXAMPLE 7 **Writing the Equation of a Line by Using Two Points**

Write an equation of the line through the points $(-2, 5)$ and $(3, 4)$. Give the final answer in slope-intercept form and then in standard form.

First, find the slope of the line, using the slope formula.

$$\text{slope } m = \frac{y_2 - y_1}{x_2 - x_1} = \frac{5 - 4}{-2 - 3} = \frac{1}{-5} = -\frac{1}{5}$$

Now use either $(-2, 5)$ or $(3, 4)$ and either slope-intercept or point-slope form.

$$y - y_1 = m(x - x_1) \qquad \text{We choose } (3, 4) \text{ and point-slope form.}$$

$$y - 4 = -\frac{1}{5}(x - 3) \qquad \text{Let } y_1 = 4,\, m = -\tfrac{1}{5},\, x_1 = 3.$$

$$y - 4 = -\frac{1}{5}x + \frac{3}{5} \qquad \text{Distributive property}$$

$$y = -\frac{1}{5}x + \frac{3}{5} + \frac{20}{5} \qquad \text{Add } 4 = \tfrac{20}{5} \text{ to each side.}$$

Slope-intercept form $\longrightarrow \quad y = -\dfrac{1}{5}x + \dfrac{23}{5} \qquad \text{Combine like terms.}$

$$5y = -x + 23 \qquad \text{Multiply by 5 to clear fractions.}$$

Standard form $\longrightarrow x + 5y = 23 \qquad \text{Add } x. \qquad \text{NOW TRY}$

NOW TRY ANSWERS
6. $y = -\frac{2}{5}x + \frac{1}{5}$

7. (a) $y = -\frac{3}{2}x + 7$

  (b) $3x + 2y = 14$

NOTE In **Example 7,** the same result would be found by using $(-2, 5)$ for (x_1, y_1). We could also substitute the slope and either given point in slope-intercept form $y = mx + b$ and then solve for b, as in **Example 5.**

A summary of the forms of linear equations follows.

Forms of Linear Equations		
Equation	**Description**	**Example**
$x = a$	**Vertical line** Slope is undefined. x-intercept is $(a, 0)$.	$x = 3$
$y = b$	**Horizontal line** Slope is 0. y-intercept is $(0, b)$.	$y = 3$
$y = mx + b$	**Slope-intercept form** Slope is m. y-intercept is $(0, b)$.	$y = \frac{3}{2}x - 6$
$y - y_1 = m(x - x_1)$	**Point-slope form** Slope is m. Line passes through (x_1, y_1).	$y + 3 = \frac{3}{2}(x - 2)$
$Ax + By = C$	**Standard form** Slope is $-\frac{A}{B}$. x-intercept is $\left(\frac{C}{A}, 0\right)$. y-intercept is $\left(0, \frac{C}{B}\right)$.	$3x - 2y = 12$

NOTE Slope-intercept form is an especially useful form for a linear equation because of the information we can determine from it. It is also the form used by graphing calculators and the one that describes *a linear function.*

OBJECTIVE 5 **Write an equation of a line that fits a data set.** If a given set of data fits a linear pattern—that is, if its graph consists of points lying close to a straight line—we can write a linear equation that models the data.

EXAMPLE 8 Writing an Equation of a Line That Describes Data

The table lists the average annual cost (in dollars) of tuition and fees for in-state students at public 4-year colleges and universities for selected years. Year 1 represents 2001, year 3 represents 2003, and so on. Plot the data and write an equation that approximates it.

Letting y represent the cost in year x, we plot the data as shown in **FIGURE 34** on the next page.

Year	Cost (in dollars)
1	3766
3	4645
5	5491
7	6185

Source: The College Board.

NOW TRY
EXERCISE 8

Use the points $(3, 4645)$ and $(5, 5491)$ to write an equation in slope-intercept form that approximates the data of **Example 8.** How well does this equation approximate the cost in 2007?

**AVERAGE ANNUAL COSTS AT
PUBLIC 4-YEAR COLLEGES**

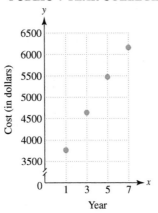

FIGURE 34

The points appear to lie approximately in a straight line. We choose the ordered pairs $(5, 5491)$ and $(7, 6185)$ from the table and find the slope of the line through these points.

$$m = \frac{y_2 - y_1}{x_2 - x_1} = \frac{6185 - 5491}{7 - 5} = 347 \qquad \text{Let } (7, 6185) = (x_2, y_2) \text{ and } (5, 5491) = (x_1, y_1).$$

The slope, 347, is positive, indicating that tuition and fees *increased* \$347 each year. Now use this slope and the point $(5, 5491)$ in the slope-intercept form to find an equation of the line.

$$
\begin{aligned}
y &= mx + b & &\text{Slope-intercept form} \\
5491 &= 347(5) + b & &\text{Substitute for } x, y, \text{ and } m. \\
5491 &= 1735 + b & &\text{Multiply.} \\
3756 &= b & &\text{Subtract 1735.}
\end{aligned}
$$

Thus, $m = 347$ and $b = 3756$, so we can write an equation of the line.

$$y = 347x + 3756$$

To see how well this equation approximates the ordered pairs in the data table, let $x = 3$ (for 2003) and find y.

$$
\begin{aligned}
y &= 347x + 3756 & &\text{Equation of the line} \\
y &= 347(3) + 3756 & &\text{Substitute 3 for } x. \\
y &= 4797 & &\text{Multiply and then add.}
\end{aligned}
$$

The corresponding value in the table for $x = 3$ is 4645, so the equation approximates the data reasonably well. With caution, the equation could be used to predict values for years that are not included in the table. NOW TRY

NOTE In **Example 8,** if we had chosen two different data points, we would have found a slightly different equation.

NOW TRY ANSWER
8. $y = 423x + 3376$;
   The equation gives $y = 6337$
   when $x = 7$, which approximates
   the data reasonably well.

3.4 EXERCISES

 MyMathLab Math XL PRACTICE WATCH DOWNLOAD READ REVIEW

🌐 *Complete solution available on the Video Resources on DVD*

Concept Check Match the description in Column I with the correct equation in Column II.

I	II
1. Slope $= -2$, passes through $(4, 1)$	**A.** $y = 4x$
2. Slope $= -2$, y-intercept $(0, 1)$	**B.** $y = \frac{1}{4}x$
3. Passes through $(0, 0)$ and $(4, 1)$	**C.** $y = -4x$
4. Passes through $(0, 0)$ and $(1, 4)$	**D.** $y = -2x + 1$
	E. $y - 1 = -2(x - 4)$

Concept Check Match each equation with the graph in A–D that would most closely resemble its graph.

5. $y = x + 3$ **6.** $y = -x + 3$ **7.** $y = x - 3$ **8.** $y = -x - 3$

A.   B.   C.   D.

Identify the slope and y-intercept of the line with each equation. **See Example 1.**

9. $y = \frac{5}{2}x - 4$ **10.** $y = \frac{7}{3}x - 6$ **11.** $y = -x + 9$

12. $y = x + 1$ **13.** $y = \frac{x}{5} - \frac{3}{10}$ **14.** $y = \frac{x}{7} - \frac{5}{14}$

Concept Check Use the geometric interpretation of slope (rise *divided by* run, *from Section 3.3*) to find the slope of each line. Then, by identifying the y-intercept from the graph, write the slope-intercept form of the equation of the line.

15.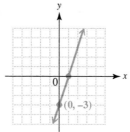

16.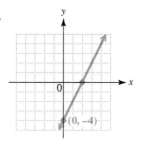

17.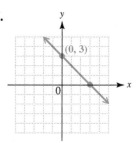

18.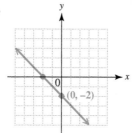

19.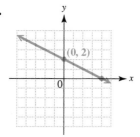

20.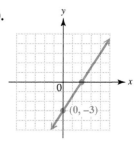

Write the equation of each line with the given slope and y-intercept. ***See Example 2.***

21. $m = 4, (0, -3)$ **22.** $m = -5, (0, 6)$ **23.** $m = -1, (0, -7)$

24. $m = 1, (0, -9)$ **25.** $m = 0, (0, 3)$ **26.** $m = 0, (0, -4)$

27. Undefined slope, $(0, -2)$ **28.** Undefined slope, $(0, 5)$

Graph each equation by using the slope and y-intercept. ***See Example 3.***

29. $y = 3x + 2$ **30.** $y = 4x - 4$ **31.** $y = -\dfrac{1}{3}x + 4$

32. $y = -\dfrac{1}{2}x + 2$ **33.** $2x + y = -5$ **34.** $3x + y = -2$

35. $4x - 5y = 20$ **36.** $6x - 5y = 30$

Graph each line passing through the given point and having the given slope. (In Exercises 45–48, recall the types of lines having slope 0 and undefined slope.) ***See Example 4.***

37. $(0, 1), m = 4$ **38.** $(0, -5), m = -2$ **39.** $(1, -5), m = -\dfrac{2}{5}$

40. $(2, -1), m = -\dfrac{1}{3}$ **41.** $(-1, 4), m = \dfrac{2}{5}$ **42.** $(-2, 2), m = \dfrac{3}{2}$

43. $(0, 0), m = -2$ **44.** $(0, 0), m = -3$

45. $(-2, 3), m = 0$ **46.** $(3, 2), m = 0$

47. $(2, 4)$, undefined slope   **48.** $(3, -2)$, undefined slope

49. *Concept Check*   What is the common name given to a vertical line whose x-intercept is the origin?

50. *Concept Check*   What is the common name given to a line with slope 0 whose y-intercept is the origin?

Write an equation for each line passing through the given point and having the given slope. Give the final answer in slope-intercept form. ***See Examples 5 and 6.***

51. $(4, 1), m = 2$ **52.** $(2, 7), m = 3$ **53.** $(-1, 3), m = -4$

54. $(-3, 1), m = -2$ **55.** $(9, 3), m = 1$ **56.** $(8, 4), m = 1$

57. $(-4, 1), m = \dfrac{3}{4}$ **58.** $(2, 1), m = \dfrac{5}{2}$ **59.** $(-2, 5), m = \dfrac{2}{3}$

60. $(4, 2), m = -\dfrac{1}{3}$ **61.** $(6, -3), m = -\dfrac{4}{5}$ **62.** $(7, -2), m = -\dfrac{7}{2}$

63. *Concept Check*   Which equations are equivalent to $2x - 3y = 6$?

  A. $y = \dfrac{2}{3}x - 2$ **B.** $-2x + 3y = -6$

  C. $y = -\dfrac{3}{2}x + 3$ **D.** $y - 2 = \dfrac{2}{3}(x - 6)$

64. *Concept Check*   In the summary box on **page 216**, we give the equations

$$y = \dfrac{3}{2}x - 6 \quad \text{and} \quad y + 3 = \dfrac{3}{2}(x - 2)$$

as examples of equations in slope-intercept form and point-slope form, respectively. Write each of these equations in standard form. What do you notice?

Write an equation for each line passing through the given pair of points. Give the final answer in (a) slope-intercept form and (b) standard form. See Example 7.

65. $(4, 10)$ and $(6, 12)$ **66.** $(8, 5)$ and $(9, 6)$ **67.** $(-4, 0)$ and $(0, 2)$

68. $(0, -2)$ and $(-3, 0)$ **69.** $(-2, -1)$ and $(3, -4)$ **70.** $(-1, -7)$ and $(-8, -2)$

71. $\left(-\dfrac{2}{3}, \dfrac{8}{3}\right)$ and $\left(\dfrac{1}{3}, \dfrac{7}{3}\right)$ **72.** $\left(\dfrac{1}{2}, \dfrac{3}{2}\right)$ and $\left(-\dfrac{1}{4}, \dfrac{5}{4}\right)$

Write an equation of the line satisfying the given conditions. Give the final answer in slope-intercept form. (Hint: Recall the relationships among slopes of parallel and perpendicular lines in Section 3.3.)

73. Perpendicular to $x - 2y = 7$; y-intercept $(0, -3)$

74. Parallel to $5x - y = 10$; y-intercept $(0, -2)$

75. Through $(2, 3)$;   parallel to $4x - y = -2$

76. Through $(4, 2)$;   perpendicular to $x - 3y = 7$

77. Through $(2, -3)$;   parallel to $3x = 4y + 5$

78. Through $(-1, 4)$;   perpendicular to $2x = -3y + 8$

*The cost y of producing x items is, in some cases, expressed as $y = mx + b$. The number b gives the **fixed cost** (the cost that is the same no matter how many items are produced), and the number m is the **variable cost** (the cost of producing an additional item). Use this information to work Exercises 79 and 80.*

79. It costs \$400 to start up a business selling snow cones. Each snow cone costs \$0.25 to produce.

   (a) What is the fixed cost?

   (b) What is the variable cost?

   (c) Write the cost equation.

   (d) What will be the cost of producing 100 snow cones, based on the cost equation?

   (e) How many snow cones will be produced if the total cost is \$775?

80. It costs \$2000 to purchase a copier, and each copy costs \$0.02 to make.

   (a) What is the fixed cost?

   (b) What is the variable cost?

   (c) Write the cost equation.

   (d) What will be the cost of producing 10,000 copies, based on the cost equation?

   (e) How many copies will be produced if the total cost is \$2600?

Solve each problem. See Example 8.

81. The table lists the average annual cost (in dollars) of tuition and fees at 2-year colleges for selected years, where year 1 represents 2004, year 2 represents 2005, and so on.

Year	Cost (in dollars)
1	2079
2	2182
3	2272
4	2361
5	2402

Source: The College Board.

(a) Write five ordered pairs from the data.

(b) Plot the ordered pairs. Do the points lie approximately in a straight line?

(c) Use the ordered pairs $(1, 2079)$ and $(4, 2361)$ to write an equation of a line that approximates the data. Give the final equation in slope-intercept form.

(d) Use the equation from part (c) to estimate the average annual cost at 2-year colleges in 2009 to the nearest dollar. (*Hint:* What is the value of x for 2009?)

82. The table gives heavy-metal nuclear waste (in thousands of metric tons) from spent reactor fuel stored temporarily at reactor sites, awaiting permanent storage. Let $x = 0$ represent 1995, $x = 5$ represent 2000 (since $2000 - 1995 = 5$), and so on. (*Source:* "Burial of Radioactive Nuclear Waste Under the Seabed," *Scientific American.*)

Year x	Waste y
1995	32
2000	42
2010*	61
2020*	76

*Estimated by the U.S. Department of Energy.

(a) For 1995, the ordered pair is $(0, 32)$. Write ordered pairs for the data for the other years given in the table.

(b) Plot the ordered pairs (x, y). Do the points lie approximately in a straight line?

(c) Use the ordered pairs $(0, 32)$ and $(25, 76)$ to write the equation of a line that approximates the other ordered pairs. Give the equation in slope-intercept form.

(d) Use the equation from part (c) to estimate the amount of nuclear waste in 2015. (*Hint:* What is the value of x for 2015?)

The points on the graph show the number of colleges that teamed up with banks to issue student ID cards which doubled as debit cards from 2002 through 2007. The graph of a linear equation that models the data is also shown.

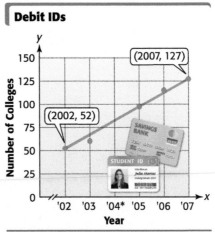

Debit IDs

Source: CR80News.
* Data for 2004 unavailable.

83. Use the ordered pairs shown on the graph to write an equation of the line that models the data. Give the equation in slope-intercept form.

84. Use the equation from **Exercise 83** to estimate the number of colleges that teamed up with banks to offer debit IDs in 2004, the year with unavailable data.

PREVIEW EXERCISES

*Evaluate each expression. **See Section 1.2.***

85. $2 \cdot 2 \cdot 2 \cdot 2 \cdot 2 \cdot 2$ **86.** $3 \cdot 3 \cdot 3$ **87.** $5 \cdot 5 \cdot 5 \cdot 5$

88. $4 \cdot 4 \cdot 4 \cdot 4 \cdot 4$ **89.** $\dfrac{2}{3} \cdot \dfrac{2}{3} \cdot \dfrac{2}{3}$ **90.** $\dfrac{5}{8} \cdot \dfrac{5}{8}$

SUMMARY EXERCISES on Linear Equations and Graphs

Graph each line, using the given information or equation.

1. $x - 2y = -4$ **2.** $2x + 3y = 12$

3. $m = 1$, y-intercept $(0, -2)$ **4.** $y = -2x + 6$

5. $m = -\frac{2}{3}$, passes through $(3, -4)$ **6.** Undefined slope, passes through $(-3.5, 0)$

7. $x - 4y = 0$ **8.** $y - 4 = -9$

9. $8x = 6y + 24$ **10.** $m = 1$, y-intercept $(0, -4)$

11. $5x + 2y = 10$ **12.** $m = -\frac{3}{4}$, passes through $(4, -4)$

13. $m = 0$, passes through $\left(0, \frac{3}{2}\right)$ **14.** $x + 5y = 0$

15. $y = -x + 6$ **16.** $4x = 3y - 24$

17. $x + 4 = 0$ **18.** $x - 3y = 6$

19. *Concept Check*   Match the description in Column I with the correct equation in Column II.

I	II
(a) Slope -0.5, $b = -2$	**A.** $y = -\frac{1}{2}x$
(b) x-intercept $(4, 0)$, y-intercept $(0, 2)$	**B.** $y = -\frac{1}{2}x - 2$
(c) Passes through $(4, -2)$ and $(0, 0)$	**C.** $x - 2y = 2$
(d) $m = \frac{1}{2}$, passes through $(-2, -2)$	**D.** $x + 2y = 4$
	E. $x = 2y$

20. *Concept Check*   Which equations are equivalent to $2x + 5y = 20$?

    A. $y = -\frac{2}{5}x + 4$ **B.** $y - 2 = -\frac{2}{5}(x - 5)$

    C. $y = \frac{5}{2}x - 4$ **D.** $2x = 5y - 20$

Write an equation for each line. Give the final answer in slope-intercept form if possible.

21. $m = -3$, $b = -6$ **22.** $m = \frac{3}{2}$, through $(-4, 6)$

23. Through $(1, -7)$ and $(-2, 5)$ **24.** Through $(0, 0)$ and $(5, 3)$

25. Through $(0, 0)$, undefined slope   **26.** Through $(3, 0)$ and $(0, -3)$

27. Through $(0, 0)$ and $(3, 2)$ **28.** $m = -2$, $b = -4$

29. Through $(5, 0)$ and $(0, -5)$ **30.** Through $(0, 0)$, $m = 0$

31. $m = \frac{5}{3}$, through $(-3, 0)$ **32.** Through $(1, -13)$ and $(-2, 2)$

Analyzing Your Test Results

An exam is a learning opportunity—learn from your mistakes. After a test is returned, do the following:

▶ **Note what you got wrong and why you had points deducted.**

▶ **Figure out how to solve the problems you missed.** Check your textbook or notes, or ask your instructor. Rework the problems correctly.

▶ **Keep all quizzes and tests that are returned to you.** Use them to study for future tests and the final exam.

Typical Reasons for Errors on Math Tests

These are test taking errors. They are easy to correct if you read carefully, show all your work, proofread, and double-check units and labels.

1. You read the directions wrong.
2. You read the question wrong or skipped over something.
3. You made a computation error.
4. You made a careless error. (For example, you incorrectly copied a correct answer onto a separate answer sheet.)
5. Your answer is not complete.
6. You labeled your answer wrong. (For example, you labeled an answer "ft" instead of "ft^2.")
7. You didn't show your work.

These are test preparation errors. You must practice the kinds of problems that you will see on tests.

8. You didn't understand a concept.
9. You were unable to set up the problem (in an application).
10. You were unable to apply a procedure.

Below are sample charts for tracking your test taking progress. Use them to find out if you tend to make certain kinds of errors on tests. Check the appropriate box when you've made an error in a particular category.

Test Taking Errors

Test	Read directions wrong	Read question wrong	Computation error	Not exact or accurate	Not complete	Labeled wrong	Didn't show work
1							
2							
3							

Test Preparation Errors

Test	Didn't understand concept	Didn't set up problem correctly	Couldn't apply concept to new situation
1			
2			
3			

What will you do to avoid these kinds of errors on your next test?

CHAPTER 3 SUMMARY

KEY TERMS

3.1

line graph
linear equation in two
  variables
ordered pair
table of values
x-axis
y-axis

origin
rectangular (Cartesian)
  coordinate system
quadrant
plane
coordinates
plot
scatter diagram

3.2

graph, graphing
y-intercept
x-intercept
horizontal line
vertical line

3.3

rise
run
slope
subscript notation
parallel lines
perpendicular lines

NEW SYMBOLS

(a, b) an ordered pair

m slope

(x_1, y_1) x-sub-one,
           y-sub-one

TEST YOUR WORD POWER

See how well you have learned the vocabulary in this chapter.

1. A **linear equation in two variables**
is an equation that can be written in
the form
  A. $Ax + By < C$
  B. $ax = b$
  C. $y = x^2$
  D. $Ax + By = C$.

2. An **ordered pair** is a pair of
numbers written
  A. in numerical order between
    brackets
  B. between parentheses or
    brackets
  C. between parentheses in which
    order is important
  D. between parentheses in which
    order does not matter.

3. An **intercept** is
  A. the point where the x-axis and
    y-axis intersect
  B. a pair of numbers written in
    parentheses in which order
    matters
  C. one of the four regions
    determined by a rectangular
    coordinate system
  D. the point where a graph intersects
    the x-axis or the y-axis.

4. The **slope** of a line is
  A. the measure of the run over the
    rise of the line
  B. the distance between two points
    on the line
  C. the ratio of the change in y to the
    change in x along the line

  D. the horizontal change compared
    with the vertical change of two
    points on the line.

5. Two lines in a plane are **parallel** if
  A. they represent the same line
  B. they never intersect
  C. they intersect at a 90° angle
  D. one has a positive slope and one
    has a negative slope.

6. Two lines in a plane are
perpendicular if
  A. they represent the same line
  B. they never intersect
  C. they intersect at a 90° angle
  D. one has a positive slope and one
    has a negative slope.

ANSWERS

1. D; *Examples:* $3x + 2y = 6, x = y - 7, y = 4x$ **2.** C; *Examples:* $(0, 3), (-3, 8), (4, 0)$ **3.** D; *Example:* The graph of the equation
$4x - 3y = 12$ has x-intercept $(3, 0)$ and y-intercept $(0, -4)$.   **4.** C; *Example:* The line through $(3, 6)$ and $(5, 4)$ has slope $\frac{4 - 6}{5 - 3} = \frac{-2}{2} = -1$.
5. B; *Example:* See **FIGURE 27** in **Section 3.3**.   **6.** C; *Example:* See **FIGURE 28** in **Section 3.3**.

QUICK REVIEW

CONCEPTS

EXAMPLES

3.1 Linear Equations in Two Variables;
The Rectangular Coordinate System

An ordered pair is a solution of an equation if it satisfies the equation.

Is $(2, -5)$ or $(0, -6)$ a solution of $4x - 3y = 18$?

$$4(2) - 3(-5) = 23 \neq 18 \qquad \bigg| \qquad 4(0) - 3(-6) = 18$$

$(2, -5)$ is not a solution. $\qquad$ $(0, -6)$ is a solution.

If a value of either variable in an equation is given, then the other variable can be found by substitution.

Complete the ordered pair $(0, \_\_)$ for $3x = y + 4$.

$$3(0) = y + 4 \qquad \text{Let } x = 0.$$

$$0 = y + 4 \qquad \text{Multiply.}$$

$$-4 = y \qquad \text{Subtract 4.}$$

The ordered pair is $(0, -4)$.

Plot the ordered pair $(-3, 4)$ by starting at the origin, moving 3 units to the left, and then moving 4 units up.

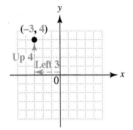

3.2 Graphing Linear Equations in Two Variables

To graph a linear equation, follow these steps.

Step 1 Find at least two ordered pairs that satisfy the equation.

Step 2 Plot the corresponding points.

Step 3 Draw a straight line through the points.

x	y
0	-2
4	0

The graph of $Ax + By = 0$ passes through the origin. Find and plot another point that satisfies the equation. Then draw the line through the two points.

The graph of $y = b$ is a horizontal line through $(0, b)$.

The graph of $x = a$ is a vertical line through $(a, 0)$.

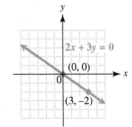

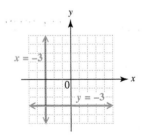

(continued)

CONCEPTS	EXAMPLES
3.3 The Slope of a Line	

3.3 The Slope of a Line

The slope of the line through (x_1, y_1) and (x_2, y_2) is

$$m = \frac{\text{change in } y}{\text{change in } x} = \frac{y_2 - y_1}{x_2 - x_1} \quad (\text{where } x_1 \neq x_2).$$

Horizontal lines have slope 0.

Vertical lines have undefined slope.

To find the slope of a line from its equation, solve for y. The slope is the coefficient of x.

The line through $(-2, 3)$ and $(4, -5)$ has slope as follows.

$$m = \frac{-5 - 3}{4 - (-2)} = \frac{-8}{6} = -\frac{4}{3}$$

The line $y = -2$ has slope 0.

The line $x = 4$ has undefined slope.

Find the slope of $3x - 4y = 12$.

$$-4y = -3x + 12 \qquad \text{Add } -3x.$$

$$y = \frac{3}{4}x - 3 \qquad \text{Divide by } -4.$$

Slope ⎯⎯

Parallel lines have the same slope.

The lines $y = 3x - 1$ and $y = 3x + 4$ are parallel because both have slope 3.

The slopes of perpendicular lines are negative reciprocals (that is, their product is -1).

The lines $y = -3x - 1$ and $y = \frac{1}{3}x + 4$ are perpendicular because their slopes are -3 and $\frac{1}{3}$, and $-3\left(\frac{1}{3}\right) = -1$.

3.4 Writing and Graphing Equations of Lines

Slope-Intercept Form

$y = mx + b$

m is the slope.
$(0, b)$ is the y-intercept.

Write an equation of the line with slope 2 and y-intercept $(0, -5)$.

$$y = 2x - 5$$

Point-Slope Form

$y - y_1 = m(x - x_1)$

m is the slope.
(x_1, y_1) is a point on the line.

Write an equation of the line with slope $-\frac{1}{2}$ through $(-4, 5)$.

$$y - 5 = -\frac{1}{2}[x - (-4)] \qquad \text{Substitute.}$$

$$y - 5 = -\frac{1}{2}(x + 4) \qquad \text{Definition of subtraction}$$

$$y - 5 = -\frac{1}{2}x - 2 \qquad \text{Distributive property}$$

$$y = -\frac{1}{2}x + 3 \qquad \text{Add 5.}$$

Standard Form

$Ax + By = C$

A, B, and C are real numbers and A and B are not both 0.

The equation $y = -\frac{1}{2}x + 3$ is written in standard form as

$$x + 2y = 6,$$

with $A = 1$, $B = 2$, and $C = 6$.

3.1

1. The line graph shows the number, in millions, of real Christmas trees purchased for the years 2002 through 2007.

(a) Between which years did the number of real trees purchased increase?

(b) Between which years did the number of real trees purchased decrease?

(c) Estimate the number of real trees purchased in 2005 and 2006.

(d) By about how much did the number of real trees purchased between 2005 and 2006 decrease?

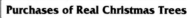

Purchases of Real Christmas Trees

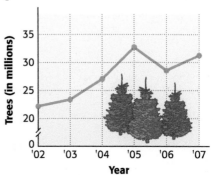

Source: National Christmas Tree Association.

Complete the given ordered pairs for each equation.

2. $y = 3x + 2$; $(-1, \_\_)$, $(0, \_\_)$, $(\_\_, 5)$

3. $4x + 3y = 6$; $(0, \_\_)$, $(\_\_, 0)$, $(-2, \_\_)$

4. $x = 3y$; $(0, \_\_)$, $(8, \_\_)$, $(\_\_, -3)$

5. $x - 7 = 0$; $(\_\_, -3)$, $(\_\_, 0)$, $(\_\_, 5)$

Determine whether the given ordered pair is a solution of the given equation.

6. $x + y = 7$; $(2, 5)$ **7.** $2x + y = 5$; $(-1, 3)$ **8.** $3x - y = 4$; $\left(\frac{1}{3}, -3\right)$

Name the quadrant in which each ordered pair lies. Then plot each pair in a rectangular coordinate system.

9. $(2, 3)$ **10.** $(-4, 2)$ **11.** $(3, 0)$ **12.** $(0, -6)$

13. *Concept Check* If $xy > 0$, in what quadrant or quadrants must (x, y) lie?

3.2 *Find the x- and y-intercepts for the line that is the graph of each equation, and graph the line.*

14. $y = 2x + 5$ **15.** $3x + 2y = 8$ **16.** $x + 2y = -4$

3.3 *Find the slope of each line.*

17. Through $(2, 3)$ and $(-4, 6)$ **18.** Through $(2, 5)$ and $(2, 8)$

19. $y = 3x - 4$ **20.** $y = 5$

21.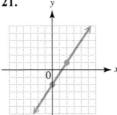

22.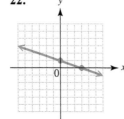

23. The line passing through these points

x	y
0	1
2	4
6	10

24. **(a)** A line parallel to the graph of $y = 2x + 3$

(b) A line perpendicular to the graph of $y = -3x + 3$

Decide whether each pair of lines is parallel, perpendicular, *or* neither.

25. $3x + 2y = 6$
$6x + 4y = 8$

26. $x - 3y = 1$
$3x + y = 4$

27. $x - 2y = 8$
$x + 2y = 8$

3.4 *Write an equation for each line. Give the final answer in slope-intercept form if possible.*

28. $m = -1, b = \frac{2}{3}$

29. Through $(2, 3)$ and $(-4, 6)$

30. Through $(4, -3), m = 1$

31. Through $(-1, 4), m = \frac{2}{3}$

32. Through $(1, -1), m = -\frac{3}{4}$

33. $m = -\frac{1}{4}, b = \frac{3}{2}$

34. Slope 0, through $(-4, 1)$

35. Through $\left(\frac{1}{3}, -\frac{5}{4}\right)$, undefined slope

MIXED REVIEW EXERCISES

Concept Check In Exercises 36–41, match each statement to the appropriate graph or graphs in A–D. Graphs may be used more than once.

A. 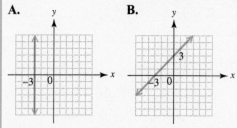 **B.** **C.** 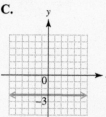 **D.**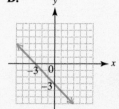

36. The line shown in the graph has undefined slope.

37. The graph of the equation has y-intercept $(0, -3)$.

38. The graph of the equation has x-intercept $(-3, 0)$.

39. The line shown in the graph has negative slope.

40. The graph is that of the equation $y = -3$.

41. The line shown in the graph has slope 1.

Find the intercepts and the slope of each line. Then graph the line.

42. $y = -2x - 5$

43. $x + 3y = 0$

44. $y - 5 = 0$

Write an equation for each line. Give the final answer in slope-intercept form.

45. $m = -\frac{1}{4}, b = -\frac{5}{4}$

46. Through $(8, 6), m = -3$

47. Through $(3, -5)$ and $(-4, -1)$

48. Slope 0, through $(5, -5)$

Also,
$$6^2 \cdot 6^3 = (6 \cdot 6)(6 \cdot 6 \cdot 6)$$
$$= 6 \cdot 6 \cdot 6 \cdot 6 \cdot 6$$
$$= 6^5.$$

Generalizing from these examples, we have

$$2^4 \cdot 2^3 = 2^{4+3} = 2^7 \quad \text{and} \quad 6^2 \cdot 6^3 = 6^{2+3} = 6^5.$$

This suggests the **product rule for exponents.**

Product Rule for Exponents

For any positive integers m and n, $a^m \cdot a^n = a^{m+n}.$
(Keep the same base and add the exponents.)

Example: $6^2 \cdot 6^5 = 6^{2+5} = 6^7$

⚠ **CAUTION**   Do not multiply the bases when using the product rule. ***Keep the same base and add the exponents.*** For example,

$$6^2 \cdot 6^5 = 6^7, \quad \textbf{\textit{not}} \quad 36^7.$$

NOW TRY
EXERCISE 3

Use the product rule for exponents to find each product if possible.

(a) $(-5)^2(-5)^4$

(b) $y^2 \cdot y \cdot y^5$

(c) $(2x^3)(4x^7)$

(d) $2^4 \cdot 5^3$

(e) $3^2 + 3^3$

EXAMPLE 3   Using the Product Rule

Use the product rule for exponents to find each product if possible.

(a) $6^3 \cdot 6^5 = 6^{3+5} = 6^8$
  [Keep the same base.]

(b) $(-4)^7(-4)^2 = (-4)^{7+2} = (-4)^9$

(c) $x^2 \cdot x = x^2 \cdot x^1 = x^{2+1} = x^3$

(d) $m^4 m^3 m^5 = m^{4+3+5} = m^{12}$

(e) $2^3 \cdot 3^2$
  The product rule does not apply, since the bases are different.
$$2^3 \cdot 3^2 = 8 \cdot 9 = 72 \qquad \text{Evaluate } 2^3 \text{ and } 3^2. \text{ Then multiply.}$$
  [Think: $2^3 = 2 \cdot 2 \cdot 2$]   [Think: $3^2 = 3 \cdot 3$]

(f) $2^3 + 2^4$
  The product rule does not apply, since this is a *sum,* not a *product.*
$$2^3 + 2^4 = 8 + 16 = 24 \qquad \text{Evaluate } 2^3 \text{ and } 2^4. \text{ Then add.}$$

(g) $(2x^3)(3x^7)$ — [$2x^3$ means $2 \cdot x^3$ and $3x^7$ means $3 \cdot x^7$.]
$$= (2 \cdot 3) \cdot (x^3 \cdot x^7) \qquad \text{Commutative and associative properties}$$
$$= 6x^{3+7} \qquad \text{Multiply; product rule}$$
$$= 6x^{10} \qquad \text{Add.} \qquad \qquad \textit{NOW TRY}$$

⚠ **CAUTION**   Be sure that you understand the difference between *adding* and *multiplying* exponential expressions. For example, consider the following.

$$8x^3 + 5x^3 = (8 + 5)x^3 = 13x^3$$
$$(8x^3)(5x^3) = (8 \cdot 5)x^{3+3} = 40x^6$$

NOW TRY ANSWERS
3. (a) $(-5)^6$ **(b)** y^8 **(c)** $8x^{10}$
  (d) The product rule does not
  apply; 2000 **(e)** The product
  rule does not apply; 36

OBJECTIVE 3 Use the rule $(a^m)^n = a^{mn}$. Consider the following.

$$(8^3)^2 = (8^3)(8^3) = 8^{3+3} = 8^6 \qquad \text{Product rule for exponents}$$

The product of the exponents in $(8^3)^2$, $3 \cdot 2$, gives the exponent in 8^6. Also

$$(5^2)^4 = 5^2 \cdot 5^2 \cdot 5^2 \cdot 5^2 \qquad \text{Definition of exponent}$$
$$= 5^{2+2+2+2} \qquad \text{Product rule}$$
$$= 5^8, \qquad \text{Add the exponents.}$$

and $2 \cdot 4 = 8$. These examples suggest **power rule (a) for exponents.**

Power Rule (a) for Exponents

For any positive integers m and n, $\quad (a^m)^n = a^{mn}$.
(Raise a power to a power by multiplying exponents.)
Example: $\quad (3^2)^4 = 3^{2 \cdot 4} = 3^8$

NOW TRY
EXERCISE 4
Simplify.
(a) $(4^7)^5$ **(b)** $(y^4)^7$

EXAMPLE 4 Using Power Rule (a)

Use power rule (a) for exponents to simplify.

(a) $(2^5)^3 = 2^{5 \cdot 3} = 2^{15}$ **(b)** $(5^7)^2 = 5^{7(2)} = 5^{14}$ **(c)** $(x^2)^5 = x^{2(5)} = x^{10}$

NOW TRY

OBJECTIVE 4 Use the rule $(ab)^m = a^m b^m$. Consider the following.

$$(4x)^3 = (4x)(4x)(4x) \qquad \text{Definition of exponent}$$
$$= (4 \cdot 4 \cdot 4)(x \cdot x \cdot x) \qquad \text{Commutative and associative properties}$$
$$= 4^3 \cdot x^3 \qquad \text{Definition of exponent}$$

This example suggests **power rule (b) for exponents.**

Power Rule (b) for Exponents

For any positive integer m, $\quad (ab)^m = a^m b^m$.
(Raise a product to a power by raising each factor to the power.)
Example: $\quad (2p)^5 = 2^5 p^5$

EXAMPLE 5 Using Power Rule (b)

Use power rule (b) for exponents to simplify.

(a) $(3xy)^2$

$\qquad = 3^2 x^2 y^2 \qquad$ Power rule (b)

$\qquad = 9x^2 y^2 \qquad 3^2 = 3 \cdot 3 = 9$

(b) $5(pq)^2$

$\qquad = 5(p^2 q^2) \qquad$ Power rule (b)

$\qquad = 5p^2 q^2 \qquad$ Multiply.

(c) $3(2m^2 p^3)^4$

$\qquad = 3[2^4 (m^2)^4 (p^3)^4] \qquad$ Power rule (b)

$\qquad = 3 \cdot 2^4 m^8 p^{12} \qquad$ Power rule (a)

$\qquad = 48m^8 p^{12} \qquad 3 \cdot 2^4 = 3 \cdot 16 = 48$

NOW TRY ANSWERS
4. **(a)** 4^{35} **(b)** y^{28}

NOW TRY
EXERCISE 5
Simplify.

(a) $(-5ab)^3$ **(b)** $3(4t^3p^5)^2$

(d) $(-5^6)^3$

$= (-1 \cdot 5^6)^3$ $-a = -1 \cdot a$

$= (-1)^3 \cdot (5^6)^3$ Power rule (b)

$\boxed{\text{Raise } -1 \text{ to the designated power.}}$

$= -1 \cdot 5^{18}$ Power rule (a)

$= -5^{18}$

NOW TRY

⚠ **CAUTION** *Power rule (b) does not apply to a sum.* For example,

$$(4x)^2 = 4^2x^2, \quad \text{but} \quad (4+x)^2 \neq 4^2 + x^2.$$

OBJECTIVE 5 **Use the rule** $\left(\frac{a}{b}\right)^m = \frac{a^m}{b^m}$. Since the quotient $\frac{a}{b}$ can be written as $a\left(\frac{1}{b}\right)$, we use this fact and power rule (b) to get **power rule (c) for exponents.**

Power Rule (c) for Exponents

For any positive integer m, $\left(\dfrac{a}{b}\right)^m = \dfrac{a^m}{b^m}$ $(b \neq 0)$.

(Raise a quotient to a power by raising both numerator and denominator to the power.)

Example: $\left(\dfrac{5}{3}\right)^2 = \dfrac{5^2}{3^2}$

NOW TRY
EXERCISE 6
Simplify.

(a) $\left(\dfrac{p}{q}\right)^5$ **(b)** $\left(\dfrac{1}{4}\right)^3$

$(q \neq 0)$

EXAMPLE 6 Using Power Rule (c)

Use power rule (c) for exponents to simplify.

(a) $\left(\dfrac{2}{3}\right)^5 = \dfrac{2^5}{3^5} = \dfrac{32}{243}$ **(b)** $\left(\dfrac{m}{n}\right)^3 = \dfrac{m^3}{n^3}$ $(n \neq 0)$

(c) $\left(\dfrac{1}{5}\right)^4 = \dfrac{1^4}{5^4} = \dfrac{1}{5^4} = \dfrac{1}{625}$ $1^4 = 1 \cdot 1 \cdot 1 \cdot 1 = 1$

NOW TRY

NOTE In **Example 6(c),** we used the fact that $1^4 = 1$.

In general, $1^n = 1$, for any integer n.

Rules for Exponents

For positive integers m and n, the following are true.

		Examples
Product rule	$a^m \cdot a^n = a^{m+n}$	$6^2 \cdot 6^5 = 6^{2+5} = 6^7$
Power rules (a)	$(a^m)^n = a^{mn}$	$(3^2)^4 = 3^{2 \cdot 4} = 3^8$
(b)	$(ab)^m = a^m b^m$	$(2p)^5 = 2^5 p^5$
(c)	$\left(\dfrac{a}{b}\right)^m = \dfrac{a^m}{b^m}$ $(b \neq 0)$	$\left(\dfrac{5}{3}\right)^2 = \dfrac{5^2}{3^2}$

OBJECTIVE 6 Use combinations of rules.

NOW TRY
EXERCISE 7

Simplify.

(a) $\left(\dfrac{3}{5}\right)^3 \cdot 3^2$ **(b)** $(8k)^5(8k)^4$

(c) $(x^4y)^5(-2x^2y^5)^3$

EXAMPLE 7 Using Combinations of Rules

Simplify.

(a) $\left(\dfrac{2}{3}\right)^2 \cdot 2^3$

$= \dfrac{2^2}{3^2} \cdot \dfrac{2^3}{1}$ Power rule (c)

$= \dfrac{2^2 \cdot 2^3}{3^2 \cdot 1}$ Multiply fractions.

$= \dfrac{2^{2+3}}{3^2}$ Product rule

$= \dfrac{2^5}{3^2},$ or $\dfrac{32}{9}$

(b) $(5x)^3(5x)^4$

$= (5x)^7$ Product rule

$= 5^7x^7$ Power rule (b)

(c) $(2x^2y^3)^4(3xy^2)^3$

$= 2^4(x^2)^4(y^3)^4 \cdot 3^3x^3(y^2)^3$ Power rule (b)

$= 2^4x^8y^{12} \cdot 3^3x^3y^6$ Power rule (a)

$= 2^4 \cdot 3^3x^8x^3y^{12}y^6$ Commutative and associative properties

$= 16 \cdot 27x^{11}y^{18},$ or $432x^{11}y^{18}$ Product rule; multiply.

Notice that $(2x^2y^3)^4$ means $2^4x^{2 \cdot 4}y^{3 \cdot 4}$, **not** $(2 \cdot 4)x^{2 \cdot 4}y^{3 \cdot 4}$.

(d) $(-x^3y)^2(-x^5y^4)^3$ ▷ Don't forget each factor of -1.

$= (-1 \cdot x^3y)^2(-1 \cdot x^5y^4)^3$ $-a = -1 \cdot a$

$= (-1)^2(x^3)^2y^2 \cdot (-1)^3(x^5)^3(y^4)^3$ Power rule (b)

$= (-1)^2(x^6)(y^2)(-1)^3(x^{15})(y^{12})$ Power rule (a)

$= (-1)^5(x^{21})(y^{14})$ Product rule

$= -x^{21}y^{14}$ Simplify.   **NOW TRY**

⚠ **CAUTION** Be aware of the distinction between $(2y)^3$ and $2y^3$.

$(2y)^3 = 2y \cdot 2y \cdot 2y = 8y^3,$ while $2y^3 = 2 \cdot y \cdot y \cdot y.$

OBJECTIVE 7 Use the rules for exponents in a geometry application.

EXAMPLE 8 Using Area Formulas

Find an expression that represents the area in **(a)** FIGURE 1 and **(b)** FIGURE 2.

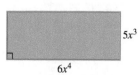

$5x^3$

$6x^4$

FIGURE 1

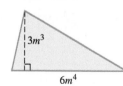

$3m^3$

$6m^4$

FIGURE 2

Assume $x > 0, m > 0.$

NOW TRY ANSWERS

7. **(a)** $\frac{243}{125}$ **(b)** 8^9k^9

  (c) $-8x^{26}y^{20}$

NOW TRY
EXERCISE 8
Write an expression that represents the area of the figure. Assume $x > 0$.

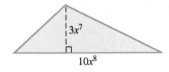

NOW TRY ANSWER
8. $15x^{15}$

(a) For **FIGURE 1**, use the formula for the area of a rectangle, $\mathcal{A} = LW$.

$$\mathcal{A} = (6x^4)(5x^3) \qquad \text{Area formula}$$

$$\mathcal{A} = 6 \cdot 5 \cdot x^{4+3} \qquad \text{Commutative property; product rule}$$

$$\mathcal{A} = 30x^7 \qquad \text{Multiply. Add the exponents.}$$

(b) **FIGURE 2** is a triangle with base $6m^4$ and height $3m^3$.

$$\mathcal{A} = \frac{1}{2}bh \qquad \text{Area formula}$$

$$\mathcal{A} = \frac{1}{2}(6m^4)(3m^3) \qquad \text{Substitute.}$$

$$\mathcal{A} = \frac{1}{2}(18m^7), \quad \text{or} \quad 9m^7 \qquad \text{Product rule; multiply.} \quad \text{NOW TRY}$$

4.1 EXERCISES

MyMathLab | Math XL PRACTICE | WATCH | DOWNLOAD | READ | REVIEW

🌐 *Complete solution available on the Video Resources on DVD*

Concept Check *Decide whether each statement is* true *or* false*. If false, tell why.*

1. $3^3 = 9$　　　　**2.** $(-3)^4 = 3^4$　　　　**3.** $(x^2)^3 = x^5$　　　　**4.** $\left(\dfrac{1}{5}\right)^2 = \dfrac{1}{5^2}$

Write each expression by using exponents. ***See Example 1.***

5. $w \cdot w \cdot w \cdot w \cdot w \cdot w$ 　　　　　　　　**6.** $t \cdot t \cdot t \cdot t \cdot t \cdot t \cdot t \cdot t$

🌐 **7.** $\left(\dfrac{1}{2}\right)\left(\dfrac{1}{2}\right)\left(\dfrac{1}{2}\right)\left(\dfrac{1}{2}\right)\left(\dfrac{1}{2}\right)\left(\dfrac{1}{2}\right)$ 　　**8.** $\left(\dfrac{1}{4}\right)\left(\dfrac{1}{4}\right)\left(\dfrac{1}{4}\right)\left(\dfrac{1}{4}\right)\left(\dfrac{1}{4}\right)$

9. $(-4)(-4)(-4)(-4)$ 　　　　　　　**10.** $(-3)(-3)(-3)(-3)(-3)(-3)$

11. $(-7y)(-7y)(-7y)(-7y)$ 　　　　　**12.** $(-8p)(-8p)(-8p)(-8p)(-8p)$

✏ **13.** Explain how the expressions $(-3)^4$ and -3^4 are different.

✏ **14.** Explain how the expressions $(5x)^3$ and $5x^3$ are different.

Identify the base and the exponent for each exponential expression. In Exercises 15–18, also evaluate each expression. ***See Example 2.***

🌐 **15.** 3^5 　　　　**16.** 2^7 　　　　🌐 **17.** $(-3)^5$ 　　　　**18.** $(-2)^7$

19. $(-6x)^4$ 　　**20.** $(-8x)^4$ 　　**21.** $-6x^4$ 　　　**22.** $-8x^4$

✏ **23.** Explain why the product rule does not apply to the expression $5^2 + 5^3$. Then evaluate the expression by finding the individual powers and adding the results.

✏ **24.** Repeat **Exercise 23** for the expression $(-4)^3 + (-4)^4$.

Use the product rule, if possible, to simplify each expression. Write each answer in exponential form. ***See Example 3.***

🌐 **25.** $5^2 \cdot 5^6$ 　　　　　**26.** $3^6 \cdot 3^7$ 　　　　　**27.** $4^2 \cdot 4^7 \cdot 4^3$

28. $5^3 \cdot 5^8 \cdot 5^2$ 　　　**29.** $(-7)^3(-7)^6$ 　　　**30.** $(-9)^8(-9)^5$

🌐 **31.** $t^3 \cdot t^8 \cdot t^{13}$ 　　　**32.** $n^5 \cdot n^6 \cdot n^9$ 　　　**33.** $(-8r^4)(7r^3)$

34. $(10a^7)(-4a^3)$ 　　🌐 **35.** $(-6p^5)(-7p^5)$ 　　**36.** $(-5w^8)(-9w^8)$

37. $(5x^2)(-2x^3)(3x^4)$ 　　**38.** $(12y^3)(4y)(-3y^5)$ 　🌐 **39.** $3^8 + 3^9$

40. $4^{12} + 4^5$ 　　　　　**41.** $5^8 \cdot 3^9$ 　　　　　**42.** $6^3 \cdot 8^9$

*Use the power rules for exponents to simplify each expression. Write each answer in exponential form. **See Examples 4–6.***

43. $(4^3)^2$ **44.** $(8^3)^6$ **45.** $(t^4)^5$ **46.** $(y^6)^5$

47. $(7r)^3$ **48.** $(11x)^4$ **49.** $(5xy)^5$ **50.** $(9pq)^6$

51. $(-5^2)^6$ **52.** $(-9^4)^8$ **53.** $(-8^3)^5$ **54.** $(-7^5)^7$

55. $8(qr)^3$ **56.** $4(vw)^5$ **57.** $\left(\dfrac{9}{5}\right)^8$

58. $\left(\dfrac{12}{7}\right)^3$ **59.** $\left(\dfrac{1}{2}\right)^3$ **60.** $\left(\dfrac{1}{3}\right)^5$

61. $\left(\dfrac{a}{b}\right)^3$ $(b \neq 0)$ **62.** $\left(\dfrac{r}{t}\right)^4$ $(t \neq 0)$ **63.** $\left(\dfrac{x}{2}\right)^3$

64. *Concept Check*   Will $(-a)^n$ ever equal a^n? If so, when?

*Simplify each expression. **See Example 7.***

65. $\left(\dfrac{5}{2}\right)^3 \cdot \left(\dfrac{5}{2}\right)^2$ **66.** $\left(\dfrac{3}{4}\right)^5 \cdot \left(\dfrac{3}{4}\right)^6$ **67.** $\left(\dfrac{9}{8}\right)^3 \cdot 9^2$

68. $\left(\dfrac{8}{5}\right)^4 \cdot 8^3$ **69.** $(2x)^9(2x)^3$ **70.** $(6y)^5(6y)^8$

71. $(-6p)^4(-6p)$ **72.** $(-13q)^3(-13q)$ **73.** $(6x^2y^3)^5$

74. $(5r^5t^6)^7$ **75.** $(x^2)^3(x^3)^5$ **76.** $(y^4)^5(y^3)^5$

77. $(2w^2x^3y)^2(x^4y)^5$ **78.** $(3x^4y^2z)^3(yz^4)^5$ **79.** $(-r^4s)^2(-r^2s^3)^5$

80. $(-ts^6)^4(-t^3s^5)^3$ **81.** $\left(\dfrac{5a^2b^5}{c^6}\right)^3$ $(c \neq 0)$ **82.** $\left(\dfrac{6x^3y^9}{z^5}\right)^4$ $(z \neq 0)$

83. *Concept Check*   A student simplified $(10^2)^3$ as 1000^6. *WHAT WENT WRONG?*

84. Explain why $(3x^2y^3)^4$ is *not* equivalent to $(3 \cdot 4)x^8y^{12}$.

*Find an expression that represents the area of each figure. **See Example 8.** (If necessary, refer to the formulas on the inside covers. The ⌐ in the figures indicate 90° right angles.)*

85.

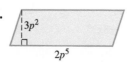

86.

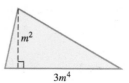

87.

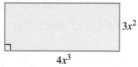

88.

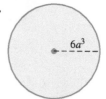

Find an expression that represents the volume of each figure. (If necessary, refer to the formulas on the inside covers.)

89.

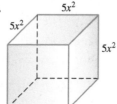

90.

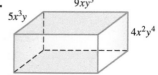

✎ **91.** Assume that a is a number greater than 1. Arrange the following terms in order from least to greatest: $-(-a)^3, -a^3, (-a)^4, -a^4$. Explain how you decided on the order.

✎ **92.** Devise a rule that tells whether an exponential expression with a negative base is positive or negative.

Compound interest is interest paid on the principal and the interest earned earlier. The formula for compound interest, which involves an exponential expression, is

$$A = P(1 + r)^n,$$

where A is the amount accumulated from a principal of P dollars left untouched for n years with an annual interest rate r (expressed as a decimal).

In Exercises 93–96, use the preceding formula and a calculator to find A to the nearest cent.

93. $P = \$250, r = 0.04, n = 5$

94. $P = \$400, r = 0.04, n = 3$

95. $P = \$1500, r = 0.035, n = 6$

96. $P = \$2000, r = 0.025, n = 4$

PREVIEW EXERCISES

*Give the reciprocal of each number. **See Section 1.1.***

97. 9

98. -3

99. $-\dfrac{1}{8}$

100. 0.5

*Perform each subtraction. **See Section 1.5.***

101. $8 - (-4)$

102. $-4 - 8$

103. Subtract -6 from -3.

104. Subtract -3 from -6.

4.2 Integer Exponents and the Quotient Rule

OBJECTIVES

1 Use 0 as an exponent.

2 Use negative numbers as exponents.

3 Use the quotient rule for exponents.

4 Use combinations of rules.

Consider the following list.

$$2^4 = 16$$
$$2^3 = 8$$
$$2^2 = 4$$

Each time we reduce the exponent by 1, the value is divided by 2 (the base). Using this pattern, we can continue the list to lesser and lesser integer exponents.

$$2^1 = 2$$
$$2^0 = 1$$
$$2^{-1} = \tfrac{1}{2}$$
$$2^{-2} = \tfrac{1}{4}$$
$$2^{-3} = \tfrac{1}{8}$$

From the preceding list, it appears that we should define 2^0 as 1 and bases raised to negative exponents as reciprocals of those bases.

OBJECTIVE 1 Use 0 as an exponent. The definitions of 0 and negative exponents must satisfy the rules for exponents from **Section 4.1.** For example, if $6^0 = 1$, then

$$6^0 \cdot 6^2 = 1 \cdot 6^2 = 6^2 \qquad \text{and} \qquad 6^0 \cdot 6^2 = 6^{0+2} = 6^2,$$

so that the product rule is satisfied. Check that the power rules are also valid for a 0 exponent. Thus, we define a 0 exponent as follows.

Zero Exponent

For any nonzero real number a, $\quad a^0 = 1$.

Example: $\quad 17^0 = 1$

**NOW TRY
EXERCISE 1**

Evaluate.

(a) 6^0

(b) -12^0

(c) $(-12x)^0 \quad (x \neq 0)$

(d) $14^0 - 12^0$

EXAMPLE 1 Using Zero Exponents

Evaluate.

(a) $60^0 = 1$

(b) $(-60)^0 = 1$

(c) $-60^0 = -(1) = -1$

(d) $y^0 = 1 \quad (y \neq 0)$

(e) $6y^0 = 6(1) = 6 \quad (y \neq 0)$

(f) $(6y)^0 = 1 \quad (y \neq 0)$

(g) $8^0 + 11^0 = 1 + 1 = 2$

(h) $-8^0 - 11^0 = -1 - 1 = -2$ NOW TRY

⚠ **CAUTION** Look again at **Examples 1(b) and 1(c).** In $(-60)^0$, the base is -60, and since any nonzero base raised to the 0 exponent is 1, $(-60)^0 = 1$. In -60^0, which can be written $-(60)^0$, the base is 60, so $-60^0 = -1$.

OBJECTIVE 2 Use negative numbers as exponents. From the lists at the beginning of this section, since $2^{-2} = \frac{1}{4}$ and $2^{-3} = \frac{1}{8}$, we can deduce that 2^{-n} should equal $\frac{1}{2^n}$. Is the product rule valid in such cases? For example,

$$6^{-2} \cdot 6^2 = 6^{-2+2} = 6^0 = 1.$$

The expression 6^{-2} behaves as if it were the reciprocal of 6^2, since their product is 1. The reciprocal of 6^2 is also $\frac{1}{6^2}$, leading us to define 6^{-2} as $\frac{1}{6^2}$.

Negative Exponents

For any nonzero real number a and any integer n, $\quad a^{-n} = \dfrac{1}{a^n}$.

Example: $\quad 3^{-2} = \dfrac{1}{3^2}$

By definition, a^{-n} and a^n are reciprocals, since

$$a^n \cdot a^{-n} = a^n \cdot \frac{1}{a^n} = 1.$$

Because $1^n = 1$, the definition of a^{-n} can also be written

$$a^{-n} = \frac{1}{a^n} = \frac{1^n}{a^n} = \left(\frac{1}{a}\right)^n.$$

NOW TRY ANSWERS
1. (a) 1 **(b)** -1 **(c)** 1 **(d)** 0

For example, $\qquad 6^{-3} = \left(\dfrac{1}{6}\right)^3 \quad$ and $\quad \left(\dfrac{1}{3}\right)^{-2} = 3^2.$

NOW TRY
EXERCISE 2

Simplify.

(a) 2^{-3} **(b)** $\left(\dfrac{1}{7}\right)^{-2}$

(c) $\left(\dfrac{3}{2}\right)^{-4}$ **(d)** $3^{-2} + 4^{-2}$

(e) p^{-4} $(p \neq 0)$

EXAMPLE 2 Using Negative Exponents

Simplify by writing with positive exponents. Assume that all variables represent nonzero real numbers.

(a) $3^{-2} = \dfrac{1}{3^2} = \dfrac{1}{9}$

(b) $5^{-3} = \dfrac{1}{5^3} = \dfrac{1}{125}$

(c) $\left(\dfrac{1}{2}\right)^{-3} = 2^3 = 8$ $\frac{1}{2}$ and 2 are reciprocals.

Notice that we can change the base to its reciprocal if we also change the sign of the exponent.

(d) $\left(\dfrac{2}{5}\right)^{-4} = \left(\dfrac{5}{2}\right)^4 = \dfrac{625}{16}$

$\frac{2}{5}$ and $\frac{5}{2}$ are reciprocals.

(e) $\left(\dfrac{4}{3}\right)^{-5} = \left(\dfrac{3}{4}\right)^5 = \dfrac{243}{1024}$

(f) $4^{-1} - 2^{-1} = \dfrac{1}{4} - \dfrac{1}{2} = \dfrac{1}{4} - \dfrac{2}{4} = -\dfrac{1}{4}$ Apply the exponents first, and then subtract.

Remember to find a common denominator.

(g) $p^{-2} = \dfrac{1}{p^2}$

(h) $\dfrac{1}{x^{-4}} = \dfrac{1^{-4}}{x^{-4}}$

It is convenient to write 1 as 1^{-4} here, because -4 is the exponent in the denominator.

$= \left(\dfrac{1}{x}\right)^{-4}$ Power rule (c)

$= x^4$ $\frac{1}{x}$ and x are reciprocals.

(i) $x^3 y^{-4} = \dfrac{x^3}{y^4}$

NOW TRY

Consider the following.

$$\dfrac{2^{-3}}{3^{-4}} = \dfrac{\frac{1}{2^3}}{\frac{1}{3^4}} = \dfrac{1}{2^3} \div \dfrac{1}{3^4} = \dfrac{1}{2^3} \cdot \dfrac{3^4}{1} = \dfrac{3^4}{2^3}$$ To divide by a fraction, multiply by its reciprocal.

Therefore, $\dfrac{2^{-3}}{3^{-4}} = \dfrac{3^4}{2^3}.$

Changing from Negative to Positive Exponents

For any nonzero numbers a and b and any integers m and n, the following are true.

$$\dfrac{a^{-m}}{b^{-n}} = \dfrac{b^n}{a^m} \quad \text{and} \quad \left(\dfrac{a}{b}\right)^{-m} = \left(\dfrac{b}{a}\right)^m$$

Examples: $\dfrac{3^{-5}}{2^{-4}} = \dfrac{2^4}{3^5}$ and $\left(\dfrac{4}{5}\right)^{-3} = \left(\dfrac{5}{4}\right)^3$

NOW TRY ANSWERS

2. (a) $\dfrac{1}{8}$ **(b)** 49 **(c)** $\dfrac{16}{81}$

(d) $\dfrac{25}{144}$ **(e)** $\dfrac{1}{p^4}$

NOW TRY
EXERCISE 3
Simplify by writing with positive exponents. Assume that all variables represent nonzero real numbers.

(a) $\dfrac{5^{-3}}{6^{-2}}$ **(b)** $m^2 n^{-4}$

(c) $\dfrac{x^2 y^{-3}}{5z^{-4}}$

EXAMPLE 3   Changing from Negative to Positive Exponents

Simplify by writing with positive exponents. Assume that all variables represent nonzero real numbers.

(a) $\dfrac{4^{-2}}{5^{-3}} = \dfrac{5^3}{4^2} = \dfrac{125}{16}$

(b) $\dfrac{m^{-5}}{p^{-1}} = \dfrac{p^1}{m^5} = \dfrac{p}{m^5}$

(c) $\dfrac{a^{-2}b}{3d^{-3}} = \dfrac{bd^3}{3a^2}$ Notice that b in the numerator and 3 in the denominator are not affected.

(d) $\left(\dfrac{x}{2y}\right)^{-4} = \left(\dfrac{2y}{x}\right)^4 = \dfrac{2^4 y^4}{x^4} = \dfrac{16y^4}{x^4}$ NOW TRY

⚠ **CAUTION**   Be careful. We cannot use this rule to change negative exponents to positive exponents if the exponents occur in a *sum or difference* of terms. For example,

$$\dfrac{5^{-2} + 3^{-1}}{7 - 2^{-3}} \quad \text{would be written with positive exponents as} \quad \dfrac{\dfrac{1}{5^2} + \dfrac{1}{3}}{7 - \dfrac{1}{2^3}}.$$

OBJECTIVE 3   Use the quotient rule for exponents. Consider the following.

$$\dfrac{6^5}{6^3} = \dfrac{6 \cdot 6 \cdot 6 \cdot 6 \cdot 6}{6 \cdot 6 \cdot 6} = 6^2$$

The difference between the exponents, $5 - 3 = 2$, is the exponent in the quotient.

Also, $\dfrac{6^2}{6^4} = \dfrac{6 \cdot 6}{6 \cdot 6 \cdot 6 \cdot 6} = \dfrac{1}{6^2} = 6^{-2}.$

Here, $2 - 4 = -2$. These examples suggest the **quotient rule for exponents.**

Quotient Rule for Exponents

For any nonzero real number a and any integers m and n,

$$\dfrac{a^m}{a^n} = a^{m-n}.$$

(Keep the same base and subtract the exponents.)

Example: $\dfrac{5^8}{5^4} = 5^{8-4} = 5^4$

⚠ **CAUTION**   A common **error** is to write $\dfrac{5^8}{5^4} = 1^{8-4} = 1^4$. By the quotient rule, the quotient must have the *same base*, 5, just as in the product rule.

$$\dfrac{5^8}{5^4} = 5^{8-4} = 5^4$$

If you are not sure, use the definition of an exponent to write out the factors.

$$\dfrac{5^8}{5^4} = \dfrac{5 \cdot 5 \cdot 5 \cdot 5 \cdot 5 \cdot 5 \cdot 5 \cdot 5}{5 \cdot 5 \cdot 5 \cdot 5} = 5^4$$

NOW TRY ANSWERS
3. (a) $\dfrac{6^2}{5^3}$, or $\dfrac{36}{125}$ (b) $\dfrac{m^2}{n^4}$
(c) $\dfrac{x^2 z^4}{5y^3}$

NOW TRY
EXERCISE 4

Simplify by writing with positive exponents. Assume that all variables represent nonzero real numbers.

(a) $\dfrac{6^3}{6^4}$ **(b)** $\dfrac{t^4}{t^{-5}}$

(c) $\dfrac{(p+q)^{-3}}{(p+q)^{-7}}$ $(p \neq -q)$

(d) $\dfrac{5^2 x y^{-3}}{3^{-1} x^{-2} y^2}$

EXAMPLE 4 Using the Quotient Rule

Simplify by writing with positive exponents. Assume that all variables represent nonzero real numbers.

(a) $\dfrac{5^8}{5^6} = 5^{8-6} = 5^2 = 25$

> Keep the same base.

(b) $\dfrac{4^2}{4^9} = 4^{2-9} = 4^{-7} = \dfrac{1}{4^7}$

(c) $\dfrac{5^{-3}}{5^{-7}} = 5^{-3-(-7)} = 5^4 = 625$

> Be careful with signs.

(d) $\dfrac{q^5}{q^{-3}} = q^{5-(-3)} = q^8$

(e) $\dfrac{3^2 x^5}{3^4 x^3}$

$= \dfrac{3^2}{3^4} \cdot \dfrac{x^5}{x^3}$

$= 3^{2-4} \cdot x^{5-3}$ Quotient rule

$= 3^{-2} x^2$ Subtract.

$= \dfrac{x^2}{3^2}$, or $\dfrac{x^2}{9}$

(f) $\dfrac{(m+n)^{-2}}{(m+n)^{-4}}$

$= (m+n)^{-2-(-4)}$

$= (m+n)^{-2+4}$

$= (m+n)^2, \quad m \neq -n$

(g) $\dfrac{7 x^{-3} y^2}{2^{-1} x^2 y^{-5}}$

$= \dfrac{7 \cdot 2^1 y^2 y^5}{x^2 x^3}$ Negative-to-positive rule

$= \dfrac{14 y^7}{x^5}$ Product rule

NOW TRY

The definitions and rules for exponents are summarized here.

Definitions and Rules for Exponents

For any integers m and n, the following are true.		**Examples**
Product rule	$a^m \cdot a^n = a^{m+n}$	$7^4 \cdot 7^5 = 7^{4+5} = 7^9$
Zero exponent	$a^0 = 1 \quad (a \neq 0)$	$(-3)^0 = 1$
Negative exponent	$a^{-n} = \dfrac{1}{a^n} \quad (a \neq 0)$	$5^{-3} = \dfrac{1}{5^3}$
Quotient rule	$\dfrac{a^m}{a^n} = a^{m-n} \quad (a \neq 0)$	$\dfrac{2^2}{2^5} = 2^{2-5} = 2^{-3} = \dfrac{1}{2^3}$
Power rule (a)	$(a^m)^n = a^{mn}$	$(4^2)^3 = 4^{2 \cdot 3} = 4^6$
Power rule (b)	$(ab)^m = a^m b^m$	$(3k)^4 = 3^4 k^4$
Power rule (c)	$\left(\dfrac{a}{b}\right)^m = \dfrac{a^m}{b^m} \quad (b \neq 0)$	$\left(\dfrac{2}{3}\right)^2 = \dfrac{2^2}{3^2}$
Negative-to-positive rules	$\dfrac{a^{-m}}{b^{-n}} = \dfrac{b^n}{a^m} \quad (a \neq 0, b \neq 0)$	$\dfrac{2^{-4}}{5^{-3}} = \dfrac{5^3}{2^4}$
	$\left(\dfrac{a}{b}\right)^{-m} = \left(\dfrac{b}{a}\right)^m$	$\left(\dfrac{4}{7}\right)^{-2} = \left(\dfrac{7}{4}\right)^2$

NOW TRY ANSWERS

4. (a) $\dfrac{1}{6}$ **(b)** t^9

(c) $(p+q)^4$ **(d)** $\dfrac{75 x^3}{y^5}$

NOW TRY
EXERCISE 5

Simplify. Assume that all variables represent nonzero real numbers.

(a) $\dfrac{3^{15}}{(3^3)^4}$ **(b)** $(4t)^5(4t)^{-3}$

(c) $\left(\dfrac{7y^4}{10}\right)^{-3}$ **(d)** $\dfrac{(a^2b^{-2}c)^{-3}}{(2ab^3c^{-4})^5}$

OBJECTIVE 4 Use combinations of rules.

EXAMPLE 5 Using Combinations of Rules

Simplify. Assume that all variables represent nonzero real numbers.

(a) $\dfrac{(4^2)^3}{4^5}$

$= \dfrac{4^6}{4^5}$ Power rule (a)

$= 4^{6-5}$ Quotient rule

$= 4^1$

$= 4$

(b) $(2x)^3(2x)^2$

$= (2x)^5$ Product rule

$= 2^5x^5$ Power rule (b)

$= 32x^5$

(c) $\left(\dfrac{2x^3}{5}\right)^{-4}$

$= \left(\dfrac{5}{2x^3}\right)^4$ Negative-to-positive rule

$= \dfrac{5^4}{2^4x^{12}}$ Power rules (a)–(c)

$= \dfrac{625}{16x^{12}}$

(d) $\left(\dfrac{3x^{-2}}{4^{-1}y^3}\right)^{-3}$

$= \dfrac{3^{-3}x^6}{4^3y^{-9}}$ Power rules (a)–(c)

$= \dfrac{x^6y^9}{4^3 \cdot 3^3}$ Negative-to-positive rule

$= \dfrac{x^6y^9}{1728}$

(e) $\dfrac{(4m)^{-3}}{(3m)^{-4}}$

$= \dfrac{4^{-3}m^{-3}}{3^{-4}m^{-4}}$ Power rule (b)

$= \dfrac{3^4m^4}{4^3m^3}$ Negative-to-positive rule

$= \dfrac{3^4m^{4-3}}{4^3}$ Quotient rule

$= \dfrac{3^4m}{4^3}$, or $\dfrac{81m}{64}$

NOW TRY

NOW TRY ANSWERS
5. (a) 3^3, or 27   **(b)** $16t^2$
    (c) $\dfrac{1000}{343y^{12}}$ **(d)** $\dfrac{c^{17}}{32a^{11}b^9}$

4.2 EXERCISES

MyMathLab   Math XL PRACTICE   WATCH   DOWNLOAD   READ   REVIEW

🌐 *Complete solution available on the Video Resources on DVD*

Decide whether each expression is equal to 0, 1, or −1. See Example 1.

🌐 **1.** 9^0 **2.** 3^0 **3.** $(-2)^0$ **4.** $(-12)^0$

5. -8^0 **6.** -6^0 **7.** $-(-6)^0$ **8.** $-(-13)^0$

9. $(-4)^0 - 4^0$ **10.** $(-11)^0 - 11^0$ **11.** $\dfrac{0^{10}}{12^0}$ **12.** $\dfrac{0^5}{2^0}$

13. $8^0 - 12^0$

14. $6^0 - 13^0$

15. $\dfrac{0^2}{2^0 + 0^2}$

16. $\dfrac{2^0}{0^2 + 2^0}$

Concept Check In Exercises 17 and 18, match each expression in Column I with the equivalent expression in Column II. Choices in Column II may be used once, more than once, or not at all. (In Exercise 17, $x \neq 0$.)

I	II		I	II
17. (a) x^0	**A.** 0		**18. (a)** -2^{-4}	**A.** 8
(b) $-x^0$	**B.** 1		**(b)** $(-2)^{-4}$	**B.** 16
(c) $7x^0$	**C.** -1		**(c)** 2^{-4}	**C.** $-\dfrac{1}{16}$
(d) $(7x)^0$	**D.** 7		**(d)** $\dfrac{1}{2^{-4}}$	**D.** -8
(e) $-7x^0$	**E.** -7		**(e)** $\dfrac{1}{-2^{-4}}$	**E.** -16
(f) $(-7x)^0$	**F.** $\dfrac{1}{7}$		**(f)** $\dfrac{1}{(-2)^{-4}}$	**F.** $\dfrac{1}{16}$

Evaluate each expression. **See Examples 1 and 2.**

19. $6^0 + 8^0$

20. $4^0 + 2^0$

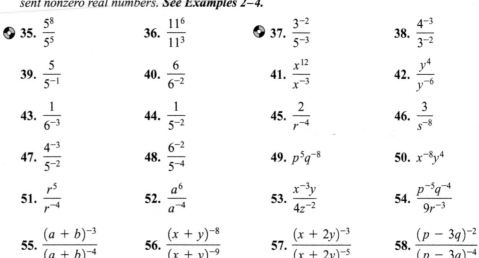 **21.** 4^{-3}

22. 5^{-4}

23. $\left(\dfrac{1}{2}\right)^{-4}$

24. $\left(\dfrac{1}{3}\right)^{-3}$

25. $\left(\dfrac{6}{7}\right)^{-2}$

26. $\left(\dfrac{2}{3}\right)^{-3}$

27. $(-3)^{-4}$

28. $(-4)^{-3}$

29. $5^{-1} + 3^{-1}$

30. $6^{-1} + 2^{-1}$

31. $3^{-2} - 2^{-1}$

32. $6^{-2} - 3^{-1}$

33. $\left(\dfrac{1}{2}\right)^{-1} + \left(\dfrac{2}{3}\right)^{-1}$

34. $\left(\dfrac{1}{3}\right)^{-1} + \left(\dfrac{4}{3}\right)^{-1}$

Simplify by writing each expression with positive exponents. Assume that all variables represent nonzero real numbers. **See Examples 2–4.**

35. $\dfrac{5^8}{5^5}$

36. $\dfrac{11^6}{11^3}$

37. $\dfrac{3^{-2}}{5^{-3}}$

38. $\dfrac{4^{-3}}{3^{-2}}$

39. $\dfrac{5}{5^{-1}}$

40. $\dfrac{6}{6^{-2}}$

41. $\dfrac{x^{12}}{x^{-3}}$

42. $\dfrac{y^4}{y^{-6}}$

43. $\dfrac{1}{6^{-3}}$

44. $\dfrac{1}{5^{-2}}$

45. $\dfrac{2}{r^{-4}}$

46. $\dfrac{3}{s^{-8}}$

47. $\dfrac{4^{-3}}{5^{-2}}$

48. $\dfrac{6^{-2}}{5^{-4}}$

49. $p^5 q^{-8}$

50. $x^{-8} y^4$

51. $\dfrac{r^5}{r^{-4}}$

52. $\dfrac{a^6}{a^{-4}}$

53. $\dfrac{x^{-3} y}{4z^{-2}}$

54. $\dfrac{p^{-5} q^{-4}}{9r^{-3}}$

55. $\dfrac{(a+b)^{-3}}{(a+b)^{-4}}$

56. $\dfrac{(x+y)^{-8}}{(x+y)^{-9}}$

57. $\dfrac{(x+2y)^{-3}}{(x+2y)^{-5}}$

58. $\dfrac{(p-3q)^{-2}}{(p-3q)^{-4}}$

FOR INDIVIDUAL OR GROUP WORK

In **Objective 1,** we showed how 6^0 acts as 1 when it is applied to the product rule, thus motivating the definition of 0 as an exponent. We can also use the quotient rule to motivate this definition. **Work Exercises 59–62 in order.**

59. Consider the expression $\frac{25}{25}$. What is its simplest form?

60. Because $25 = 5^2$, the expression $\frac{25}{25}$ can be written as the quotient of powers of 5. Write the expression in this way.

61. Apply the quotient rule for exponents to the expression you wrote in **Exercise 60.** Give the answer as a power of 5.

62. Your answers in **Exercises 59 and 61** must be equal because they both represent $\frac{25}{25}$. Write this equality. What definition does this result support?

Simplify by writing each expression with positive exponents. Assume that all variables represent nonzero real numbers. **See Example 5.**

63. $\dfrac{(7^4)^3}{7^9}$ **64.** $\dfrac{(5^3)^2}{5^2}$ **65.** $x^{-3} \cdot x^5 \cdot x^{-4}$ **66.** $y^{-8} \cdot y^5 \cdot y^{-2}$

67. $\dfrac{(3x)^{-2}}{(4x)^{-3}}$ **68.** $\dfrac{(2y)^{-3}}{(5y)^{-4}}$ ◉ **69.** $\left(\dfrac{x^{-1}y}{z^2}\right)^{-2}$ **70.** $\left(\dfrac{p^{-4}q}{r^{-3}}\right)^{-3}$

71. $(6x)^4(6x)^{-3}$ **72.** $(10y)^9(10y)^{-8}$ **73.** $\dfrac{(m^7n)^{-2}}{m^{-4}n^3}$ **74.** $\dfrac{(m^8n^{-4})^2}{m^{-2}n^5}$

75. $\dfrac{(x^{-1}y^2z)^{-2}}{(x^{-3}y^3z)^{-1}}$ **76.** $\dfrac{(a^{-2}b^{-3}c^{-4})^{-5}}{(a^2b^3c^4)^{-4}}$ **77.** $\left(\dfrac{xy^{-2}}{x^2y}\right)^{-3}$ **78.** $\left(\dfrac{wz^{-5}}{w^{-3}z}\right)^{-2}$

Brain Busters   Simplify by writing each expression wth positive exponents. Assume that all variables represent nonzero real numbers.

79. $\dfrac{(4a^2b^3)^{-2}(2ab^{-1})^3}{(a^3b)^{-4}}$ **80.** $\dfrac{(m^6n)^{-2}(m^2n^{-2})^3}{m^{-1}n^{-2}}$

81. $\dfrac{(2y^{-1}z^2)^2(3y^{-2}z^{-3})^3}{(y^3z^2)^{-1}}$ **82.** $\dfrac{(3p^{-2}q^3)^2(5p^{-1}q^{-4})^{-1}}{(p^2q^{-2})^{-3}}$

83. $\dfrac{(9^{-1}z^{-2}x)^{-1}(4z^2x^4)^{-2}}{(5z^{-2}x^{-3})^2}$ **84.** $\dfrac{(4^{-1}a^{-1}b^{-2})^{-2}(5a^{-3}b^4)^{-2}}{(3a^{-3}b^{-5})^2}$

85. *Concept Check*   A student simplified $\frac{16^3}{2^2}$ as shown.

$$\frac{16^3}{2^2} = \left(\frac{16}{2}\right)^{3-2} = 8^1 = 8$$

WHAT WENT WRONG? Give the correct answer.

86. *Concept Check*   A student simplified -5^4 as shown.

$$-5^4 = (-5)^4 = 625$$

WHAT WENT WRONG? Give the correct answer.

Evaluate.

87. $10(6428)$ **88.** $100(72.79)$ **89.** $1000(1.53)$ **90.** $10,000(36.94)$

91. $38 \div 10$ **92.** $6504 \div 100$ **93.** $277 \div 1000$ **94.** $49 \div 10,000$

SUMMARY EXERCISES on the Rules for Exponents

Simplify each expression. Use only positive exponents in your answers. Assume that all variables represent nonzero real numbers.

1. $(10x^2y^4)^2(10xy^2)^3$

2. $(-2ab^3c)^4(-2a^2b)^3$

3. $\left(\dfrac{9wx^3}{y^4}\right)^3$

4. $(4x^{-2}y^{-3})^{-2}$

5. $\dfrac{c^{11}(c^2)^4}{(c^3)^3(c^2)^{-6}}$

6. $\left(\dfrac{k^4t^2}{k^2t^{-4}}\right)^{-2}$

7. $5^{-1} + 6^{-1}$

8. $\dfrac{(3y^{-1}z^3)^{-1}(3y^2)}{(y^3z^2)^{-3}}$

9. $\dfrac{(2xy^{-1})^3}{2^3x^{-3}y^2}$

10. $-4^0 + (-4)^0$

11. $(z^4)^{-3}(z^{-2})^{-5}$

12. $\left(\dfrac{r^2st^5}{3r}\right)^{-2}$

13. $\dfrac{(3^{-1}x^{-3}y)^{-1}(2x^2y^{-3})^2}{(5x^{-2}y^2)^{-2}}$

14. $\left(\dfrac{5x^2}{3x^{-4}}\right)^{-1}$

15. $\left(\dfrac{-9x^{-2}}{9x^2}\right)^{-2}$

16. $\dfrac{(x^{-4}y^2)^3(x^2y)^{-1}}{(xy^2)^{-3}}$

17. $\dfrac{(a^{-2}b^3)^{-4}}{(a^{-3}b^2)^{-2}(ab)^{-4}}$

18. $(2a^{-30}b^{-29})(3a^{31}b^{30})$

19. $5^{-2} + 6^{-2}$

20. $\left[\dfrac{(x^{43}y^{23})^2}{x^{-26}y^{-42}}\right]^0$

21. $\left(\dfrac{7a^2b^3}{2}\right)^3$

22. $-(-19^0)$

23. $-(-13)^0$

24. $\dfrac{0^{13}}{13^0}$

25. $\dfrac{(2xy^{-3})^{-2}}{(3x^{-2}y^4)^{-3}}$

26. $\left(\dfrac{a^2b^3c^4}{a^{-2}b^{-3}c^{-4}}\right)^{-2}$

27. $(6x^{-5}z^3)^{-3}$

28. $(2p^{-2}qr^{-3})(2p)^{-4}$

29. $\dfrac{(xy)^{-3}(xy)^5}{(xy)^{-4}}$

30. $52^0 - (-8)^0$

31. $\dfrac{(7^{-1}x^{-3})^{-2}(x^4)^{-6}}{7^{-1}x^{-3}}$

32. $\left(\dfrac{3^{-4}x^{-3}}{3^{-3}x^{-6}}\right)^{-2}$

33. $(5p^{-2}q)^{-3}(5pq^3)^4$

34. $8^{-1} + 6^{-1}$

35. $\left[\dfrac{4r^{-6}s^{-2}t}{2r^8s^{-4}t^2}\right]^{-1}$

36. $(13x^{-6}y)(13x^{-6}y)^{-1}$

37. $\dfrac{(8pq^{-2})^4}{(8p^{-2}q^{-3})^3}$

38. $\left(\dfrac{mn^{-2}p}{m^2np^4}\right)^{-2}\left(\dfrac{mn^{-2}p}{m^2np^4}\right)^3$

39. $-(-8^0)^0$

40. *Concept Check* Match each expression (a)–(j) in Column I with the equivalent expression A–J in Column II. Choices in Column II may be used once, more than once, or not at all.

I		II	
(a) $2^0 + 2^0$	**(b)** $2^1 \cdot 2^0$	**A.** 0	**B.** 1
(c) $2^0 - 2^{-1}$	**(d)** $2^1 - 2^0$	**C.** -1	**D.** 2
(e) $2^0 \cdot 2^{-2}$	**(f)** $2^1 \cdot 2^1$	**E.** $\dfrac{1}{2}$	**F.** 4
(g) $2^{-2} - 2^{-1}$	**(h)** $2^0 \cdot 2^0$	**G.** -2	**H.** -4
(i) $2^{-2} \div 2^{-1}$	**(j)** $2^0 \div 2^{-2}$	**I.** $-\dfrac{1}{4}$	**J.** $\dfrac{1}{4}$

4.3   An Application of Exponents: Scientific Notation

OBJECTIVES

1   Express numbers in scientific notation.
2   Convert numbers in scientific notation to numbers without exponents.
3   Use scientific notation in calculations.

OBJECTIVE 1 **Express numbers in scientific notation.** Numbers occurring in science are often extremely large (such as the distance from Earth to the sun, 93,000,000 mi) or extremely small (the wavelength of yellow-green light, approximately 0.0000006 m). Because of the difficulty of working with many zeros, scientists often express such numbers with exponents, using a form called *scientific notation*.

Scientific Notation

A number is written in **scientific notation** when it is expressed in the form

$$a \times 10^n, \quad \text{where } 1 \le |a| < 10 \text{ and } n \text{ is an integer.}$$

In scientific notation, there is always one nonzero digit before the decimal point.

$3.19 \times 10^1 = 3.19 \times 10 = 31.9$	Decimal point moves 1 place to the right.
$3.19 \times 10^2 = 3.19 \times 100 = 319.$	Decimal point moves 2 places to the right.
$3.19 \times 10^3 = 3.19 \times 1000 = 3190.$	Decimal point moves 3 places to the right.
$3.19 \times 10^{-1} = 3.19 \times 0.1 = 0.319$	Decimal point moves 1 place to the left.
$3.19 \times 10^{-2} = 3.19 \times 0.01 = 0.0319$	Decimal point moves 2 places to the left.
$3.19 \times 10^{-3} = 3.19 \times 0.001 = 0.00319$	Decimal point moves 3 places to the left.

NOTE In work with scientific notation, the times symbol, $\times$, is commonly used.

A number in scientific notation is always written with the decimal point after the first nonzero digit and then multiplied by the appropriate power of 10. For example, 56,200 is written 5.62×10^4, since

$$56{,}200 = 5.62 \times 10{,}000 = 5.62 \times 10^4.$$

Other examples include

42,000,000	written	$4.2 \times 10^7,$
0.000586	written	$5.86 \times 10^{-4},$
and 2,000,000,000	written	$2 \times 10^9.$

> It is not necessary to write 2.0.

To write a number in scientific notation, follow these steps. (For a negative number, follow these steps using the *absolute value* of the number. Then make the result negative.)

Writing a Number in Scientific Notation

Step 1 Move the decimal point to the right of the first nonzero digit.

Step 2 Count the number of places you moved the decimal point.

Step 3 The number of places in Step 2 is the absolute value of the exponent on 10.

Step 4 The exponent on 10 is positive if the original number is greater than the number in Step 1. The exponent is negative if the original number is less than the number in Step 1. If the decimal point is not moved, the exponent is 0.

NOW TRY
EXERCISE 1

Write each number in scientific notation.

(a) 12,600,000

(b) 0.00027

(c) −0.0000341

EXAMPLE 1 Using Scientific Notation

Write each number in scientific notation.

(a) 93,000,000

Move the decimal point to follow the first nonzero digit (the 9). Count the number of places the decimal point was moved.

$$93{,}000{,}000. \longleftarrow \text{Decimal point}$$
7 places

The number will be written in scientific notation as 9.3×10^n. To find the value of n, first compare the original number, 93,000,000, with 9.3. Since 93,000,000 is *greater* than 9.3, we must multiply by a *positive* power of 10 so that the product 9.3×10^n will equal the larger number.

Since the decimal point was moved seven places, and since n is positive,

$$93{,}000{,}000 = 9.3 \times 10^7.$$

(b) $63{,}200{,}000{,}000 = 6.3200000000 = 6.32 \times 10^{10}$
10 places

(c) 0.00462

Move the decimal point to the right of the first nonzero digit, and count the number of places the decimal point was moved.

$$0.00462 \qquad \text{3 places}$$

Since 0.00462 is *less* than 4.62, the exponent must be *negative*.

$$0.00462 = 4.62 \times 10^{-3}$$

(d) $-0.0000762 = -7.62 \times 10^{-5}$
5 places

> Remember the negative sign.

NOW TRY

NOTE To choose the exponent when you write a positive number in scientific notation, think as follows.

1. If the original number is "large," like 93,000,000, use a *positive* exponent on 10, since positive is greater than negative.

2. If the original number is "small," like 0.00462, use a *negative* exponent on 10, since negative is less than positive.

OBJECTIVE 2 **Convert numbers in scientific notation to numbers without exponents.** To do this, we work in reverse. *Multiplying a positive number by a positive power of 10 will make the number greater. Multiplying by a negative power of 10 will make the number less.*

EXAMPLE 2 Writing Numbers without Exponents

Write each number without exponents.

(a) 6.2×10^3

Since the exponent is positive, we make 6.2 greater by moving the decimal point three places to the right. We attach two zeros.

$$6.2 \times 10^3 = 6.200 = 6200$$

NOW TRY ANSWERS
1. **(a)** 1.26×10^7
(b) 2.7×10^{-4}
(c) -3.41×10^{-5}

NOW TRY EXERCISE 2

Write each number without exponents.

(a) 5.71×10^4

(b) 2.72×10^{-5}

(b) $4.283 \times 10^6 = 4.283000 = 4,283,000$ Move 6 places to the right. Attach zeros as necessary.

(c) $7.04 \times 10^{-3} = 0.00704$ Move 3 places to the left.

The exponent tells the number of places and the direction that the decimal point is moved.   NOW TRY

OBJECTIVE 3 Use scientific notation in calculations.

NOW TRY EXERCISE 3

Perform each calculation. Write answers in scientific notation and also without exponents.

(a) $(6 \times 10^7)(7 \times 10^{-4})$

(b) $\dfrac{18 \times 10^{-3}}{6 \times 10^4}$

EXAMPLE 3 Multiplying and Dividing with Scientific Notation

Perform each calculation.

(a) $(7 \times 10^3)(5 \times 10^4)$

$= (7 \times 5)(10^3 \times 10^4)$ Commutative and associative properties

$= 35 \times 10^7$ Multiply; product rule

> Don't stop! This number is *not* in scientific notation, since 35 is not between 1 and 10.

$= (3.5 \times 10^1) \times 10^7$ Write 35 in scientific notation.

$= 3.5 \times (10^1 \times 10^7)$ Associative property

$= 3.5 \times 10^8$ Product rule

$= 350,000,000$ Write without exponents.

(b) $\dfrac{4 \times 10^{-5}}{2 \times 10^3} = \dfrac{4}{2} \times \dfrac{10^{-5}}{10^3} = 2 \times 10^{-8} = 0.00000002$ NOW TRY

NOTE Multiplying or dividing numbers written in scientific notation may produce an answer in the form $a \times 10^0$. Since $10^0 = 1$, $a \times 10^0 = a$. For example,

$$(8 \times 10^{-4})(5 \times 10^4) = 40 \times 10^0 = 40.   10^0 = 1$$

Also, if $a = 1$, then $a \times 10^n = 10^n$. For example, we could write 1,000,000 as 10^6 instead of 1×10^6.

NOW TRY EXERCISE 4

See **Example 4.** About how much would 8,000,000 nanometers measure in inches?

EXAMPLE 4 Using Scientific Notation to Solve an Application

A *nanometer* is a very small unit of measure that is equivalent to about 0.00000003937 in. About how much would 700,000 nanometers measure in inches? (*Source: World Almanac and Book of Facts.*)

Write each number in scientific notation, and then multiply.

$700,000(0.00000003937)$

$= (7 \times 10^5)(3.937 \times 10^{-8})$ Write in scientific notation.

$= (7 \times 3.937)(10^5 \times 10^{-8})$ Properties of real numbers

$= 27.559 \times 10^{-3}$ Multiply; product rule

> Don't stop here.

$= (2.7559 \times 10^1) \times 10^{-3}$ Write 27.559 in scientific notation.

$= 2.7559 \times 10^{-2}$ Product rule

$= 0.027559$ Write without exponents.

Thus, 700,000 nanometers would measure

$$2.7559 \times 10^{-2} \text{ in.,} \quad \text{or} \quad 0.027559 \text{ in.}$$ NOW TRY

NOW TRY ANSWERS

2. **(a)** 57,100   **(b)** 0.0000272

3. **(a)** 4.2×10^4, or 42,000
   (b) 3×10^{-7}, or 0.0000003

4. 3.1496×10^{-1} in., or 0.31496 in.

NOW TRY
EXERCISE 5

The land area of California is approximately 1.6×10^5 mi^2, and the 2008 estimated population of California was approximately 4×10^7 people. Use this information to estimate the number of square miles per California resident in 2008. (*Source:* U.S. Census Bureau.)

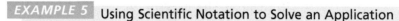

EXAMPLE 5 Using Scientific Notation to Solve an Application

In 2008, the national debt was $\$1.0025 \times 10^{13}$ (which is more than \$10 trillion). The population of the United States was approximately 304 million that year. About how much would each person have had to contribute in order to pay off the national debt? (*Source:* Bureau of Public Land; U.S. Census Bureau.)

Write the population in scientific notation. Then divide to obtain the per person contribution.

$$\frac{1.0025 \times 10^{13}}{304,000,000} = \frac{1.0025 \times 10^{13}}{3.04 \times 10^8} \qquad \text{Write 304 million in scientific notation.}$$

$$= \frac{1.0025}{3.04} \times 10^5 \qquad \text{Quotient rule}$$

$$= 0.32977 \times 10^5 \qquad \text{Divide. Round to 5 decimal places.}$$

$$= 32,977 \qquad \text{Write without exponents.}$$

Each person would have to pay about \$32,977.

 NOW TRY

CONNECTIONS

In 1935, Charles F. Richter devised a scale to compare the intensities of earthquakes. The *intensity* of an earthquake is measured relative to the intensity of a standard *zero-level* earthquake of intensity I_0. The relationship is equivalent to $I = I_0 \times 10^R$, where R is the **Richter scale** measure.

For example, if an earthquake has magnitude 5.0 on the Richter scale, then its intensity is calculated as

$$I = I_0 \times 10^{5.0} = I_0 \times 100,000,$$

which is 100,000 times as intense as a zero-level earthquake.

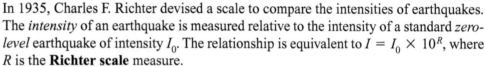

To compare two earthquakes, a ratio of the intensities is calculated. For example, to compare an earthquake that measures 8.0 on the Richter scale with one that measures 5.0, find the ratio of the intensities.

$$\frac{\text{intensity } 8.0}{\text{intensity } 5.0} = \frac{I_0 \times 10^{8.0}}{I_0 \times 10^{5.0}} = \frac{10^8}{10^5} = 10^{8-5} = 10^3 = 1000$$

Therefore, an earthquake that measures 8.0 on the Richter scale is 1000 times as intense as one that measures 5.0.

For Discussion or Writing

Year	Earthquake Location	Richter Scale Measurement
1964	Prince William Sound, Alaska	9.2
2004	Sumatra, Indonesia	9.0
2007	Central Peru	8.0
2008	E. Sichuan Province, China	7.9
2002	Hindu Kush, Afghanistan	5.9

Source: U.S. Geological Survey.

NOW TRY ANSWER
5. 4×10^{-3} mi^2, or 0.004 mi^2

1. Compare the intensity of the 2004 Indonesia earthquake with the 2007 Peru earthquake.

2. Compare the intensity of the 2002 Afghanistan earthquake with the 2008 China earthquake.

3. Compare the intensity of the 1964 Alaska earthquake with the 2008 China earthquake. (*Hint:* Use a calculator.)

4. Suppose an earthquake measures 7.2 on the Richter scale. How would the intensity of a second earthquake compare if its Richter scale measure differed by $+3.0$?   By -1.0?

4.3 EXERCISES

MyMathLab   PRACTICE   WATCH   DOWNLOAD   READ REVIEW

⊕ *Complete solution available on the Video Resources on DVD*

Concept Check   Match each number written in scientific notation in Column I with the correct choice from Column II. Not all choices in Column II will be used.

	I	II		I	II
1.	(a) 4.6×10^{-4}	**A.** 46,000	2.	(a) 1×10^{9}	**A.** 1 billion
	(b) 4.6×10^{4}	**B.** 460,000		(b) 1×10^{6}	**B.** 100 million
	(c) 4.6×10^{5}	**C.** 0.00046		(c) 1×10^{8}	**C.** 1 million
	(d) 4.6×10^{-5}	**D.** 0.000046		(d) 1×10^{10}	**D.** 10 billion
		E. 4600			**E.** 100 billion

Concept Check   Determine whether or not each number is written in scientific notation as defined in **Objective 1.** If it is not, write it as such.

3. 4.56×10^{4} 4. 7.34×10^{6} 5. 5,600,000   6. 34,000

7. 0.8×10^{2} 8. 0.9×10^{3} 9. 0.004   10. 0.0007

✎ 11. Explain what it means for a number to be written in scientific notation. Give examples.

✎ 12. Explain how to multiply a number by a positive power of 10. Then explain how to multiply a number by a negative power of 10.

*Write each number in scientific notation. **See Example 1.***

⊕ 13. 5,876,000,000   14. 9,994,000,000   15. 82,350   16. 78,330

17. 0.000007   18. 0.0000004   19. 0.00203   20. 0.0000578

21. $-13,000,000$ 22. $-25,000,000,000$ 23. -0.006 24. -0.01234

*Write each number without exponents. **See Example 2.***

⊕ 25. 7.5×10^{5} 26. 8.8×10^{6} 27. 5.677×10^{12} 28. 8.766×10^{9}

29. 1×10^{12} 30. 1×10^{7} 31. 6.21×10^{0} 32. 8.56×10^{0}

33. 7.8×10^{-4} 34. 8.9×10^{-5} 35. 5.134×10^{-9} 36. 7.123×10^{-10}

37. -4×10^{-3} 38. -6×10^{-4} 39. -8.1×10^{5} 40. -9.6×10^{6}

*Perform the indicated operations. Write each answer **(a)** in scientific notation and **(b)** without exponents. **See Example 3.***

41. $(2 \times 10^{8})(3 \times 10^{3})$ 42. $(4 \times 10^{7})(3 \times 10^{3})$

⊕ 43. $(5 \times 10^{4})(3 \times 10^{2})$ 44. $(8 \times 10^{5})(2 \times 10^{3})$

45. $(3 \times 10^{-4})(-2 \times 10^8)$ **46.** $(4 \times 10^{-3})(-2 \times 10^7)$

47. $(6 \times 10^3)(4 \times 10^{-2})$ **48.** $(7 \times 10^5)(3 \times 10^{-4})$

49. $(9 \times 10^4)(7 \times 10^{-7})$ **50.** $(6 \times 10^4)(8 \times 10^{-8})$

51. $\dfrac{9 \times 10^{-5}}{3 \times 10^{-1}}$ **52.** $\dfrac{12 \times 10^{-4}}{4 \times 10^{-3}}$ **53.** $\dfrac{8 \times 10^3}{-2 \times 10^2}$

54. $\dfrac{15 \times 10^4}{-3 \times 10^3}$ **55.** $\dfrac{2.6 \times 10^{-3}}{2 \times 10^2}$ **56.** $\dfrac{9.5 \times 10^{-1}}{5 \times 10^3}$

57. $\dfrac{4 \times 10^5}{8 \times 10^2}$ **58.** $\dfrac{3 \times 10^9}{6 \times 10^5}$ **59.** $\dfrac{-4.5 \times 10^4}{1.5 \times 10^{-2}}$

60. $\dfrac{-7.2 \times 10^3}{6.0 \times 10^{-1}}$ **61.** $\dfrac{-8 \times 10^{-4}}{-4 \times 10^3}$ **62.** $\dfrac{-5 \times 10^{-6}}{-2 \times 10^2}$

TECHNOLOGY INSIGHTS   EXERCISES 63–68

Graphing calculators such as the TI-83/84 Plus can display numbers in scientific notation (when in scientific mode), using the format shown in the screen on the left. For 5400, the calculator displays 5.4E3 to represent 5.4×10^3. The display 5.4E‑4 means 5.4×10^{-4}. The calculator will also perform operations with numbers entered in scientific notation, as shown in the screen on the right. Notice how the rules for exponents are applied.

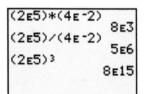

```
5400
             5.4E3
5.4*10^(-4)
             5.4E-4
```

```
(2E5)*(4E-2)
             8E3
(2E5)/(4E-2)
             5E6
(2E5)³
             8E15
```

Predict the display the calculator would give for the expression shown in each screen.

63.
```
.00000047
```

64.
```
.000021
```

65.
```
(8E5)/(4E-2)
```

66.
```
(9E-4)/(3E3)
```

67.
```
(2E6)*(2E-3)/(4E
2)
```

68.
```
(5E-3)*(1E9)/(5E
3)
```

Brain Busters   *Use scientific notation to calculate the answer to each problem. Write answers in scientific notation.*

69. $\dfrac{650{,}000{,}000(0.0000032)}{0.00002}$ **70.** $\dfrac{3{,}400{,}000{,}000(0.000075)}{0.00025}$

71. $\dfrac{0.00000072(0.00023)}{0.000000018}$ **72.** $\dfrac{0.000000081(0.000036)}{0.00000048}$

73. $\dfrac{0.0000016(240{,}000{,}000)}{0.00002(0.0032)}$ **74.** $\dfrac{0.000015(42{,}000{,}000)}{0.000009(0.000005)}$

Each statement comes from Astronomy! A Brief Edition *by James B. Kaler (Addison-Wesley). If the number in boldface italics is in scientific notation, write it without exponents. If the number is written without exponents, write it in scientific notation.*

75. Multiplying this view over the whole sky yields a galaxy count of more than **10 billion.** (page 496)

Spiral Galaxy M81   Spitzer Space Telescope • IRAC
NASA / JPL-Caltech / S. Willner (Harvard-Smithsonian CfA)

76. The circumference of the solar orbit is . . . about **4.7 million** km . . . . (in reference to the orbit of Jupiter, page 395)

77. The solar luminosity requires that 2×10^9 kg of mass be converted into energy every second. (page 327)

78. At maximum, a cosmic ray particle—a mere atomic nucleus of only 10^{-13} cm across—can carry the energy of a professionally pitched baseball. (page 445)

Each statement contains a number in boldface italics. Write the number in scientific notation.

79. At the end of 2007, the total number of cellular telephone subscriptions in the world reached about **3,305,000,000.** (*Source*: International Telecommunications Union.)

80. In 2007, the leading U.S. advertiser was the Procter and Gamble Company, which spent approximately **$5,230,000,000.** (*Source*: Crain Communications, Inc.)

81. During 2008, worldwide motion picture box office receipts (in U.S. dollars) totaled **$28,100,000,000.** (*Source*: Motion Picture Association of America.)

82. In 2007, assets of the insured commercial banks in the United States totaled about **$13,039,000,000,000.** (*Source*: U.S. Federal Deposit Insurance Corporation.)

Use scientific notation to calculate the answer to each problem. See Examples 3–5.

83. The body of a 150-lb person contains about 2.3×10^{-4} lb of copper. How much copper is contained in the bodies of 1200 such people?

84. In 2007, the state of Minnesota had about 7.9×10^4 farms with an average of 3.5×10^2 acres per farm. What was the total number of acres devoted to farmland in Minnesota that year? (*Source*: U.S. Department of Agriculture.)

85. Venus is 6.68×10^7 mi from the sun. If light travels at a speed of 1.86×10^5 mi per sec, how long does it take light to travel from the sun to Venus? (*Source*: World Almanac and Book of Facts.)

86. (a) The distance to Earth from Pluto is 4.58×10^9 km. In April 1983, *Pioneer 10* transmitted radio signals from Pluto to Earth at the speed of light, 3.00×10^5 km per sec. How long (in seconds) did it take for the signals to reach Earth?

    (b) How many hours did it take for the signals to reach Earth?

87. During the 2007–2008 season, Broadway shows grossed a total of 9.38×10^8 dollars. Total attendance for the season was 1.23×10^7. What was the average ticket price for a Broadway show? (*Source*: The Broadway League.)

88. In 2007, 9.63×10^9 dollars were spent to attend motion pictures in the United States. Domestic admissions (the total number of tickets sold) for that year totaled 1.4 billion. What was the average ticket price? (*Source*: Motion Picture Association of America.)

89. On February 17, 2009, Congress raised the U.S. government's debt limit to $\$1.2 \times 10^{13}$. When this national debt limit is reached, about how much will it be for every man, women, and child in the country? Use 300 million as the population of the United States. (*Source:* The Concord Coalition.)

90. In theory there are 1×10^9 possible Social Security numbers. The population of the United States is about 3×10^8. How many Social Security numbers are available for each person? (*Source:* U.S. Census Bureau.)

91. Astronomers using the Spitzer Space Telescope discovered a twisted double-helix nebula, a conglomeration of dust and gas stretching across the center of the Milky Way galaxy. This nebula is 25,000 light-years from Earth. If one light-year is about 6,000,000,000,000 (that is, 6 trillion) miles, about how many miles is the twisted double-helix nebula from Earth? (*Source:* http://articles.news.aol.com)

92. A computer can perform 466,000,000 calculations per second. How many calculations can it perform per minute?   Per hour?

93. In 2008, the U.S. government collected about $4013 per person in personal income taxes. If the population was 304,000,000, how much did the government collect in taxes for 2008? (*Source:* U.S. Office of Management and Budget.)

94. Pollux, one of the brightest stars in the night sky, is 33.7 light-years from Earth. If one light-year is about 6,000,000,000,000 mi, about how many miles is Pollux from Earth? (*Source: World Almanac and Book of Facts.*)

95. In September of 2009, the population of the United States was about 307.5 million. To the nearest dollar, calculate how much each person in the United States would have had to contribute in order to make one lucky person a trillionaire (that is, to give that person $1,000,000,000,000). (*Source:* U.S. Census Bureau.)

96. In 2006, national expenditures for health care reached $2,106,000,000,000. Using 300 million as the population of the United States, about how much, to the nearest dollar, was spent on health care per person in 2006? (*Source:* U.S. Centers for Medicare and Medicaid Services.)

PREVIEW EXERCISES

Simplify. ***See Section 1.8.***

97. $-3(2x + 4) + 4(2x - 6)$ **98.** $-8(-3x + 7) - 4(2x + 3)$

Evaluate each expression for $x = 3$. ***See Sections 1.3 and 1.6.***

99. $2x^2 - 3x + 10$ **100.** $3x^2 - 3x + 4$

101. $4x^3 - 5x^2 + 2x - 5$ **102.** $-4x^3 + 2x^2 - 9x - 2$

4.4

Adding and Subtracting Polynomials; Graphing Simple Polynomials

OBJECTIVES

1. Identify terms and coefficients.
2. Add like terms.
3. Know the vocabulary for polynomials.
4. Evaluate polynomials.
5. Add and subtract polynomials.
6. Graph equations defined by polynomials of degree 2.

OBJECTIVE 1 Identify terms and coefficients. In an expression such as

$$4x^3 + 6x^2 + 5x + 8,$$

the quantities $4x^3$, $6x^2$, $5x$, and 8 are called **terms.** (See **Section 1.8.**) In the first (or *leading*) term $4x^3$, the number 4 is called the **numerical coefficient,** or simply the **coefficient,** of x^3. In the same way, 6 is the coefficient of x^2 in the term $6x^2$, and 5 is the coefficient of x in the term $5x$. The constant term 8 can be thought of as $8 \cdot 1 = 8x^0$, since $x^0 = 1$, so 8 is the coefficient in the term 8.

 NOW TRY EXERCISE 1

Name the coefficient of each term in the expression.

$$t - 10t^2$$

EXAMPLE 1 Identifying Coefficients

Name the coefficient of each term in these expressions.

(a) $x - 6x^4$ can be written as $1x + (-6x^4)$.

The coefficients are 1 and −6.

(b) $5 - v^3$ can be written as $5v^0 + (-1v^3)$.

The coefficients are 5 and −1.

NOW TRY

OBJECTIVE 2 Add like terms. Recall from **Section 1.8** that **like terms** have exactly the same combination of variables, with the same exponents on the variables. *Only the coefficients may differ.*

$19m^5$ and $14m^5$		
$6y^9$, $-37y^9$, and y^9	Examples of like terms	
$3pq$ and $-2pq$		
$2xy^2$ and $-xy^2$		

$7x$ and $7y$		
z^4 and z	Examples of unlike terms	
$2pq$ and $2p$		
$-4xy^2$ and $5x^2y$		

Using the distributive property, we combine, or add, like terms by adding their coefficients.

NOW TRY EXERCISE 2

Simplify by adding like terms.

$$3x^2 - x^2 + 2x$$

EXAMPLE 2 Adding Like Terms

Simplify by adding like terms.

(a) $-4x^3 + 6x^3$

$= (-4 + 6)x^3$ Distributive property

$= 2x^3$ Add.

(b) $9x^6 - 14x^6 + x^6$

$= (9 - 14 + 1)x^6$ $x^6 = 1x^6$

$= -4x^6$

(c) $12m^2 + 5m + 4m^2$

$= (12 + 4)m^2 + 5m$

$= 16m^2 + 5m$

(d) $3x^2y + 4x^2y - x^2y$

$= (3 + 4 - 1)x^2y$

$= 6x^2y$

NOW TRY

NOW TRY ANSWERS

1. 1; −10
2. $2x^2 + 2x$

⚠ **CAUTION** In **Example 2(c)**, we cannot combine $16m^2$ and $5m$, because the exponents on the variables are different. *Unlike terms have different variables or different exponents on the same variables.*

OBJECTIVE 3 **Know the vocabulary for polynomials.** A **polynomial in** x is a term or the sum of a finite number of terms of the form ax^n, for any real number a and any whole number n. For example,

$$16x^8 - 7x^6 + 5x^4 - 3x^2 + 4$$

Polynomial in x
(The 4 can be written as $4x^0$.)

is a polynomial in x. This polynomial is written in **descending powers** of the variable, since the exponents on x decrease from left to right. By contrast,

$$2x^3 - x^2 + \frac{4}{x}, \quad \text{or} \quad 2x^3 - x^2 + 4x^{-1}, \quad \text{Not a polynomial}$$

is not a polynomial in x. A variable appears in a denominator or to a negative power.

NOTE We can define *polynomial* using any variable and not just x, as in **Example 2(c)**. Polynomials may have terms with more than one variable, as in **Example 2(d)**.

The **degree of a term** is the sum of the exponents on the variables. The **degree of a polynomial** is the greatest degree of any nonzero term of the polynomial. The table gives several examples.

Term	Degree	Polynomial	Degree
$3x^4$	4	$3x^4 - 5x^2 + 6$	4
$5x$, or $5x^1$	1	$5x + 7$	1
-7, or $-7x^0$	0	$x^2y + xy - 5y^2$	3
$2x^2y$, or $2x^2y^1$	$2 + 1 = 3$	$x^5 + 3x^6$	6

Three types of polynomials are common and are given special names. A polynomial with only one term is called a **monomial.** (*Mono* means "one," as in *mono*rail.)

$$9m, \quad -6y^5, \quad a^2, \quad \text{and} \quad 6 \quad \text{Monomials}$$

A polynomial with exactly two terms is called a **binomial.** (*Bi-* means "two," as in *bi*cycle.)

$$-9x^4 + 9x^3, \quad 8m^2 + 6m, \quad \text{and} \quad 3m^5 - 9m^2 \quad \text{Binomials}$$

A polynomial with exactly three terms is called a **trinomial.** (*Tri-* means "three," as in *tri*angle.)

$$9m^3 - 4m^2 + 6, \quad \frac{19}{3}y^2 + \frac{8}{3}y + 5, \quad \text{and} \quad -3m^5 - 9m^2 + 2 \quad \text{Trinomials}$$

NOW TRY
EXERCISE 3
Simplify, give the degree, and tell whether the simplified polynomial is a *monomial*, a *binomial*, a *trinomial*, or *none of these.*
$$x^2 + 4x - 2x - 8$$

NOW TRY ANSWER
3. $x^2 + 2x - 8$; degree 2; trinomial

EXAMPLE 3 Classifying Polynomials

For each polynomial, first simplify, if possible. Then give the degree and tell whether the polynomial is a *monomial,* a *binomial,* a *trinomial,* or *none of these.*

(a) $2x^3 + 5$ The polynomial cannot be simplified. It is a binomial of degree 3.

(b) $4xy - 5xy + 2xy$

Add like terms: $4xy - 5xy + 2xy = xy$, which is a monomial of degree 2.

NOW TRY

OBJECTIVE 4 Evaluate polynomials. A polynomial usually represents different numbers for different values of the variable.

NOW TRY
EXERCISE 4

Find the value for $t = -3$.

$$4t^3 - t^2 - t$$

EXAMPLE 4 Evaluating a Polynomial

Find the value of $3x^4 + 5x^3 - 4x - 4$ for **(a)** $x = -2$ and **(b)** $x = 3$.

(a) First, substitute -2 for x.

$$3x^4 + 5x^3 - 4x - 4$$

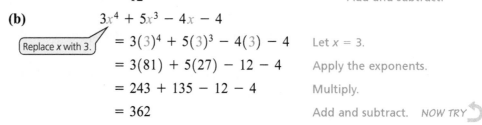

$= 3(-2)^4 + 5(-2)^3 - 4(-2) - 4$	Let $x = -2$.

Use parentheses to avoid errors.

$= 3(16) + 5(-8) - 4(-2) - 4$	Apply the exponents.
$= 48 - 40 + 8 - 4$	Multiply.
$= 12$	Add and subtract.

(b) $3x^4 + 5x^3 - 4x - 4$

Replace x with 3.

$= 3(3)^4 + 5(3)^3 - 4(3) - 4$	Let $x = 3$.
$= 3(81) + 5(27) - 12 - 4$	Apply the exponents.
$= 243 + 135 - 12 - 4$	Multiply.
$= 362$	Add and subtract. NOW TRY

⚠ **CAUTION** Use parentheses around the numbers that are substituted for the variable, as in **Example 4**. *Be particularly careful when substituting a negative number for a variable that is raised to a power, or a sign error may result.*

OBJECTIVE 5 Add and subtract polynomials.

Adding Polynomials

To add two polynomials, add like terms.

NOW TRY
EXERCISE 5

Add $4y^3 - 2y^2 + y - 1$ and $y^3 - y - 7$ vertically.

EXAMPLE 5 Adding Polynomials Vertically

(a) Add $6x^3 - 4x^2 + 3$ and $-2x^3 + 7x^2 - 5$.

$$\begin{array}{r} 6x^3 - 4x^2 + 3 \\ -2x^3 + 7x^2 - 5 \end{array}$$

Write like terms in columns.

Now add, column by column.

Combine the coefficients only. Do *not* add the exponents.

$$\begin{array}{ccc} 6x^3 & -4x^2 & 3 \\ -2x^3 & 7x^2 & -5 \\ \hline 4x^3 & 3x^2 & -2 \end{array}$$

Add the three sums together.

$$4x^3 + 3x^2 + (-2) = 4x^3 + 3x^2 - 2 \leftarrow \text{Final sum}$$

(b) Add $2x^2 - 4x + 3$ and $x^3 + 5x$.

Write like terms in columns and add column by column.

$$\begin{array}{r} 2x^2 - 4x + 3 \\ x^3 \qquad + 5x \qquad \\ \hline x^3 + 2x^2 + \ x + 3 \end{array}$$

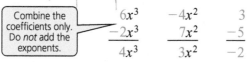

Leave spaces for missing terms.

NOW TRY

NOW TRY ANSWERS
4. -114
5. $5y^3 - 2y^2 - 8$

The polynomials in **Example 5** also can be added horizontally.

NOW TRY
EXERCISE 6
Add $10x^4 - 3x^2 - x$ and $x^4 - 3x^2 + 5x$ horizontally.

EXAMPLE 6 Adding Polynomials Horizontally

(a) Add $6x^3 - 4x^2 + 3$ and $-2x^3 + 7x^2 - 5$.
Combine like terms.

$(6x^3 - 4x^2 + 3) + (-2x^3 + 7x^2 - 5) = 4x^3 + 3x^2 - 2$ Same answer as found in **Example 5(a)**

(b) Add $2x^2 - 4x + 3$ and $x^3 + 5x$.

$$(2x^2 - 4x + 3) + (x^3 + 5x)$$
$$= x^3 + 2x^2 - 4x + 5x + 3 \quad \text{Commutative property}$$
$$= x^3 + 2x^2 + x + 3 \quad \text{Combine like terms.}$$

NOW TRY

In **Section 1.5**, we defined the difference $x - y$ as $x + (-y)$. (We find the difference $x - y$ by adding x and the opposite of y.) For example,

$$7 - 2 = 7 + (-2) = 5 \quad \text{and} \quad -8 - (-2) = -8 + 2 = -6.$$

A similar method is used to subtract polynomials.

Subtracting Polynomials

To subtract two polynomials, change all the signs in the second polynomial and add the result to the first polynomial.

NOW TRY
EXERCISE 7
Subtract $5t^4 - 3t^2 + 1$ from $4t^4 - t^2 + 7$.

EXAMPLE 7 Subtracting Polynomials Horizontally

(a) Perform the subtraction $(5x - 2) - (3x - 8)$.
$$(5x - 2) - (3x - 8)$$
$$= (5x - 2) + [-(3x - 8)] \quad \text{Definition of subtraction}$$
$$= (5x - 2) + [-1(3x - 8)] \quad -a = -1a$$
$$= (5x - 2) + (-3x + 8) \quad \text{Distributive property}$$
$$= 2x + 6 \quad \text{Combine like terms.}$$

(b) Subtract $6x^3 - 4x^2 + 2$ from $11x^3 + 2x^2 - 8$.
$$(11x^3 + 2x^2 - 8) - (6x^3 - 4x^2 + 2)$$ Be careful to write the problem in the correct order.
$$= (11x^3 + 2x^2 - 8) + (-6x^3 + 4x^2 - 2)$$
$$= 5x^3 + 6x^2 - 10 \quad \text{Answer}$$

CHECK To check a subtraction problem, use the fact that
$$\text{if} \quad a - b = c, \quad \text{then} \quad a = b + c.$$
Here, add $6x^3 - 4x^2 + 2$ and $5x^3 + 6x^2 - 10$.
$$(6x^3 - 4x^2 + 2) + (5x^3 + 6x^2 - 10)$$
$$= 11x^3 + 2x^2 - 8 \checkmark$$

NOW TRY

NOW TRY ANSWERS
6. $11x^4 - 6x^2 + 4x$
7. $-t^4 + 2t^2 + 6$

We use vertical subtraction in **Section 4.7** when we divide polynomials.

NOW TRY
EXERCISE 8

Subtract by columns.

$(12x^2 - 9x + 4)$
$\quad - (-10x^2 - 3x + 7)$

EXAMPLE 8 Subtracting Polynomials Vertically

Subtract by columns to find

$$(14y^3 - 6y^2 + 2y - 5) - (2y^3 - 7y^2 - 4y + 6).$$

$$\begin{array}{l} 14y^3 - 6y^2 + 2y - 5 \\ \underline{2y^3 - 7y^2 - 4y + 6} \end{array}$$ Arrange like terms in columns.

Change all signs in the second row, and then add.

$$\begin{array}{l} 14y^3 - 6y^2 + 2y - 5 \\ \underline{-2y^3 + 7y^2 + 4y - 6} \quad \text{Change all signs.} \\ 12y^3 + y^2 + 6y - 11 \quad \text{Add.} \end{array}$$ NOW TRY

NOW TRY
EXERCISE 9

Subtract.

$(4x^2 - 2xy + y^2)$
$\quad - (6x^2 - 7xy + 2y^2)$

EXAMPLE 9 Adding and Subtracting Polynomials with More Than One Variable

Add or subtract as indicated.

(a) $(4a + 2ab - b) + (3a - ab + b)$

$\quad = 4a + 2ab - b + 3a - ab + b$

$\quad = 7a + ab$ Combine like terms.

(b) $(2x^2y + 3xy + y^2) - (3x^2y - xy - 2y^2)$

$\quad = 2x^2y + 3xy + y^2 - 3x^2y + xy + 2y^2$

$\quad = -x^2y + 4xy + 3y^2$ Be careful with signs. The coefficient of xy is 1. NOW TRY

OBJECTIVE 6 Graph equations defined by polynomials of degree 2. In **Chapter 3,** we introduced graphs of linear equations (which are actually polynomial equations of degree 1). By plotting points selectively, we can graph polynomial equations of degree 2.

EXAMPLE 10 Graphing Equations Defined by Polynomials of Degree 2

Graph each equation.

(a) $y = x^2$

Select values for x. Then find the corresponding y-values. Selecting $x = 2$ gives

$$y = x^2 = 2^2 = 4,$$

so the point $(2, 4)$ is on the graph of $y = x^2$. (Recall that in an ordered pair such as $(2, 4)$, *the x-value comes first and the y-value second.*) We show some ordered pairs that satisfy $y = x^2$ in the table with **FIGURE 3** on the next page. If we plot the ordered pairs from the table on a coordinate system and draw a smooth curve through them, we obtain the graph shown in **FIGURE 3**.

NOW TRY ANSWERS
8. $22x^2 - 6x - 3$
9. $-2x^2 + 5xy - y^2$

NOW TRY
EXERCISE 10

Graph $y = -x^2 - 1$.

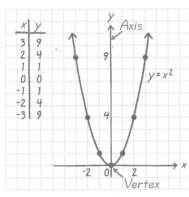

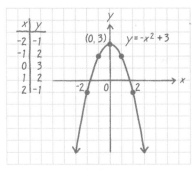

FIGURE 3   **FIGURE 4**

The graph of $y = x^2$ in **FIGURE 3** is called a **parabola.** The point $(0, 0)$, the *lowest* point on this graph, is called the **vertex** of the parabola. The vertical line through the vertex (the y-axis here) is called the **axis** of the parabola. The axis of a parabola is a **line of symmetry** for the graph. If the graph is folded on this line, the two halves will match.

(b) $y = -x^2 + 3$

Once again, plot points to obtain the graph. For example, if $x = -2$, then

$$y = -(-2)^2 + 3 = -4 + 3 = -1.$$

The point $(-2, -1)$ and several others are shown in the table that accompanies the graph in **FIGURE 4**. The vertex of this parabola is $(0, 3)$. Now the vertex is the *highest* point on the graph. The graph opens downward because x^2 has a negative coefficient.

NOW TRY

NOW TRY ANSWER

10.

NOTE *All polynomials of degree 2 have parabolas as their graphs.* When graphing, find points until the vertex and points on either side of it are located. (In this section, all parabolas have their vertices on the x-axis or the y-axis.)

4.4 EXERCISES **MyMathLab** Math XL PRACTICE WATCH DOWNLOAD READ REVIEW

🌐 *Complete solution available on the Video Resources on DVD*

Concept Check *Fill in each blank with the correct response.*

1. In the term $4x^6$, the coefficient is _____ and the exponent is _____.

2. The expression $4x^3 - 5x^2$ has _____ term(s).
(how many?)

3. The degree of the term $-3x^9$ is _____.

4. The polynomial $4x^2 + y^2$ _____ an example of a trinomial.
(is/is not)

5. When $x^2 + 10$ is evaluated for $x = 3$, the result is _____.

6. $5x^{\underline{}} + 3x^3 - 7x$ is a trinomial of degree 6.

7. $-3xy - 2xy + 5xy =$ _____

8. _____ is an example of a monomial with coefficient 8, in the variable x, having degree 5.

For each polynomial, determine the number of terms and name the coefficients of the terms. **See Example 1.**

9. $6x^4$ **10.** $-9y^5$ **11.** t^4 **12.** s^7

13. $-19r^2 - r$ **14.** $2y^3 - y$ **15.** $x + 8x^2 + 5x^3$ **16.** $v - 2v^3 - v^7$

In each polynomial, add like terms whenever possible. Write the result in descending powers of the variable. **See Example 2.**

17. $-3m^5 + 5m^5$ **18.** $-4y^3 + 3y^3$ **19.** $2r^5 + (-3r^5)$

20. $9y^2 + (-19y^2)$ **21.** $0.2m^5 - 0.5m^2$ **22.** $-0.9y + 0.9y^2$

23. $-3x^5 + 3x^5 - 5x^5$ **24.** $6x^3 - 9x^3 + 10x^3$

25. $-4p^7 + 8p^7 + 5p^9$ **26.** $-3a^8 + 4a^8 - 3a^2$

27. $-4xy^2 + 3xy^2 - 2xy^2 + xy^2$ **28.** $3pr^5 - 8pr^5 + pr^5 + 2pr^5$

For each polynomial, first simplify, if possible, and write it in descending powers of the variable. Then give the degree of the resulting polynomial and tell whether it is a monomial, *a* binomial, *a* trinomial, *or none of these.* **See Example 3.**

29. $6x^4 - 9x$ **30.** $7t^3 - 3t$

31. $5m^4 - 3m^2 + 6m^4 - 7m^3$ **32.** $6p^5 + 4p^3 - 8p^5 + 10p^2$

33. $\dfrac{5}{3}x^4 - \dfrac{2}{3}x^4$ **34.** $\dfrac{4}{5}r^6 + \dfrac{1}{5}r^6$

35. $0.8x^4 - 0.3x^4 - 0.5x^4 + 7$ **36.** $1.2t^3 - 0.9t^3 - 0.3t^3 + 9$

*Find the value of each polynomial for **(a)** $x = 2$ and **(b)** $x = -1$.* **See Example 4.**

37. $2x^2 - 3x - 5$ **38.** $x^2 + 5x - 10$

39. $-3x^2 + 14x - 2$ **40.** $-2x^2 + 5x - 1$

41. $2x^5 - 4x^4 + 5x^3 - x^2$ **42.** $x^4 - 6x^3 + x^2 - x$

Add. **See Example 5.**

43. $\begin{array}{r} 2x^2 - 4x \\ 3x^2 + 2x \\ \hline \end{array}$ **44.** $\begin{array}{r} -5y^3 + 3y \\ 8y^3 - 4y \\ \hline \end{array}$ **45.** $\begin{array}{r} 3m^2 + 5m + 6 \\ 2m^2 - 2m - 4 \\ \hline \end{array}$

46. $\begin{array}{r} 4a^3 - 4a^2 - 4 \\ 6a^3 + 5a^2 - 8 \\ \hline \end{array}$ **47.** $\begin{array}{r} \frac{2}{3}x^2 + \frac{1}{5}x + \frac{1}{6} \\ \frac{1}{2}x^2 - \frac{1}{3}x + \frac{2}{3} \\ \hline \end{array}$ **48.** $\begin{array}{r} \frac{4}{7}y^2 - \frac{1}{5}y + \frac{7}{9} \\ \frac{1}{3}y^2 - \frac{1}{3}y + \frac{2}{5} \\ \hline \end{array}$

49. $9m^3 - 5m^2 + 4m - 8$ and $-3m^3 + 6m^2 - 6$

50. $12r^5 + 11r^4 - 7r^3 - 2r^2$ and $-8r^5 + 3r^3 + 2r^2$

Subtract. **See Example 8.**

51. $\begin{array}{r} 5y^3 - 3y^2 \\ 2y^3 + 8y^2 \\ \hline \end{array}$ **52.** $\begin{array}{r} -6t^3 + 4t^2 \\ 8t^3 - 6t^2 \\ \hline \end{array}$

53. $\begin{array}{r} 12x^4 - x^2 + x \\ 8x^4 + 3x^2 - 3x \\ \hline \end{array}$ **54.** $\begin{array}{r} 13y^5 - y^3 - 8y^2 \\ 7y^5 + 5y^3 + y^2 \\ \hline \end{array}$

55. $\begin{array}{r} 12m^3 - 8m^2 + 6m + 7 \\ -3m^3 + 5m^2 - 2m - 4 \\ \hline \end{array}$ **56.** $\begin{array}{r} 5a^4 - 3a^3 + 2a^2 - a + 6 \\ -6a^4 + a^3 - a^2 + a - 1 \\ \hline \end{array}$

57. After reading **Examples 5–8,** do you have a preference regarding horizontal or vertical addition and subtraction of polynomials? Explain your answer.

58. Write a paragraph explaining how to add and subtract polynomials. Give an example using addition.

Perform each indicated operation. ***See Examples 6 and 7.***

🌐 **59.** $(8m^2 - 7m) - (3m^2 + 7m - 6)$ **60.** $(x^2 + x) - (3x^2 + 2x - 1)$

🌐 **61.** $(16x^3 - x^2 + 3x) + (-12x^3 + 3x^2 + 2x)$

62. $(-2b^6 + 3b^4 - b^2) + (b^6 + 2b^4 + 2b^2)$

63. Subtract $18y^4 - 5y^2 + y$ from $7y^4 + 3y^2 + 2y$.

64. Subtract $19t^5 - 6t^3 + t$ from $8t^5 + 3t^3 + 5t$.

65. $(9a^4 - 3a^2 + 2) + (4a^4 - 4a^2 + 2) + (-12a^4 + 6a^2 - 3)$

66. $(4m^2 - 3m + 2) + (5m^2 + 13m - 4) + (-16m^2 - 4m + 3)$

67. $[(8m^2 + 4m - 7) - (2m^2 - 5m + 2)] - (m^2 + m + 1)$

68. $[(9b^3 - 4b^2 + 3b + 2) - (-2b^3 - 3b^2 + b)] - (8b^3 + 6b + 4)$

69. $[(3x^2 - 2x + 7) - (4x^2 + 2x - 3)] - [(9x^2 + 4x - 6) + (-4x^2 + 4x + 4)]$

70. $[(6t^2 - 3t + 1) - (12t^2 + 2t - 6)] - [(4t^2 - 3t - 8) + (-6t^2 + 10t - 12)]$

71. *Concept Check*   Without actually performing the operations, determine mentally the coefficient of the x^2-term in the simplified form of

$$(-4x^2 + 2x - 3) - (-2x^2 + x - 1) + (-8x^2 + 3x - 4).$$

72. *Concept Check*   Without actually performing the operations, determine mentally the coefficient of the x-term in the simplified form of

$$(-8x^2 - 3x + 2) - (4x^2 - 3x + 8) - (-2x^2 - x + 7).$$

Add or subtract as indicated. ***See Example 9.***

🌐 **73.** $(6b + 3c) + (-2b - 8c)$ **74.** $(-5t + 13s) + (8t - 3s)$

75. $(4x + 2xy - 3) - (-2x + 3xy + 4)$ **76.** $(8ab + 2a - 3b) - (6ab - 2a + 3b)$

77. $(5x^2y - 2xy + 9xy^2) - (8x^2y + 13xy + 12xy^2)$

78. $(16t^3s^2 + 8t^2s^3 + 9ts^4) - (-24t^3s^2 + 3t^2s^3 - 18ts^4)$

Find a polynomial that represents the perimeter of each rectangle, square, or triangle.

79.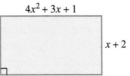
$4x^2 + 3x + 1$
$x + 2$

80.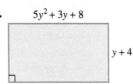
$5y^2 + 3y + 8$
$y + 4$

81.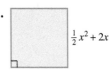
$\frac{1}{2}x^2 + 2x$

82.
$\frac{3}{4}x^2 + x$

83.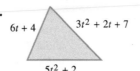
$6t + 4$ $3t^2 + 2t + 7$
$5t^2 + 2$

84.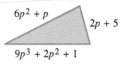
$6p^2 + p$ $2p + 5$
$9p^3 + 2p^2 + 1$

*Find **(a)** a polynomial that represents the perimeter of each triangle and **(b)** the degree measures of the angles of the triangle.*

85.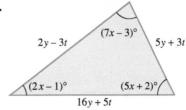
$2y - 3t$ $(7x - 3)°$ $5y + 3t$
$(2x - 1)°$ $(5x + 2)°$
$16y + 5t$

86.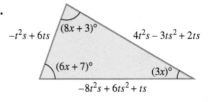
$-t^2s + 6ts$ $(8x + 3)°$ $4t^2s - 3ts^2 + 2ts$
$(6x + 7)°$ $(3x)°$
$-8t^2s + 6ts^2 + ts$

Perform each indicated operation.

87. Find the difference between the sum of $5x^2 + 2x - 3$ and $x^2 - 8x + 2$ and the sum of $7x^2 - 3x + 6$ and $-x^2 + 4x - 6$.

88. Subtract the sum of $9t^3 - 3t + 8$ and $t^2 - 8t + 4$ from the sum of $12t + 8$ and $t^2 - 10t + 3$.

Graph each equation by completing the table of values. **See Example 10.**

89. $y = x^2 - 4$

x	y
-2	
-1	
0	
1	
2	

90. $y = x^2 - 6$

x	y
-2	
-1	
0	
1	
2	

91. $y = 2x^2 - 1$

x	y
-2	
-1	
0	
1	
2	

92. $y = 2x^2 + 2$

x	y
-2	
-1	
0	
1	
2	

93. $y = -x^2 + 4$

x	y
-2	
-1	
0	
1	
2	

94. $y = -x^2 + 2$

x	y
-2	
-1	
0	
1	
2	

95. $y = (x + 3)^2$

x	-5	-4	-3	-2	-1
y					

96. $y = (x - 4)^2$

x	2	3	4	5	6
y					

RELATING CONCEPTS EXERCISES 97–100

FOR INDIVIDUAL OR GROUP WORK

The polynomial equation

$$y = -0.0545x^2 + 5.047x + 11.78$$

*gives a good approximation of the age of a dog in human years y, where x represents age in dog years. Each time we evaluate this polynomial for a value of x, we get one and only one output value y. For example, if a dog is 4 in dog years, let x = 4 to find that y ≈ 31.1. (Verify this.) This means that the dog is about 31 yr old in human years. This illustrates the concept of a **function**, one of the most important topics in mathematics.*

*Exercises 97–100 further illustrate the function concept with polynomials. **Work these exercises in order.***

97. It used to be thought that each dog year was about 7 human years, so that $y = 7x$ gave the number of human years for x dog years. Evaluate y for $x = 9$, and interpret the result.

98. Use the polynomial equation given in the directions above to find the number of human years equivalent to 3 dog years.

99. If an object is projected upward under certain conditions, its height in feet is given by the trinomial

$$-16x^2 + 60x + 80,$$

where x is in seconds. Evaluate this polynomial for $x = 2.5$. Use the result to fill in the blanks: If ____ seconds have elapsed, the height of the object is ____ feet.

100. If it costs $15 to rent a chain saw, plus $2 per day, the binomial $2x + 15$ gives the cost to rent the chain saw for x days. Evaluate this polynomial for $x = 6$. Use the result to fill in the blanks: If the saw is rented for ____ days, the cost is ____.

PREVIEW EXERCISES

Multiply. See Section 1.8.

101. $5(x + 4)$ **102.** $-3(x^2 + 7)$ **103.** $4(2a + 6b)$ **104.** $\dfrac{1}{2}(4m - 8n)$

Multiply. See Section 4.1.

105. $(2a)(-5ab)$ **106.** $(3xz)(4x)$ **107.** $(-m^2)(m^5)$ **108.** $(2c)(3c^2)$

4.5 Multiplying Polynomials

OBJECTIVES

1 Multiply a monomial and a polynomial.

2 Multiply two polynomials.

3 Multiply binomials by the FOIL method.

OBJECTIVE 1 **Multiply a monomial and a polynomial.** As shown in **Section 4.1,** we find the product of two monomials by using the rules for exponents and the commutative and associative properties. Consider this example.

$$-8m^6(-9n^6)$$
$$= -8(-9)(m^6)(n^6)$$
$$= 72m^6n^6$$

> ⚠ **CAUTION** *Do not confuse addition of terms with multiplication of terms.* For instance,
> $$7q^5 + 2q^5 = 9q^5, \qquad \text{but} \qquad (7q^5)(2q^5) = 7 \cdot 2q^{5+5} = 14q^{10}.$$

NOW TRY
EXERCISE 1

Find the product.

$$-3x^5(2x^3 - 5x^2 + 10)$$

EXAMPLE 1 Multiplying Monomials and Polynomials

Find each product.

(a) $4x^2(3x + 5)$

$$4x^2(3x + 5) = 4x^2(3x) + 4x^2(5) \qquad \text{Distributive property}$$
$$= 12x^3 + 20x^2 \qquad \text{Multiply monomials.}$$

(b) $-8m^3(4m^3 + 3m^2 + 2m - 1)$

$$= -8m^3(4m^3) + (-8m^3)(3m^2)$$
$$+ (-8m^3)(2m) + (-8m^3)(-1) \qquad \text{Distributive property}$$
$$= -32m^6 - 24m^5 - 16m^4 + 8m^3 \qquad \text{Multiply monomials.} \qquad \text{NOW TRY} \circlearrowright$$

OBJECTIVE 2 **Multiply two polynomials.** To find the product of the polynomials $x^2 + 3x + 5$ and $x - 4$, we can think of $x - 4$ as a single quantity and use the distributive property as follows.

$$(x^2 + 3x + 5)(x - 4)$$
$$= x^2(x - 4) + 3x(x - 4) + 5(x - 4) \qquad \text{Distributive property}$$
$$= x^2(x) + x^2(-4) + 3x(x) + 3x(-4) + 5(x) + 5(-4)$$
$$\qquad\qquad\qquad\qquad\qquad\qquad\qquad \text{Distributive property again}$$
$$= x^3 - 4x^2 + 3x^2 - 12x + 5x - 20 \qquad \text{Multiply monomials.}$$
$$= x^3 - x^2 - 7x - 20 \qquad \text{Combine like terms.}$$

NOW TRY ANSWER
1. $-6x^8 + 15x^7 - 30x^5$

Multiplying Polynomials

To multiply two polynomials, multiply each term of the second polynomial by each term of the first polynomial and add the products.

NOW TRY
EXERCISE 2

Multiply.

$(x^2 - 4)(2x^2 - 5x + 3)$

EXAMPLE 2   Multiplying Two Polynomials

Multiply $(m^2 + 5)(4m^3 - 2m^2 + 4m)$.

$$(m^2 + 5)(4m^3 - 2m^2 + 4m) \qquad \text{Multiply each term of the second polynomial by each term of the first.}$$

$$= m^2(4m^3) + m^2(-2m^2) + m^2(4m) + 5(4m^3) + 5(-2m^2) + 5(4m)$$

$$= 4m^5 - 2m^4 + 4m^3 + 20m^3 - 10m^2 + 20m$$

$$= 4m^5 - 2m^4 + 24m^3 - 10m^2 + 20m \qquad \text{Combine like terms.} \quad \textit{NOW TRY}$$

NOW TRY
EXERCISE 3

Multiply.

$$5t^2 - 7t + 4$$
$$\underline{\qquad 2t - 6}$$

EXAMPLE 3   Multiplying Polynomials Vertically

Multiply $(x^3 + 2x^2 + 4x + 1)(3x + 5)$ vertically.

$$x^3 + 2x^2 + 4x + 1 \qquad \text{Write the polynomials}$$
$$\underline{\qquad\qquad 3x + 5} \qquad \text{vertically}$$

Begin by multiplying each of the terms in the top row by 5.

$$x^3 + 2x^2 + 4x + 1$$
$$\underline{\qquad\qquad 3x + 5}$$
$$5x^3 + 10x^2 + 20x + 5 \qquad 5(x^3 + 2x^2 + 4x + 1)$$

Now multiply each term in the top row by $3x$. Then add like terms.

$$x^3 + 2x^2 + 4x + 1 \qquad \text{This process is similar to}$$
$$\underline{\qquad\qquad 3x + 5} \qquad \text{multiplication of whole numbers.}$$

> Place like terms in columns so they can be added.

$$5x^3 + 10x^2 + 20x + 5$$
$$\underline{3x^4 + 6x^3 + 12x^2 + 3x} \qquad 3x(x^3 + 2x^2 + 4x + 1)$$
$$3x^4 + 11x^3 + 22x^2 + 23x + 5 \leftarrow \text{Product} \qquad\qquad \textit{NOW TRY}$$

NOW TRY
EXERCISE 4

Find the product of
$9x^3 - 12x^2 + 3$ and $\frac{1}{3}x^2 - \frac{2}{3}$.

EXAMPLE 4   Multiplying Polynomials with Fractional Coefficients Vertically

Find the product of $4m^3 - 2m^2 + 4m$ and $\frac{1}{2}m^2 + \frac{5}{2}$.

$$4m^3 - 2m^2 + 4m$$
$$\underline{\qquad\qquad \tfrac{1}{2}m^2 + \tfrac{5}{2}}$$
$$10m^3 - 5m^2 + 10m \qquad \text{Terms of top row are multiplied by } \tfrac{5}{2}.$$
$$\underline{2m^5 - m^4 + 2m^3 \qquad\qquad} \quad \text{Terms of top row are multiplied by } \tfrac{1}{2}m^2.$$
$$2m^5 - m^4 + 12m^3 - 5m^2 + 10m \qquad \text{Add.} \qquad \textit{NOW TRY}$$

We can use a rectangle to model polynomial multiplication. For example, to find

$$(2x + 1)(3x + 2),$$

label a rectangle with each term as shown next on the left. Then put the product of each pair of monomials in the appropriate box, as shown on the right.

NOW TRY ANSWERS
2. $2x^4 - 5x^3 - 5x^2 + 20x - 12$
3. $10t^3 - 44t^2 + 50t - 24$
4. $3x^5 - 4x^4 - 6x^3 + 9x^2 - 2$

	$3x$	2
$2x$		
1		

	$3x$	2
$2x$	$6x^2$	$4x$
1	$3x$	2

The product of the binomials is the sum of the four monomial products.

$$(2x + 1)(3x + 2)$$
$$= 6x^2 + 4x + 3x + 2$$
$$= 6x^2 + 7x + 2$$

This approach can be extended to polynomials with any number of terms.

OBJECTIVE 3 **Multiply binomials by the FOIL method.** When multiplying binomials, the **FOIL method** reduces the rectangle method to a systematic approach without the rectangle. Consider this example.

$$(x + 3)(x + 5)$$

$= (x + 3)x + (x + 3)5$	Distributive property
$= x(x) + 3(x) + x(5) + 3(5)$	Distributive property again
$= x^2 + 3x + 5x + 15$	Multiply.
$= x^2 + 8x + 15$	Combine like terms.

The letters of the word FOIL originate as shown.

$(x + 3)(x + 5)$ Multiply the **First terms:** $x(x)$.   F

$(x + 3)(x + 5)$ Multiply the **Outer terms:** $x(5)$.   O
This is the **outer product.**

$(x + 3)(x + 5)$ Multiply the **Inner terms:** $3(x)$.   I
This is the **inner product.**

$(x + 3)(x + 5)$ Multiply the **Last terms:** $3(5)$.   L

The outer product, $5x$, and the inner product, $3x$, should be added mentally to get $8x$ so that the three terms of the answer can be written without extra steps.

$$(x + 3)(x + 5)$$
$$= x^2 + 8x + 15$$

Multiplying Binomials by the FOIL Method

Step 1 Multiply the two **First** terms of the binomials to get the first term of the answer.

Step 2 Find the **Outer** product and the **Inner** product and add them (when possible) to get the middle term of the answer.

Step 3 Multiply the two **Last** terms of the binomials to get the last term of the answer.

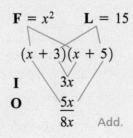

$$\mathbf{F} = x^2 \qquad \mathbf{L} = 15$$
$$(x + 3)(x + 5)$$
$$\mathbf{I} \qquad 3x$$
$$\mathbf{O} \qquad 5x$$
$$\qquad 8x \qquad \text{Add.}$$

**NOW TRY
EXERCISE 5**

Use the FOIL method to find the product.

$$(t - 6)(t + 5)$$

EXAMPLE 5 Using the FOIL Method

Use the FOIL method to find the product $(x + 8)(x - 6)$.

Step 1   F   Multiply the First terms: $x(x) = x^2$.

Step 2   O   Find the Outer product: $x(-6) = -6x$.

   I   Find the Inner product: $8(x) = 8x$.

   Add the outer and inner products mentally: $-6x + 8x = 2x$.

Step 3   L   Multiply the Last terms: $8(-6) = -48$.

$$(x + 8)(x - 6) = x^2 + 2x - 48 \qquad \text{Add the terms found in Steps 1–3.}$$

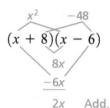

Shortcut:

The product $(9x - 2)(3y + 1)$ steps...

NOW TRY

**NOW TRY
EXERCISE 6**

Multiply.

$$(7y - 3)(2x + 5)$$

EXAMPLE 6 Using the FOIL Method

Multiply $(9x - 2)(3y + 1)$.

First	$(9x - 2)(3y + 1)$	$27xy$
Outer	$(9x - 2)(3y + 1)$	$9x$
Inner	$(9x - 2)(3y + 1)$	$-6y$
Last	$(9x - 2)(3y + 1)$	-2

These unlike terms cannot be combined.

$$\qquad\qquad\qquad\quad \text{F}\quad\ \text{O}\quad\ \text{I}\quad\ \text{L}$$

The product $(9x - 2)(3y + 1)$ is $27xy + 9x - 6y - 2$.   NOW TRY

**NOW TRY
EXERCISE 7**

Find each product.

(a) $(3p - 5q)(4p - q)$

(b) $5x^2(3x + 1)(x - 5)$

EXAMPLE 7 Using the FOIL Method

Find each product.

(a) $(2k + 5y)(k + 3y)$

$$\qquad\ \text{F}\quad\ \ \text{O}\quad\ \ \ \text{I}\quad\ \ \text{L}$$

$$= 2k(k) + 2k(3y) + 5y(k) + 5y(3y)$$

$$= 2k^2 + 6ky + 5ky + 15y^2 \qquad\qquad \text{Multiply.}$$

$$= 2k^2 + 11ky + 15y^2 \qquad\qquad\qquad \text{Combine like terms.}$$

(b) $(7p + 2q)(3p - q)$ **(c)** $2x^2(x - 3)(3x + 4)$

$$= 21p^2 - pq - 2q^2 \quad \text{FOIL} \qquad\qquad = 2x^2(3x^2 - 5x - 12) \quad \text{FOIL}$$

$$\qquad\qquad\qquad\qquad\qquad\qquad\qquad = 6x^4 - 10x^3 - 24x^2 \quad \begin{array}{l}\text{Distributive}\\\text{property}\end{array}$$

NOW TRY

NOTE Alternatively, **Example 7(c)** can be solved as follows.

$$2x^2(x - 3)(3x + 4) \qquad\qquad \text{Multiply } 2x^2 \text{ and } x - 3 \text{ first.}$$

$$= (2x^3 - 6x^2)(3x + 4) \qquad \text{Multiply that product and } 3x + 4.$$

$$= 6x^4 - 10x^3 - 24x^2 \qquad \text{Same answer}$$

4.5 EXERCISES

 MyMathLab Math XL PRACTICE WATCH DOWNLOAD READ REVIEW

⊕ *Complete solution available on the Video Resources on DVD*

Concept Check In Exercises 1 and 2, match each product in Column I with the correct polynomial in Column II.

I	II		I	II
1. (a) $5x^3(6x^7)$	**A.** $125x^{21}$		**2. (a)** $(x - 5)(x + 4)$	**A.** $x^2 + 9x + 20$
(b) $-5x^7(6x^3)$	**B.** $30x^{10}$		**(b)** $(x + 5)(x + 4)$	**B.** $x^2 - 9x + 20$
(c) $(5x^7)^3$	**C.** $-216x^9$		**(c)** $(x - 5)(x - 4)$	**C.** $x^2 - x - 20$
(d) $(-6x^3)^3$	**D.** $-30x^{10}$		**(d)** $(x + 5)(x - 4)$	**D.** $x^2 + x - 20$

*Find each product. **See Objective 1.***

3. $5y^4(3y^7)$ **4.** $10p^2(5p^3)$ **5.** $-15a^4(-2a^5)$

6. $-3m^6(-5m^4)$ **7.** $5p(3q^2)$ **8.** $4a^3(3b^2)$

9. $-6m^3(3n^2)$ **10.** $9r^3(-2s^2)$ **11.** $y^5 \cdot 9y \cdot y^4$

12. $x^2 \cdot 3x^3 \cdot 2x$ **13.** $(4x^3)(2x^2)(-x^5)$ **14.** $(7t^5)(3t^4)(-t^8)$

*Find each product. **See Example 1.***

⊕ **15.** $2m(3m + 2)$ **16.** $4x(5x + 3)$

17. $3p(-2p^3 + 4p^2)$ **18.** $4x(3 + 2x + 5x^3)$

19. $-8z(2z + 3z^2 + 3z^3)$ **20.** $-7y(3 + 5y^2 - 2y^3)$

21. $2y^3(3 + 2y + 5y^4)$ **22.** $2m^4(6 + 5m + 3m^2)$

23. $-4r^3(-7r^2 + 8r - 9)$ **24.** $-9a^5(-3a^6 - 2a^4 + 8a^2)$

25. $3a^2(2a^2 - 4ab + 5b^2)$ **26.** $4z^3(8z^2 + 5zy - 3y^2)$

27. $7m^3n^2(3m^2 + 2mn - n^3)$ **28.** $2p^2q(3p^2q^2 - 5p + 2q^2)$

*Find each product. **See Examples 2–4.***

⊕ **29.** $(6x + 1)(2x^2 + 4x + 1)$ **30.** $(9a + 2)(9a^2 + a + 1)$

31. $(9y - 2)(8y^2 - 6y + 1)$ **32.** $(2r - 1)(3r^2 + 4r - 4)$

⊕ **33.** $(4m + 3)(5m^3 - 4m^2 + m - 5)$ **34.** $(2y + 8)(3y^4 - 2y^2 + 1)$

35. $(2x - 1)(3x^5 - 2x^3 + x^2 - 2x + 3)$ **36.** $(2a + 3)(a^4 - a^3 + a^2 - a + 1)$

37. $(5x^2 + 2x + 1)(x^2 - 3x + 5)$ **38.** $(2m^2 + m - 3)(m^2 - 4m + 5)$

⊕ **39.** $(6x^4 - 4x^2 + 8x)\left(\dfrac{1}{2}x + 3\right)$ **40.** $(8y^6 + 4y^4 - 12y^2)\left(\dfrac{3}{4}y^2 + 2\right)$

*Find each product. Use the FOIL method. **See Examples 5–7.***

⊕ **41.** $(m + 7)(m + 5)$ **42.** $(n + 9)(n + 3)$ **43.** $(n - 1)(n + 4)$

44. $(t - 3)(t + 8)$ **45.** $(x + 5)(x - 5)$ **46.** $(y + 8)(y - 8)$

47. $(2x + 3)(6x - 4)$ **48.** $(3y + 5)(8y - 6)$ **49.** $(9 + t)(9 - t)$

50. $(10 + r)(10 - r)$ **51.** $(3x - 2)(3x - 2)$ **52.** $(4m + 3)(4m + 3)$

53. $(5a + 1)(2a + 7)$ **54.** $(b + 8)(6b - 2)$ **55.** $(6 - 5m)(2 + 3m)$

56. $(8 - 3a)(2 + a)$ **57.** $(5 - 3x)(4 + x)$ **58.** $(6 - 5x)(2 + x)$

59. $(3t - 4s)(t + 3s)$ **60.** $(2m - 3n)(m + 5n)$ ⊕ **61.** $(4x + 3)(2y - 1)$

62. $(5x + 7)(3y - 8)$ ⊕ **63.** $(3x + 2y)(5x - 3y)$ **64.** $(5a + 3b)(5a - 4b)$

65. $3y^3(2y + 3)(y - 5)$

66. $2x^2(2x - 5)(x + 3)$

67. $-8r^3(5r^2 + 2)(5r^2 - 2)$

68. $-5t^4(2t^4 + 1)(2t^4 - 1)$

*Find polynomials that represent **(a)** the area and **(b)** the perimeter of each square or rectangle. (If necessary, refer to the formulas on the inside covers.)*

69.

$3y + 7$

$y + 1$

70.

$6x + 2$

Find each product. In Exercises 81–84, 89, and 90, apply the meaning of exponents.

71. $\left(3p + \dfrac{5}{4}q\right)\left(2p - \dfrac{5}{3}q\right)$

72. $\left(2x + \dfrac{2}{3}y\right)\left(3x - \dfrac{3}{4}y\right)$

73. $(x + 7)^2$

74. $(m + 6)^2$

75. $(a - 4)(a + 4)$

76. $(b - 10)(b + 10)$

77. $(2p - 5)^2$

78. $(3m - 1)^2$

79. $(5k + 3q)^2$

80. $(8m + 3n)^2$

81. $(m - 5)^3$

82. $(p - 3)^3$

83. $(2a + 1)^3$

84. $(3m + 1)^3$

85. $-3a(3a + 1)(a - 4)$

86. $-4r(3r + 2)(2r - 5)$

87. $7(4m - 3)(2m + 1)$

88. $5(3k - 7)(5k + 2)$

89. $(3r - 2s)^4$

90. $(2z - 5y)^4$

91. $3p^3(2p^2 + 5p)(p^3 + 2p + 1)$

92. $5k^2(k^3 - 3)(k^2 - k + 4)$

93. $-2x^5(3x^2 + 2x - 5)(4x + 2)$

94. $-4x^3(3x^4 + 2x^2 - x)(-2x + 1)$

The figures in Exercises 95–98 are composed of triangles, squares, rectangles, and circles. Find a polynomial that represents the area of each shaded region. In Exercises 97 and 98, leave π in your answers. (If necessary, refer to the formulas on the inside covers.)

95.

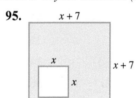

$x + 7$

x

x

$x + 7$

96.

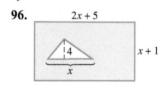

$2x + 5$

4

x

$x + 1$

97.

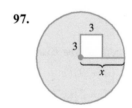

3

3

x

98.

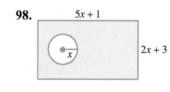

$5x + 1$

x

$2x + 3$

*Apply a power rule for exponents. **See Section 4.1.***

99. $(3m)^2$

100. $(5p)^2$

101. $(-2r)^2$

102. $(-5a)^2$

103. $(4x^2)^2$

104. $(8y^3)^2$

4.6   Special Products

OBJECTIVES

1 Square binomials.
2 Find the product of the sum and difference of two terms.
3 Find greater powers of binomials.

NOW TRY
EXERCISE 1
Find $(x + 5)^2$.

OBJECTIVE 1 Square binomials. The square of a binomial can be found quickly by using the method suggested by **Example 1.**

EXAMPLE 1 Squaring a Binomial

Find $(m + 3)^2$.

$$(m + 3)(m + 3)$$

$(m + 3)^2$ means $(m + 3)(m + 3)$.

$$= m^2 + 3m + 3m + 9 \qquad \text{FOIL}$$

$$= m^2 + 6m + 9$$

Combine like terms. This is the answer.

This result has the squares of the first and the last terms of the binomial.

$$m^2 = m^2 \quad \text{and} \quad 3^2 = 9$$

The middle term, 6m, is twice the product of the two terms of the binomial, since the outer and inner products are $m(3)$ and $3(m)$. Then we find their sum.

$$m(3) + 3(m) = 2(m)(3) = 6m \qquad \text{NOW TRY}$$

Square of a Binomial

The square of a binomial is a trinomial consisting of

the square of the first term $+$ twice the product of the two terms $+$ the square of the last term.

For x and y, the following are true.

$$(x + y)^2 = x^2 + 2xy + y^2$$

$$(x - y)^2 = x^2 - 2xy + y^2$$

EXAMPLE 2 Squaring Binomials

Find each binomial square and simplify.

$$(x - y)^2 = x^2 - 2 \cdot x \cdot y + y^2$$

(a) $(5z - 1)^2 = (5z)^2 - 2(5z)(1) + (1)^2$

$$= 25z^2 - 10z + 1 \qquad (5z)^2 = 5^2 z^2 = 25z^2$$

(b) $(3b + 5r)^2$

$$= (3b)^2 + 2(3b)(5r) + (5r)^2$$

$$= 9b^2 + 30br + 25r^2$$

(c) $(2a - 9x)^2$

$$= (2a)^2 - 2(2a)(9x) + (9x)^2$$

$$= 4a^2 - 36ax + 81x^2$$

(d) $\left(4m + \dfrac{1}{2} \right)^2$

$$= (4m)^2 + 2(4m)\left(\frac{1}{2}\right) + \left(\frac{1}{2}\right)^2$$

$$= 16m^2 + 4m + \frac{1}{4}$$

NOW TRY ANSWER
1. $x^2 + 10x + 25$

NOW TRY
EXERCISE 2

Find each binomial square and simplify.

(a) $(3x - 1)^2$

(b) $(4p - 5q)^2$

(c) $\left(6t - \frac{1}{3}\right)^2$

(d) $m(2m + 3)^2$

(e) $x(4x - 3)^2$ ⟵ Remember the middle term.

$= x(16x^2 - 24x + 9)$ Square the binomial.

$= 16x^3 - 24x^2 + 9x$ Distributive property   NOW TRY

In the square of a sum, all of the terms are positive, as in Examples 2(b) and (d). *In the square of a difference, the middle term is negative,* as in Examples 2(a), (c), and (e).

⚠ CAUTION   A common error when squaring a binomial is to forget the middle term of the product. In general,

$$(x + y)^2 = x^2 + 2xy + y^2, \quad not \quad x^2 + y^2,$$

and

$$(x - y)^2 = x^2 - 2xy + y^2, \quad not \quad x^2 - y^2.$$

OBJECTIVE 2   Find the product of the sum and difference of two terms. In binomial products of the form $(x + y)(x - y)$, one binomial is the sum of two terms and the other is the difference of the *same* two terms. Consider $(x + 2)(x - 2)$.

$$(x + 2)(x - 2)$$
$$= x^2 - 2x + 2x - 4 \quad \text{FOIL}$$
$$= x^2 - 4 \quad \text{Combine like terms.}$$

Thus, the product of $x + y$ and $x - y$ is the difference of two squares.

Product of the Sum and Difference of Two Terms

$$(x + y)(x - y) = x^2 - y^2$$

 NOW TRY
EXERCISE 3

Find the product.

$(t + 10)(t - 10)$

EXAMPLE 3   Finding the Product of the Sum and Difference of Two Terms

Find each product.

(a) $(x + 4)(x - 4)$

Use the rule for the product of the sum and difference of two terms.

$$(x + 4)(x - 4)$$
$$= x^2 - 4^2$$
$$= x^2 - 16$$

(b) $\left(\frac{2}{3} - w\right)\left(\frac{2}{3} + w\right)$

$$= \left(\frac{2}{3} + w\right)\left(\frac{2}{3} - w\right) \quad \text{Commutative property}$$

$$= \left(\frac{2}{3}\right)^2 - w^2 \quad (x + y)(x - y) = x^2 - y^2$$

$$= \frac{4}{9} - w^2 \quad \text{Square } \frac{2}{3}.$$ NOW TRY

NOW TRY ANSWERS

2. (a) $9x^2 - 6x + 1$
   (b) $16p^2 - 40pq + 25q^2$
   (c) $36t^2 - 4t + \frac{1}{9}$
   (d) $4m^3 + 12m^2 + 9m$
3. $t^2 - 100$

NOW TRY
EXERCISE 4

Find each product.

(a) $(4x - 6)(4x + 6)$

(b) $\left(5r - \frac{4}{5}\right)\left(5r + \frac{4}{5}\right)$

(c) $y(3y + 1)(3y - 1)$

EXAMPLE 4 **Finding the Product of the Sum and Difference of Two Terms**

Find each product.

$$(x + y) \quad (x \ - \ y)$$
$$\downarrow \quad \quad \downarrow \quad \downarrow \quad \quad \downarrow$$

(a) $(5m + 3)(5m - 3)$

Use the rule for the product of the sum and difference of two terms.

$$(5m + 3)(5m - 3)$$
$$= (5m)^2 - 3^2 \qquad (x + y)(x - y) = x^2 - y^2$$
$$= 25m^2 - 9 \qquad \text{Apply the exponents.}$$

(b) $(4x + y)(4x - y)$

$$= (4x)^2 - y^2$$
$$= 16x^2 - y^2$$

(c) $\left(z - \frac{1}{4}\right)\left(z + \frac{1}{4}\right)$

$$= z^2 - \frac{1}{16}$$

(d) $p(2p + 1)(2p - 1)$

$$= p(4p^2 - 1)$$
$$= 4p^3 - p \qquad \text{Distributive property}$$

NOW TRY

OBJECTIVE 3 **Find greater powers of binomials.** The methods used in the previous section and this section can be combined to find greater powers of binomials.

NOW TRY
EXERCISE 5

Find the product.

$$(2m - 1)^3$$

EXAMPLE 5 **Finding Greater Powers of Binomials**

Find each product.

(a) $(x + 5)^3$

$$= (x + 5)^2(x + 5) \qquad a^3 = a^2 \cdot a$$
$$= (x^2 + 10x + 25)(x + 5) \qquad \text{Square the binomial.}$$
$$= x^3 + 10x^2 + 25x + 5x^2 + 50x + 125 \qquad \text{Multiply polynomials.}$$
$$= x^3 + 15x^2 + 75x + 125 \qquad \text{Combine like terms.}$$

(b) $(2y - 3)^4$

$$= (2y - 3)^2(2y - 3)^2 \qquad a^4 = a^2 \cdot a^2$$
$$= (4y^2 - 12y + 9)(4y^2 - 12y + 9) \qquad \text{Square each binomial.}$$
$$= 16y^4 - 48y^3 + 36y^2 - 48y^3 + 144y^2 \qquad \text{Multiply polynomials.}$$
$$\quad - 108y + 36y^2 - 108y + 81$$
$$= 16y^4 - 96y^3 + 216y^2 - 216y + 81 \qquad \text{Combine like terms.}$$

(c) $-2r(r + 2)^3$

$$= -2r(r + 2)(r + 2)^2 \qquad a^3 = a \cdot a^2$$
$$= -2r(r + 2)(r^2 + 4r + 4) \qquad \text{Square the binomial.}$$
$$= -2r(r^3 + 4r^2 + 4r + 2r^2 + 8r + 8) \qquad \text{Multiply polynomials.}$$
$$= -2r(r^3 + 6r^2 + 12r + 8) \qquad \text{Combine like terms.}$$
$$= -2r^4 - 12r^3 - 24r^2 - 16r \qquad \text{Multiply.} \qquad \text{NOW TRY}$$

NOW TRY ANSWERS

4. **(a)** $16x^2 - 36$
   (b) $25r^2 - \frac{16}{25}$
   (c) $9y^3 - y$
5. $8m^3 - 12m^2 + 6m - 1$

4.6 EXERCISES

Complete solution available on the Video Resources on DVD

1. *Concept Check* Consider the square $(4x + 3)^2$.

(a) What is the simplest form of the square of the first term, $(4x)^2$?

(b) What is the simplest form of twice the product of the two terms, $2(4x)(3)$?

(c) What is the simplest form of the square of the last term, 3^2?

(d) Write the final product, which is a trinomial, using your results in parts (a)–(c).

2. Explain in your own words how to square a binomial. Give an example.

*Find each product. **See Examples 1 and 2.***

3. $(m + 2)^2$ **4.** $(x + 8)^2$ **5.** $(r - 3)^2$

6. $(z - 5)^2$ **7.** $(x + 2y)^2$ **8.** $(p - 3m)^2$

9. $(5p + 2q)^2$ **10.** $(8a + 3b)^2$ **11.** $(4a + 5b)^2$

12. $(9y + 4z)^2$ **13.** $\left(6m - \dfrac{4}{5}n\right)^2$ **14.** $\left(5x + \dfrac{2}{5}y\right)^2$

15. $t(3t - 1)^2$ **16.** $x(2x + 5)^2$ **17.** $3t(4t + 1)^2$

18. $2x(7x - 2)^2$ **19.** $-(4r - 2)^2$ **20.** $-(3y - 8)^2$

21. *Concept Check* Consider the product $(7x + 3y)(7x - 3y)$.

(a) What is the simplest form of the product of the first terms, $7x(7x)$?

(b) Multiply the outer terms, $7x(-3y)$. Then multiply the inner terms, $3y(7x)$. Add the results. What is this sum?

(c) What is the simplest form of the product of the last terms, $3y(-3y)$?

(d) Write the final product, using your results in parts (a) and (c). Why is the sum found in part (b) omitted here?

22. Explain in your own words how to find the product of the sum and the difference of two terms. Give an example.

*Find each product. **See Examples 3 and 4.***

23. $(k + 5)(k - 5)$ **24.** $(a + 8)(a - 8)$ **25.** $(4 - 3t)(4 + 3t)$

26. $(7 - 2x)(7 + 2x)$ **27.** $(5x + 2)(5x - 2)$ **28.** $(2m + 5)(2m - 5)$

29. $(5y + 3x)(5y - 3x)$ **30.** $(3x + 4y)(3x - 4y)$ **31.** $(10x + 3y)(10x - 3y)$

32. $(13r + 2z)(13r - 2z)$ **33.** $(2x^2 - 5)(2x^2 + 5)$ **34.** $(9y^2 - 2)(9y^2 + 2)$

35. $\left(\dfrac{3}{4} - x\right)\left(\dfrac{3}{4} + x\right)$ **36.** $\left(\dfrac{2}{3} + r\right)\left(\dfrac{2}{3} - r\right)$ **37.** $\left(9y + \dfrac{2}{3}\right)\left(9y - \dfrac{2}{3}\right)$

38. $\left(7x + \dfrac{3}{7}\right)\left(7x - \dfrac{3}{7}\right)$ **39.** $q(5q - 1)(5q + 1)$ **40.** $p(3p + 7)(3p - 7)$

41. Does $(a + b)^2$ equal $a^2 + b^2$ in general? Explain.

42. Does $(a + b)^3$ equal $a^3 + b^3$ in general? Explain.

*Find each product. **See Example 5.***

43. $(x + 1)^3$ **44.** $(y + 2)^3$ **45.** $(t - 3)^3$ **46.** $(m - 5)^3$

47. $(r + 5)^3$ **48.** $(p + 3)^3$ **49.** $(2a + 1)^3$ **50.** $(3m + 1)^3$

51. $(4x - 1)^4$ **52.** $(2x - 1)^4$ **53.** $(3r - 2t)^4$ **54.** $(2z + 5y)^4$

55. $2x(x + 1)^3$ **56.** $3y(y + 2)^3$ **57.** $-4t(t + 3)^3$

58. $-5r(r + 1)^3$ **59.** $(x + y)^2(x - y)^2$ **60.** $(s + 2)^2(s - 2)^2$

RELATING CONCEPTS EXERCISES 61–70

FOR INDIVIDUAL OR GROUP WORK

Special products can be illustrated by using areas of rectangles. Use the figure, and **work Exercises 61–66 in order** *to justify the special product*

$$(a + b)^2 = a^2 + 2ab + b^2.$$

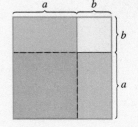

61. Express the area of the large square as the square of a binomial.

62. Give the monomial that represents the area of the red square.

63. Give the monomial that represents the sum of the areas of the blue rectangles.

64. Give the monomial that represents the area of the yellow square.

65. What is the sum of the monomials you obtained in **Exercises 62–64**?

66. Explain why the binomial square you found in **Exercise 61** must equal the polynomial you found in **Exercise 65**.

To understand how the special product $(a + b)^2 = a^2 + 2ab + b^2$ *can be applied to a purely numerical problem,* **work Exercises 67–70 in order.**

67. Evaluate 35^2, using either traditional paper-and-pencil methods or a calculator.

68. The number 35 can be written as $30 + 5$. Therefore, $35^2 = (30 + 5)^2$. Use the special product for squaring a binomial with $a = 30$ and $b = 5$ to write an expression for $(30 + 5)^2$. Do not simplify at this time.

69. Use the order of operations to simplify the expression you found in **Exercise 68**.

70. How do the answers in **Exercises 67 and 69** compare?

The special product

$$(x + y)(x - y) = x^2 - y^2$$

can be used to perform some multiplication problems. Here are two examples.

$$
\begin{aligned}
51 \times 49 &= (50 + 1)(50 - 1) \\
&= 50^2 - 1^2 \\
&= 2500 - 1 \\
&= 2499
\end{aligned}
\qquad
\begin{aligned}
102 \times 98 &= (100 + 2)(100 - 2) \\
&= 100^2 - 2^2 \\
&= 10{,}000 - 4 \\
&= 9996
\end{aligned}
$$

Once these patterns are recognized, multiplications of this type can be done mentally. Use this method to calculate each product mentally.

71. 101×99

72. 103×97

73. 201×199

74. 301×299

75. $20\frac{1}{2} \times 19\frac{1}{2}$

76. $30\frac{1}{3} \times 29\frac{2}{3}$

Determine a polynomial that represents the area of each figure. (If necessary, refer to the formulas on the inside covers.)

77.
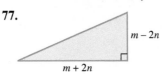

78.

79.
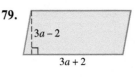

80.

81.

82.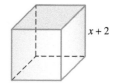

In Exercises 83 and 84, refer to the figure shown here.

83. Find a polynomial that represents the volume of the cube (in cubic units).

84. If the value of x is 6, what is the volume of the cube (in cubic units)?

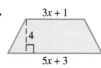

PREVIEW EXERCISES

Write each product as a sum of terms. Write answers with positive exponents only. Simplify each term. ***See Section 1.8.***

85. $\dfrac{1}{2p}(4p^2 + 2p + 8)$

86. $\dfrac{1}{5x}(5x^2 - 10x + 45)$

87. $\dfrac{1}{3m}(m^3 + 9m^2 - 6m)$

88. $\dfrac{1}{4y}(y^4 + 6y^2 + 8)$

Find each product. ***See Section 4.5.***

89. $-3k(8k^2 - 12k + 2)$

90. $(3r + 5)(2r + 1)$

91. $(-2k + 1)(8k^2 + 9k + 3)$

92. $(x^2 - 2)(3x^2 + x + 4)$

Subtract. ***See Section 4.4.***

93. $\begin{array}{r} 5t^2 + 2t - 6 \\ \underline{5t^2 - 3t - 9} \end{array}$

94. $\begin{array}{r} x^5 + x^3 - 2x^2 + 3 \\ \underline{-4x^5 \qquad + 3x^2 - 8} \end{array}$

4.7 Dividing Polynomials

OBJECTIVES

1 Divide a polynomial by a monomial.

2 Divide a polynomial by a polynomial.

OBJECTIVE 1 **Divide a polynomial by a monomial.** We add two fractions with a common denominator as follows.

$$\frac{a}{c} + \frac{b}{c} = \frac{a + b}{c}$$

In reverse, this statement gives a rule for dividing a polynomial by a monomial.

> **Dividing a Polynomial by a Monomial**
>
> To divide a polynomial by a monomial, divide each term of the polynomial by the monomial.
>
> $$\frac{a + b}{c} = \frac{a}{c} + \frac{b}{c} \quad (c \neq 0)$$
>
> *Examples:* $\quad \dfrac{2 + 5}{3} = \dfrac{2}{3} + \dfrac{5}{3} \quad$ and $\quad \dfrac{x + 3z}{2y} = \dfrac{x}{2y} + \dfrac{3z}{2y}$

The parts of a division problem are named here.

$$\text{Dividend} \rightarrow \frac{12x^2 + 6x}{6x} = 2x + 1 \leftarrow \text{Quotient}$$
$$\text{Divisor} \rightarrow$$

NOW TRY
EXERCISE 1

Divide $16a^6 - 12a^4$ by $4a^2$.

EXAMPLE 1 Dividing a Polynomial by a Monomial

Divide $5m^5 - 10m^3$ by $5m^2$.

$$\frac{5m^5 - 10m^3}{5m^2}$$

$$= \frac{5m^5}{5m^2} - \frac{10m^3}{5m^2} \qquad \text{Use the preceding rule,}$$
$$\qquad\qquad\qquad\qquad \text{with } + \text{ replaced by } -.$$

$$= m^3 - 2m \qquad \text{Quotient rule}$$

CHECK Multiply: $5m^2 \cdot (m^3 - 2m) = 5m^5 - 10m^3.$
$$\qquad\qquad\qquad\uparrow\qquad\quad\uparrow \qquad\qquad\qquad \text{Original polynomial}$$
$$\qquad\qquad\text{Divisor}\quad\text{Quotient}\qquad\qquad \text{(Dividend)}$$

Because division by 0 is undefined, the quotient $\frac{5m^5 - 10m^3}{5m^2}$ is undefined if $5m^2 = 0$, or $m = 0$. From now on, we assume that no denominators are 0.   NOW TRY

NOW TRY
EXERCISE 2

Divide.

$$\frac{36x^5 + 24x^4 - 12x^3}{6x^4}$$

EXAMPLE 2 Dividing a Polynomial by a Monomial

Divide.

$$\frac{16a^5 - 12a^4 + 8a^2}{4a^3}$$

> This becomes $\frac{2}{a}$, **not** $2a$.

$$= \frac{16a^5}{4a^3} - \frac{12a^4}{4a^3} + \frac{8a^2}{4a^3} \qquad \text{Divide each term by } 4a^3.$$

$$= 4a^2 - 3a + \frac{2}{a} \qquad \text{Quotient rule}$$

The quotient $4a^2 - 3a + \frac{2}{a}$ is *not* a polynomial because of the presence of the expression $\frac{2}{a}$, which has a variable in the denominator. While the sum, difference, and product of two polynomials are always polynomials, the quotient of two polynomials may not be a polynomial.

CHECK $4a^3\left(4a^2 - 3a + \frac{2}{a}\right)$ Divisor $\times$ Quotient should equal Dividend.

$$= 4a^3(4a^2) + 4a^3(-3a) + 4a^3\left(\frac{2}{a}\right) \qquad \text{Distributive property}$$

$$= 16a^5 - 12a^4 + 8a^2 \;\checkmark \qquad \text{Dividend} \qquad\qquad \text{NOW TRY}$$

⚠ **CAUTION** The most frequent error in a problem like that in **Example 2** is with the last term of the quotient.

$$\frac{8a^2}{4a^3} = \frac{8}{4}a^{2-3} = 2a^{-1} = 2\left(\frac{1}{a}\right) = \frac{2}{a}$$

NOW TRY ANSWERS

1. $4a^4 - 3a^2$

2. $6x + 4 - \frac{2}{x}$

NOW TRY
EXERCISE 3
Divide $7y^4 - 40y^5 + 100y^2$ by $-5y^2$.

EXAMPLE 3 Dividing a Polynomial by a Monomial with a Negative Coefficient

Divide $-7x^3 + 12x^4 - 4x$ by $-4x$.

Write the polynomial in descending powers as $12x^4 - 7x^3 - 4x$ before dividing.

$$\frac{12x^4 - 7x^3 - 4x}{-4x}$$

[Write in descending powers.]

$$= \frac{12x^4}{-4x} - \frac{7x^3}{-4x} - \frac{4x}{-4x}$$ Divide each term by $-4x$.

$$= -3x^3 - \frac{7x^2}{-4} - (-1)$$ Quotient rule

$$= -3x^3 + \frac{7x^2}{4} + 1$$ [Be sure to include 1 in the answer.]

Check by multiplying.

NOW TRY

NOW TRY
EXERCISE 4
Divide $35m^5n^4 - 49m^2n^3 + 12mn$ by $7m^2n$.

EXAMPLE 4 Dividing a Polynomial by a Monomial

Divide $180x^4y^{10} - 150x^3y^8 + 120x^2y^6 - 90xy^4 + 100y$ by $30xy^2$.

$$\frac{180x^4y^{10} - 150x^3y^8 + 120x^2y^6 - 90xy^4 + 100y}{30xy^2}$$

$$= \frac{180x^4y^{10}}{30xy^2} - \frac{150x^3y^8}{30xy^2} + \frac{120x^2y^6}{30xy^2} - \frac{90xy^4}{30xy^2} + \frac{100y}{30xy^2}$$

$$= 6x^3y^8 - 5x^2y^6 + 4xy^4 - 3y^2 + \frac{10}{3xy}$$

NOW TRY

OBJECTIVE 2 Divide a polynomial by a polynomial. As shown in the box, we use a method of "long division" to divide a polynomial by a polynomial (other than a monomial). *Both polynomials must first be written in descending powers.*

Dividing Whole Numbers	Dividing Polynomials
Step 1	
Divide 6696 by 27.	Divide $8x^3 - 4x^2 - 14x + 15$ by $2x + 3$.
$27\overline{)6696}$	$2x + 3\overline{)8x^3 - 4x^2 - 14x + 15}$
Step 2	
66 divided by 27 $= 2$.	$8x^3$ divided by $2x = 4x^2$.
$2 \cdot 27 = 54$	$4x^2(2x + 3) = 8x^3 + 12x^2$
$\begin{array}{r} 2 \\ 27\overline{)6696} \\ 54 \end{array}$	$\begin{array}{r} 4x^2 \\ 2x + 3\overline{)8x^3 - 4x^2 - 14x + 15} \\ 8x^3 + 12x^2 \end{array}$

(continued)

NOW TRY ANSWERS
3. $8y^3 - \frac{7y^2}{5} - 20$

4. $5m^3n^3 - 7n^2 + \frac{12}{7m}$

Step 3

Subtract. Then bring down the next digit.

$$\begin{array}{r} 2 \\ 27\overline{)6696} \\ 54\downarrow \\ \hline 129 \end{array}$$

Subtract. Then bring down the next term.

$$\begin{array}{r} 4x^2 \\ 2x + 3\overline{)8x^3 - 4x^2 - 14x + 15} \\ 8x^3 + 12x^2\downarrow \\ \hline -16x^2 - 14x \end{array}$$

(To subtract two polynomials, change the signs of the second and then add.)

Step 4

129 divided by $27 = 4$.
$4 \cdot 27 = 108$

$$\begin{array}{r} 24 \\ 27\overline{)6696} \\ 54 \\ \hline 129 \\ 108 \end{array}$$

$-16x^2$ divided by $2x = -8x$.
$-8x(2x + 3) = -16x^2 - 24x$

$$\begin{array}{r} 4x^2 - 8x \\ 2x + 3\overline{)8x^3 - 4x^2 - 14x + 15} \\ 8x^3 + 12x^2 \\ \hline -16x^2 - 14x \\ -16x^2 - 24x \end{array}$$

Step 5

Subtract. Then bring down the next digit.

$$\begin{array}{r} 24 \\ 27\overline{)6696} \\ 54\mid \\ \hline 129\downarrow \\ 108\downarrow \\ \hline 216 \end{array}$$

Subtract. Then bring down the next term.

$$\begin{array}{r} 4x^2 - 8x \\ 2x + 3\overline{)8x^3 - 4x^2 - 14x + 15} \\ 8x^3 + 12x^2 \\ \hline -16x^2 - 14x \\ -16x^2 - 24x\downarrow \\ \hline 10x + 15 \end{array}$$

Step 6

216 divided by $27 = 8$.
$8 \cdot 27 = 216$

$$\begin{array}{r} 248 \\ 27\overline{)6696} \\ 54 \\ \hline 129 \\ 108 \\ \hline 216 \\ 216 \end{array}$$

Remainder $\longrightarrow 0$

6696 divided by 27 is 248. The remainder is 0.

$10x$ divided by $2x = 5$.
$5(2x + 3) = 10x + 15$

$$\begin{array}{r} 4x^2 - 8x + 5 \\ 2x + 3\overline{)8x^3 - 4x^2 - 14x + 15} \\ 8x^3 + 12x^2 \\ \hline -16x^2 - 14x \\ -16x^2 - 24x \\ \hline 10x + 15 \\ 10x + 15 \end{array}$$

Remainder $\longrightarrow 0$

$8x^3 - 4x^2 - 14x + 15$ divided by $2x + 3$ is $4x^2 - 8x + 5$. The remainder is 0.

Step 7

CHECK Multiply.

$$27 \cdot 248 = 6696 \ \checkmark$$

CHECK Multiply.

$$(2x + 3)(4x^2 - 8x + 5)$$
$$= 8x^3 - 4x^2 - 14x + 15 \ \checkmark$$

NOW TRY
EXERCISE 5

Divide.

$$\frac{4x^2 + x - 18}{x - 2}$$

EXAMPLE 5 Dividing a Polynomial by a Polynomial

Divide. $\dfrac{3x^2 - 5x - 28}{x - 4}$

Step 1 $3x^2$ divided by x is $3x$.
$3x(x - 4) = 3x^2 - 12x$

Step 2 Subtract $3x^2 - 12x$ from $3x^2 - 5x$. Bring down -28.

Step 3 $7x$ divided by x is 7.
$7(x - 4) = 7x - 28$

Step 4 Subtract $7x - 28$ from $7x - 28$. The remainder is 0.

$$
\begin{array}{r}
3x + 7 \quad \leftarrow \text{Quotient} \\
x - 4 \overline{)3x^2 - 5x - 28} \quad \leftarrow \text{Dividend} \\
\underline{3x^2 - 12x} \\
7x - 28 \\
\underline{7x - 28} \\
0
\end{array}
$$

Divisor

CHECK Multiply the divisor, $x - 4$, by the quotient, $3x + 7$. The product must be the original dividend, $3x^2 - 5x - 28$.

$$(x - 4)(3x + 7) = 3x^2 + 7x - 12x - 28$$
$$= 3x^2 - 5x - 28 \; \checkmark$$

Divisor Quotient

Dividend

NOW TRY

EXAMPLE 6 Dividing a Polynomial by a Polynomial

Divide. $\dfrac{5x + 4x^3 - 8 - 4x^2}{2x - 1}$

The first polynomial must be written in descending powers as $4x^3 - 4x^2 + 5x - 8$. Then divide by $2x - 1$.

$$
\begin{array}{r}
2x^2 - x + 2 \\
2x - 1 \overline{)4x^3 - 4x^2 + 5x - 8} \\
\underline{4x^3 - 2x^2} \\
-2x^2 + 5x \\
\underline{-2x^2 + x} \\
4x - 8 \\
\underline{4x - 2} \\
-6 \quad \leftarrow \text{Remainder}
\end{array}
$$

Write in descending powers.

Each time you subtract, add the opposite.

Step 1 $4x^3$ divided by $2x$ is $2x^2$. $2x^2(2x - 1) = 4x^3 - 2x^2$

Step 2 Subtract. Bring down the next term.

Step 3 $-2x^2$ divided by $2x$ is $-x$. $-x(2x - 1) = -2x^2 + x$

Step 4 Subtract. Bring down the next term.

Step 5 $4x$ divided by $2x$ is 2. $2(2x - 1) = 4x - 2$

Step 6 Subtract. The remainder is -6. Write the remainder as the numerator of a fraction that has $2x - 1$ as its denominator. Because of the nonzero remainder, the answer is not a polynomial.

Remember to add $\frac{\text{remainder}}{\text{divisor}}$. Don't forget the + sign.

$$\text{Dividend} \rightarrow \dfrac{4x^3 - 4x^2 + 5x - 8}{2x - 1} \leftarrow \text{Divisor} = \underbrace{2x^2 - x + 2}_{\substack{\text{Quotient} \\ \text{polynomial}}} + \underbrace{\dfrac{-6}{2x - 1}}_{\substack{\text{Fractional part} \\ \text{of quotient}}} \begin{array}{l} \leftarrow \text{Remainder} \\ \leftarrow \text{Divisor} \end{array}$$

NOW TRY ANSWER
5. $4x + 9$

CHAPTER (4)   SUMMARY

KEY TERMS

4.1

base
exponent
power
exponential expression

4.3

scientific notation

4.4

term
numerical coefficient
like terms
polynomial
descending powers
degree of a term
degree of a polynomial

monomial
binomial
trinomial
parabola
vertex
axis
line of symmetry

4.5

outer product
inner product
FOIL

NEW SYMBOLS

x^{-n} x to the negative n power

TEST YOUR WORD POWER

See how well you have learned the vocabulary in this chapter.

1. A **polynomial** is an algebraic expression made up of
   A. a term or a finite product of terms with positive coefficients and exponents
   B. a term or a finite sum of terms with real coefficients and whole number exponents
   C. the product of two or more terms with positive exponents
   D. the sum of two or more terms with whole number coefficients and exponents.

2. The **degree of a term** is
   A. the number of variables in the term

   B. the product of the exponents on the variables
   C. the least exponent on the variables
   D. the sum of the exponents on the variables.

3. **FOIL** is a method for
   A. adding two binomials
   B. adding two trinomials
   C. multiplying two binomials
   D. multiplying two trinomials.

4. A **binomial** is a polynomial with
   A. only one term
   B. exactly two terms
   C. exactly three terms
   D. more than three terms.

5. A **monomial** is a polynomial with
   A. only one term
   B. exactly two terms
   C. exactly three terms
   D. more than three terms.

6. A **trinomial** is a polynomial with
   A. only one term
   B. exactly two terms
   C. exactly three terms
   D. more than three terms.

ANSWERS

1. B; *Example:* $5x^3 + 2x^2 - 7$ **2.** D; *Examples:* The term 6 has degree 0, $3x$ has degree 1, $-2x^8$ has degree 8, and $5x^2y^4$ has degree 6.

3. C; *Example:* $(m + 4)(m - 3) = m(m) - 3m + 4m + 4(-3) = m^2 + m - 12$ **4.** B; *Example:* $3t^3 + 5t$ **5.** A; *Examples:* -5 and $4xy^5$
6. C; *Example:* $2a^2 - 3ab + b^2$

QUICK REVIEW

CONCEPTS	EXAMPLES

4.1 The Product Rule and Power Rules for Exponents

For any integers m and n, the following are true.

Product Rule $a^m \cdot a^n = a^{m+n}$

Power Rules   **(a)** $(a^m)^n = a^{mn}$

          (b) $(ab)^m = a^m b^m$

          (c) $\left(\dfrac{a}{b}\right)^m = \dfrac{a^m}{b^m}$ $(b \neq 0)$

Perform the operations by using rules for exponents.

$$2^4 \cdot 2^5 = 2^{4+5} = 2^9$$

$$(3^4)^2 = 3^{4 \cdot 2} = 3^8$$

$$(6a)^5 = 6^5 a^5$$

$$\left(\frac{2}{3}\right)^4 = \frac{2^4}{3^4}$$

4.2 Integer Exponents and the Quotient Rule

If $a \neq 0$, then for integers m and n, the following are true.

Zero Exponent $a^0 = 1$

Negative Exponent $a^{-n} = \dfrac{1}{a^n}$

Quotient Rule $\dfrac{a^m}{a^n} = a^{m-n}$

Negative-to-Positive Rules

$$\frac{a^{-m}}{b^{-n}} = \frac{b^n}{a^m} \quad (b \neq 0)$$

$$\left(\frac{a}{b}\right)^{-m} = \left(\frac{b}{a}\right)^m \quad (b \neq 0)$$

Simplify by using the rules for exponents.

$$15^0 = 1$$

$$5^{-2} = \frac{1}{5^2} = \frac{1}{25}$$

$$\frac{4^8}{4^3} = 4^{8-3} = 4^5$$

$$\frac{4^{-2}}{3^{-5}} = \frac{3^5}{4^2}$$

$$\left(\frac{6}{5}\right)^{-3} = \left(\frac{5}{6}\right)^3$$

4.3 An Application of Exponents: Scientific Notation

To write a number in scientific notation

$$a \times 10^n, \quad \text{where} \quad 1 \le |a| < 10,$$

move the decimal point to follow the first nonzero digit.

1. If moving the decimal point makes the number less, n is positive.
2. If it makes the number greater, n is negative.
3. If the decimal point is not moved, n is 0.

Write in scientific notation.

$$247 = 2.47 \times 10^2$$

$$0.0051 = 5.1 \times 10^{-3}$$

$$4.8 = 4.8 \times 10^0$$

Write without exponents.

$$3.25 \times 10^5 = 325{,}000$$

$$8.44 \times 10^{-6} = 0.00000844$$

4.4 Adding and Subtracting Polynomials; Graphing Simple Polynomials

Adding Polynomials
Add like terms.

Add.
$$\begin{array}{r} 2x^2 + 5x - 3 \\ 5x^2 - 2x + 7 \\ \hline 7x^2 + 3x + 4 \end{array}$$

Subtracting Polynomials
Change the signs of the terms in the second polynomial and add the second polynomial to the first.

Subtract.
$$(2x^2 + 5x - 3) - (5x^2 - 2x + 7)$$
$$= (2x^2 + 5x - 3) + (-5x^2 + 2x - 7)$$
$$= -3x^2 + 7x - 10$$

(continued)

CONCEPTS	EXAMPLES

Graphing Simple Polynomials

To graph a simple polynomial equation such as $y = x^2 - 2$, plot points near the vertex. (In this chapter, all parabolas have a vertex on the x-axis or the y-axis.)

Graph $y = x^2 - 2$.

x	y
-2	2
-1	-1
0	-2
1	-1
2	2

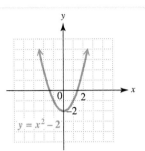

$y = x^2 - 2$

4.5 Multiplying Polynomials

General Method for Multiplying Polynomials

Multiply each term of the first polynomial by each term of the second polynomial. Then add like terms.

Multiply.

$$
\begin{array}{r}
3x^3 - 4x^2 + 2x - 7 \\
4x + 3 \\
\hline
9x^3 - 12x^2 + 6x - 21 \\
12x^4 - 16x^3 + 8x^2 - 28x \\
\hline
12x^4 - 7x^3 - 4x^2 - 22x - 21
\end{array}
$$

FOIL Method for Multiplying Binomials

Step 1 Multiply the two **F**irst terms to get the first term of the product.

Step 2 Find the **O**uter product and the **I**nner product, and mentally add them, when possible, to get the middle term of the product.

Step 3 Multiply the two **L**ast terms to get the last term of the product.

Add the terms found in Steps 1–3.

Multiply. $(2x + 3)(5x - 4)$

$$2x(5x) = 10x^2 \qquad \textbf{F}$$

$$2x(-4) + 3(5x) = 7x \qquad \textbf{O, I}$$

$$3(-4) = -12 \qquad \textbf{L}$$

The product is $10x^2 + 7x - 12$.

4.6 Special Products

Square of a Binomial

$$(x + y)^2 = x^2 + 2xy + y^2$$
$$(x - y)^2 = x^2 - 2xy + y^2$$

Multiply.

$$(3x + 1)^2 = 9x^2 + 6x + 1$$
$$(2m - 5n)^2 = 4m^2 - 20mn + 25n^2$$

Product of the Sum and Difference of Two Terms

$$(x + y)(x - y) = x^2 - y^2$$

$$(4a + 3)(4a - 3) = 16a^2 - 9$$

4.7 Dividing Polynomials

Dividing a Polynomial by a Monomial

Divide each term of the polynomial by the monomial.

$$\frac{a + b}{c} = \frac{a}{c} + \frac{b}{c}$$

Divide.

$$\frac{4x^3 - 2x^2 + 6x - 9}{2x} = 2x^2 - x + 3 - \frac{9}{2x}$$

Divide each term in the numerator by $2x$.

Dividing a Polynomial by a Polynomial

Use "long division."

$$
\begin{array}{r}
2x - 5 \\
3x + 4 \overline{)6x^2 - 7x - 21} \\
6x^2 + 8x \\
\hline
-15x - 21 \\
-15x - 20 \\
\hline
-1 \leftarrow \text{Remainder}
\end{array}
$$

The final answer is $2x - 5 + \frac{-1}{3x + 4}$.

CHAPTER **4**

REVIEW EXERCISES

4.1 *Use the product rule, power rules, or both to simplify each expression. Write the answers in exponential form.*

1. $4^3 \cdot 4^8$

2. $(-5)^6(-5)^5$

3. $(-8x^4)(9x^3)$

4. $(2x^2)(5x^3)(x^9)$

5. $(19x)^5$

6. $(-4y)^7$

7. $5(pt)^4$

8. $\left(\dfrac{7}{5}\right)^6$

9. $(3x^2y^3)^3$

10. $(t^4)^8(t^2)^5$

11. $(6x^2z^4)^2(x^3yz^2)^4$

12. $\left(\dfrac{2m^3n}{p^2}\right)^3$

13. Why does the product rule for exponents not apply to the expression $7^2 + 7^4$?

4.2 *Evaluate each expression.*

14. $6^0 + (-6)^0$

15. $-(-23)^0$

16. -10^0

Simplify. Write each answer with only positive exponents. Assume that all variables represent nonzero real numbers.

17. -7^{-2}

18. $\left(\dfrac{5}{8}\right)^{-2}$

19. $(5^{-2})^{-4}$

20. $9^3 \cdot 9^{-5}$

21. $2^{-1} + 4^{-1}$

22. $\dfrac{6^{-5}}{6^{-3}}$

23. $\dfrac{x^{-7}}{x^{-9}}$

24. $\dfrac{y^4 \cdot y^{-2}}{y^{-5}}$

25. $(3r^{-2})^{-4}$

26. $(3p)^4(3p^{-7})$

27. $\dfrac{ab^{-3}}{a^4b^2}$

28. $\dfrac{(6r^{-1})^2(2r^{-4})}{r^{-5}(r^2)^{-3}}$

4.3 *Write each number in scientific notation.*

29. 48,000,000

30. 28,988,000,000

31. 0.0000000824

Write each number without exponents.

32. 2.4×10^4

33. 7.83×10^7

34. 8.97×10^{-7}

Perform each indicated operation and write the answer without exponents.

35. $(2 \times 10^{-3}) \times (4 \times 10^5)$

36. $\dfrac{8 \times 10^4}{2 \times 10^{-2}}$

37. $\dfrac{12 \times 10^{-5} \times 5 \times 10^4}{4 \times 10^3 \times 6 \times 10^{-2}}$

Write each boldface italic number in the quote without exponents.

38. The muon, a close relative of the electron produced by the bombardment of cosmic rays against the upper atmosphere, has a half-life of 2 millionths of a second (*2×10^{-6}* s). (Excerpt from *Conceptual Physics*, 6th edition, by Paul G. Hewitt. Copyright © by Paul G. Hewitt. Published by HarperCollins College Publishers.)

39. There are 13 red balls and 39 black balls in a box. Mix them up and draw 13 out one at a time without returning any ball . . . the probability that the 13 drawings each will produce a red ball is . . . *1.6×10^{-12}*. (Weaver, Warren, *Lady Luck*.)

Write each boldface italic number in scientific notation.

40. An electron and a positron attract each other in two ways: the electromagnetic attraction of their opposite electric charges, and the gravitational attraction of their two masses. The electromagnetic attraction is

$$4,200,000,000,000,000,000,000,000,000,000,000,000,000$$

times as strong as the gravitational. (Asimov, Isaac, *Isaac Asimov's Book of Facts.*)

41. The aircraft carrier USS John Stennis is a *97,000*-ton nuclear powered floating city with a crew of *5000*. (*Source:* Seelye, Katharine Q., "Staunch Allies Hard to Beat: Defense Dept., Hollywood," *New York Times,* in *Plain Dealer.*)

42. A googol is

$$10,000,000,000,000,000,000,000,000,000,000,000,000,000,000,000,$$
$$000,000,000,000,000,000,000,000,000,000,000,000,000,000,000.$$

The Web search engine Google is named after a googol. Sergey Brin, president and cofounder of Google, Inc., was a mathematics major. He chose the name Google to describe the vast reach of this search engine. (*Source: The Gazette.*)

43. According to Campbell, Mitchell, and Reece in *Biology Concepts and Connections* (Benjamin Cummings, 1994, p. 230), "The amount of DNA in a human cell is about *1000* times greater than the DNA in *E. coli.* Does this mean humans have 1000 times as many genes as the *2000* in *E. coli?* The answer is probably no; the human genome is thought to carry between *50,000* and *100,000* genes, which code for various proteins (as well as for tRNA and rRNA)."

4.4 *In Exercises 44–48, combine like terms where possible in each polynomial. Write the answer in descending powers of the variable. Give the degree of the answer. Identify the polynomial as a* monomial, *a* binomial, *a* trinomial, *or* none of these.

44. $9m^2 + 11m^2 + 2m^2$
45. $-4p + p^3 - p^2 + 8p + 2$

46. $12a^5 - 9a^4 + 8a^3 + 2a^2 - a + 3$
47. $-7y^5 - 8y^4 - y^5 + y^4 + 9y$

48. $(12r^4 - 7r^3 + 2r^2) - (5r^4 - 3r^3 + 2r^2 - 1)$

49. Simplify. $(5x^3y^2 - 3xy^5 + 12x^2) - (-9x^2 - 8x^3y^2 + 2xy^5)$

Add or subtract as indicated.

50. Add.

$$-2a^3 + 5a^2$$
$$\underline{3a^3 - a^2}$$

51. Subtract.

$$6y^2 - 8y + 2$$
$$\underline{5y^2 + 2y - 7}$$

52. Subtract.

$$-12k^4 - 8k^2 + 7k$$
$$\underline{k^4 + 7k^2 - 11k}$$

Graph each equation by completing the table of values.

53. $y = -x^2 + 5$

x	-2	-1	0	1	2
y					

54. $y = 3x^2 - 2$

x	-2	-1	0	1	2
y					

4.5 *Find each product.*

55. $(a + 2)(a^2 - 4a + 1)$
56. $(3r - 2)(2r^2 + 4r - 3)$

57. $(5p^2 + 3p)(p^3 - p^2 + 5)$
58. $(m - 9)(m + 2)$

59. $(3k - 6)(2k + 1)$
60. $(a + 3b)(2a - b)$

61. $(6k + 5q)(2k - 7q)$
62. $(s - 1)^3$

4.6 *Find each product.*

63. $(a + 4)^2$

64. $(2r + 5t)^2$

65. $(6m - 5)(6m + 5)$

66. $(5a + 6b)(5a - 6b)$

67. $(r + 2)^3$

68. $t(5t - 3)^2$

69. Choose values for x and y to show that, in general, the following hold true.

    (a) $(x + y)^2 \neq x^2 + y^2$ **(b)** $(x + y)^3 \neq x^3 + y^3$

70. Write an explanation on how to raise a binomial to the third power. Give an example.

71. Refer to **Exercise 69.** Suppose that you happened to let $x = 0$ and $y = 1$. Would your results be sufficient to illustrate the truth, in general, of the inequalities shown? If not, what would you need to do as your next step in working the exercise?

In Exercises 72 and 73, if necessary, refer to the formulas on the inside covers.

72. Find a polynomial that represents, in cubic centimeters, the volume of a cube with one side having length $(x^2 + 2)$ centimeters.

73. Find a polynomial that represents, in cubic inches, the volume of a sphere with radius $(x + 1)$ inches.

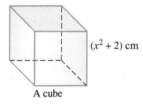

$(x^2 + 2)$ cm

A cube

$(x + 1)$ in.

A sphere

4.7 *Perform each division.*

74. $\dfrac{-15y^4}{9y^2}$

75. $\dfrac{6y^4 - 12y^2 + 18y}{6y}$

76. $(-10m^4n^2 + 5m^3n^2 + 6m^2n^4) \div (5m^2n)$

77. *Concept Check* What polynomial, when multiplied by $6m^2n$, gives the product

$$12m^3n^2 + 18m^6n^3 - 24m^2n^2?$$

78. *Concept Check* One of your friends in class simplified

$$\frac{6x^2 - 12x}{6} \quad \text{as} \quad x^2 - 12x.$$

WHAT WENT WRONG? Give the correct answer.

Perform each division.

79. $\dfrac{2r^2 + 3r - 14}{r - 2}$

80. $\dfrac{10a^3 + 9a^2 - 14a + 9}{5a - 3}$

81. $\dfrac{x^4 - 5x^2 + 3x^3 - 3x + 4}{x^2 - 1}$

82. $\dfrac{m^4 + 4m^3 - 12m - 5m^2 + 6}{m^2 - 3}$

83. $\dfrac{16x^2 - 25}{4x + 5}$

84. $\dfrac{25y^2 - 100}{5y + 10}$

85. $\dfrac{y^3 - 8}{y - 2}$

86. $\dfrac{1000x^6 + 1}{10x^2 + 1}$

87. $\dfrac{6y^4 - 15y^3 + 14y^2 - 5y - 1}{3y^2 + 1}$

88. $\dfrac{4x^5 - 8x^4 - 3x^3 + 22x^2 - 15}{4x^2 - 3}$

MIXED REVIEW EXERCISES

Perform each indicated operation. Write answers with only positive exponents. Assume that all variables represent nonzero real numbers.

89. $5^0 + 7^0$

90. $\left(\dfrac{6r^2 p}{5}\right)^3$

91. $(12a + 1)(12a - 1)$

92. 2^{-4}

93. $(8^{-3})^4$

94. $\dfrac{2p^3 - 6p^2 + 5p}{2p^2}$

95. $\dfrac{(2m^{-5})(3m^2)^{-1}}{m^{-2}(m^{-1})^2}$

96. $(3k - 6)(2k^2 + 4k + 1)$

97. $\dfrac{r^9 \cdot r^{-5}}{r^{-2} \cdot r^{-7}}$

98. $(2r + 5s)^2$

99. $(-5y^2 + 3y - 11) + (4y^2 - 7y + 15)$ **100.** $(2r + 5)(5r - 2)$

101. $\dfrac{2y^3 + 17y^2 + 37y + 7}{2y + 7}$

102. $(25x^2 y^3 - 8xy^2 + 15x^3 y) \div (10x^2 y^3)$

103. $(6p^2 - p - 8) - (-4p^2 + 2p - 3)$

104. $\dfrac{3x^3 - 2x + 5}{x - 3}$

105. $(-7 + 2k)^2$

106. $\left(\dfrac{x}{y^{-3}}\right)^{-4}$

107. Find polynomials that represent, in appropriate units, the **(a)** perimeter and **(b)** area of the rectangle shown.

$2x - 3$

$x + 2$

108. If the side of a square has a measure represented by $5x^4 + 2x^2$, what polynomials, in appropriate units, represent its **(a)** perimeter and **(b)** area?

$5x^4 + 2x^2$

CHAPTER 4

TEST   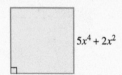   **CHAPTER Test Prep VIDEOS**

Step-by-step test solutions are found on the Chapter Test Prep Videos available via the Video Resources on DVD, in *MyMathLab* , or on You Tube (search "LialCombinedAlgebra").

View the complete solutions to all Chapter Test exercises on the Video Resources on DVD.

Evaluate each expression.

1. 5^{-4}

2. $(-3)^0 + 4^0$

3. $4^{-1} + 3^{-1}$

4. Simplify $\dfrac{(3x^2 y)^2 (xy^3)^2}{(xy)^3}$. Assume that x and y represent nonzero numbers.

Simplify, and write the answer using only positive exponents. Assume that all variables represent nonzero numbers.

5. $\dfrac{8^{-1} \cdot 8^4}{8^{-2}}$

6. $\dfrac{(x^{-3})^{-2}(x^{-1} y)^2}{(xy^{-2})^2}$

7. Determine whether each expression represents a number that is *positive, negative,* or *zero.*

   (a) 3^{-4} **(b)** $(-3)^4$ **(c)** -3^4 **(d)** 3^0 **(e)** $(-3)^0 - 3^0$ **(f)** $(-3)^{-3}$

8. (a) Write 45,000,000,000 using scientific notation.

   (b) Write 3.6×10^{-6} without using exponents.

   (c) Write the quotient without using exponents: $\dfrac{9.5 \times 10^{-1}}{5 \times 10^3}$.

9. A satellite galaxy of the Milky Way, known as the Large Magellanic Cloud, is **1000** light-years across. A *light-year* is equal to **5,890,000,000,000** mi. (*Source:* "Images of Brightest Nebula Unveiled," *USA Today*.)

   (a) Write the two boldface italic numbers in scientific notation.

   (b) How many miles across is the Large Magellanic Cloud?

For each polynomial, combine like terms when possible and write the polynomial in descending powers of the variable. Give the degree of the simplified polynomial. Decide whether the simplified polynomial is a monomial, *a* binomial, *a* trinomial, *or* none of these.

10. $5x^2 + 8x - 12x^2$ **11.** $13n^3 - n^2 + n^4 + 3n^4 - 9n^2$

12. Use the table to complete a set of ordered pairs that lie on the graph of $y = 2x^2 - 4$. Then graph the equation.

x	-2	-1	0	1	2
y					

Perform each indicated operation.

13. $(2y^2 - 8y + 8) + (-3y^2 + 2y + 3) - (y^2 + 3y - 6)$

14. $(-9a^3b^2 + 13ab^5 + 5a^2b^2) - (6ab^5 + 12a^3b^2 + 10a^2b^2)$

15. Subtract.   **16.** $3x^2(-9x^3 + 6x^2 - 2x + 1)$

   $9t^3 - 4t^2 + 2t + 2$
   $\underline{9t^3 + 8t^2 - 3t - 6}$

17. $(t - 8)(t + 3)$ **18.** $(4x + 3y)(2x - y)$

19. $(5x - 2y)^2$ **20.** $(10v + 3w)(10v - 3w)$

21. $(2r - 3)(r^2 + 2r - 5)$

22. What polynomial expression represents, in appropriate units, the perimeter of this square? The area?

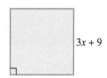

$3x + 9$

Perform each division.

23. $\dfrac{8y^3 - 6y^2 + 4y + 10}{2y}$ **24.** $(-9x^2y^3 + 6x^4y^3 + 12xy^3) \div (3xy)$

25. $\dfrac{5x^2 - x - 18}{5x + 9}$ **26.** $(3x^3 - x + 4) \div (x - 2)$

CHAPTERS (1–4) CUMULATIVE REVIEW EXERCISES

Write each fraction in lowest terms.

1. $\dfrac{28}{16}$

2. $\dfrac{55}{11}$

3. A contractor installs sheds. Each requires $1\frac{1}{4}$ yd³ of concrete. How much concrete would be needed for 25 sheds?

4. A retailer has $34,000 invested in her business. She finds that last year she earned 5.4% on this investment. How much did she earn?

5. List all positive integer factors of 45.

6. If $x = -2$ and $y = 4$, find the value of $\dfrac{4x - 2y}{x + y}$.

Perform each indicated operation.

7. $\dfrac{(-13 + 15) - (3 + 2)}{6 - 12}$

8. $-7 - 3[2 + (5 - 8)]$

Decide which property justifies each statement.

9. $(9 + 2) + 3 = 9 + (2 + 3)$

10. $6(4 + 2) = 6(4) + 6(2)$

11. Simplify the expression $-3(2x^2 - 8x + 9) - (4x^2 + 3x + 2)$.

Solve each equation.

12. $2 - 3(t - 5) = 4 + t$

13. $2(5x + 1) = 10x + 4$

14. $d = rt$ for r

15. $\dfrac{x}{5} = \dfrac{x - 2}{7}$

16. $\dfrac{1}{3}p - \dfrac{1}{6}p = -2$

17. $0.05x + 0.15(50 - x) = 5.50$

18. $4 - (3x + 12) = (2x - 9) - (5x - 1)$

Solve each problem.

19. A husky running the Iditarod burns $5\frac{3}{8}$ calories in exertion for every 1 calorie burned in thermoregulation in extreme cold. According to one scientific study, a husky in top condition burns an amazing total of 11,200 calories per day. How many calories are burned for exertion, and how many are burned for regulation of body temperature? Round answers to the nearest whole number.

2008 XXXVI Iditarod

20. One side of a triangle is twice as long as a second side. The third side of the triangle is 17 ft long. The perimeter of the triangle cannot be more than 50 ft. Find the longest possible values for the other two sides of the triangle.

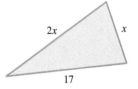

Solve each inequality.

21. $-2(x + 4) > 3x + 6$ **22.** $-3 \le 2x + 5 < 9$

23. Graph $y = -3x + 6$.

24. Consider the two points $(-1, 5)$ and $(2, 8)$.

    (a) Find the slope of the line joining them.

    (b) Find the equation of the line joining them.

Evaluate each expression.

25. $4^{-1} + 3^0$ **26.** $\dfrac{8^{-5} \cdot 8^7}{8^2}$

27. Write with positive exponents only. $\dfrac{(a^{-3}b^2)^2}{(2a^{-4}b^{-3})^{-1}}$

28. It takes about 3.6×10^1 sec at a speed of 3.0×10^5 km per sec for light from the sun to reach Venus. How far is Venus from the sun? (*Source: World Almanac and Book of Facts.*)

29. Graph $y = (x + 4)^2$, using the x-values $-6, -5, -4, -3$, and -2 to obtain a set of points.

Perform each indicated operation.

30. $(7x^3 - 12x^2 - 3x + 8) + (6x^2 + 4) - (-4x^3 + 8x^2 - 2x - 2)$

31. $(7x + 4)(9x + 3)$ **32.** $\dfrac{y^3 - 3y^2 + 8y - 6}{y - 1}$

Factoring and Applications

Wireless communication uses radio waves to carry signals and messages across distances. Cellular phones, one of the most popular forms of wireless communication, have become an invaluable tool for people to stay connected to family, friends, and work while on the go. In 2007, there were about 243 million cell phone subscribers in the United States, with 81% of the population having cell phone service. Total revenue from this service was about $133 billion. (*Source:* CITA—The Wireless Association.)

In **Exercise 37** of **Section 5.6,** we use a *quadratic equation* to model the number of cell phone subscribers in the United States.

5.1

The Greatest Common Factor; Factoring by Grouping

OBJECTIVES

1 Find the greatest common factor of a list of terms.

2 Factor out the greatest common factor.

3 Factor by grouping.

Recall from **Section 1.1** that to **factor** means "to write a quantity as a product." That is, factoring is the opposite of multiplying.

Multiplying	*Factoring*
$6 \cdot 2 = 12$	$12 = 6 \cdot 2$
↑ ↑ ↑	↑ ↑ ↑
Factors Product	Product Factors

Other **factored forms** of 12 are

$$-6(-2), \quad 3 \cdot 4, \quad -3(-4), \quad 12 \cdot 1, \quad \text{and} \quad -12(-1).$$

More than two factors may be used, so another factored form of 12 is $2 \cdot 2 \cdot 3$.

OBJECTIVE 1 Find the greatest common factor of a list of terms. An integer that is a factor of two or more integers is a **common factor** of those integers. For example, 6 is a common factor of 18 and 24, since 6 is a factor of both 18 and 24. Other common factors of 18 and 24 are 1, 2, and 3.

The **greatest common factor (GCF)** of a list of integers is the largest common factor of those integers. Thus, 6 is the greatest common factor of 18 and 24, since it is the largest of their common factors.

NOTE *Factors* of a number are also *divisors* of the number. The *greatest common factor* is actually the same as the *greatest common divisor.* Here are some useful divisibility rules for deciding what numbers divide into a given number.

A Whole Number Divisible by	Must Have the Following Property:
2	Ends in 0, 2, 4, 6, or 8
3	Sum of digits divisible by 3
4	Last two digits form a number divisible by 4
5	Ends in 0 or 5
6	Divisible by both 2 and 3
8	Last three digits form a number divisible by 8
9	Sum of digits divisible by 9
10	Ends in 0

Finding the Greatest Common Factor (GCF)

Step 1 **Factor.** Write each number in prime factored form.

Step 2 **List common factors.** List each prime number or each variable that is a factor of every term in the list. (If a prime does not appear in one of the prime factored forms, it cannot appear in the greatest common factor.)

Step 3 **Choose least exponents.** Use as exponents on the common prime factors the *least* exponents from the prime factored forms.

Step 4 **Multiply** the primes from Step 3. If there are no primes left after Step 3, the greatest common factor is 1.

NOW TRY
EXERCISE 1

Find the greatest common factor for each list of numbers.

(a) 24, 36

(b) 54, 90, 108

(c) 15, 19, 25

EXAMPLE 1 Finding the Greatest Common Factor for Numbers

Find the greatest common factor for each list of numbers.

(a) 30, 45

$$30 = 2 \cdot 3 \cdot 5$$
$$45 = 3 \cdot 3 \cdot 5$$

Write the prime factored form of each number.

Use each prime the least number of times it appears in all the factored forms. There is no 2 in the prime factored form of 45, so there will be no 2 in the greatest common factor. The least number of times 3 appears in all the factored forms is 1, and the least number of times 5 appears is also 1.

$$GCF = 3^1 \cdot 5^1 = 15$$

(b) 72, 120, 432

$$72 = 2 \cdot 2 \cdot 2 \cdot 3 \cdot 3$$
$$120 = 2 \cdot 2 \cdot 2 \cdot 3 \cdot 5$$
$$432 = 2 \cdot 2 \cdot 2 \cdot 2 \cdot 3 \cdot 3 \cdot 3$$

Write the prime factored form of each number.

The least number of times 2 appears in all the factored forms is 3, and the least number of times 3 appears is 1. There is no 5 in the prime factored form of either 72 or 432.

$$GCF = 2^3 \cdot 3^1 = 24$$

(c) 10, 11, 14

$$10 = 2 \cdot 5$$
$$11 = 11$$
$$14 = 2 \cdot 7$$

Write the prime factored form of each number.

There are no primes common to all three numbers, so the GCF is 1. *NOW TRY*

The greatest common factor can also be found for a list of variable terms. For example, the terms $x^4, x^5, x^6,$ and x^7 have x^4 as the greatest common factor because each of these terms can be written with x^4 as a factor.

$$x^4 = 1 \cdot x^4, \quad x^5 = x \cdot x^4, \quad x^6 = x^2 \cdot x^4, \quad x^7 = x^3 \cdot x^4$$

NOTE *The exponent on a variable in the GCF is the least exponent that appears in all the common factors.*

EXAMPLE 2 Finding the Greatest Common Factor for Variable Terms

Find the greatest common factor for each list of terms.

(a) $21m^7, 18m^6, 45m^8, 24m^5$

$$21m^7 = 3 \cdot 7 \cdot m^7$$
$$18m^6 = 2 \cdot 3 \cdot 3 \cdot m^6$$
$$45m^8 = 3 \cdot 3 \cdot 5 \cdot m^8$$
$$24m^5 = 2 \cdot 2 \cdot 2 \cdot 3 \cdot m^5$$

Here, 3 is the greatest common factor of the coefficients 21, 18, 45, and 24. The least exponent on m is 5.

$$GCF = 3m^5$$

NOW TRY ANSWERS
1. (a) 12 (b) 18 (c) 1

*NOW TRY
EXERCISE 2*

Find the greatest common factor for each list of terms.

(a) $25k^3, 15k^2, 35k^5$

(b) m^3n^5, m^4n^4, m^5n^2

(b) $x^4y^2, \quad x^7y^5, \quad x^3y^7, \quad y^{15}$

$x^4y^2 = x^4 \cdot y^2$ There is no x in the last term, y^{15}, so x will not appear in the greatest common factor. There is a y in each term, however, and 2 is the least exponent on y.

$x^7y^5 = x^7 \cdot y^5$

$x^3y^7 = x^3 \cdot y^7$

$y^{15} = y^{15}$

$$\text{GCF} = y^2$$

NOW TRY

OBJECTIVE 2 **Factor out the greatest common factor.** Writing a polynomial (a sum) in factored form as a product is called **factoring.** For example, the polynomial

$$3m + 12$$

has two terms: $3m$ and 12. The greatest common factor of these two terms is 3. We can write $3m + 12$ so that each term is a product with 3 as one factor.

$$3m + 12$$

$$= 3 \cdot m + 3 \cdot 4 \qquad \text{GCF} = 3$$

$$= 3(m + 4) \qquad \text{Distributive property}$$

The factored form of $3m + 12$ is $3(m + 4)$. This process is called **factoring out the greatest common factor.**

⚠ **CAUTION** The polynomial $3m + 12$ is *not* in factored form when written as

$$3 \cdot m + 3 \cdot 4. \qquad \text{Not in factored form}$$

The *terms* are factored, but the polynomial is not. The factored form of $3m + 12$ is the *product*

$$3(m + 4). \qquad \text{In factored form}$$

EXAMPLE 3 **Factoring Out the Greatest Common Factor**

Write in factored form by factoring out the greatest common factor.

(a) $5y^2 + 10y$

$$= 5y(y) + 5y(2) \qquad \text{GCF} = 5y$$

$$= 5y(y + 2) \qquad \text{Distributive property}$$

CHECK   Multiply the factored form.

$$5y(y + 2)$$

$$= 5y(y) + 5y(2) \qquad \text{Distributive property}$$

$$= 5y^2 + 10y \checkmark \qquad \text{Original polynomial}$$

(b) $20m^5 + 10m^4 + 15m^3$

$$= 5m^3(4m^2) + 5m^3(2m) + 5m^3(3) \qquad \text{GCF} = 5m^3$$

$$= 5m^3(4m^2 + 2m + 3) \qquad \text{Factor out } 5m^3.$$

CHECK $5m^3(4m^2 + 2m + 3)$

$$= 20m^5 + 10m^4 + 15m^3 \checkmark \qquad \text{Original polynomial}$$

NOW TRY ANSWERS
2. (a) $5k^2$ **(b)** m^3n^2

NOW TRY
EXERCISE 3

Write in factored form by factoring out the greatest common factor.

(a) $7t^4 - 14t^3$

(b) $8x^6 - 20x^5 + 28x^4$

(c) $30m^4n^3 - 42m^2n^2$

(c) $x^5 + x^3$

$$= x^3(x^2) + x^3(1) \qquad \text{GCF} = x^3$$

$$= x^3(x^2 + 1) \longleftarrow \boxed{\text{Don't forget the 1.}}$$

Check mentally by distributing x^3 over each term inside the parentheses.

(d) $20m^7p^2 - 36m^3p^4$

$$= 4m^3p^2(5m^4) - 4m^3p^2(9p^2) \qquad \text{GCF} = 4m^3p^2$$

$$= 4m^3p^2(5m^4 - 9p^2) \qquad \text{Factor out } 4m^3p^2. \qquad \text{NOW TRY}$$

⚠ **CAUTION** Be sure to include the 1 in a problem like **Example 3(c).** *Check that the factored form can be multiplied out to give the original polynomial.*

NOW TRY
EXERCISE 4

Write in factored form by factoring out the greatest common factor.

(a) $x(x + 2) + 5(x + 2)$

(b) $a(t + 10) - b(t + 10)$

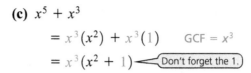
EXAMPLE 4 Factoring Out the Greatest Common Factor

Write in factored form by factoring out the greatest common factor.

$$\overbrace{\qquad}^{\text{Same}}$$

(a) $a(a + 3) + 4(a + 3)$ The binomial $a + 3$ is the greatest common factor.

$$= (a + 3)(a + 4) \qquad \text{Factor out } a + 3.$$

(b) $x^2(x + 1) - 5(x + 1)$

$$= (x + 1)(x^2 - 5) \qquad \text{Factor out } x + 1. \qquad \text{NOW TRY}$$

NOTE In factored forms like those in **Example 4,** the order of the factors does not matter because of the commutative property of multiplication.

$$(a + 3)(a + 4) \quad \text{can also be written} \quad (a + 4)(a + 3).$$

OBJECTIVE 3 Factor by grouping. *When a polynomial has four terms, common factors can sometimes be used to factor by grouping.*

EXAMPLE 5 Factoring by Grouping

Factor by grouping.

(a) $2x + 6 + ax + 3a$

Group the first two terms and the last two terms, since the first two terms have a common factor of 2 and the last two terms have a common factor of a.

$$2x + 6 + ax + 3a$$

$$= (2x + 6) + (ax + 3a) \qquad \text{Group the terms.}$$

$$= 2(x + 3) + a(x + 3) \qquad \text{Factor each group.}$$

The expression is still not in factored form because it is the *sum* of two terms. Now, however, $x + 3$ is a common factor and can be factored out.

$$= 2(x + 3) + a(x + 3) \qquad x + 3 \text{ is a common factor.}$$

$\boxed{(2 + a)(x + 3) \atop \text{is also correct.}} \longrightarrow = (x + 3)(2 + a) \qquad \text{Factor out } x + 3.$

NOW TRY ANSWERS

3. (a) $7t^3(t - 2)$
   (b) $4x^4(2x^2 - 5x + 7)$
   (c) $6m^2n^2(5m^2n - 7)$
4. (a) $(x + 2)(x + 5)$
   (b) $(t + 10)(a - b)$

NOW TRY
EXERCISE 5

Factor by grouping.

(a) $ab + 3a + 5b + 15$

(b) $12xy + 3x + 4y + 1$

(c) $x^3 + 5x^2 - 8x - 40$

The final result $(x + 3)(2 + a)$ is in factored form because it is a ***product.***

CHECK $(x + 3)(2 + a)$

$\qquad = 2x + ax + 6 + 3a \qquad$ FOIL (Section 5.5)

$\qquad = 2x + 6 + ax + 3a \;\checkmark \quad$ Rearrange terms to obtain
the original polynomial.

(b) $6ax + 24x + a + 4$

$\qquad = (6ax + 24x) + (a + 4) \qquad$ Group the terms.

$\qquad = 6x(a + 4) + 1(a + 4) \qquad$ Factor each group.

$\qquad\qquad\qquad$ `Remember the 1.`

$\qquad = (a + 4)(6x + 1) \qquad$ Factor out $a + 4$.

CHECK $(a + 4)(6x + 1)$

$\qquad\qquad = 6ax + a + 24x + 4 \qquad$ FOIL

$\qquad\qquad = 6ax + 24x + a + 4 \;\checkmark \quad$ Rearrange terms to obtain the
original polynomial.

(c) $2x^2 - 10x + 3xy - 15y$

$\qquad = (2x^2 - 10x) + (3xy - 15y) \qquad$ Group the terms.

$\qquad = 2x(x - 5) + 3y(x - 5) \qquad$ Factor each group.

$\qquad = (x - 5)(2x + 3y) \qquad$ Factor out $x - 5$.

CHECK $(x - 5)(2x + 3y)$

$\qquad\qquad = 2x^2 + 3xy - 10x - 15y \qquad$ FOIL

$\qquad\qquad = 2x^2 - 10x + 3xy - 15y \;\checkmark \quad$ Original polynomial

(d) $t^3 + 2t^2 - 3t - 6$

$\qquad\qquad\qquad$ `Write a + sign between the groups.`

$\qquad = (t^3 + 2t^2) + (-3t - 6) \qquad$ Group the terms.

$\qquad = t^2(t + 2) - 3(t + 2) \qquad$ Factor out -3 so there is a common factor,
$t + 2$; $-3(t + 2) = -3t - 6$.

$\qquad\qquad\qquad$ `Be careful with signs.`

$\qquad = (t + 2)(t^2 - 3) \qquad$ Factor out $t + 2$.

Check by multiplying.

NOW TRY

⚠ CAUTION   *Be careful with signs when grouping* in a problem like **Example 5(d).**
It is wise to check the factoring in the second step, as shown in the side comment in
that example, before continuing.

Factoring a Polynomial with Four Terms by Grouping

Step 1   **Group terms.** Collect the terms into two groups so that each group
has a common factor.

Step 2   **Factor within groups.** Factor out the greatest common factor from
each group.

Step 3   **Factor the entire polynomial.** Factor out a common binomial
factor from the results of Step 2.

Step 4   **If necessary, rearrange terms.** If Step 2 does not result in a
common binomial factor, try a different grouping.

NOW TRY ANSWERS

5. (a) $(b + 3)(a + 5)$
(b) $(4y + 1)(3x + 1)$
(c) $(x + 5)(x^2 - 8)$

56. $3t^3 + 27t^2 + 24t$ **57.** $2x^6 + 8x^5 - 42x^4$ **58.** $4y^5 + 12y^4 - 40y^3$

59. $5m^5 + 25m^4 - 40m^2$ **60.** $12k^5 - 6k^3 + 10k^2$

61. $m^3n - 10m^2n^2 + 24mn^3$ **62.** $y^3z + 3y^2z^2 - 54yz^3$

Brain Busters *Factor each polynomial.*

63. $a^5 + 3a^4b - 4a^3b^2$ **64.** $m^3n - 2m^2n^2 - 3mn^3$ **65.** $y^3z + y^2z^2 - 6yz^3$

66. $k^7 - 2k^6m - 15k^5m^2$ **67.** $z^{10} - 4z^9y - 21z^8y^2$ **68.** $x^9 + 5x^8w - 24x^7w^2$

69. $(a + b)x^2 + (a + b)x - 12(a + b)$

70. $(x + y)n^2 + (x + y)n - 20(x + y)$

71. $(2p + q)r^2 - 12(2p + q)r + 27(2p + q)$

72. $(3m - n)k^2 - 13(3m - n)k + 40(3m - n)$

PREVIEW EXERCISES

Find each product. **See Section 4.5.**

73. $(2y - 7)(y + 4)$ **74.** $(3a + 2)(2a + 1)$ **75.** $(5z + 2)(3z - 2)$

5.3 More on Factoring Trinomials

OBJECTIVES

1 Factor trinomials by grouping when the coefficient of the second-degree term is not 1.

2 Factor trinomials by using the FOIL method.

Trinomials such as $2x^2 + 7x + 6$, in which the coefficient of the second-degree term is *not* 1, are factored with extensions of the methods from the previous sections.

OBJECTIVE 1 **Factor trinomials by grouping when the coefficient of the second-degree term is not 1.** A trinomial such as $m^2 + 3m + 2$ is factored by finding two numbers whose product is 2 and whose sum is 3. To factor $2x^2 + 7x + 6$, we look for two integers whose product is $2 \cdot 6 = 12$ and whose sum is 7.

Sum is 7.

$$2x^2 + 7x + 6$$

Product is $2 \cdot 6 = 12$.

By considering pairs of positive integers whose product is 12, we find the required integers, 3 and 4. We use these integers to write the middle term, $7x$, as $7x = 3x + 4x$.

$$2x^2 + 7x + 6$$
$$= 2x^2 + \underbrace{3x + 4x}_{7x} + 6$$
$$= (2x^2 + 3x) + (4x + 6) \qquad \text{Group the terms.}$$
$$= x(2x + 3) + 2(2x + 3) \qquad \text{Factor each group.}$$

Must be the same factor

$$= (2x + 3)(x + 2) \qquad \text{Factor out } 2x + 3.$$

CHECK Multiply $(2x + 3)(x + 2)$ to obtain $2x^2 + 7x + 6$. ✓

NOTE In the preceding example, we could have written $7x$ as $4x + 3x$, rather than as $3x + 4x$. Factoring by grouping would give the same answer. Try this.

NOW TRY
EXERCISE 1

Factor.

(a) $2z^2 + 5z + 3$

(b) $15m^2 + m - 2$

(c) $8x^2 - 2xy - 3y^2$

EXAMPLE 1 Factoring Trinomials by Grouping

Factor each trinomial.

(a) $6r^2 + r - 1$

We must find two integers with a product of $6(-1) = -6$ and a sum of 1.

Sum is 1.

$$6r^2 + 1r - 1$$

Product is $6(-1) = -6$.

The integers are -2 and 3. We write the middle term, r, as $-2r + 3r$.

$$6r^2 + r - 1$$

$$= 6r^2 - 2r + 3r - 1 \qquad r = -2r + 3r$$

$$= (6r^2 - 2r) + (3r - 1) \qquad \text{Group the terms.}$$

$$= 2r(3r - 1) + 1(3r - 1) \qquad \text{The binomials must be the same.}$$

Remember the 1.

$$= (3r - 1)(2r + 1) \qquad \text{Factor out } 3r - 1.$$

CHECK Multiply $(3r - 1)(2r + 1)$ to obtain $6r^2 + r - 1$. ✓

(b) $12z^2 - 5z - 2$

Look for two integers whose product is $12(-2) = -24$ and whose sum is -5. The required integers are 3 and -8.

$$12z^2 - 5z - 2$$

$$= 12z^2 + 3z - 8z - 2 \qquad -5z = 3z - 8z$$

$$= (12z^2 + 3z) + (-8z - 2) \qquad \text{Group the terms.}$$

$$= 3z(4z + 1) - 2(4z + 1) \qquad \text{Factor each group.}$$

Be careful with signs.

$$= (4z + 1)(3z - 2) \qquad \text{Factor out } 4z + 1.$$

CHECK Multiply $(4z + 1)(3z - 2)$ to obtain $12z^2 - 5z - 2$. ✓

(c) $10m^2 + mn - 3n^2$

Two integers whose product is $10(-3) = -30$ and whose sum is 1 are -5 and 6.

$$10m^2 + mn - 3n^2$$

$$= 10m^2 - 5mn + 6mn - 3n^2 \qquad mn = -5mn + 6mn$$

$$= (10m^2 - 5mn) + (6mn - 3n^2) \qquad \text{Group the terms.}$$

$$= 5m(2m - n) + 3n(2m - n) \qquad \text{Factor each group.}$$

$$= (2m - n)(5m + 3n) \qquad \text{Factor out } 2m - n.$$

NOW TRY ANSWERS
1. (a) $(2z + 3)(z + 1)$
 (b) $(3m - 1)(5m + 2)$
 (c) $(4x - 3y)(2x + y)$

CHECK Multiply $(2m - n)(5m + 3n)$ to obtain $10m^2 + mn - 3n^2$. ✓

NOW TRY

NOW TRY
EXERCISE 2
Factor $15z^6 + 18z^5 - 24z^4$.

EXAMPLE 2   Factoring a Trinomial with a Common Factor by Grouping

Factor $28x^5 - 58x^4 - 30x^3$.

$$28x^5 - 58x^4 - 30x^3$$
$$= 2x^3(14x^2 - 29x - 15) \qquad \text{Factor out the greatest common factor, } 2x^3.$$

To factor $14x^2 - 29x - 15$, find two integers whose product is $14(-15) = -210$ and whose sum is -29. Factoring 210 into prime factors helps find these integers.

$$210 = 2 \cdot 3 \cdot 5 \cdot 7$$

Combine the prime factors of $210 = 2 \cdot 3 \cdot 5 \cdot 7$ into pairs in different ways, using one positive and one negative (to get -210). The factors 6 and -35 have the correct sum, -29.

$$28x^5 - 58x^4 - 30x^3$$
$$= 2x^3(14x^2 - 29x - 15)$$

Remember the common factor.
$$= 2x^3(14x^2 + 6x - 35x - 15) \qquad -29x = 6x - 35x$$
$$= 2x^3[(14x^2 + 6x) + (-35x - 15)] \qquad \text{Group the terms.}$$
$$= 2x^3[2x(7x + 3) - 5(7x + 3)] \qquad \text{Factor each group.}$$
$$= 2x^3[(7x + 3)(2x - 5)] \qquad \text{Factor out } 7x + 3.$$
$$= 2x^3(7x + 3)(2x - 5) \qquad \text{Check by multiplying.} \qquad \text{NOW TRY}$$

OBJECTIVE 2   **Factor trinomials by using the FOIL method.** There is an alternative method of factoring trinomials that uses trial and error.

To factor $2x^2 + 7x + 6$ (the trinomial factored at the beginning of this section) by trial and error, we use the FOIL method in reverse. We want to write $2x^2 + 7x + 6$ as the product of two binomials.

$$2x^2 + 7x + 6$$
$$= (\underline{\quad})(\underline{\quad})$$

The product of the two first terms of the binomials is $2x^2$. The possible factors of $2x^2$ are $2x$ and x or $-2x$ and $-x$. Since all terms of the trinomial are positive, we consider only positive factors. Thus, we have the following.

$$2x^2 + 7x + 6$$
$$= (2x\underline{\quad})(x\underline{\quad})$$

The product of the two last terms, 6, can be factored as $1 \cdot 6, 6 \cdot 1, 2 \cdot 3$, or $3 \cdot 2$. Try each pair to find the pair that gives the correct middle term, $7x$.

$(2x + 1)(x + 6)$ Incorrect $(2x + 6)(x + 1)$ Incorrect
         x $6x$
       $12x$ $2x$
       $13x$ Add. $8x$ Add.

Since $2x + 6 = 2(x + 3)$, the binomial $2x + 6$ has a common factor of 2, while $2x^2 + 7x + 6$ has no common factor other than 1. The product $(2x + 6)(x + 1)$ cannot be correct.

NOTE   If the terms of the original polynomial have greatest common factor 1, then each factor of that polynomial will also have terms with GCF 1.

NOW TRY ANSWER
2. $3z^4(5z - 4)(z + 2)$

Now try the numbers 2 and 3 as factors of 6. Because of the common factor 2 in $2x + 2$, the product $(2x + 2)(x + 3)$ will not work, so we try $(2x + 3)(x + 2)$.

$$(2x + 3)(x + 2) = 2x^2 + 7x + 6 \quad \text{Correct}$$

$$\begin{array}{c} 3x \\ 4x \\ \hline 7x \quad \text{Add.} \end{array}$$

Thus, $2x^2 + 7x + 6$ factors as $(2x + 3)(x + 2)$.

NOW TRY
EXERCISE 3
Factor $8y^2 + 22y + 5$.

EXAMPLE 3 Factoring a Trinomial with All Positive Terms by Using FOIL

Factor $8p^2 + 14p + 5$.

The number 8 has several possible pairs of factors, but 5 has only 1 and 5 or -1 and -5, so begin by considering the factors of 5. Ignore the negative factors, since all coefficients in the trinomial are positive. The factors will have this form.

$$(\underline{\quad} + 5)(\underline{\quad} + 1)$$

The possible pairs of factors of $8p^2$ are $8p$ and p, or $4p$ and $2p$. Try various combinations, checking in each case to see if the middle term is $14p$.

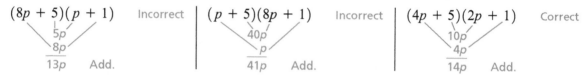

Since the combination on the right produces $14p$, the correct middle term,

$$8p^2 + 14p + 5 \quad \text{factors as} \quad (4p + 5)(2p + 1).$$

CHECK Multiply $(4p + 5)(2p + 1)$ to obtain $8p^2 + 14p + 5$ ✓ NOW TRY

NOW TRY
EXERCISE 4
Factor $10x^2 - 9x + 2$.

EXAMPLE 4 Factoring a Trinomial with a Negative Middle Term by Using FOIL

Factor $6x^2 - 11x + 3$.

Since 3 has only 1 and 3 or -1 and -3 as factors, it is better here to begin by factoring 3. The last (constant) term of the trinomial $6x^2 - 11x + 3$ is positive and the middle term has a negative coefficient, so we consider only negative factors. We need two negative factors, because the *product* of two negative factors is positive and their *sum* is negative, as required. Try -3 and -1 as factors of 3.

$$(\underline{\quad} - 3)(\underline{\quad} - 1)$$

The factors of $6x^2$ may be either $6x$ and x or $2x$ and $3x$.

$$(6x - 3)(x - 1) \quad \text{Incorrect}$$

$$\begin{array}{c} -3x \\ -6x \\ \hline -9x \quad \text{Add.} \end{array}$$

$$(2x - 3)(3x - 1) \quad \text{Correct}$$

$$\begin{array}{c} -9x \\ -2x \\ \hline -11x \quad \text{Add.} \end{array}$$

The factors $2x$ and $3x$ produce $-11x$, the correct middle term. (Check by multiplying.)

$$6x^2 - 11x + 3 \quad \text{factors as} \quad (2x - 3)(3x - 1).$$

NOW TRY

NOTE In **Example 4,** we might also realize that our initial attempt to factor $6x^2 - 11x + 3$ as $(6x - 3)(x - 1)$ *cannot* be correct, since the terms of $6x - 3$ have a common factor of 3, while those of the original polynomial do not.

NOW TRY ANSWERS
3. $(4y + 1)(2y + 5)$
4. $(5x - 2)(2x - 1)$

NOW TRY
EXERCISE 5
Factor $10a^2 + 31a - 14$.

EXAMPLE 5 Factoring a Trinomial with a Negative Constant Term by Using FOIL

Factor $8x^2 + 6x - 9$.

The integer 8 has several possible pairs of factors, as does -9. Since the constant term is negative, one positive factor and one negative factor of -9 are needed. Since the coefficient of the middle term is relatively small, it is wise to avoid large factors such as 8 or 9. We try $4x$ and $2x$ as factors of $8x^2$, and 3 and -3 as factors of -9.

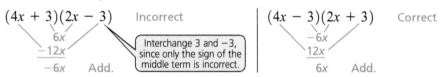

The combination on the right produces the correct middle term.

$$8x^2 + 6x - 9 \quad \text{factors as} \quad (4x - 3)(2x + 3).$$

NOW TRY

NOW TRY
EXERCISE 6
Factor $8z^2 + 2wz - 15w^2$.

EXAMPLE 6 Factoring a Trinomial with Two Variables

Factor $12a^2 - ab - 20b^2$.

There are several pairs of factors of $12a^2$, including

$$12a \text{ and } a, \quad 6a \text{ and } 2a, \quad \text{and} \quad 3a \text{ and } 4a.$$

There are also many pairs of factors of $-20b^2$, including

$$20b \text{ and } -b, \quad -20b \text{ and } b, \quad 10b \text{ and } -2b, \quad -10b \text{ and } 2b,$$

$$4b \text{ and } -5b, \quad \text{and} \quad -4b \text{ and } 5b.$$

Once again, since the coefficient of the desired middle term is relatively small, avoid the larger factors. Try the factors $6a$ and $2a$, and $4b$ and $-5b$.

$$(6a + 4b)(2a - 5b)$$

This cannot be correct, since there is a factor of 2 in $6a + 4b$, while 2 is not a factor of the given trinomial. Try $3a$ and $4a$ with $4b$ and $-5b$.

$$(3a + 4b)(4a - 5b)$$

$$= 12a^2 + ab - 20b^2 \quad \text{Incorrect}$$

Here the middle term is ab rather than $-ab$, so we interchange the signs of the last two terms in the factors.

$$12a^2 - ab - 20b^2 \quad \text{factors as} \quad (3a - 4b)(4a + 5b).$$

Check by multiplying.

NOW TRY

EXAMPLE 7 Factoring Trinomials with Common Factors

Factor each trinomial.

(a) $15y^3 + 55y^2 + 30y$

$$= 5y(3y^2 + 11y + 6) \quad \text{Factor out the greatest common factor, } 5y.$$

To factor $3y^2 + 11y + 6$, try $3y$ and y as factors of $3y^2$, and 2 and 3 as factors of 6.

$$(3y + 2)(y + 3)$$

$$= 3y^2 + 11y + 6 \quad \text{Correct}$$

NOW TRY ANSWERS
5. $(5a - 2)(2a + 7)$
6. $(4z - 5w)(2z + 3w)$

NOW TRY
EXERCISE 7
Factor $-10x^3 - 45x^2 + 90x$.

This leads to the completely factored form.

$$15y^3 + 55y^2 + 30y$$

Remember the common factor.
$$= 5y(3y + 2)(y + 3)$$

CHECK $5y(3y + 2)(y + 3)$

$\quad = 5y(3y^2 + 11y + 6)$ FOIL; Combine like terms.

$\quad = 15y^3 + 55y^2 + 30y$ ✓ Distributive property

(b) $-24a^3 - 42a^2 + 45a$

The common factor could be $3a$ or $-3a$. If we factor out $-3a$, the first term of the trinomial will be positive, which makes it easier to factor the remaining trinomial.

$$-24a^3 - 42a^2 + 45a$$

$\qquad = -3a(8a^2 + 14a - 15)$ Factor out $-3a$.

$\qquad = -3a(4a - 3)(2a + 5)$ Factor the trinomial.

Check by multiplying.

NOW TRY

NOW TRY ANSWER
7. $-5x(2x - 3)(x + 6)$

⚠ CAUTION   ***Include the common factor in the final factored form.***

5.3 EXERCISES

MyMathLab | MathXL PRACTICE | WATCH | DOWNLOAD | READ | REVIEW

🌐 *Complete solution available on the Video Resources on DVD*

Concept Check *The middle term of each trinomial has been rewritten. Now factor by grouping.*

1. $10t^2 + 9t + 2$
$\quad = 10t^2 + 5t + 4t + 2$

2. $6x^2 + 13x + 6$
$\quad = 6x^2 + 9x + 4x + 6$

3. $15z^2 - 19z + 6$
$\quad = 15z^2 - 10z - 9z + 6$

4. $12p^2 - 17p + 6$
$\quad = 12p^2 - 9p - 8p + 6$

5. $8s^2 + 2st - 3t^2$
$\quad = 8s^2 - 4st + 6st - 3t^2$

6. $3x^2 - xy - 14y^2$
$\quad = 3x^2 - 7xy + 6xy - 14y^2$

Concept Check *Complete the steps to factor each trinomial by grouping.*

7. $2m^2 + 11m + 12$

  (a) Find two integers whose product is
_____ · _____ = _____
and whose sum is _____.

  (b) The required integers are _____ and _____.

  (c) Write the middle term, $11m$, as _____ + _____.

  (d) Rewrite the given trinomial as _____.

  (e) Factor the polynomial in part (d) by grouping.

  (f) Check by multiplying.

8. $6y^2 - 19y + 10$

  (a) Find two integers whose product is
_____ · _____ = _____
and whose sum is _____.

  (b) The required integers are _____ and _____.

  (c) Write the middle term, $-19y$, as _____ + _____.

  (d) Rewrite the given trinomial as _____.

  (e) Factor the polynomial in part (d) by grouping.

  (f) Check by multiplying.

9. *Concept Check* Which pair of integers would be used to rewrite the middle term when one is factoring $12y^2 + 5y - 2$ by grouping?

   A. $-8, 3$ **B.** $8, -3$

   C. $-6, 4$ **D.** $6, -4$

10. *Concept Check* Which pair of integers would be used to rewrite the middle term when one is factoring $20b^2 - 13b + 2$ by grouping?

    A. $10, 3$ **B.** $-10, -3$

    C. $8, 5$ **D.** $-8, -5$

Concept Check *Which is the correct factored form of the given polynomial?*

11. $2x^2 - x - 1$

    A. $(2x - 1)(x + 1)$

    B. $(2x + 1)(x - 1)$

12. $3a^2 - 5a - 2$

    A. $(3a + 1)(a - 2)$

    B. $(3a - 1)(a + 2)$

13. $4y^2 + 17y - 15$

    A. $(y + 5)(4y - 3)$

    B. $(2y - 5)(2y + 3)$

14. $12c^2 - 7c - 12$

    A. $(6c - 2)(2c + 6)$

    B. $(4c + 3)(3c - 4)$

Complete each factoring. ***See Examples 1–7.***

15. $6a^2 + 7ab - 20b^2$
    $= (3a - 4b)(\underline{\hspace{1.5cm}})$

16. $9m^2 + 6mn - 8n^2$
    $= (3m - 2n)(\underline{\hspace{1.5cm}})$

17. $2x^2 + 6x - 8$
    $= 2(\underline{\hspace{2cm}})$
    $= 2(\underline{\hspace{0.8cm}})(\underline{\hspace{0.8cm}})$

18. $3x^2 + 9x - 30$
    $= 3(\underline{\hspace{2cm}})$
    $= 3(\underline{\hspace{0.8cm}})(\underline{\hspace{0.8cm}})$

19. $4z^3 - 10z^2 - 6z$
    $= 2z(\underline{\hspace{2cm}})$
    $= 2z(\underline{\hspace{0.8cm}})(\underline{\hspace{0.8cm}})$

20. $15r^3 - 39r^2 - 18r$
    $= 3r(\underline{\hspace{2cm}})$
    $= 3r(\underline{\hspace{0.8cm}})(\underline{\hspace{0.8cm}})$

21. The polynomial $12x^2 + 7x - 12$ does not have 2 as a factor. Explain why the binomial $2x - 6$, then, cannot be a factor of the polynomial.

22. *Concept Check* On a quiz, a student factored $3k^3 - 12k^2 - 15k$ by first factoring out the common factor $3k$ to get $3k(k^2 - 4k - 5)$. Then the student wrote the following.

$$k^2 - 4k - 5$$
$$= k^2 - 5k + k - 5$$
$$= k(k - 5) + 1(k - 5)$$
$$= (k - 5)(k + 1) \qquad \text{Her answer}$$

WHAT WENT WRONG? What is the correct factored form?

Factor each trinomial completely. ***See Examples 1–7.*** *(Hint: In Exercises 55–58, first write the trinomial in descending powers and then factor.)*

23. $3a^2 + 10a + 7$

24. $7r^2 + 8r + 1$

25. $2y^2 + 7y + 6$

26. $5z^2 + 12z + 4$

27. $15m^2 + m - 2$

28. $6x^2 + x - 1$

29. $12s^2 + 11s - 5$

30. $20x^2 + 11x - 3$

31. $10m^2 - 23m + 12$

32. $6x^2 - 17x + 12$

33. $8w^2 - 14w + 3$

34. $9p^2 - 18p + 8$

35. $20y^2 - 39y - 11$

36. $10x^2 - 11x - 6$

37. $3x^2 - 15x + 16$

38. $2t^2 - 14t + 15$

39. $20x^2 + 22x + 6$

40. $36y^2 + 81y + 45$

41. $24x^2 - 42x + 9$

42. $48b^2 - 74b - 10$

43. $40m^2q + mq - 6q$　　　　　　**44.** $15a^2b + 22ab + 8b$

🌐 **45.** $15n^4 - 39n^3 + 18n^2$　　　　**46.** $24a^4 + 10a^3 - 4a^2$

🌐 **47.** $15x^2y^2 - 7xy^2 - 4y^2$　　　**48.** $14a^2b^3 + 15ab^3 - 9b^3$

49. $5a^2 - 7ab - 6b^2$　　　　　　**50.** $6x^2 - 5xy - y^2$

🌐 **51.** $12s^2 + 11st - 5t^2$　　　　　**52.** $25a^2 + 25ab + 6b^2$

53. $6m^6n + 7m^5n^2 + 2m^4n^3$　　**54.** $12k^3q^4 - 4k^2q^5 - kq^6$

55. $5 - 6x + x^2$　　　　　　　　**56.** $7 - 8x + x^2$

57. $16 + 16x + 3x^2$　　　　　　**58.** $18 + 65x + 7x^2$

59. $-10x^3 + 5x^2 + 140x$　　　　**60.** $-18k^3 - 48k^2 + 66k$

61. $12x^2 - 47x - 4$　　　　　　**62.** $12x^2 - 19x - 10$

63. $24y^2 - 41xy - 14x^2$　　　　**64.** $24x^2 + 19xy - 5y^2$

65. $36x^4 - 64x^2y + 15y^2$　　　**66.** $36x^4 + 59x^2y + 24y^2$

67. $48a^2 - 94ab - 4b^2$　　　　　**68.** $48t^2 - 147ts + 9s^2$

69. $10x^4y^5 + 39x^3y^5 - 4x^2y^5$　**70.** $14x^7y^4 - 31x^6y^4 + 6x^5y^4$

71. $36a^3b^2 - 104a^2b^2 - 12ab^2$　**72.** $36p^4q + 129p^3q - 60p^2q$

73. $24x^2 - 46x + 15$　　　　　　**74.** $24x^2 - 94x + 35$

75. $24x^4 + 55x^2 - 24$　　　　　**76.** $24x^4 + 17x^2 - 20$

77. $24x^2 + 38xy + 15y^2$　　　　**78.** $24x^2 + 62xy + 33y^2$

If a trinomial has a negative coefficient for the squared term, as in $-2x^2 + 11x - 12$, it is usually easier to factor by first factoring out the common factor -1.

$$-2x^2 + 11x - 12$$
$$= -1(2x^2 - 11x + 12)$$
$$= -1(2x - 3)(x - 4)$$

Use this method to factor each trinomial. ***See Example 7(b).***

79. $-x^2 - 4x + 21$　　　　　　　**80.** $-x^2 + x + 72$

81. $-3x^2 - x + 4$　　　　　　　**82.** $-5x^2 + 2x + 16$

83. $-2a^2 - 5ab - 2b^2$　　　　　**84.** $-3p^2 + 13pq - 4q^2$

Brain Busters   *Factor each polynomial. (Hint: As the first step, factor out the greatest common factor.)*

85. $25q^2(m + 1)^3 - 5q(m + 1)^3 - 2(m + 1)^3$

86. $18x^2(y - 3)^2 - 21x(y - 3)^2 - 4(y - 3)^2$

87. $9x^2(r + 3)^3 + 12xy(r + 3)^3 + 4y^2(r + 3)^3$

88. $4t^2(k + 9)^7 + 20ts(k + 9)^7 + 25s^2(k + 9)^7$

Brain Busters   *Find all integers k so that the trinomial can be factored by the methods of this section.*

89. $5x^2 + kx - 1$　　　　　　　**90.** $2x^2 + kx - 3$

91. $2m^2 + km + 5$　　　　　　　**92.** $3y^2 + ky + 4$

PREVIEW EXERCISES

Find each product. ***See Section 4.6.***

93. $(7p + 3)(7p - 3)$　　　　　　**94.** $(3h + 5k)(3h - 5k)$

95. $(x + 6)^2$　　　　　　　　　**96.** $(3t + 4)^2$

5.4 Special Factoring Techniques

OBJECTIVES

1. Factor a difference of squares.
2. Factor a perfect square trinomial.
3. Factor a difference of cubes.
4. Factor a sum of cubes.

By reversing the rules for multiplication of binomials from **Section 4.6,** we get rules for factoring polynomials in certain forms.

OBJECTIVE 1 **Factor a difference of squares.** The formula for the product of the sum and difference of the same two terms is

$$(x + y)(x - y) = x^2 - y^2.$$

Reversing this rule leads to the following special factoring rule.

Factoring a Difference of Squares

$$x^2 - y^2 = (x + y)(x - y)$$

For example, $m^2 - 16$

$$= m^2 - 4^2$$

$$= (m + 4)(m - 4).$$

The following conditions must be true for a binomial to be a difference of squares.

1. Both terms of the binomial must be squares, such as

$$x^2, \quad 9y^2 = (3y)^2, \quad 25 = 5^2, \quad 1 = 1^2, \quad m^4 = (m^2)^2.$$

2. The terms of the binomial must have different signs (one positive and one negative).

NOW TRY
EXERCISE 1

Factor each binomial if possible.

(a) $x^2 - 100$ **(b)** $x^2 + 49$

EXAMPLE 1 **Factoring Differences of Squares**

Factor each binomial if possible.

$$x^2 - y^2 = (x + y)(x - y)$$

(a) $a^2 - 49 = a^2 - 7^2 = (a + 7)(a - 7)$ **(b)** $y^2 - m^2 = (y + m)(y - m)$

(c) $x^2 - 8$

Because 8 is not the square of an integer, this binomial does not satisfy the conditions above. It is a prime polynomial.

(d) $p^2 + 16$

Since $p^2 + 16$ is a *sum* of squares, it is not equal to $(p + 4)(p - 4)$. Also, we use FOIL and try the following.

$$(p - 4)(p - 4)$$
$$= p^2 - 8p + 16, \quad \text{not} \quad p^2 + 16.$$
$$(p + 4)(p + 4)$$
$$= p^2 + 8p + 16, \quad \text{not} \quad p^2 + 16.$$

Thus, $p^2 + 16$ is a prime polynomial.   NOW TRY

NOW TRY ANSWERS
1. **(a)** $(x + 10)(x - 10)$
   (b) prime

⚠ **CAUTION**   *As **Example 1(d)** suggests, after any common factor is removed, a sum of squares cannot be factored.*

NOW TRY
EXERCISE 2

Factor each difference of squares.

(a) $9t^2 - 100$

(b) $36a^2 - 49b^2$

EXAMPLE 2 Factoring Differences of Squares

Factor each difference of squares.

$$x^2 \;\; - \;\; y^2 \; = \;\; (x \;\; + \;\; y) \, (x \;\; - \;\; y)$$

(a) $25m^2 - 16 = (5m)^2 - 4^2 = (5m + 4)(5m - 4)$

(b) $49z^2 - 64t^2$

$= (7z)^2 - (8t)^2$ Write each term as a square.

$= (7z + 8t)(7z - 8t)$ Factor the difference of squares.   *NOW TRY*

NOTE *Always check a factored form by multiplying.*

NOW TRY
EXERCISE 3

Factor completely.

(a) $16k^2 - 64$

(b) $m^4 - 144$

(c) $v^4 - 625$

EXAMPLE 3 Factoring More Complex Differences of Squares

Factor completely.

(a) $81y^2 - 36$

$= 9(9y^2 - 4)$ Factor out the GCF, 9.

$= 9[(3y)^2 - 2^2]$ Write each term as a square.

$= 9(3y + 2)(3y - 2)$ Factor the difference of squares.

(b) $p^4 - 36$

$= (p^2)^2 - 6^2$ Write each term as a square.

$\boxed{\text{Neither binomial can}\atop\text{be factored further.}} = (p^2 + 6)(p^2 - 6)$ Factor the difference of squares.

(c) $m^4 - 16$

$= (m^2)^2 - 4^2$

$= (m^2 + 4)(m^2 - 4)$ Factor the difference of squares.

$\boxed{\text{Don't stop}\atop\text{here.}} = (m^2 + 4)(m + 2)(m - 2)$ Factor the difference of squares again.

NOW TRY

⚠ **CAUTION** *Factor again when any of the factors is a difference of squares,* as in **Example 3(c)**. Check by multiplying.

OBJECTIVE 2 Factor a perfect square trinomial. The expressions 144, $4x^2$, and $81m^6$ are called **perfect squares** because

$$144 = 12^2, \quad 4x^2 = (2x)^2, \quad \text{and} \quad 81m^6 = (9m^3)^2.$$

A **perfect square trinomial** is a trinomial that is the square of a binomial. For example, $x^2 + 8x + 16$ is a perfect square trinomial because it is the square of the binomial $x + 4$.

$$x^2 + 8x + 16$$

$$= (x + 4)(x + 4)$$

$$= (x + 4)^2$$

NOW TRY ANSWERS

2. (a) $(3t + 10)(3t - 10)$

   (b) $(6a + 7b)(6a - 7b)$

3. (a) $16(k + 2)(k - 2)$

   (b) $(m^2 + 12)(m^2 - 12)$

   (c) $(v^2 + 25)(v + 5)(v - 5)$

On the one hand, a necessary condition for a trinomial to be a perfect square is that *two of its terms be perfect squares*. For this reason, $16x^2 + 4x + 15$ is not a perfect square trinomial, because only the term $16x^2$ is a perfect square.

On the other hand, even if two of the terms are perfect squares, the trinomial may not be a perfect square trinomial. For example, $x^2 + 6x + 36$ has two perfect square terms, x^2 and 36, but it is *not* a perfect square trinomial.

Factoring Perfect Square Trinomials

$$x^2 + 2xy + y^2 = (x + y)^2$$
$$x^2 - 2xy + y^2 = (x - y)^2$$

The middle term of a perfect square trinomial is always twice the product of the two terms in the squared binomial (as shown in Section 4.6). Use this rule to check any attempt to factor a trinomial that appears to be a perfect square.

NOW TRY
EXERCISE 4
Factor $y^2 + 14y + 49$.

EXAMPLE 4 Factoring a Perfect Square Trinomial

Factor $x^2 + 10x + 25$.

The x^2-term is a perfect square, and so is 25.

Try to factor $x^2 + 10x + 25$ as $(x + 5)^2$.

To check, take twice the product of the two terms in the squared binomial.

$$2 \cdot x \cdot 5 = 10x \longleftarrow \text{Middle term of } x^2 + 10x + 25$$

Twice   First term   Last term
of binomial   of binomial

Since $10x$ is the middle term of the trinomial, the trinomial is a perfect square.

$$x^2 + 10x + 25 \quad \text{factors as} \quad (x + 5)^2.$$

NOW TRY

EXAMPLE 5 Factoring Perfect Square Trinomials

Factor each trinomial.

(a) $x^2 - 22x + 121$

The first and last terms are perfect squares $(121 = 11^2 \text{ or } (-11)^2)$. Check to see whether the middle term of $x^2 - 22x + 121$ is twice the product of the first and last terms of the binomial $x - 11$.

$$2 \cdot x \cdot (-11) = -22x \longleftarrow \text{Middle term of } x^2 - 22x + 121$$

Twice   First   Last
term   term

Thus, $x^2 - 22x + 121$ is a perfect square trinomial.

$$x^2 - 22x + 121 \quad \text{factors as} \quad (x - 11)^2.$$

Same sign

Notice that the sign of the second term in the squared binomial is the same as the sign of the middle term in the trinomial.

NOW TRY ANSWER
4. $(y + 7)^2$

NOW TRY
EXERCISE 5

Factor each trinomial.

(a) $t^2 - 18t + 81$

(b) $4p^2 - 28p + 49$

(c) $9x^2 + 6x + 4$

(d) $80x^3 + 120x^2 + 45x$

(b) $9m^2 - 24m + 16 = (3m)^2 + 2(3m)(-4) + (-4)^2 = (3m - 4)^2$

Twice —— First term —— Last term

(c) $25y^2 + 20y + 16$

The first and last terms are perfect squares.

$$25y^2 = (5y)^2 \quad \text{and} \quad 16 = 4^2$$

Twice the product of the first and last terms of the binomial $5y + 4$ is

$$2 \cdot 5y \cdot 4 = 40y,$$

which is *not* the middle term of

$$25y^2 + 20y + 16.$$

This trinomial is not a perfect square. In fact, the trinomial cannot be factored even with the methods of the previous sections. It is a prime polynomial.

(d) $12z^3 + 60z^2 + 75z$

$$= 3z(4z^2 + 20z + 25) \qquad \text{Factor out the common factor, } 3z.$$

$$= 3z[(2z)^2 + 2(2z)(5) + 5^2] \qquad 4z^2 + 20z + 25 \text{ is a perfect square trinomial.}$$

$$= 3z(2z + 5)^2 \qquad \text{Factor.} \qquad \text{NOW TRY}$$

NOTE

1. The sign of the second term in the squared binomial is always the same as the sign of the middle term in the trinomial.

2. The first and last terms of a perfect square trinomial must be *positive*, because they are squares. For example, the polynomial $x^2 - 2x - 1$ cannot be a perfect square, because the last term is negative.

3. Perfect square trinomials can also be factored by using grouping or the FOIL method, although using the method of this section is often easier.

OBJECTIVE 3 **Factor a difference of cubes.** We can factor a **difference of cubes** by using the following pattern.

Factoring a Difference of Cubes

$$x^3 - y^3 = (x - y)(x^2 + xy + y^2)$$

This pattern for factoring a difference of cubes should be memorized. To see that the pattern is correct, multiply $(x - y)(x^2 + xy + y^2)$.

$$
\begin{array}{r}
x^2 + xy + y^2 \\
x - y \\
\hline
-x^2y - xy^2 - y^3 \\
x^3 + x^2y + xy^2 \\
\hline
x^3 \qquad\qquad - y^3
\end{array}
$$

Multiply vertically.
(Section 4.5)

$-y(x^2 + xy + y^2)$

$x(x^2 + xy + y^2)$

Add.

Notice the pattern of the terms in the factored form of $x^3 - y^3$.

- $x^3 - y^3 =$ (a binomial factor)(a trinomial factor)
- The binomial factor has the difference of the cube roots of the given terms.
- The terms in the trinomial factor are all positive.
- The terms in the binomial factor help to determine the trinomial factor.

$$x^3 - y^3 = (x - y)(\underset{\substack{\text{First term} \\ \text{squared}}}{x^2} + \underset{\substack{\text{positive} \\ \text{product of} \\ \text{the terms}}}{xy} + \underset{\substack{\text{second term} \\ \text{squared}}}{y^2})$$

> ⚠ **CAUTION** The polynomial $x^3 - y^3$ is not equivalent to $(x - y)^3$.
>
> $$x^3 - y^3$$
> $$= (x - y)(x^2 + xy + y^2)$$
>
> $$(x - y)^3$$
> $$= (x - y)(x - y)(x - y)$$
> $$= (x - y)(x^2 - 2xy + y^2)$$

NOW TRY
EXERCISE 6
Factor each polynomial.
(a) $a^3 - 27$
(b) $8t^3 - 125$
(c) $3k^3 - 192$
(d) $125x^3 - 343y^6$

EXAMPLE 6 Factoring Differences of Cubes

Factor each polynomial.

(a) $m^3 - 125$

Let $x = m$ and $y = 5$ in the pattern for the difference of cubes.

$$x^3 - y^3 = (x - y)(x^2 + xy + y^2)$$

$$m^3 - 125 = m^3 - 5^3 = (m - 5)(m^2 + 5m + 5^2) \qquad \text{Let } x = m, y = 5.$$
$$= (m - 5)(m^2 + 5m + 25) \qquad 5^2 = 25$$

(b) $8p^3 - 27$

$$= (2p)^3 - 3^3 \qquad\qquad 8p^3 = (2p)^3 \text{ and } 27 = 3^3.$$
$$= (2p - 3)[(2p)^2 + (2p)3 + 3^2] \qquad \text{Let } x = 2p, y = 3.$$
$$= (2p - 3)(4p^2 + 6p + 9) \qquad \text{Apply the exponents. Multiply.}$$

> $(2p)^2 = 2^2 p^2 = 4p^2$, NOT $2p^2$.

(c) $4m^3 - 32$

$$= 4(m^3 - 8) \qquad\qquad \text{Factor out the common factor, 4.}$$
$$= 4(m^3 - 2^3) \qquad\qquad 8 = 2^3$$
$$= 4(m - 2)(m^2 + 2m + 4) \qquad \text{Factor the difference of cubes.}$$

(d) $125t^3 - 216s^6$

$$= (5t)^3 - (6s^2)^3 \qquad\qquad \text{Write each term as a cube.}$$
$$= (5t - 6s^2)[(5t)^2 + 5t(6s^2) + (6s^2)^2] \qquad \text{Factor the difference of cubes.}$$
$$= (5t - 6s^2)(25t^2 + 30ts^2 + 36s^4) \qquad \text{Apply the exponents. Multiply.}$$

NOW TRY

NOW TRY ANSWERS
6. (a) $(a - 3)(a^2 + 3a + 9)$
(b) $(2t - 5)(4t^2 + 10t + 25)$
(c) $3(k - 4)(k^2 + 4k + 16)$
(d) $(5x - 7y^2) \cdot$
$\quad (25x^2 + 35xy^2 + 49y^4)$

⚠ **CAUTION**   A common error in factoring a difference of cubes, such as $x^3 - y^3 = (x - y)(x^2 + xy + y^2)$, is to try to factor $x^2 + xy + y^2$. This is usually not possible.

OBJECTIVE 4   **Factor a sum of cubes.**   A sum of squares, such as $m^2 + 25$, cannot be factored by using real numbers, but a **sum of cubes** can.

Factoring a Sum of Cubes

$$x^3 + y^3 = (x + y)(x^2 - xy + y^2)$$

Compare the pattern for the *sum* of cubes with that for the *difference* of cubes.

$$x^3 - y^3 = (x - y)(x^2 + xy + y^2)$$

Same sign — Opposite sign   Positive

Difference of cubes

The only difference between the patterns is the positive and negative signs.

$$x^3 + y^3 = (x + y)(x^2 - xy + y^2)$$

Same sign — Opposite sign   Positive

Sum of cubes

NOW TRY
EXERCISE 7

Factor each polynomial.

(a) $x^3 + 125$

(b) $27a^3 + 8b^3$

EXAMPLE 7   **Factoring Sums of Cubes**

Factor each polynomial.

(a) $k^3 + 27$

$= k^3 + 3^3$ $\quad 27 = 3^3$

$= (k + 3)(k^2 - 3k + 3^2)$ Factor the sum of cubes.

$= (k + 3)(k^2 - 3k + 9)$ Apply the exponent.

(b) $8m^3 + 125n^3$

$= (2m)^3 + (5n)^3$ $\quad 8m^3 = (2m)^3$ and $125n^3 = (5n)^3$.

$= (2m + 5n)[(2m)^2 - 2m(5n) + (5n)^2]$ Factor the sum of cubes.

$= (2m + 5n)(4m^2 - 10mn + 25n^2)$

Be careful: $(2m)^2 = 2^2m^2$ and $(5n)^2 = 5^2n^2$.

(c) $1000a^6 + 27b^3$

$= (10a^2)^3 + (3b)^3$

$= (10a^2 + 3b)[(10a^2)^2 - (10a^2)(3b) + (3b)^2]$ Factor the sum of cubes.

$= (10a^2 + 3b)(100a^4 - 30a^2b + 9b^2)$ $(10a^2)^2 = 10^2(a^2)^2 = 100a^4$

NOW TRY ANSWERS

7. (a) $(x + 5)(x^2 - 5x + 25)$

(b) $(3a + 2b)(9a^2 - 6ab + 4b^2)$

NOW TRY ↻

The methods of factoring discussed in this section are summarized here.

Special Factorizations

Difference of squares	$x^2 - y^2 = (x + y)(x - y)$
Perfect square trinomials	$x^2 + 2xy + y^2 = (x + y)^2$
	$x^2 - 2xy + y^2 = (x - y)^2$
Difference of cubes	$x^3 - y^3 = (x - y)(x^2 + xy + y^2)$
Sum of cubes	$x^3 + y^3 = (x + y)(x^2 - xy + y^2)$

The sum of squares can be factored only if the terms have a common factor.

5.4 EXERCISES

MyMathLab   Math XL PRACTICE   WATCH   DOWNLOAD   READ   REVIEW

Complete solution available on the Video Resources on DVD

1. *Concept Check*   To help you factor the difference of squares, complete the following list of squares.

$1^2 =$ _____ $2^2 =$ _____ $3^2 =$ _____ $4^2 =$ _____ $5^2 =$ _____

$6^2 =$ _____ $7^2 =$ _____ $8^2 =$ _____ $9^2 =$ _____ $10^2 =$ _____

$11^2 =$ _____ $12^2 =$ _____ $13^2 =$ _____ $14^2 =$ _____ $15^2 =$ _____

$16^2 =$ _____ $17^2 =$ _____ $18^2 =$ _____ $19^2 =$ _____ $20^2 =$ _____

2. *Concept Check*   The following powers of x are all perfect squares: $x^2, x^4, x^6, x^8, x^{10}$. On the basis of this observation, we may make a conjecture (an educated guess) that if the power of a variable is divisible by _____ (with 0 remainder), then we have a perfect square.

3. *Concept Check*   To help you factor the sum or difference of cubes, complete the following list of cubes.

$1^3 =$ _____ $2^3 =$ _____ $3^3 =$ _____ $4^3 =$ _____ $5^3 =$ _____

$6^3 =$ _____ $7^3 =$ _____ $8^3 =$ _____ $9^3 =$ _____ $10^3 =$ _____

4. *Concept Check*   The following powers of x are all perfect cubes: $x^3, x^6, x^9, x^{12}, x^{15}$. On the basis of this observation, we may make a conjecture that if the power of a variable is divisible by _____ (with 0 remainder), then we have a perfect cube.

5. *Concept Check*   Identify each monomial as a *perfect square*, a *perfect cube*, *both of these*, or *neither of these*.

(a) $64x^6y^{12}$ (b) $125t^6$ (c) $49x^{12}$ (d) $81r^{10}$

6. *Concept Check*   What must be true for x^n to be both a perfect square and a perfect cube?

*Factor each binomial completely. If the binomial is prime, say so. Use your answers from Exercises 1 and 2 as necessary. **See Examples 1–3.***

7. $y^2 - 25$ **8.** $t^2 - 16$ **9.** $x^2 - 144$

10. $x^2 - 400$ **11.** $m^2 + 64$ **12.** $k^2 + 49$

13. $4m^2 + 16$ **14.** $9x^2 + 81$ **15.** $9r^2 - 4$

16. $4x^2 - 9$ **17.** $36x^2 - 16$ **18.** $32a^2 - 8$

19. $196p^2 - 225$ **20.** $361q^2 - 400$ **21.** $16r^2 - 25a^2$

22. $49m^2 - 100p^2$ **23.** $100x^2 + 49$ **24.** $81w^2 + 16$

25. $p^4 - 49$ **26.** $r^4 - 25$ **27.** $x^4 - 1$

28. $y^4 - 10,000$ **29.** $p^4 - 256$ **30.** $k^4 - 81$

31. *Concept Check* When a student was directed to factor $k^4 - 81$ from **Exercise 30** completely, his teacher did not give him full credit for the answer

$$(k^2 + 9)(k^2 - 9).$$

The student argued that since his answer does indeed give $k^4 - 81$ when multiplied out, he should be given full credit. *WHAT WENT WRONG?* Give the correct factored form.

32. *Concept Check* The binomial $4x^2 + 36$ is a sum of squares that *can* be factored. How is this binomial factored? When can the sum of squares be factored?

Concept Check *Find the value of the indicated variable.*

33. Find b so that $x^2 + bx + 25$ factors as $(x + 5)^2$.

34. Find c so that $4m^2 - 12m + c$ factors as $(2m - 3)^2$.

35. Find a so that $ay^2 - 12y + 4$ factors as $(3y - 2)^2$.

36. Find b so that $100a^2 + ba + 9$ factors as $(10a + 3)^2$.

Factor each trinomial completely. **See Examples 4 and 5.**

🔘 **37.** $w^2 + 2w + 1$ **38.** $p^2 + 4p + 4$

🔘 **39.** $x^2 - 8x + 16$ **40.** $x^2 - 10x + 25$

41. $2x^2 + 24x + 72$ **42.** $3y^2 + 48y + 192$

43. $16x^2 - 40x + 25$ **44.** $36y^2 - 60y + 25$

45. $49x^2 - 28xy + 4y^2$ **46.** $4z^2 - 12zw + 9w^2$

47. $64x^2 + 48xy + 9y^2$ **48.** $9t^2 + 24tr + 16r^2$

49. $50h^2 - 40hy + 8y^2$ **50.** $18x^2 - 48xy + 32y^2$

51. $4k^3 - 4k^2 + 9k$ **52.** $9r^3 - 6r^2 + 16r$

53. $25z^4 + 5z^3 + z^2$ **54.** $4x^4 + 2x^3 + x^2$

Factor each binomial completely. Use your answers from **Exercises 3 and 4** *as necessary.* **See Examples 6 and 7.**

🔘 **55.** $a^3 - 1$ **56.** $m^3 - 8$ 🔘 **57.** $m^3 + 8$

58. $b^3 + 1$ **59.** $k^3 + 1000$ **60.** $p^3 + 512$

61. $27x^3 - 64$ **62.** $64y^3 - 27$ **63.** $6p^3 + 6$

64. $81x^3 + 3$ **65.** $5x^3 + 40$ **66.** $128y^3 + 54$

67. $y^3 - 8x^3$ **68.** $w^3 - 216z^3$

69. $2x^3 - 16y^3$ **70.** $27w^3 - 216z^3$

71. $8p^3 + 729q^3$ **72.** $64x^3 + 125y^3$

73. $27a^3 + 64b^3$ **74.** $125m^3 + 8p^3$

75. $125t^3 + 8s^3$ **76.** $27r^3 + 1000s^3$

77. $8x^3 - 125y^6$ **78.** $27t^3 - 64s^6$

79. $27m^6 + 8n^3$ **80.** $1000r^6 + 27s^3$

81. $x^9 + y^9$ **82.** $x^9 - y^9$

Although we usually factor polynomials using integers, we can apply the same concepts to factoring using fractions and decimals.

$$z^2 - \frac{9}{16}$$

$$= z^2 - \left(\frac{3}{4}\right)^2 \qquad \frac{9}{16} = \left(\frac{3}{4}\right)^2$$

$$= \left(z + \frac{3}{4}\right)\left(z - \frac{3}{4}\right) \qquad \text{Factor the difference of squares.}$$

Apply the special factoring rules of this section to factor each binomial or trinomial.

83. $p^2 - \dfrac{1}{9}$

84. $q^2 - \dfrac{1}{4}$

85. $36m^2 - \dfrac{16}{25}$

86. $100b^2 - \dfrac{4}{49}$

87. $x^2 - 0.64$

88. $y^2 - 0.36$

89. $t^2 + t + \dfrac{1}{4}$

90. $m^2 + \dfrac{2}{3}m + \dfrac{1}{9}$

91. $x^2 - 1.0x + 0.25$

92. $y^2 - 1.4y + 0.49$

93. $x^3 + \dfrac{1}{8}$

94. $x^3 + \dfrac{1}{64}$

Brain Busters   *Factor each polynomial completely.*

95. $(m + n)^2 - (m - n)^2$

96. $(a - b)^3 - (a + b)^3$

97. $m^2 - p^2 + 2m + 2p$

98. $3r - 3k + 3r^2 - 3k^2$

PREVIEW EXERCISES

*Solve each equation. **See Sections 2.1 and 2.2.***

99. $m - 4 = 0$

100. $3t + 2 = 0$

101. $2t + 10 = 0$

102. $7x = 0$

SUMMARY EXERCISES on Factoring

As you factor a polynomial, ask yourself these questions to decide on a suitable factoring technique.

Factoring a Polynomial

1. **Is there a common factor?** If so, factor it out.

2. **How many terms are in the polynomial?**

   Two terms: Check to see whether it is a difference of squares or a sum or difference of cubes. If so, factor as in **Section 5.4.**

   Three terms: Is it a perfect square trinomial? If the trinomial is not a perfect square, check to see whether the coefficient of the second-degree term is 1. If so, use the method of **Section 5.2.** If the coefficient of the second-degree term of the trinomial is not 1, use the general factoring methods of **Section 5.3.**

   Four terms: Try to factor the polynomial by grouping, as in **Section 5.1.**

3. **Can any factors be factored further?** If so, factor them.

(continued)

Match each polynomial in Column I with the best choice for factoring it in Column II. The choices in Column II may be used once, more than once, or not at all.

I	**II**
1. $12x^2 + 20x + 8$	**A.** Factor out the GCF. No further factoring is possible.
2. $x^2 - 17x + 72$	**B.** Factor a difference of squares.
3. $16m^2n + 24mn - 40mn^2$	**C.** Factor a difference of cubes.
4. $64a^2 - 121b^2$	**D.** Factor a sum of cubes.
5. $36p^2 - 60pq + 25q^2$	**E.** Factor a perfect square trinomial.
6. $z^2 - 4z + 6$	**F.** Factor by grouping.
7. $8r^3 - 125$	**G.** Factor out the GCF. Then factor a trinomial by grouping or trial and error.
8. $x^6 + 4x^4 - 3x^2 - 12$	**H.** Factor into two binomials by finding two integers whose product is the constant in the trinomial and whose sum is the coefficient of the middle term.
9. $4w^2 + 49$	
10. $z^2 - 24z + 144$	**I.** The polynomial is prime.

Factor each polynomial completely.

11. $a^2 - 4a - 12$ **12.** $a^2 + 17a + 72$

13. $6y^2 - 6y - 12$ **14.** $7y^6 + 14y^5 - 168y^4$

15. $6a + 12b + 18c$ **16.** $m^2 - 3mn - 4n^2$

17. $p^2 - 17p + 66$ **18.** $z^2 - 6z + 7z - 42$

19. $10z^2 - 7z - 6$ **20.** $2m^2 - 10m - 48$

21. $17x^3y^2 + 51xy$ **22.** $15y + 5$

23. $8a^5 - 8a^4 - 48a^3$ **24.** $8k^2 - 10k - 3$

25. $z^2 - 3za - 10a^2$ **26.** $50z^2 - 100$

27. $x^2 - 4x - 5x + 20$ **28.** $100n^2r^2 + 30nr^3 - 50n^2r$

29. $6n^2 - 19n + 10$ **30.** $9y^2 + 12y - 5$

31. $16x + 20$ **32.** $m^2 + 2m - 15$

33. $6y^2 - 5y - 4$ **34.** $m^2 - 81$

35. $6z^2 + 31z + 5$ **36.** $12x^2 + 47x - 4$

37. $4k^2 - 12k + 9$ **38.** $8p^2 + 23p - 3$

39. $54m^2 - 24z^2$ **40.** $8m^2 - 2m - 3$

41. $3k^2 + 4k - 4$ **42.** $45a^3b^5 - 60a^4b^2 + 75a^6b^4$

43. $14k^3 + 7k^2 - 70k$ **44.** $5 + r - 5s - rs$

45. $y^4 - 16$ **46.** $20y^5 - 30y^4$

47. $8m - 16m^2$ **48.** $k^2 - 16$

49. $z^3 - 8$ **50.** $y^2 - y - 56$

51. $k^2 + 9$ **52.** $27p^{10} - 45p^9 - 252p^8$

53. $32m^9 + 16m^5 + 24m^3$ **54.** $8m^3 + 125$

55. $16r^2 + 24rm + 9m^2$ **56.** $z^2 - 12z + 36$

57. $15h^2 + 11hg - 14g^2$ **58.** $5z^3 - 45z^2 + 70z$

59. $k^2 - 11k + 30$ **60.** $64p^2 - 100m^2$

61. $3k^3 - 12k^2 - 15k$

62. $y^2 - 4yk - 12k^2$

63. $1000p^3 + 27$

64. $64r^3 - 343$

65. $6 + 3m + 2p + mp$

66. $2m^2 + 7mn - 15n^2$

67. $16z^2 - 8z + 1$

68. $125m^4 - 400m^3n + 195m^2n^2$

69. $108m^2 - 36m + 3$

70. $100a^2 - 81y^2$

71. $x^2 - xy + y^2$

72. $4y^2 - 25$

73. $32z^3 + 56z^2 - 16z$

74. $10m^2 + 25m - 60$

75. $20 + 5m + 12n + 3mn$

76. $4 - 2q - 6p + 3pq$

77. $6a^2 + 10a - 4$

78. $36y^6 - 42y^5 - 120y^4$

79. $a^3 - b^3 + 2a - 2b$

80. $16k^2 - 48k + 36$

81. $64m^2 - 80mn + 25n^2$

82. $72y^3z^2 + 12y^2 - 24y^4z^2$

83. $8k^2 - 2kh - 3h^2$

84. $2a^2 - 7a - 30$

85. $2x^3 + 128$

86. $8a^3 - 27$

87. $10y^2 - 7yz - 6z^2$

88. $m^2 - 4m + 4$

89. $8a^2 + 23ab - 3b^2$

90. $a^4 - 625$

RELATING CONCEPTS   EXERCISES 91–98

FOR INDIVIDUAL OR GROUP WORK

*A binomial may be both a difference of squares and a difference of cubes. One example of such a binomial is $x^6 - 1$. With the techniques of **Section 5.4,** one factoring method will give the completely factored form, while the other will not. **Work Exercises 91–98 in order** to determine the method to use if you have to make such a decision.*

91. Factor $x^6 - 1$ as the difference of squares.

92. The factored form obtained in **Exercise 91** consists of a difference of cubes multiplied by a sum of cubes. Factor each binomial further.

93. Now start over and factor $x^6 - 1$ as the difference of cubes.

94. The factored form obtained in **Exercise 93** consists of a binomial that is a difference of squares and a trinomial. Factor the binomial further.

95. Compare your results in **Exercises 92 and 94.** Which one of these is factored completely?

96. Verify that the trinomial in the factored form in **Exercise 94** is the product of the two trinomials in the factored form in **Exercise 92.**

97. Use the results of **Exercises 91–96** to complete the following statement: In general, if I must choose between factoring first with the method for the difference of squares or the method for the difference of cubes, I should choose the _____ method to eventually obtain the completely factored form.

98. Find the *completely* factored form of $x^6 - 729$ by using the knowledge you gained in **Exercises 91–97.**

STUDY SKILLS

Preparing for Your Math Final Exam

Your math final exam is likely to be a comprehensive exam, which means it will cover material from the entire term.

1. **Figure out the grade you need to earn on the final exam to get the course grade you want.** Check your course syllabus for grading policies, or ask your instructor if you are not sure.

   How many points do you need to earn on your math final exam to get the grade you want?

2. **Create a final exam week plan.** Set priorities that allow you to spend extra time studying. This may mean making adjustments, in advance, in your work schedule or enlisting extra help with family responsibilities.

   What adjustments do you need to make for final exam week?

3. **Use the following suggestions to guide your studying and reviewing.**

   ▶ **Begin reviewing several days before the final exam.** DON'T wait until the last minute.

   ▶ **Know exactly which chapters and sections will be covered on the exam.**

   ▶ **Divide up the chapters.** Decide how much you will review each day.

   ▶ **Use returned quizzes and tests to review earlier material.**

   ▶ **Practice all types of problems. Use the Cumulative Reviews** that are at the end of each chapter in your textbook. All answers, with section references, are given in the answer section.

   ▶ **Review or rewrite your notes** to create summaries of important information.

   ▶ **Make study cards for all types of problems.** Carry the cards with you, and review them whenever you have a few minutes.

   ▶ **Take plenty of short breaks to reduce physical and mental stress.** Exercising, listening to music, and enjoying a favorite activity are effective stress busters.

   Finally, *DON'T* stay up all night the night before an exam—*get a good night's sleep.*

   Select several suggestions to use as you study for your math final exam.

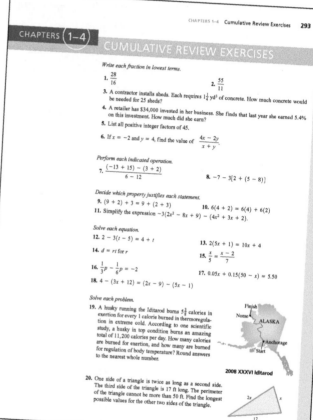

5.5

Solving Quadratic Equations by Factoring

OBJECTIVES

1 Solve quadratic equations by factoring.

2 Solve other equations by factoring.

Galileo Galilei (1564–1642)

Galileo Galilei developed theories to explain physical phenomena and set up experiments to test his ideas. According to legend, Galileo dropped objects of different weights from the Leaning Tower of Pisa to disprove the belief that heavier objects fall faster than lighter objects. He developed the formula

$$d = 16t^2$$

describing the motion of freely falling objects. In this formula, d is the distance in feet that an object falls (disregarding air resistance) in t seconds, regardless of weight.

The equation $d = 16t^2$ is a *quadratic equation*. A quadratic equation contains a second-degree term and no terms of greater degree.

> **Quadratic Equation**
>
> A **quadratic equation** is an equation that can be written in the form
>
> $$ax^2 + bx + c = 0,$$
>
> where a, b, and c are real numbers, with $a \neq 0$.

The form $ax^2 + bx + c = 0$ is the **standard form** of a quadratic equation.

$$x^2 + 5x + 6 = 0, \quad 2x^2 - 5x = 3, \quad x^2 = 4 \qquad \text{Quadratic equations}$$

Of these quadratic equations, only $x^2 + 5x + 6 = 0$ is in standard form.

We have factored many quadratic *expressions* of the form $ax^2 + bx + c$. In this section, we use factored quadratic expressions to solve quadratic *equations*.

OBJECTIVE 1 **Solve quadratic equations by factoring.** We use the **zero-factor property** to solve a quadratic equation by factoring.

> **Zero-Factor Property**
>
> **If a and b are real numbers and if $ab = 0$, then $a = 0$ or $b = 0$.**
>
> That is, if the product of two numbers is 0, then at least one of the numbers must be 0. One number *must* be 0, but both *may* be 0.

EXAMPLE 1 **Using the Zero-Factor Property**

Solve each equation.

(a) $(x + 3)(2x - 1) = 0$

The product $(x + 3)(2x - 1)$ is equal to 0. By the zero-factor property, the only way that the product of these two factors can be 0 is if at least one of the factors equals 0. Therefore, either $x + 3 = 0$ or $2x - 1 = 0$.

$$x + 3 = 0 \quad \text{or} \quad 2x - 1 = 0 \qquad \text{Zero-factor property}$$
$$x = -3 \qquad\qquad 2x = 1 \qquad \text{Solve each equation.}$$
$$x = \frac{1}{2} \qquad \text{Divide each side by 2.}$$

NOW TRY
EXERCISE 1

Solve each equation.

(a) $(x - 4)(3x + 1) = 0$

(b) $y(4y - 5) = 0$

The original equation, $(x + 3)(2x - 1) = 0$, has two solutions, -3 and $\frac{1}{2}$. Check these solutions by substituting -3 for x in this equation. **_Then start over_** and substitute $\frac{1}{2}$ for x.

CHECK   Let $x = -3$.

$$(x + 3)(2x - 1) = 0$$

$$(-3 + 3)[2(-3) - 1] \stackrel{?}{=} 0$$

$$0(-7) = 0 \checkmark \text{ True}$$

Let $x = \frac{1}{2}$.

$$(x + 3)(2x - 1) = 0$$

$$\left(\frac{1}{2} + 3\right)\left(2 \cdot \frac{1}{2} - 1\right) \stackrel{?}{=} 0$$

$$\frac{7}{2}(1 - 1) \stackrel{?}{=} 0$$

$$\frac{7}{2} \cdot 0 = 0 \checkmark \text{ True}$$

Both -3 and $\frac{1}{2}$ result in true equations, so the solution set is $\left\{-3, \frac{1}{2}\right\}$.

(b)

$$y(3y - 4) = 0$$

$$y = 0 \quad \text{or} \quad 3y - 4 = 0 \qquad \text{Zero-factor property}$$

Don't forget that 0 is a solution.

$$3y = 4$$

$$y = \frac{4}{3}$$

Check these solutions by substituting each one into the original equation. The solution set is $\left\{0, \frac{4}{3}\right\}$.

NOW TRY

NOTE   The word _or_ as used in **Example 1** means "one or the other or both."

If the polynomial in an equation is not already factored, first make sure that the equation is in standard form. Then factor.

EXAMPLE 2   Solving Quadratic Equations

Solve each equation.

(a) $x^2 - 5x = -6$

First, rewrite the equation in standard form by adding 6 to each side.

Don't factor x out at this step.

$$x^2 - 5x = -6$$

$$x^2 - 5x + 6 = 0 \qquad \text{Add 6.}$$

Now factor $x^2 - 5x + 6$. Find two numbers whose product is 6 and whose sum is -5. These two numbers are -2 and -3, so we factor as follows.

$$(x - 2)(x - 3) = 0 \qquad \text{Factor.}$$

$$x - 2 = 0 \quad \text{or} \quad x - 3 = 0 \qquad \text{Zero-factor property}$$

$$x = 2 \quad \text{or} \qquad x = 3 \qquad \text{Solve each equation.}$$

NOW TRY ANSWERS

1. **(a)** $\left\{-\frac{1}{3}, 4\right\}$ **(b)** $\left\{0, \frac{5}{4}\right\}$

NOW TRY
EXERCISE 2
Solve $t^2 = -3t + 18$.

CHECK   Let $x = 2$.

$$x^2 - 5x = -6$$
$$2^2 - 5(2) \stackrel{?}{=} -6$$
$$4 - 10 \stackrel{?}{=} -6$$
$$-6 = -6 \checkmark \quad \text{True}$$

Let $x = 3$.

$$x^2 - 5x = -6$$
$$3^2 - 5(3) \stackrel{?}{=} -6$$
$$9 - 15 \stackrel{?}{=} -6$$
$$-6 = -6 \checkmark \quad \text{True}$$

Both solutions check, so the solution set is $\{2, 3\}$.

(b)
$$y^2 = y + 20 \quad \boxed{\text{Write this equation in standard form.}}$$

Standard form $\longrightarrow$ $y^2 - y - 20 = 0$ Subtract y and 20.

$$(y - 5)(y + 4) = 0$$ Factor.

$$y - 5 = 0 \quad \text{or} \quad y + 4 = 0$$ Zero-factor property

$$y = 5 \quad \text{or} \quad y = -4$$ Solve each equation.

Check each solution to verify that the solution set is $\{-4, 5\}$.   NOW TRY

Solving a Quadratic Equation by Factoring

Step 1 **Write the equation in standard form**—that is, with all terms on one side of the equals symbol in descending powers of the variable and 0 on the other side.

Step 2 **Factor** completely.

Step 3 **Use the zero-factor property** to set each factor with a variable equal to 0.

Step 4 **Solve** the resulting equations.

Step 5 **Check** each solution in the original equation.

NOTE Not all quadratic equations can be solved by factoring. A more general method for solving such equations is given in **Chapter 11.**

NOW TRY
EXERCISE 3
Solve $10p^2 + 65p = 35$.

EXAMPLE 3 Solving a Quadratic Equation with a Common Factor

Solve $4p^2 + 40 = 26p$.

$$4p^2 + 40 = 26p$$

$$4p^2 - 26p + 40 = 0$$ Standard form

$$\boxed{\text{This 2 is } \textit{not} \text{ a solution of the equation.}} \; 2(2p^2 - 13p + 20) = 0$$ Factor out 2.

$$2p^2 - 13p + 20 = 0$$ Divide each side by 2.

$$(2p - 5)(p - 4) = 0$$ Factor.

$$2p - 5 = 0 \quad \text{or} \quad p - 4 = 0$$ Zero-factor property

$$2p = 5 \qquad\qquad p = 4$$ Solve each equation.

$$p = \frac{5}{2}$$

NOW TRY ANSWERS
2. $\{-6, 3\}$ **3.** $\left\{-7, \frac{1}{2}\right\}$

Check each solution to verify that the solution set is $\left\{\frac{5}{2}, 4\right\}$.   NOW TRY

> ⚠ **CAUTION** A common error is to include the common factor 2 as a solution in **Example 3.** *Only factors containing variables lead to solutions,* such as the factor y in the equation $y(3y - 4) = 0$ in **Example 1(b).**

**NOW TRY
EXERCISE 4**

Solve each equation.

(a) $9x^2 - 64 = 0$

(b) $m^2 = 5m$

(c) $p(6p - 1) = 2$

EXAMPLE 4 Solving Quadratic Equations

Solve each equation.

(a)
$$16m^2 - 25 = 0$$
$$(4m + 5)(4m - 5) = 0 \quad \text{Factor the difference of squares. (Section 6.4)}$$
$$4m + 5 = 0 \quad \text{or} \quad 4m - 5 = 0 \quad \text{Zero-factor property}$$
$$4m = -5 \quad \text{or} \quad 4m = 5 \quad \text{Solve each equation.}$$
$$m = -\frac{5}{4} \quad \text{or} \quad m = \frac{5}{4}$$

Check the solutions, $-\frac{5}{4}$ and $\frac{5}{4}$, in the original equation. The solution set is $\left\{-\frac{5}{4}, \frac{5}{4}\right\}$.

(b)
$$y^2 = 2y$$
$$y^2 - 2y = 0 \quad \text{Standard form}$$
$$y(y - 2) = 0 \quad \text{Factor.}$$
$$y = 0 \quad \text{or} \quad y - 2 = 0 \quad \text{Zero-factor property}$$
$$y = 2 \quad \text{Solve.}$$

Don't forget to set the variable factor y equal to 0.

The solution set is $\{0, 2\}$.

(c)
$$k(2k + 1) = 3 \quad \text{To be in standard form, 0 must be on the right side.}$$
$$2k^2 + k = 3 \quad \text{Distributive property}$$
$$\text{Standard form} \rightarrow 2k^2 + k - 3 = 0 \quad \text{Subtract 3.}$$
$$(2k + 3)(k - 1) = 0 \quad \text{Factor.}$$
$$2k + 3 = 0 \quad \text{or} \quad k - 1 = 0 \quad \text{Zero-factor property}$$
$$2k = -3 \qquad k = 1 \quad \text{Solve each equation.}$$
$$k = -\frac{3}{2}$$

The solution set is $\left\{-\frac{3}{2}, 1\right\}$.

NOW TRY

> ⚠ **CAUTION** In **Example 4(b),** it is tempting to begin by dividing both sides of
> $$y^2 = 2y$$
> by y to get $y = 2$. Note, however, that we do not get the other solution, 0, if we divide by a variable. (We *may* divide each side of an equation by a *nonzero* real number, however. For instance, in **Example 3** we divided each side by 2.)
>   In **Example 4(c),** we could not use the zero-factor property to solve the equation
> $$k(2k + 1) = 3$$
> in its given form because of the 3 on the right. *The zero-factor property applies only to a product that equals 0.*

NOW TRY ANSWERS

4. (a) $\left\{-\frac{8}{3}, \frac{8}{3}\right\}$ (b) $\{0, 5\}$

(c) $\left\{-\frac{1}{2}, \frac{2}{3}\right\}$

PREVIEW EXERCISES

*Solve each problem. **See Sections 2.4 and 2.5.***

83. If a number is doubled and 6 is subtracted from this result, the answer is 3684. The unknown number is the year that Texas was admitted to the Union. What year was Texas admitted?

84. The length of the rectangle is 3 m more than its width. The perimeter of the rectangle is 34 m. Find the width of the rectangle.

x

$x + 3$

85. Twice the sum of two consecutive integers is 28 more than the greater integer. Find the integers.

86. The area of a triangle with base 12 in. is 48 in.^{2}. Find the height of the triangle.

5.6 Applications of Quadratic Equations

OBJECTIVES

1 Solve problems involving geometric figures.

2 Solve problems involving consecutive integers.

3 Solve problems by applying the Pythagorean theorem.

4 Solve problems by using given quadratic models.

We use factoring to solve quadratic equations that arise in application problems. We follow the same six problem-solving steps given in **Section 2.4.**

Solving an Applied Problem

Step 1 **Read** the problem carefully. What information is given? What are you asked to find?

Step 2 **Assign a variable** to represent the unknown value. Use a sketch, diagram, or table, as needed. If necessary, express any other unknown values in terms of the variable.

Step 3 **Write an equation,** using the variable expression(s).

Step 4 **Solve** the equation.

Step 5 **State the answer.** Label it appropriately. Does it seem reasonable?

Step 6 **Check** the answer in the words of the original problem.

OBJECTIVE 1 Solve problems involving geometric figures. Refer to the formulas given on the inside covers of the text, if necessary.

EXAMPLE 1 Solving an Area Problem

Abe Biggs wants to plant a triangular flower bed in a corner of his garden. One leg of the right-triangular flower bed will be 2 m shorter than the other leg. He wants the bed to have an area of 24 m^2. See **FIGURE 1**. Find the lengths of the legs.

Step 1 **Read** the problem. We need to find the lengths of the legs of a right triangle with area 24 m^2.

Step 2 **Assign a variable.**

Let x = the length of one leg.

Then $x - 2$ = the length of the other leg.

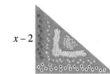

$x - 2$

x

FIGURE 1

↷NOW TRY
↬EXERCISE 1
A right triangle has one leg that is 4 ft shorter than the other leg. The area of the triangle is 6 ft². Determine the lengths of the legs.

Step 3 **Write an equation.** The area of a right triangle is given by the formula

$$\text{area} = \frac{1}{2} \times \text{base} \times \text{height}.$$

In a right triangle, the legs are the base and height, so we substitute 24 for the area, x for the base, and $x - 2$ for the height in the formula.

$$\mathcal{A} = \frac{1}{2}bh \qquad \text{Formula for the area of a triangle}$$

$$24 = \frac{1}{2}x(x - 2) \qquad \text{Let } \mathcal{A} = 24, b = x, h = x - 2.$$

Step 4 **Solve.**
$$48 = x(x - 2) \qquad \text{Multiply by 2.}$$
$$48 = x^2 - 2x \qquad \text{Distributive property}$$
$$x^2 - 2x - 48 = 0 \qquad \text{Standard form}$$
$$(x + 6)(x - 8) = 0 \qquad \text{Factor.}$$
$$x + 6 = 0 \quad \text{or} \quad x - 8 = 0 \qquad \text{Zero-factor property}$$
$$x = -6 \quad \text{or} \qquad x = 8 \qquad \text{Solve each equation.}$$

Step 5 **State the answer.** The solutions are -6 and 8. Because a triangle cannot have a side of negative length, we discard the solution -6. Then the lengths of the legs will be 8 m and $8 - 2 = 6$ m.

Step 6 **Check.** The length of one leg is 2 m less than the length of the other leg, and the area is

$$\frac{1}{2}(8)(6) = 24 \text{ m}^2, \quad \text{as required.} \qquad \text{NOW TRY}↷$$

⚠ CAUTION   *In solving applied problems, always check solutions against physical facts* and discard any answers that are not appropriate.

OBJECTIVE 2 Solve problems involving consecutive integers. Recall from our work in **Section 2.4** that **consecutive integers** are integers that are next to each other on a number line, such as 3 and 4, or -11 and -10. See **FIGURE 2(a)**.

Consecutive odd integers are *odd* integers that are next to each other, such as 3 and 5, or -13 and -11. **Consecutive even integers** are defined similarly—for example, 4 and 6 are consecutive even integers, as are -10 and -8. See **FIGURE 2(b)**.

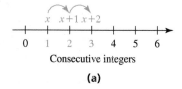

Consecutive integers

(a)

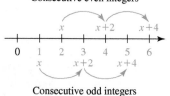

Consecutive even integers

Consecutive odd integers

(b)

FIGURE 2

PROBLEM-SOLVING HINT

If x represents the lesser integer, then, for any

two consecutive integers, use	$x, \ x + 1;$
three consecutive integers, use	$x, \ x + 1, \ x + 2;$
two consecutive even or odd integers, use	$x, \ x + 2;$
three consecutive even or odd integers, use	$x, \ x + 2, \ x + 4.$

As a general rule in this book, we list consecutive integers in increasing order when solving applications.

NOW TRY ANSWER
1. 2 ft, 6 ft

NOW TRY
EXERCISE 2

The product of the first and second of three consecutive integers is 2 more than 8 times the third integer. Find the integers.

EXAMPLE 2 Solving a Consecutive Integer Problem

The product of the second and third of three consecutive integers is 2 more than 7 times the first integer. Find the integers.

Step 1   **Read** the problem. Note that the integers are consecutive.

Step 2   **Assign a variable.**

Let $x =$ the first integer.

Then $x + 1 =$ the second integer,

and $x + 2 =$ the third integer.

Step 3   **Write an equation.**

The product of the second and third   is   2 more than 7 times the first.

$$(x + 1)(x + 2) = 7x + 2$$

Step 4   **Solve.**

$$x^2 + 3x + 2 = 7x + 2 \qquad \text{Multiply.}$$
$$x^2 - 4x = 0 \qquad \text{Standard form}$$
$$x(x - 4) = 0 \qquad \text{Factor.}$$
$$x = 0 \quad \text{or} \quad x = 4 \qquad \text{Zero-factor property}$$

Step 5   **State the answer.** The solutions 0 and 4 each lead to a correct answer.

0, 1, 2   or   4, 5, 6

Step 6   **Check.** The product of the second and third integers must equal 2 more than 7 times the first. Since $1 \cdot 2 = 7 \cdot 0 + 2$ and $5 \cdot 6 = 7 \cdot 4 + 2$, both sets of consecutive integers satisfy the statement of the problem.

NOW TRY

OBJECTIVE 3   **Solve problems by applying the Pythagorean theorem.**

Pythagorean Theorem

If a right triangle has longest side of length c and two other sides of lengths a and b, then

$$a^2 + b^2 = c^2.$$

The longest side, the **hypotenuse,** is opposite the right angle. The two shorter sides are the **legs** of the triangle.

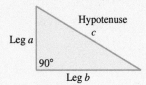

EXAMPLE 3   Applying the Pythagorean Theorem

Patricia Walker and Ali Ulku leave their office, Patricia traveling north and Ali traveling east. When Ali is 1 mi farther than Patricia from the office, the distance between them is 2 mi more than Patricia's distance from the office. Find their distances from the office and the distance between them.

Step 1   **Read** the problem again. There will be three answers to this problem.

NOW TRY ANSWER
2. 9, 10, 11   or $-2, -1, 0$

NOW TRY
EXERCISE 3
The longer leg of a right triangle is 7 ft longer than the shorter leg and the hypotenuse is 8 ft longer than the shorter leg. Find the lengths of the sides of the triangle.

Step 2 **Assign a variable.**

Let x = Patricia's distance from the office.

Then $x + 1$ = Ali's distance from the office,

and $x + 2$ = the distance between them.

Place these expressions on a right triangle, as in **FIGURE 3**.

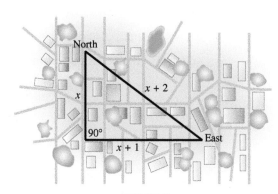

FIGURE 3

Step 3 **Write an equation.** Use the Pythagorean theorem.

$$a^2 + b^2 = c^2$$
$$x^2 + (x + 1)^2 = (x + 2)^2$$

> Be careful to substitute properly.

Step 4 **Solve.** $x^2 + x^2 + 2x + 1 = x^2 + 4x + 4$ Square each binomial.

$x^2 - 2x - 3 = 0$ Standard form

$(x - 3)(x + 1) = 0$ Factor.

$x - 3 = 0$ or $x + 1 = 0$ Zero-factor property

$x = 3$ or $x = -1$ Solve each equation.

Step 5 **State the answer.** Since -1 cannot represent a distance, 3 is the only possible answer. Patricia's distance is 3 mi, Ali's distance is $3 + 1 = 4$ mi, and the distance between them is $3 + 2 = 5$ mi.

Step 6 **Check.** Since $3^2 + 4^2 = 5^2$, the answers are correct. NOW TRY

PROBLEM-SOLVING HINT

In solving a problem involving the Pythagorean theorem, be sure that the expressions for the sides are properly placed.

$$(\text{one leg})^2 + (\text{other leg})^2 = \text{hypotenuse}^2$$

OBJECTIVE 4 Solve problems by using given quadratic models. In **Examples 1–3**, we wrote quadratic equations to model, or mathematically describe, various situations and then solved the equations. In the last two examples of this section, we are given the quadratic models and must use them to determine data.

NOW TRY ANSWER
3. 5 ft, 12 ft, 13 ft

**NOW TRY
EXERCISE 4**

Refer to **Example 4.** How long will it take for the ball to reach a height of 50 ft?

EXAMPLE 4   Finding the Height of a Ball

A tennis player's serve travels 180 ft per sec (123 mph). If she hits the ball directly upward, the height h of the ball in feet at time t in seconds is modeled by the quadratic equation

$$h = -16t^2 + 180t + 6.$$

How long will it take for the ball to reach a height of 206 ft?

A height of 206 ft means that $h = 206$, so we substitute 206 for h in the equation.

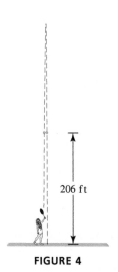

FIGURE 4

$$h = -16t^2 + 180t + 6$$

$$206 = -16t^2 + 180t + 6 \qquad \text{Let } h = 206.$$

$$-16t^2 + 180t + 6 = 206 \qquad \text{Interchange sides.}$$

$$-16t^2 + 180t - 200 = 0 \qquad \text{Standard form}$$

$$4t^2 - 45t + 50 = 0 \qquad \text{Divide by } -4.$$

$$(4t - 5)(t - 10) = 0 \qquad \text{Factor.}$$

$$4t - 5 = 0 \quad \text{or} \quad t - 10 = 0 \qquad \text{Zero-factor property}$$

$$4t = 5 \quad \text{or} \qquad t = 10 \qquad \text{Solve each equation.}$$

$$t = \frac{5}{4}$$

Since we found two acceptable answers, the ball will be 206 ft above the ground twice, once on its way up and once on its way down, at $\frac{5}{4}$ sec and at 10 sec. See **FIGURE 4**.

NOW TRY

EXAMPLE 5   Modeling the Foreign-Born Population of the United States

The foreign-born population of the United States over the years 1930–2007 can be modeled by the quadratic equation

$$y = 0.01048x^2 - 0.5400x + 15.43,$$

where $x = 0$ represents 1930, $x = 10$ represents 1940, and so on, and y is the number of people in millions. (*Source*: U.S. Census Bureau.)

(a) Use the model to find the foreign-born population in 1980 to the nearest tenth of a million.

Since $x = 0$ represents 1930, $x = 50$ represents 1980. Substitute 50 for x in the equation.

$$y = 0.01048\,(50)^2 - 0.5400\,(50) + 15.43 \qquad \text{Let } x = 50.$$

$$y = 14.6 \qquad\qquad\qquad\qquad\qquad \text{Round to the nearest tenth.}$$

In 1980, the foreign-born population of the United States was about 14.6 million.

(b) Repeat part (a) for 2007.

$$y = 0.01048\,(77)^2 - 0.5400\,(77) + 15.43 \qquad \text{For 2007, let } x = 77.$$

$$y = 36.0 \qquad\qquad\qquad\qquad\qquad \text{Round to the nearest tenth.}$$

In 2007, the foreign-born population of the United States was about 36.0 million.

NOW TRY ANSWER

4. $\frac{1}{4}$ sec and 11 sec

Use the model in **Example 5** to find the foreign-born population of the United States in the year 2000. Give your answer to the nearest tenth of a million. How does it compare to the actual value from the table?

(c) The model used in parts (a) and (b) was developed using the data in the table below. How do the results in parts (a) and (b) compare to the actual data from the table?

Year	Foreign-Born Population (millions)
1930	14.2
1940	11.6
1950	10.3
1960	9.7
1970	9.6
1980	14.1
1990	19.8
2000	28.4
2007	37.3

NOW TRY ANSWER
5. 29.0 million; The actual value is 28.4 million, so the answer using the model is slightly high.

From the table, the actual value for 1980 is 14.1 million. Our answer in part (a), 14.6 million, is slightly high. For 2007, the actual value is 37.3 million, so our answer of 36.0 million in part (b) is somewhat low. *NOW TRY*

5.6 EXERCISES

1. *Concept Check* To review the six problem-solving steps first introduced in **Section 2.4,** complete each statement.

Step 1: _____ the problem carefully.

Step 2: Assign a _____ to represent the unknown value.

Step 3: Write a(n) _____ using the variable expression(s).

Step 4: _____ the equation.

Step 5: State the _____ .

Step 6: _____ the answer in the words of the _____ problem.

2. A student solves an applied problem and gets 6 or -3 for the length of the side of a square. Which of these answers is reasonable? Explain.

In Exercises 3–6, a figure and a corresponding geometric formula are given. Using x as the variable, complete Steps 3–6 for each problem. (Refer to the steps in **Exercise 1** *as needed.)*

3.

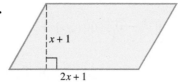

Area of a parallelogram: $\mathcal{A} = bh$

The area of this parallelogram is 45 sq. units. Find its base and height.

4.

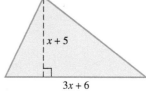

Area of a triangle: $\mathcal{A} = \dfrac{1}{2}bh$

The area of this triangle is 60 sq. units. Find its base and height.

5.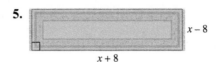

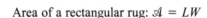

Area of a rectangular rug: $\mathcal{A} = LW$

The area of this rug is 80 sq. units. Find its length and width.

6.

Volume of a rectangular Chinese box: $V = LWH$

The volume of this box is 192 cu. units. Find its length and width.

Solve each problem. Check your answers to be sure that they are reasonable. Refer to the formulas on the inside covers. ***See Example 1.***

7. The length of a standard jewel case is 2 cm more than its width. The area of the rectangular top of the case is 168 cm². Find the length and width of the jewel case.

8. A standard DVD case is 6 cm longer than it is wide. The area of the rectangular top of the case is 247 cm². Find the length and width of the case.

9. The area of a triangle is 30 in.². The base of the triangle measures 2 in. more than twice the height of the triangle. Find the measures of the base and the height.

10. A certain triangle has its base equal in measure to its height. The area of the triangle is 72 m². Find the equal base and height measure.

11. A 10-gal aquarium is 3 in. higher than it is wide. Its length is 21 in., and its volume is 2730 in.³. What are the height and width of the aquarium?

12. A toolbox is 2 ft high, and its width is 3 ft less than its length. If its volume is 80 ft³, find the length and width of the box.

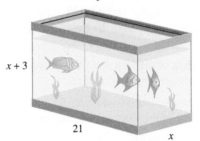

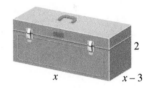

13. The dimensions of an HPf1905 flat-panel monitor are such that its length is 3 in. more than its width. If the length were doubled and if the width were decreased by 1 in., the area would be increased by 150 in.². What are the length and width of the flat panel?

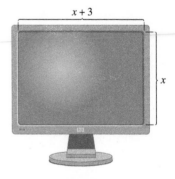

14. The keyboard that accompanies the monitor in **Exercise 13** is 11 in. longer than it is wide. If the length were doubled and if 2 in. were added to the width, the area would be increased by 198 in.². What are the length and width of the keyboard? (*Source:* Author's computer.)

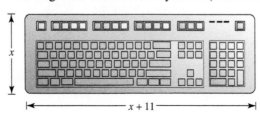

15. A square mirror has sides measuring 2 ft less than the sides of a square painting. If the difference between their areas is 32 ft^2, find the lengths of the sides of the mirror and the painting.

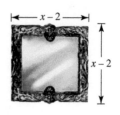

16. The sides of one square have length 3 m more than the sides of a second square. If the area of the larger square is subtracted from 4 times the area of the smaller square, the result is 36 m^2. What are the lengths of the sides of each square?

*Solve each problem. **See Example 2.***

17. The product of the numbers on two consecutive volumes of research data is 420. Find the volume numbers. See the figure.

18. The product of the page numbers on two facing pages of a book is 600. Find the page numbers.

19. The product of the second and third of three consecutive integers is 2 more than 10 times the first integer. Find the integers.

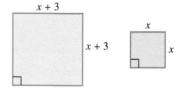

20. The product of the first and third of three consecutive integers is 3 more than 3 times the second integer. Find the integers.

21. Find three consecutive odd integers such that 3 times the sum of all three is 18 more than the product of the first and second integers.

22. Find three consecutive odd integers such that the sum of all three is 42 less than the product of the second and third integers.

23. Find three consecutive even integers such that the sum of the squares of the first and second integers is equal to the square of the third integer.

24. Find three consecutive even integers such that the square of the sum of the first and second integers is equal to twice the third integer.

*Solve each problem. **See Example 3.***

25. The hypotenuse of a right triangle is 1 cm longer than the longer leg. The shorter leg is 7 cm shorter than the longer leg. Find the length of the longer leg of the triangle.

26. The longer leg of a right triangle is 1 m longer than the shorter leg. The hypotenuse is 1 m shorter than twice the shorter leg. Find the length of the shorter leg of the triangle.

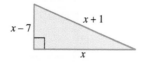

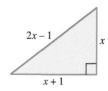

27. Tram works due north of home. Her husband Alan works due east. They leave for work at the same time. By the time Tram is 5 mi from home, the distance between them is 1 mi more than Alan's distance from home. How far from home is Alan?

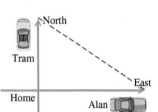

28. Two cars left an intersection at the same time. One traveled north. The other traveled 14 mi farther, but to the east. How far apart were they at that time if the distance between them was 4 mi more than the distance traveled east?

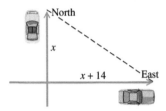

29. A ladder is leaning against a building. The distance from the bottom of the ladder to the building is 4 ft less than the length of the ladder. How high up the side of the building is the top of the ladder if that distance is 2 ft less than the length of the ladder?

30. A lot has the shape of a right triangle with one leg 2 m longer than the other. The hypotenuse is 2 m less than twice the length of the shorter leg. Find the length of the shorter leg.

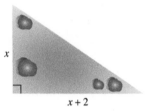

If an object is projected upward with an initial velocity of 128 ft per sec, its height h after t seconds is

$$h = -16t^2 + 128t.$$

Find the height of the object after each time listed. ***See Example 4.***

31. 1 sec   **32.** 2 sec   **33.** 4 sec

34. How long does it take the object just described to return to the ground? (*Hint:* When the object hits the ground, $h = 0$.)

Solve each problem. ***See Examples 4 and 5.***

35. An object projected from a height of 48 ft with an initial velocity of 32 ft per sec after t seconds has height

$$h = -16t^2 + 32t + 48.$$

(a) After how many seconds is the height 64 ft? (*Hint:* Let $h = 64$ and solve.)

(b) After how many seconds is the height 60 ft?

(c) After how many seconds does the object hit the ground?

(d) The quadratic equation from part (c) has two solutions, yet only one of them is appropriate for answering the question. Why is this so?

36. If an object is projected upward from ground level with an initial velocity of 64 ft per sec, its height h in feet t seconds later is

$$h = -16t^2 + 64t.$$

(a) After how many seconds is the height 48 ft?

(b) The object reaches its maximum height 2 sec after it is projected. What is this maximum height?

(c) After how many seconds does the object hit the ground?

(d) Find the number of seconds after which the height is 60 ft.

(e) What is the physical interpretation of why part (d) has two answers?

(f) The quadratic equation from part (c) has two solutions, yet only one of them is appropriate for answering the question. Why is this so?

37. The table shows the number of cellular phone subscribers (in millions) in the United States.

Year	Subscribers (in millions)
1990	5
1992	11
1994	24
1996	44
1998	69
2000	109
2002	141
2004	182
2006	233
2008	263

Source: CTIA—The Wireless Association.

We used the preceding data to develop the quadratic equation

$$y = 0.590x^2 + 4.523x + 0.136,$$

which models the number y of cellular phone subscribers (in millions) in the year x, where $x = 0$ represents 1990, $x = 2$ represents 1992, and so on.

(a) Use the model to find the number of subscribers in 2000, to the nearest tenth. How does the result compare with the actual data in the table?

(b) What value of x corresponds to 2008?

(c) Use the model to find the number of cellular phone subscribers in 2008, to the nearest tenth. How does the result compare with the actual data in the table?

(d) Assuming that the trend in the data continues, use the quadratic equation to estimate the number of cellular phone subscribers in 2010, to the nearest tenth.

38. Annual revenue in billions of dollars for eBay is shown in the table.

Year	Annual Revenue (in billions of dollars)
2002	1.21
2003	2.17
2004	3.27
2005	4.55
2006	5.97
2007	7.67

Source: eBay.

47. $m^2 - 5m + 4 = 0$

48. $x^2 = -15 + 8x$

49. $3z^2 - 11z - 20 = 0$

50. $81t^2 - 64 = 0$

51. $y^2 = 8y$

52. $n(n - 5) = 6$

53. $t^2 - 14t + 49 = 0$

54. $t^2 = 12(t - 3)$

55. $(5z + 2)(z^2 + 3z + 2) = 0$

56. $x^2 = 9$

5.6   *Solve each problem.*

57. The length of a rug is 6 ft more than the width. The area is 40 ft². Find the length and width of the rug.

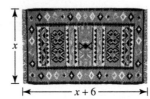

58. The surface area S of a box is given by

$$S = 2WH + 2WL + 2LH.$$

A treasure chest from a sunken galleon has the dimensions shown in the figure. Its surface area is 650 ft². Find its width.

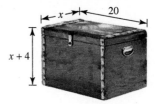

59. The product of two consecutive integers is 29 more than their sum. What are the integers?

60. Two cars left an intersection at the same time. One traveled west, and the other traveled 14 mi less, but to the south. How far apart were they at that time, if the distance between them was 16 mi more than the distance traveled south?

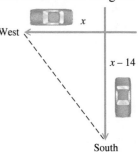

61. If an object is dropped, the distance d in feet it falls in t seconds (disregarding air resistance) is given by the quadratic equation

$$d = 16t^2.$$

Find the distance an object would fall in **(a)** 4 sec and **(b)** 8 sec.

62. The numbers of alternative-fueled vehicles in use in the United States, in thousands, for the years 2001–2006 are given in the table.

Year	Number (in thousands)
2001	425
2002	471
2003	534
2004	565
2005	592
2006	635

Source: Energy Information Administration.

Using statistical methods, we developed the quadratic equation

$$y = -2.84x^2 + 61.1x + 366$$

to model the number of vehicles y in year x. Here, we used $x = 1$ for 2001, $x = 2$ for 2002, and so on.

(a) Use the model to find the number of alternative-fueled vehicles in 2005, to the nearest thousand. How does the result compare with the actual data in the table?

(b) Use the model to estimate the number of alternative-fueled vehicles in 2007, to the nearest thousand.

(c) Why might the estimate for 2007 be unreliable?

MIXED REVIEW EXERCISES

63. *Concept Check* Which of the following is *not* factored completely?

    A. $3(7t)$ **B.** $3x(7t + 4)$ **C.** $(3 + x)(7t + 4)$ **D.** $3(7t + 4) + x(7t + 4)$

64. A student factored $6x^2 + 16x - 32$ as $(2x + 8)(3x - 4)$. Explain why the polynomial is not factored completely, and give the completely factored form.

Factor completely.

65. $3k^2 + 11k + 10$ **66.** $z^2 - 11zx + 10x^2$

67. $y^4 - 625$ **68.** $15m^2 + 20m - 12mp - 16p$

69. $24ab^3c^2 - 56a^2bc^3 + 72a^2b^2c$ **70.** $6m^3 - 21m^2 - 45m$

71. $12x^2yz^3 + 12xy^2z - 30x^3y^2z^4$ **72.** $25a^2 + 15ab + 9b^2$

73. $12r^2 + 18rq - 10r - 15q$ **74.** $2a^5 - 8a^4 - 24a^3$

75. $49t^2 + 56t + 16$ **76.** $1000a^3 + 27$

Solve.

77. $t(t - 7) = 0$ **78.** $x^2 + 3x = 10$ **79.** $25x^2 + 20x + 4 = 0$

80. The product of the first and second of three consecutive integers is equal to 23 plus the third. Find the integers.

81. A pyramid has a rectangular base with a length that is 2 m more than its width. The height of the pyramid is 6 m, and its volume is 48 m³. Find the length and width of the base.

82. A lot is in the shape of a right triangle. The hypotenuse is 3 m longer than the longer leg. The longer leg is 6 m longer than twice the length of the shorter leg. Find the lengths of the sides of the lot.

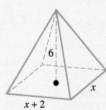

83. The triangular sail of a schooner has an area of 30 m². The height of the sail is 4 m more than the base. Find the base of the sail.

84. The floor plan for a house is a rectangle with length 7 m more than its width. The area is 170 m². Find the width and length of the house.

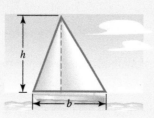

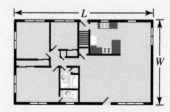

CHAPTER (5)

TEST

View the complete solutions to all Chapter Test exercises on the Video Resources on DVD.

1. *Concept Check*   Which one of the following is the correct completely factored form of $2x^2 - 2x - 24$?

A. $(2x + 6)(x - 4)$ **B.** $(x + 3)(2x - 8)$

C. $2(x + 4)(x - 3)$ **D.** $2(x + 3)(x - 4)$

Factor each polynomial completely. If the polynomial is prime, say so.

2. $12x^2 - 30x$

3. $2m^3n^2 + 3m^3n - 5m^2n^2$

4. $2ax - 2bx + ay - by$

5. $x^2 - 5x - 24$

6. $2x^2 + x - 3$

7. $10z^2 - 17z + 3$

8. $t^2 + 2t + 3$

9. $x^2 + 36$

10. $12 - 6a + 2b - ab$

11. $9y^2 - 64$

12. $4x^2 - 28xy + 49y^2$

13. $-2x^2 - 4x - 2$

14. $6t^4 + 3t^3 - 108t^2$

15. $r^3 - 125$

16. $8k^3 + 64$

17. $x^4 - 81$

18. $81x^4 - 16y^4$

19. $9x^6y^4 + 12x^3y^2 + 4$

Solve each equation.

20. $2r^2 - 13r + 6 = 0$

21. $25x^2 - 4 = 0$

22. $t^2 = 9t$

23. $x(x - 20) = -100$

24. $(s + 8)(6s^2 + 13s - 5) = 0$

Solve each problem.

25. The length of a rectangular flower bed is 3 ft less than twice its width. The area of the bed is 54 ft². Find the dimensions of the flower bed.

26. Find two consecutive integers such that the square of the sum of the two integers is 11 more than the first integer.

27. A carpenter needs to cut a brace to support a wall stud, as shown in the figure. The brace should be 7 ft less than three times the length of the stud. If the brace will be anchored on the floor 15 ft away from the stud, how long should the brace be?

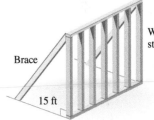

28. The public debt y (in billions of dollars) of the United States from 2000 through 2008 can be approximated by the quadratic equation

$$y = 29.92x^2 + 305.8x + 5581,$$

where $x = 0$ represents 2000, $x = 1$ represents 2001, and so on. (*Source:* Bureau of Public Debt.) Use the model to estimate the public debt, to the nearest billion dollars, in the year 2006.

Solve each equation.

1. $3x + 2(x - 4) = 4(x - 2)$

2. $0.3x + 0.9x = 0.06$

3. $\frac{2}{3}m - \frac{1}{2}(m - 4) = 3$

4. Solve for P: $A = P + Prt$.

5. Find the measures of the marked angles.

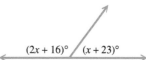

$(2x + 16)°$ $(x + 23)°$

Solve each problem.

6. At the 2006 Winter Olympics in Torino, Italy, the top medal winner was Germany, which won a total of 29 medals. Germany won 1 more silver medal than gold and 5 more gold medals than bronze. Find the number of each type of medal won. (*Source:* www.infoplease.com.)

7. From a list of "technology-related items," adults were recently surveyed as to those items they couldn't live without. Complete the results shown in the table if 500 adults were surveyed.

Item	Percent That Couldn't Live Without	Number That Couldn't Live Without
Personal computer	46%	
Cell phone	41%	
High-speed Internet		190
MP3 player		60

(Other items included digital cable, HDTV, and electronic gaming console.)
Source: Ipsos for AP.

8. Fill in each blank with *positive* or *negative*. The point with coordinates (a, b) is in

  (a) quadrant II if a is _____ and b is _____.

  (b) quadrant III if a is _____ and b is _____.

9. Consider the equation $y = 12x + 3$. Find the following.

  (a) The x- and y-intercepts   **(b)** The slope   **(c)** The graph

10. The points on the graph show the total retail sales of prescription drugs in the United States in the years 2001–2007, along with a graph of a linear equation that models the data.

  (a) Use the ordered pairs shown on the graph to find the slope of the line to the nearest whole number. Interpret the slope.

  (b) Use the graph to estimate sales in the year 2005. Write your answer as an ordered pair of the form (year, sales in billions of dollars).

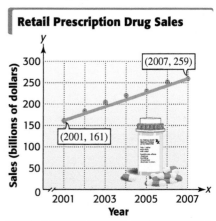

Retail Prescription Drug Sales

(2007, 259)

(2001, 161)

Sales (billions of dollars)

Year

Source: National Association of Chain Drug Stores.

NOTE *The numerator of a rational expression may be any real number.* If the numerator equals 0 and the denominator does not equal 0, then the rational expression equals 0. See **Example 1(b).**

Determining When a Rational Expression Is Undefined

Step 1   Set the denominator of the rational expression equal to 0.

Step 2   Solve this equation.

Step 3   The solutions of the equation are the values that make the rational expression undefined. The variable *cannot* equal these values.

~ NOW TRY
↪ EXERCISE 2

Find any values of the variable for which each rational expression is undefined.

(a) $\dfrac{k - 4}{2k - 1}$

(b) $\dfrac{2x}{x^2 + 5x - 14}$

(c) $\dfrac{y + 10}{y^2 + 10}$

EXAMPLE 2   Finding Values That Make Rational Expressions Undefined

Find any values of the variable for which each rational expression is undefined.

(a) $\dfrac{x + 5}{3x + 2}$ We must find any value of x that makes the *denominator* equal to 0, since division by 0 is undefined.

Step 1   Set the denominator equal to 0.

$$3x + 2 = 0$$

Step 2   Solve. $3x = -2$ Subtract 2.

$$x = -\dfrac{2}{3}$$ Divide by 3.

Step 3   The given expression is undefined for $-\frac{2}{3}$, so $x \neq -\frac{2}{3}$.

(b) $\dfrac{8x^2 + 1}{x - 3}$ The denominator $x - 3 = 0$ when x is 3. The given expression is undefined for 3, so $x \neq 3$.

(c) $\dfrac{9m^2}{m^2 - 5m + 6}$

$$m^2 - 5m + 6 = 0 \quad \text{Set the denominator equal to 0.}$$
$$(m - 2)(m - 3) = 0 \quad \text{Factor.}$$
$$m - 2 = 0 \quad \text{or} \quad m - 3 = 0 \quad \text{Zero-factor property}$$
$$m = 2 \quad \text{or} \quad m = 3 \quad \text{Solve for } m.$$

The given expression is undefined for 2 and 3, so $m \neq 2$, $m \neq 3$.

(d) $\dfrac{2r}{r^2 + 1}$ This denominator will not equal 0 for any value of r, because r^2 is always greater than or equal to 0, and adding 1 makes the sum greater than or equal to 1. There are no values for which this expression is undefined.

NOW TRY ↩

OBJECTIVE 3   **Write rational expressions in lowest terms.** A fraction such as $\frac{2}{3}$ is said to be in *lowest terms.*

Lowest Terms

A rational expression $\dfrac{P}{Q}$ $(Q \neq 0)$ is in **lowest terms** if the greatest common factor of its numerator and denominator is 1.

NOW TRY ANSWERS
2. (a) $k \neq \frac{1}{2}$ (b) $x \neq -7, x \neq 2$
(c) never undefined

We use the **fundamental property of rational expressions** to write a rational expression in lowest terms.

> ### Fundamental Property of Rational Expressions
>
> If $\frac{P}{Q}$ ($Q \neq 0$) is a rational expression and if K represents any polynomial, where $K \neq 0$, then the following is true.
>
> $$\frac{PK}{QK} = \frac{P}{Q}$$

This property is based on the identity property of multiplication.

$$\frac{PK}{QK} = \frac{P}{Q} \cdot \frac{K}{K} = \frac{P}{Q} \cdot 1 = \frac{P}{Q}$$

NOW TRY
EXERCISE 3

Write the rational expression in lowest terms.

$$\frac{21y^5}{7y^2}$$

EXAMPLE 3 Writing in Lowest Terms

Write each rational expression in lowest terms.

(a) $\dfrac{30}{72}$

Begin by factoring.

$$\frac{30}{72} = \frac{2 \cdot 3 \cdot 5}{2 \cdot 2 \cdot 2 \cdot 3 \cdot 3}$$

(b) $\dfrac{14k^2}{2k^3}$

Write k^2 as $k \cdot k$ and k^3 as $k \cdot k \cdot k$.

$$\frac{14k^2}{2k^3} = \frac{2 \cdot 7 \cdot k \cdot k}{2 \cdot k \cdot k \cdot k}$$

Group any factors common to the numerator and denominator.

$$\frac{30}{72} = \frac{5 \cdot (2 \cdot 3)}{2 \cdot 2 \cdot 3 \cdot (2 \cdot 3)}$$

$$\frac{14k^2}{2k^3} = \frac{7(2 \cdot k \cdot k)}{k(2 \cdot k \cdot k)}$$

Use the fundamental property.

$$\frac{30}{72} = \frac{5}{2 \cdot 2 \cdot 3} = \frac{5}{12}$$

$$\frac{14k^2}{2k^3} = \frac{7}{k}$$

NOW TRY

> ### Writing a Rational Expression in Lowest Terms
>
> **Step 1** **Factor** the numerator and denominator completely.
>
> **Step 2** **Use the fundamental property** to divide out any common factors.

EXAMPLE 4 Writing in Lowest Terms

Write each rational expression in lowest terms.

(a) $\dfrac{3x - 12}{5x - 20}$

$x \neq 4$, since the denominator is 0 for this value.

$$= \frac{3(x - 4)}{5(x - 4)} \qquad \text{Factor. (Step 1)}$$

$$= \frac{3}{5} \qquad \text{Fundamental property (Step 2)}$$

The given expression is equal to $\frac{3}{5}$ for all values of x, where $x \neq 4$ (since the denominator of the original rational expression is 0 when x is 4).

NOW TRY
EXERCISE 4

Write each rational expression in lowest terms.

(a) $\dfrac{3x + 15}{5x + 25}$

(b) $\dfrac{k^2 - 36}{k^2 + 8k + 12}$

(b) $\dfrac{2y^2 - 8}{2y + 4}$

> $y \neq -2$, since the denominator is 0 for this value.

$= \dfrac{2(y^2 - 4)}{2(y + 2)}$ Factor. (Step 1)

$= \dfrac{2(y + 2)(y - 2)}{2(y + 2)}$ Factor the numerator completely.

$= y - 2$ Fundamental property (Step 2)

(c) $\dfrac{m^2 + 2m - 8}{2m^2 - m - 6}$

$= \dfrac{(m + 4)(m - 2)}{(2m + 3)(m - 2)}$

> $m \neq -\frac{3}{2}$, $m \neq 2$

Factor. (Step 1)

$= \dfrac{m + 4}{2m + 3}$ Fundamental property (Step 2)   NOW TRY

We write statements of equality of rational expressions with the understanding that they apply only to real numbers that make neither denominator equal to 0.

⚠ **CAUTION** *Rational expressions cannot be written in lowest terms until after the numerator and denominator have been factored.*

$$\dfrac{6x + 9}{4x + 6} = \dfrac{3(2x + 3)}{2(2x + 3)} = \dfrac{3}{2} \qquad \Bigg| \qquad \dfrac{6 + x}{4x} \leftarrow \text{Numerator cannot be factored.}$$

Divide out the common factor.   Already in lowest terms

NOW TRY
EXERCISE 5

Write in lowest terms.

$\dfrac{10 - a^2}{a^2 - 10}$

EXAMPLE 5 Writing in Lowest Terms (Factors Are Opposites)

Write $\dfrac{x - y}{y - x}$ in lowest terms.

To get a common factor, the denominator $y - x$ can be factored as follows.

$y - x$ We are factoring out -1, **NOT** multiplying by it.

$= -1(-y + x)$ Factor out -1.

$= -1(x - y)$ Commutative property

With this result in mind, we simplify.

$$\dfrac{x - y}{y - x}$$

$= \dfrac{1(x - y)}{-1(x - y)}$ $y - x = -1(x - y)$ from above.

$= \dfrac{1}{-1}$, or -1 Fundamental property   NOW TRY

NOTE The numerator *or* the denominator could have been factored in the first step in **Example 5.** Factor -1 from the numerator, and confirm that the result is the same.

In **Example 5,** notice that $y - x$ is the **opposite** (or **additive inverse**) of $x - y$.

Quotient of Opposites

If the numerator and the denominator of a rational expression are opposites, as in $\frac{x - y}{y - x}$, then the rational expression is equal to -1.

Based on this result, the following are true.

Numerator and
denominator
are opposites.
$$\frac{q - 7}{7 - q} = -1 \quad \text{and} \quad \frac{-5a + 2b}{5a - 2b} = -1$$

However, the following expression cannot be simplified further.

$$\frac{x - 2}{x + 2} \quad \begin{array}{l} \text{Numerator and denominator} \\ \text{are } not \text{ opposites.} \end{array}$$

⌒ NOW TRY
⮡ EXERCISE 6

Write each rational expression in lowest terms.

(a) $\dfrac{p - 4}{4 - p}$ **(b)** $\dfrac{4m^2 - n^2}{2n - 4m}$

(c) $\dfrac{x + y}{x - y}$

EXAMPLE 6 Writing in Lowest Terms (Factors Are Opposites)

Write each rational expression in lowest terms.

(a) $\dfrac{2 - m}{m - 2}$ Since $2 - m$ and $m - 2$ are opposites, this expression equals -1.

(b) $\dfrac{4x^2 - 9}{6 - 4x}$

$$= \frac{(2x + 3)(2x - 3)}{2(3 - 2x)} \qquad \text{Factor the numerator and denominator.}$$

$$= \frac{(2x + 3)(2x - 3)}{2(-1)(2x - 3)} \qquad \begin{array}{l} \text{Write } 3 - 2x \text{ in the denominator} \\ \text{as } -1(2x - 3). \end{array}$$

$$= \frac{2x + 3}{2(-1)} \qquad \text{Fundamental property}$$

$$= \frac{2x + 3}{-2}, \quad \text{or} \quad -\frac{2x + 3}{2} \qquad \frac{a}{-b} = -\frac{a}{b}$$

(c) $\dfrac{3 + r}{3 - r}$ $\quad 3 - r$ is not the opposite of $3 + r$.

This rational expression is already in lowest terms. NOW TRY ⟳

OBJECTIVE 4 **Recognize equivalent forms of rational expressions.** The common fraction $-\frac{5}{6}$ can also be written $\frac{-5}{6}$ and $\frac{5}{-6}$.

Consider the final rational expression from **Example 6(b).**

$$-\frac{2x + 3}{2}$$

The $-$ sign representing the factor -1 is in front of the expression, even with the fraction bar. The factor -1 may instead be placed in the numerator or denominator.

Use parentheses.

$$\frac{-(2x + 3)}{2} \quad \text{and} \quad \frac{2x + 3}{-2}$$

NOW TRY ANSWERS
6. (a) -1
  (b) $\frac{2m + n}{-2}$, or $-\frac{2m + n}{2}$
  (c) already in lowest terms

The distributive property can also be applied.

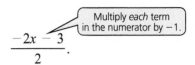
Multiply *each* term in the numerator by −1.

$$\frac{-(2x + 3)}{2} \quad \text{can also be written} \quad \frac{-2x - 3}{2}.$$

⚠ **CAUTION** $\frac{-2x + 3}{2}$ is *not* an equivalent form of $\frac{-(2x + 3)}{2}$. The sign preceding 3 in the numerator of $\frac{-2x + 3}{2}$ should be − rather than +. **Be careful to apply the distributive property correctly.**

NOW TRY EXERCISE 7

Write four equivalent forms of the rational expression.

$$-\frac{4k - 9}{k + 3}$$

EXAMPLE 7 Writing Equivalent Forms of a Rational Expression

Write four equivalent forms of the rational expression.

$$-\frac{3x + 2}{x - 6}$$

If we apply the negative sign to the numerator, we obtain these equivalent forms.

①→ $\dfrac{-(3x + 2)}{x - 6}$ and, by the distributive property, $\dfrac{-3x - 2}{x - 6}$ ←②

If we apply the negative sign to the denominator, we obtain two more forms.

③→ $\dfrac{3x + 2}{-(x - 6)}$ or, distributing once again, $\dfrac{3x + 2}{-x + 6}$ ←④

NOW TRY

⚠ **CAUTION** Recall that $-\frac{5}{6} \neq \frac{-5}{-6}$. Thus, in **Example 7**, it would be incorrect to distribute the negative sign in $-\frac{3x + 2}{x - 6}$ to *both* the numerator *and* the denominator. (Doing this would actually lead to the *opposite* of the original expression.)

CONNECTIONS

In **Section 4.7,** we used long division to find the quotient of two polynomials such as $(2x^2 + 5x - 12) \div (2x - 3)$, as shown on the left. The quotient is $x + 4$. We get the same quotient by expressing the division problem as a rational expression (fraction) and writing this rational expression in lowest terms, as shown on the right.

$$\begin{array}{r} x + 4 \\ 2x - 3 \overline{)2x^2 + 5x - 12} \\ \underline{2x^2 - 3x} \\ 8x - 12 \\ \underline{8x - 12} \\ 0 \end{array}$$

$$\frac{2x^2 + 5x - 12}{2x - 3}$$

$$= \frac{(2x - 3)(x + 4)}{2x - 3} \qquad \text{Factor.}$$

$$= x + 4 \qquad \text{Fundamental property}$$

For Discussion or Writing

What kind of division problem has a quotient that cannot be found by writing a fraction in lowest terms? Try using rational expressions to solve each division problem. Then use long division and compare.

1. $(3x^2 + 11x + 8) \div (x + 2)$ **2.** $(x^3 - 8) \div (x^2 + 2x + 4)$

NOW TRY ANSWER

7. $\dfrac{-(4k - 9)}{k + 3}$, $\dfrac{-4k + 9}{k + 3}$, $\dfrac{4k - 9}{-(k + 3)}$, $\dfrac{4k - 9}{-k - 3}$

Complete solution available on the Video Resources on DVD

*Find the numerical value of each rational expression for **(a)** $x = 2$ and **(b)** $x = -3$. See Example 1.*

1. $\dfrac{3x + 1}{5x}$

2. $\dfrac{5x - 2}{4x}$

3. $\dfrac{x^2 - 4}{2x + 1}$

4. $\dfrac{2x^2 - 4x}{3x - 1}$

5. $\dfrac{(-2x)^3}{3x + 9}$

6. $\dfrac{(-3x)^2}{4x + 12}$

7. $\dfrac{7 - 3x}{3x^2 - 7x + 2}$

8. $\dfrac{5x + 2}{4x^2 - 5x - 6}$

9. $\dfrac{(x + 3)(x - 2)}{500x}$

10. $\dfrac{(x - 2)(x + 3)}{1000x}$

11. $\dfrac{x^2 - 4}{x^2 - 9}$

12. $\dfrac{x^2 - 9}{x^2 - 4}$

13. Define *rational expression* in your own words, and give an example.

14. *Concept Check*   Fill in each blank with the correct response: The rational expression $\dfrac{x + 5}{x - 3}$ is undefined when x is _____, so $x \neq$ _____. This rational expression is equal to 0 when $x =$ _____.

15. Why can't the denominator of a rational expression equal 0?

16. If 2 is substituted for x in the rational expression $\dfrac{x - 2}{x^2 - 4}$, the result is $\dfrac{0}{0}$. An often-heard statement is "Any number divided by itself is 1." Does this mean that this expression is equal to 1 for $x = 2$? If not, explain.

Find any values of the variable for which each rational expression is undefined. Write answers with the symbol $\neq$. See Example 2.

17. $\dfrac{12}{5y}$

18. $\dfrac{-7}{3z}$

19. $\dfrac{x + 1}{x - 6}$

20. $\dfrac{m - 2}{m - 5}$

21. $\dfrac{4x^2}{3x + 5}$

22. $\dfrac{2x^3}{3x + 4}$

23. $\dfrac{5m + 2}{m^2 + m - 6}$

24. $\dfrac{2r - 5}{r^2 - 5r + 4}$

25. $\dfrac{x^2 + 3x}{4}$

26. $\dfrac{x^2 - 4x}{6}$

27. $\dfrac{3x - 1}{x^2 + 2}$

28. $\dfrac{4q + 2}{q^2 + 9}$

29. **(a)** Identify the two *terms* in the numerator and the two *terms* in the denominator of the rational expression $\dfrac{x^2 + 4x}{x + 4}$.

(b) Describe the steps you would use to write the rational expression in part (a) in lowest terms. (*Hint:* It simplifies to x.)

30. *Concept Check*   Which one of these rational expressions can be simplified?

A. $\dfrac{x^2 + 2}{x^2}$ **B.** $\dfrac{x^2 + 2}{2}$ **C.** $\dfrac{x^2 + y^2}{y^2}$ **D.** $\dfrac{x^2 - 5x}{x}$

Write each rational expression in lowest terms. See Examples 3 and 4.

31. $\dfrac{18r^3}{6r}$

32. $\dfrac{27p^4}{3p}$

33. $\dfrac{4(y - 2)}{10(y - 2)}$

34. $\dfrac{15(m - 1)}{9(m - 1)}$

35. $\dfrac{(x + 1)(x - 1)}{(x + 1)^2}$

36. $\dfrac{(t + 5)(t - 3)}{(t + 5)^2}$

37. $\dfrac{7m + 14}{5m + 10}$

38. $\dfrac{16x + 8}{14x + 7}$

39. $\dfrac{6m - 18}{7m - 21}$

6.3 Least Common Denominators

OBJECTIVES

1. Find the least common denominator for a group of fractions.
2. Write equivalent rational expressions.

OBJECTIVE 1 Find the least common denominator for a group of fractions. Adding or subtracting rational expressions often requires a **least common denominator (LCD)**. The LCD is the simplest expression that is divisible by all of the denominators in all of the expressions. For example, the fractions

$$\frac{2}{9} \quad \text{and} \quad \frac{5}{12} \quad \text{have LCD 36,}$$

because 36 is the least positive number divisible by both 9 and 12.

We can often find least common denominators by inspection. In other cases, we find the LCD by a procedure similar to that used in **Section 5.1** for finding the greatest common factor.

Finding the Least Common Denominator (LCD)

Step 1 **Factor** each denominator into prime factors.

Step 2 **List each different denominator factor** the *greatest* number of times it appears in any of the denominators.

Step 3 **Multiply** the denominator factors from Step 2 to get the LCD.

When each denominator is factored into prime factors, every prime factor must be a factor of the least common denominator.

NOW TRY EXERCISE 1

Find the LCD for each pair of fractions.

(a) $\dfrac{5}{48}, \dfrac{1}{30}$ (b) $\dfrac{3}{10y}, \dfrac{1}{6y}$

EXAMPLE 1 Finding the LCD

Find the LCD for each pair of fractions.

(a) $\dfrac{1}{24}, \dfrac{7}{15}$

(b) $\dfrac{1}{8x}, \dfrac{3}{10x}$

Step 1 Write each denominator in factored form with numerical coefficients in prime factored form.

$$24 = 2 \cdot 2 \cdot 2 \cdot 3 = 2^3 \cdot 3 \qquad\qquad 8x = 2 \cdot 2 \cdot 2 \cdot x = 2^3 \cdot x$$

$$15 = 3 \cdot 5 \qquad\qquad\qquad\qquad\quad 10x = 2 \cdot 5 \cdot x$$

Step 2 Find the LCD by taking each different factor the *greatest* number of times it appears as a factor in any of the denominators.

The factor 2 appears three times in one product and not at all in the other, so the greatest number of times 2 appears is three. The greatest number of times both 3 and 5 appear is one.

Here, 2 appears three times in one product and once in the other, so the greatest number of times 2 appears is three. The greatest number of times 5 appears is one, and the greatest number of times x appears in either product is one.

Step 3
$$\text{LCD} = 2 \cdot 2 \cdot 2 \cdot 3 \cdot 5 \qquad\qquad \text{LCD} = 2 \cdot 2 \cdot 2 \cdot 5 \cdot x$$
$$= 2^3 \cdot 3 \cdot 5 \qquad\qquad\qquad = 2^3 \cdot 5 \cdot x$$
$$= 120 \qquad\qquad\qquad\qquad = 40x \qquad \text{NOW TRY}$$

NOW TRY ANSWERS
1. (a) 240 (b) $30y$

NOW TRY
EXERCISE 2

Find the LCD for the pair of fractions.

$$\frac{5}{6x^4} \quad \text{and} \quad \frac{7}{8x^3}$$

EXAMPLE 2   Finding the LCD

Find the LCD for $\dfrac{5}{6r^2}$ and $\dfrac{3}{4r^3}$.

Step 1   Factor each denominator.

$$6r^2 = 2 \cdot 3 \cdot r^2$$
$$4r^3 = 2 \cdot 2 \cdot r^3 = 2^2 \cdot r^3$$

Step 2   The greatest number of times 2 appears is two, the greatest number of times 3 appears is one, and the greatest number of times r appears is three.

Step 3 $\text{LCD} = 2^2 \cdot 3 \cdot r^3 = 12r^3$ NOW TRY

⚠️ **CAUTION**   When finding the LCD, use each factor the *greatest* number of times it appears in any *single* denominator, not the *total* number of times it appears. For instance, the greatest number of times r appears as a factor in one denominator in **Example 2** is 3, *not* 5.

NOW TRY
EXERCISE 3

Find the LCD for the fractions in each list.

(a) $\dfrac{3t}{2t^2 - 10t}, \dfrac{t+4}{t^2 - 25}$

(b) $\dfrac{1}{x^2 + 7x + 12},$

$\dfrac{2}{x^2 + 6x + 9}, \dfrac{5}{x^2 + 2x - 8}$

(c) $\dfrac{2}{a-4}, \dfrac{1}{4-a}$

EXAMPLE 3   Finding LCDs

Find the LCD for the fractions in each list.

(a) $\dfrac{6}{5m}, \dfrac{4}{m^2 - 3m}$

$$\left.\begin{array}{l} 5m = 5 \cdot m \\[4pt] m^2 - 3m = m(m - 3) \end{array}\right\} \text{Factor each denominator.}$$

Use each different factor the greatest number of times it appears.

$$\text{LCD} = 5 \cdot m \cdot (m - 3) = 5m(m - 3)$$

Be sure to include m as a factor in the LCD.

Because m is not a *factor* of $m - 3$, both m and $m - 3$ must appear in the LCD.

(b) $\dfrac{1}{r^2 - 4r - 5}, \dfrac{3}{r^2 - r - 20}, \dfrac{1}{r^2 - 10r + 25}$

$$\left.\begin{array}{l} r^2 - 4r - 5 = (r - 5)(r + 1) \\[4pt] r^2 - r - 20 = (r - 5)(r + 4) \\[4pt] r^2 - 10r + 25 = (r - 5)^2 \end{array}\right\} \text{Factor each denominator.}$$

Use each different factor the greatest number of times it appears as a factor.

$$\text{LCD} = (r - 5)^2(r + 1)(r + 4)$$

Be sure to include the exponent 2.

(c) $\dfrac{1}{q - 5}, \dfrac{3}{5 - q}$

The expressions $q - 5$ and $5 - q$ are opposites of each other. This means that if we multiply $q - 5$ by -1, we will get $5 - q$.

$$-(q - 5) = -q + 5 = 5 - q$$

Therefore, either $q - 5$ or $5 - q$ can be used as the LCD.   NOW TRY

NOW TRY ANSWERS
2. $24x^4$
3. (a) $2t(t - 5)(t + 5)$
    (b) $(x + 3)^2(x + 4)(x - 2)$
    (c) either $a - 4$ or $4 - a$

OBJECTIVE 2 Write equivalent rational expressions. Once the LCD has been found, the next step in preparing to add or subtract two rational expressions is to use the fundamental property to write equivalent rational expressions.

Writing a Rational Expression with a Specified Denominator

Step 1   **Factor** both denominators.

Step 2   **Decide what factor(s) the denominator must be multiplied by** in order to equal the specified denominator.

Step 3   **Multiply** the rational expression by that factor divided by itself. (That is, multiply by 1.)

NOW TRY
EXERCISE 4

Rewrite each rational expression with the indicated denominator.

(a) $\dfrac{2}{9} = \dfrac{?}{27}$ **(b)** $\dfrac{4t}{11} = \dfrac{?}{33t}$

EXAMPLE 4   Writing Equivalent Rational Expressions

Rewrite each rational expression with the indicated denominator.

(a) $\dfrac{3}{8} = \dfrac{?}{40}$ **(b)** $\dfrac{9k}{25} = \dfrac{?}{50k}$

Step 1   For each example, first factor the denominator on the right. Then compare the denominator on the left with the one on the right to decide what factors are missing. (It may sometimes be necessary to factor both denominators.)

$$\dfrac{3}{8} = \dfrac{?}{5 \cdot 8} \qquad\qquad \dfrac{9k}{25} = \dfrac{?}{25 \cdot 2k}$$

Step 2   A factor of 5 is missing.   Factors of 2 and k are missing.

Step 3   Multiply $\dfrac{3}{8}$ by $\dfrac{5}{5}$.   Multiply $\dfrac{9k}{25}$ by $\dfrac{2k}{2k}$.

$$\dfrac{3}{8} = \dfrac{3}{8} \cdot \dfrac{5}{5} = \dfrac{15}{40} \qquad \dfrac{9k}{25} = \dfrac{9k}{25} \cdot \dfrac{2k}{2k} = \dfrac{18k^2}{50k}$$

$$\dfrac{5}{5} = 1 \qquad\qquad\qquad \dfrac{2k}{2k} = 1$$

NOW TRY

EXAMPLE 5   Writing Equivalent Rational Expressions

Rewrite each rational expression with the indicated denominator.

(a) $\dfrac{8}{3x + 1} = \dfrac{?}{12x + 4}$

$\dfrac{8}{3x + 1} = \dfrac{?}{4(3x + 1)}$ Factor the denominator on the right.

The missing factor is 4, so multiply the fraction on the left by $\dfrac{4}{4}$.

$$\dfrac{8}{3x + 1} \cdot \dfrac{4}{4} = \dfrac{32}{12x + 4}$$ Fundamental property

NOW TRY ANSWERS

4. **(a)** $\dfrac{6}{27}$ **(b)** $\dfrac{12t^2}{33t}$

NOW TRY
EXERCISE 5

Rewrite each rational expression with the indicated denominator.

(a) $\dfrac{8k}{5k - 2} = \dfrac{?}{25k - 10}$

(b) $\dfrac{2t - 1}{t^2 + 4t} = \dfrac{?}{t^3 + 12t^2 + 32t}$

(b) $\dfrac{12p}{p^2 + 8p} = \dfrac{?}{p^3 + 4p^2 - 32p}$

Factor the denominator in each rational expression.

$$\dfrac{12p}{p(p + 8)} = \dfrac{?}{p(p + 8)(p - 4)}$$

$p^3 + 4p^2 - 32p$
$= p(p^2 + 4p - 32)$
$= p(p + 8)(p - 4)$

The factor $p - 4$ is missing, so multiply $\dfrac{12p}{p(p + 8)}$ by $\dfrac{p - 4}{p - 4}$.

$$\dfrac{12p}{p^2 + 8p} = \dfrac{12p}{p(p + 8)} \cdot \dfrac{p - 4}{p - 4} \qquad \text{Fundamental property}$$

$$= \dfrac{12p(p - 4)}{p(p + 8)(p - 4)} \qquad \begin{array}{l}\text{Multiply numerators.}\\ \text{Multiply denominators.}\end{array}$$

$$= \dfrac{12p^2 - 48p}{p^3 + 4p^2 - 32p} \qquad \text{Multiply the factors.} \qquad \text{NOW TRY}$$

NOW TRY ANSWERS

5. (a) $\dfrac{40k}{25k - 10}$

(b) $\dfrac{2t^2 + 15t - 8}{t^3 + 12t^2 + 32t}$

NOTE While it is beneficial to leave the denominator in factored form, we multiplied the factors in the denominator in **Example 5** to give the answer in the same form as the original problem.

6.3 EXERCISES

MyMathLab | Math XL PRACTICE | WATCH | DOWNLOAD | READ | REVIEW

Complete solution available on the Video Resources on DVD

Concept Check Choose the correct response in Exercises 1–4.

1. Suppose that the greatest common factor of x and y is 1. What is the least common denominator for $\dfrac{1}{x}$ and $\dfrac{1}{y}$?

  A. x **B.** y **C.** xy **D.** 1

2. If x is a factor of y, what is the least common denominator for $\dfrac{1}{x}$ and $\dfrac{1}{y}$?

  A. x **B.** y **C.** xy **D.** 1

3. What is the least common denominator for $\dfrac{9}{20}$ and $\dfrac{1}{2}$?

  A. 40 **B.** 2 **C.** 20 **D.** none of these

4. Suppose that we wish to write the fraction $\dfrac{1}{(x - 4)^2(y - 3)}$ with denominator $(x - 4)^3(y - 3)^2$. By what must we multiply both the numerator and the denominator?

  A. $(x - 4)(y - 3)$ **B.** $(x - 4)^2$ **C.** $x - 4$ **D.** $(x - 4)^2(y - 3)$

Find the LCD for the fractions in each list. **See Examples 1–3.**

5. $\dfrac{7}{15}, \dfrac{21}{20}$

6. $\dfrac{9}{10}, \dfrac{13}{25}$

7. $\dfrac{17}{100}, \dfrac{23}{120}, \dfrac{43}{180}$

8. $\dfrac{17}{250}, \dfrac{21}{300}, \dfrac{1}{360}$

9. $\dfrac{9}{x^2}, \dfrac{8}{x^5}$

10. $\dfrac{12}{m^7}, \dfrac{14}{m^8}$

11. $\dfrac{-2}{5p}, \dfrac{13}{6p}$

12. $\dfrac{-14}{15k}, \dfrac{11}{4k}$

13. $\dfrac{17}{15y^2}, \dfrac{55}{36y^4}$

14. $\dfrac{4}{25m^3}, \dfrac{7}{10m^4}$

15. $\dfrac{5}{21r^3}, \dfrac{7}{12r^5}$

16. $\dfrac{6}{35t^2}, \dfrac{5}{49t^6}$

NOW TRY
EXERCISE 8

Subtract. Write the answer in lowest terms.

$$\frac{2m}{m-4} - \frac{m-12}{4-m}$$

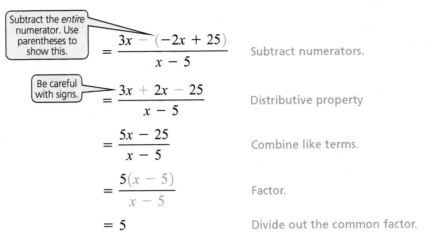

Subtract the *entire* numerator. Use parentheses to show this.

$$= \frac{3x - (-2x + 25)}{x - 5}$$ Subtract numerators.

Be careful with signs.

$$= \frac{3x + 2x - 25}{x - 5}$$ Distributive property

$$= \frac{5x - 25}{x - 5}$$ Combine like terms.

$$= \frac{5(x - 5)}{x - 5}$$ Factor.

$$= 5$$ Divide out the common factor.

NOW TRY

NOW TRY
EXERCISE 9

Subtract. Write the answer in lowest terms.

$$\frac{5}{t^2 - 6t + 9} - \frac{2t}{t^2 - 9}$$

EXAMPLE 9 Subtracting Rational Expressions

Subtract. Write the answer in lowest terms.

$$\frac{6x}{x^2 - 2x + 1} - \frac{1}{x^2 - 1}$$

$$= \frac{6x}{(x-1)^2} - \frac{1}{(x-1)(x+1)}$$ Factor the denominators.
LCD $= (x-1)(x-1)(x+1)$, or $(x-1)^2(x+1)$

$$= \frac{6x(x+1)}{(x-1)^2(x+1)} - \frac{1(x-1)}{(x-1)(x-1)(x+1)}$$ Fundamental property

$$= \frac{6x(x+1) - 1(x-1)}{(x-1)^2(x+1)}$$ Subtract numerators.

$$= \frac{6x^2 + 6x - x + 1}{(x-1)^2(x+1)}$$ Distributive property

$$= \frac{6x^2 + 5x + 1}{(x-1)^2(x+1)}, \quad \text{or} \quad \frac{(2x+1)(3x+1)}{(x-1)^2(x+1)}$$ Combine like terms. Factor the numerator.

NOW TRY

NOW TRY ANSWERS

8. 3

9. $\dfrac{-2t^2 + 11t + 15}{(t-3)^2(t+3)}$

6.4 EXERCISES

 MyMathLab   Math XL PRACTICE   WATCH   DOWNLOAD   READ   REVIEW

⊙ *Complete solution available on the Video Resources on DVD*

Concept Check   Match each expression in Column I with the correct sum or difference in Column II.

I   II

1. $\dfrac{x}{x+8} + \dfrac{8}{x+8}$ **2.** $\dfrac{2x}{x-8} - \dfrac{16}{x-8}$ **A.** 2   **B.** $\dfrac{x-8}{x+8}$

3. $\dfrac{8}{x-8} - \dfrac{x}{x-8}$ **4.** $\dfrac{8}{x+8} - \dfrac{x}{x+8}$ **C.** -1 **D.** $\dfrac{8+x}{8x}$

5. $\dfrac{x}{x+8} - \dfrac{8}{x+8}$ **6.** $\dfrac{1}{x} + \dfrac{1}{8}$ **E.** 1   **F.** 0

7. $\dfrac{1}{8} - \dfrac{1}{x}$ **8.** $\dfrac{1}{8x} - \dfrac{1}{8x}$ **G.** $\dfrac{x-8}{8x}$ **H.** $\dfrac{8-x}{x+8}$

Note: When adding and subtracting rational expressions, several different equivalent forms of the answer often exist. If your answer does not look exactly like the one given in the back of the book, check to see whether you have written an equivalent form.

*Add or subtract. Write each answer in lowest terms. **See Examples 1 and 6.***

9. $\dfrac{4}{m} + \dfrac{7}{m}$ **10.** $\dfrac{5}{p} + \dfrac{12}{p}$ **11.** $\dfrac{5}{y+4} - \dfrac{1}{y+4}$

12. $\dfrac{6}{t+3} - \dfrac{3}{t+3}$ **13.** $\dfrac{x}{x+y} + \dfrac{y}{x+y}$ **14.** $\dfrac{a}{a+b} + \dfrac{b}{a+b}$

15. $\dfrac{5m}{m+1} - \dfrac{1+4m}{m+1}$ **16.** $\dfrac{4x}{x+2} - \dfrac{2+3x}{x+2}$ **17.** $\dfrac{a+b}{2} - \dfrac{a-b}{2}$

18. $\dfrac{x-y}{2} - \dfrac{x+y}{2}$ **19.** $\dfrac{x^2}{x+5} + \dfrac{5x}{x+5}$ **20.** $\dfrac{t^2}{t-3} + \dfrac{-3t}{t-3}$

21. $\dfrac{y^2-3y}{y+3} + \dfrac{-18}{y+3}$ **22.** $\dfrac{r^2-8r}{r-5} + \dfrac{15}{r-5}$

23. $\dfrac{x}{x^2-9} - \dfrac{-3}{x^2-9}$ **24.** $\dfrac{-4}{y^2-16} - \dfrac{-y}{y^2-16}$

*Add or subtract. Write each answer in lowest terms. **See Examples 2, 3, 4, and 7.***

25. $\dfrac{z}{5} + \dfrac{1}{3}$ **26.** $\dfrac{p}{8} + \dfrac{4}{5}$ **27.** $\dfrac{5}{7} - \dfrac{r}{2}$

28. $\dfrac{20}{9} - \dfrac{z}{3}$ **29.** $-\dfrac{3}{4} - \dfrac{1}{2x}$ **30.** $-\dfrac{7}{8} - \dfrac{3}{2a}$

31. $\dfrac{6}{5x} + \dfrac{9}{2x}$ **32.** $\dfrac{3}{2x} + \dfrac{3}{7x}$ **33.** $\dfrac{x+1}{6} + \dfrac{3x+3}{9}$

34. $\dfrac{2x-6}{4} + \dfrac{x+5}{6}$ **35.** $\dfrac{x+3}{3x} + \dfrac{2x+2}{4x}$ **36.** $\dfrac{x+2}{5x} + \dfrac{6x+3}{3x}$

37. $\dfrac{7}{3p^2} - \dfrac{2}{p}$ **38.** $\dfrac{12}{5m^2} - \dfrac{5}{m}$ **39.** $\dfrac{1}{k+4} - \dfrac{2}{k}$

40. $\dfrac{3}{m+1} - \dfrac{4}{m}$ **41.** $\dfrac{x}{x-2} + \dfrac{-8}{x^2-4}$ **42.** $\dfrac{2x}{x-1} + \dfrac{-4}{x^2-1}$

43. $\dfrac{4m}{m^2+3m+2} + \dfrac{2m-1}{m^2+6m+5}$ **44.** $\dfrac{a}{a^2+3a-4} + \dfrac{4a}{a^2+7a+12}$

45. $\dfrac{4y}{y^2-1} - \dfrac{5}{y^2+2y+1}$ **46.** $\dfrac{2x}{x^2-16} - \dfrac{3}{x^2+8x+16}$

47. $\dfrac{t}{t+2} + \dfrac{5-t}{t} - \dfrac{4}{t^2+2t}$ **48.** $\dfrac{2p}{p-3} + \dfrac{2+p}{p} - \dfrac{-6}{p^2-3p}$

49. *Concept Check*   What are the two possible LCDs that could be used for the sum $\dfrac{10}{m-2} + \dfrac{5}{2-m}$?

50. *Concept Check*   If one form of the correct answer to a sum or difference of rational expressions is $\dfrac{4}{k-3}$, what would an alternative form of the answer be if the denominator is $3-k$?

*Add or subtract. Write each answer in lowest terms. **See Examples 5 and 8.***

51. $\dfrac{4}{x-5} + \dfrac{6}{5-x}$ **52.** $\dfrac{10}{m-2} + \dfrac{5}{2-m}$ **53.** $\dfrac{-1}{1-y} - \dfrac{4y-3}{y-1}$

54. $\dfrac{-4}{p-3} - \dfrac{p+1}{3-p}$

55. $\dfrac{2}{x-y^2} + \dfrac{7}{y^2-x}$

56. $\dfrac{-8}{p-q^2} + \dfrac{3}{q^2-p}$

57. $\dfrac{x}{5x-3y} - \dfrac{y}{3y-5x}$

58. $\dfrac{t}{8t-9s} - \dfrac{s}{9s-8t}$

59. $\dfrac{3}{4p-5} + \dfrac{9}{5-4p}$

60. $\dfrac{8}{3-7y} - \dfrac{2}{7y-3}$

*In these subtraction problems, the rational expression that follows the subtraction sign has a numerator with more than one term. **Be careful with signs** and find each difference. **See Example 9.***

61. $\dfrac{2m}{m-n} - \dfrac{5m+n}{2m-2n}$

62. $\dfrac{5p}{p-q} - \dfrac{3p+1}{4p-4q}$

63. $\dfrac{5}{x^2-9} - \dfrac{x+2}{x^2+4x+3}$

64. $\dfrac{1}{a^2-1} - \dfrac{a-1}{a^2+3a-4}$

65. $\dfrac{2q+1}{3q^2+10q-8} - \dfrac{3q+5}{2q^2+5q-12}$

66. $\dfrac{4y-1}{2y^2+5y-3} - \dfrac{y+3}{6y^2+y-2}$

*Perform each indicated operation. **See Examples 1–9.***

67. $\dfrac{4}{r^2-r} + \dfrac{6}{r^2+2r} - \dfrac{1}{r^2+r-2}$

68. $\dfrac{6}{k^2+3k} - \dfrac{1}{k^2-k} + \dfrac{2}{k^2+2k-3}$

69. $\dfrac{x+3y}{x^2+2xy+y^2} + \dfrac{x-y}{x^2+4xy+3y^2}$

70. $\dfrac{m}{m^2-1} + \dfrac{m-1}{m^2+2m+1}$

71. $\dfrac{r+y}{18r^2+9ry-2y^2} + \dfrac{3r-y}{36r^2-y^2}$

72. $\dfrac{2x-z}{2x^2+xz-10z^2} - \dfrac{x+z}{x^2-4z^2}$

73. Refer to the rectangle in the figure.

   (a) Find an expression that represents its perimeter. Give the simplified form.

   (b) Find an expression that represents its area. Give the simplified form.

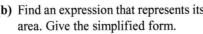
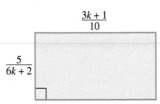

74. Refer to the triangle in the figure. Find an expression that represents its perimeter.

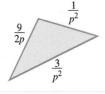

*A **concours d'elegance** is a competition in which a maximum of 100 points is awarded to a car based on its general attractiveness. The rational expression*

$$\dfrac{1010}{49(101-x)} - \dfrac{10}{49}$$

approximates the cost, in thousands of dollars, of restoring a car so that it will win x points.

   *Use this information to work **Exercises 75 and 76.***

75. Simplify the given expression by performing the indicated subtraction.

76. Use the simplified expression from **Exercise 75** to determine how much it would cost to win 95 points.

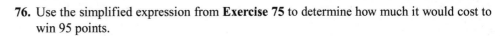

PREVIEW EXERCISES

Perform the indicated operations, using the order of operations as necessary. **See Section 1.1.**

77. $\dfrac{\dfrac{5}{6}}{\dfrac{2}{3}}$ **78.** $\dfrac{\dfrac{3}{8}}{\dfrac{1}{4}}$ **79.** $\dfrac{\dfrac{3}{2}}{\dfrac{7}{4}}$ **80.** $\dfrac{\dfrac{5}{7}}{\dfrac{5}{3}}$

6.5 Complex Fractions

OBJECTIVES

1 Simplify a complex fraction by writing it as a division problem (Method 1).

2 Simplify a complex fraction by multiplying numerator and denominator by the least common denominator (Method 2).

3 Simplify rational expressions with negative exponents.

The quotient of two mixed numbers in arithmetic, such as $2\frac{1}{2} \div 3\frac{1}{4}$, can be written as a fraction.

$$2\frac{1}{2} \div 3\frac{1}{4} = \frac{2\frac{1}{2}}{3\frac{1}{4}} = \frac{2 + \frac{1}{2}}{3 + \frac{1}{4}}$$

We do this to illustrate a *complex fraction.*

In algebra, some rational expressions have fractions in the numerator, or denominator, or both.

Complex Fraction

A quotient with one or more fractions in the numerator, or denominator, or both, is called a **complex fraction.**

$$\frac{2 + \frac{1}{2}}{3 + \frac{1}{4}}, \quad \frac{\frac{3x^2 - 5x}{6x^2}}{2x - \frac{1}{x}}, \quad \text{and} \quad \frac{3 + x}{5 - \frac{2}{x}}$$ Complex fractions

The parts of a complex fraction are named as follows.

$$\frac{\dfrac{2}{p} - \dfrac{1}{q}}{\dfrac{3}{p} + \dfrac{5}{q}}$$

← Numerator of complex fraction
← Main fraction bar
← Denominator of complex fraction

OBJECTIVE 1 Simplify a complex fraction by writing it as a division problem (Method 1). Since the main fraction bar represents division in a complex fraction, one method of simplifying a complex fraction involves division.

Method 1 for Simplifying a Complex Fraction

Step 1   Write both the numerator and denominator as single fractions.

Step 2   Change the complex fraction to a division problem.

Step 3   Perform the indicated division.

NOW TRY
EXERCISE 1
Simplify each complex fraction.

(a) $\dfrac{\dfrac{2}{5}+\dfrac{1}{4}}{\dfrac{1}{6}+\dfrac{3}{8}}$ (b) $\dfrac{2+\dfrac{4}{x}}{\dfrac{5}{6}+\dfrac{5x}{12}}$

EXAMPLE 1 Simplifying Complex Fractions (Method 1)

Simplify each complex fraction.

(a) $\dfrac{\dfrac{2}{3}+\dfrac{5}{9}}{\dfrac{1}{4}+\dfrac{1}{12}}$

(b) $\dfrac{6+\dfrac{3}{x}}{\dfrac{x}{4}+\dfrac{1}{8}}$

Step 1   First, write each numerator as a single fraction.

$$\frac{2}{3}+\frac{5}{9}=\frac{2(3)}{3(3)}+\frac{5}{9}$$

$$=\frac{6}{9}+\frac{5}{9}=\frac{11}{9}$$

$$6+\frac{3}{x}=\frac{6}{1}+\frac{3}{x}$$

$$=\frac{6x}{x}+\frac{3}{x}=\frac{6x+3}{x}$$

Now, write each denominator as a single fraction.

$$\frac{1}{4}+\frac{1}{12}=\frac{1(3)}{4(3)}+\frac{1}{12}$$

$$=\frac{3}{12}+\frac{1}{12}=\frac{4}{12}$$

$$\frac{x}{4}+\frac{1}{8}=\frac{x(2)}{4(2)}+\frac{1}{8}$$

$$=\frac{2x}{8}+\frac{1}{8}=\frac{2x+1}{8}$$

Step 2   Write the equivalent complex fraction as a division problem.

$$\frac{\dfrac{11}{9}}{\dfrac{4}{12}}=\frac{11}{9}\div\frac{4}{12}$$

$$\frac{\dfrac{6x+3}{x}}{\dfrac{2x+1}{8}}=\frac{6x+3}{x}\div\frac{2x+1}{8}$$

Step 3   Use the rule for division and the fundamental property.

Multiply by the reciprocal.

$$\frac{11}{9}\div\frac{4}{12}=\frac{11}{9}\cdot\frac{12}{4}$$

$$=\frac{11\cdot3\cdot4}{3\cdot3\cdot4}$$

$$=\frac{11}{3}$$

Multiply by the reciprocal.

$$\frac{6x+3}{x}\div\frac{2x+1}{8}=\frac{6x+3}{x}\cdot\frac{8}{2x+1}$$

$$=\frac{3(2x+1)}{x}\cdot\frac{8}{2x+1}$$

$$=\frac{24}{x}$$

NOW TRY

NOW TRY
EXERCISE 2
Simplify the complex fraction.

$$\frac{\dfrac{a^2b}{c}}{\dfrac{ab^2}{c^3}}$$

NOW TRY ANSWERS

1. (a) $\dfrac{6}{5}$ (b) $\dfrac{24}{5x}$

2. $\dfrac{ac^2}{b}$

EXAMPLE 2 Simplifying a Complex Fraction (Method 1)

Simplify the complex fraction.

$$\frac{\dfrac{xp}{q^3}}{\dfrac{p^2}{qx^2}}$$

The numerator and denominator are single fractions, so use the definition of division and then the fundamental property.

$$\frac{xp}{q^3}\div\frac{p^2}{qx^2}$$

$$=\frac{xp}{q^3}\cdot\frac{qx^2}{p^2}$$

$$=\frac{x^3}{q^2p}$$

NOW TRY

NOW TRY
EXERCISE 3

Simplify the complex fraction.

$$\dfrac{5 + \dfrac{2}{a - 3}}{\dfrac{1}{a - 3} - 2}$$

EXAMPLE 3 Simplifying a Complex Fraction (Method 1)

Simplify the complex fraction.

$$\dfrac{\dfrac{3}{x + 2} - 4}{\dfrac{2}{x + 2} + 1}$$

$$= \dfrac{\dfrac{3}{x + 2} - \dfrac{4(x + 2)}{x + 2}}{\dfrac{2}{x + 2} + \dfrac{1(x + 2)}{x + 2}} \qquad \text{Write both second terms with a denominator of } x + 2.$$

$$= \dfrac{\dfrac{3 - 4(x + 2)}{x + 2}}{\dfrac{2 + 1(x + 2)}{x + 2}} \qquad \begin{array}{l}\text{Subtract in the numerator.}\\[2ex]\text{Add in the denominator.}\end{array}$$

Be careful with signs. $= \dfrac{\dfrac{3 - 4x - 8}{x + 2}}{\dfrac{2 + x + 2}{x + 2}} \qquad \text{Distributive property}$

$$= \dfrac{\dfrac{-5 - 4x}{x + 2}}{\dfrac{4 + x}{x + 2}} \qquad \text{Combine like terms.}$$

$$= \dfrac{-5 - 4x}{x + 2} \cdot \dfrac{x + 2}{4 + x} \qquad \text{Multiply by the reciprocal of the denominator (divisor).}$$

$$= \dfrac{-5 - 4x}{4 + x} \qquad \text{Divide out the common factor.}$$

NOW TRY

OBJECTIVE 2 **Simplify a complex fraction by multiplying numerator and denominator by the least common denominator (Method 2).** Any expression can be multiplied by a form of 1 to get an equivalent expression. Thus we can multiply both the numerator and the denominator of a complex fraction by the same nonzero expression to get an equivalent rational expression. If we choose the expression to be the LCD of all the fractions within the complex fraction, the complex fraction can then be simplified. This is Method 2.

Method 2 for Simplifying a Complex Fraction
Step 1 Find the LCD of all fractions within the complex fraction.
Step 2 Multiply both the numerator and the denominator of the complex fraction by this LCD using the distributive property as necessary. Write in lowest terms.

NOW TRY ANSWER

3. $\dfrac{5a - 13}{7 - 2a}$

NOW TRY
EXERCISE 3
Solve, and check the proposed solution.

$$4 + \frac{6}{x - 3} = \frac{2x}{x - 3}$$

EXAMPLE 3 **Solving an Equation with Rational Expressions**

Solve, and check the proposed solution.

$$\frac{x}{x - 2} = \frac{2}{x - 2} + 2$$

x cannot equal 2, since 2 causes both denominators to equal 0.

$$(x - 2)\left(\frac{x}{x - 2}\right) = (x - 2)\left(\frac{2}{x - 2} + 2\right)$$

Multiply each side by the LCD, $x - 2$.

$$(x - 2)\left(\frac{x}{x - 2}\right) = (x - 2)\left(\frac{2}{x - 2}\right) + (x - 2)(2)$$

Distributive property

$$x = 2 + 2x - 4$$

Simplify.

$$x = -2 + 2x$$

Combine like terms.

$$-x = -2$$

Subtract 2x.

$$x = 2$$

Multiply by −1.

As noted, x cannot equal 2, since replacing x with 2 in the original equation causes the denominators to equal 0.

CHECK

$$\frac{x}{x - 2} = \frac{2}{x - 2} + 2$$

Original equation

$$\frac{2}{2 - 2} \overset{?}{=} \frac{2}{2 - 2} + 2$$

Let $x = 2$.

Division by 0 is undefined.

$$\frac{2}{0} \overset{?}{=} \frac{2}{0} + 2$$

Subtract in the denominators.

Thus, 2 must be rejected as a solution, and the solution set is $\emptyset$.   NOW TRY

A proposed solution that is not an actual solution of the original equation, such as 2 in **Example 3,** is called an **extraneous solution,** or **extraneous value.** Some students like to determine which numbers cannot be solutions *before* solving the equation, as we did in **Example 3.**

Solving an Equation with Rational Expressions

Step 1 **Multiply each side of the equation by the LCD** to clear the equation of fractions. Be sure to distribute to *every* term on *both* sides.

Step 2 **Solve** the resulting equation.

Step 3 **Check** each proposed solution by substituting it into the original equation. Reject any that cause a denominator to equal 0.

EXAMPLE 4 **Solving an Equation with Rational Expressions**

Solve, and check the proposed solution.

$$\frac{2}{x^2 - x} = \frac{1}{x^2 - 1}$$

NOW TRY ANSWER
3. $\emptyset$

Step 1

$$\frac{2}{x(x - 1)} = \frac{1}{(x + 1)(x - 1)}$$

Factor the denominators to find the LCD, $x(x + 1)(x - 1)$.

NOW TRY
EXERCISE 4

Solve, and check the proposed solution.

$$\frac{3}{2x^2 - 8x} = \frac{1}{x^2 - 16}$$

Notice that 0, 1, and -1 cannot be solutions. Otherwise a denominator will equal 0.

$$\frac{2}{x(x - 1)} = \frac{1}{(x + 1)(x - 1)} \qquad \text{The LCD is } x(x + 1)(x - 1).$$

$$x(x + 1)(x - 1)\frac{2}{x(x - 1)} = x(x + 1)(x - 1)\frac{1}{(x + 1)(x - 1)} \qquad \text{Multiply by the LCD.}$$

Step 2
$$2(x + 1) = x \qquad \text{Divide out the common factors.}$$
$$2x + 2 = x \qquad \text{Distributive property}$$
$$x + 2 = 0 \qquad \text{Subtract } x.$$
$$x = -2 \qquad \text{Subtract 2.}$$

Step 3 The proposed solution is -2, which does not make any denominator equal 0.

CHECK
$$\frac{2}{x^2 - x} = \frac{1}{x^2 - 1} \qquad \text{Original equation}$$

$$\frac{2}{(-2)^2 - (-2)} \overset{?}{=} \frac{1}{(-2)^2 - 1} \qquad \text{Let } x = -2.$$

$$\frac{2}{4 + 2} \overset{?}{=} \frac{1}{4 - 1} \qquad \text{Apply the exponents.}$$

$$\frac{1}{3} = \frac{1}{3} \checkmark \qquad \text{True}$$

The solution set is $\{-2\}$. NOW TRY

NOW TRY
EXERCISE 5

Solve, and check the proposed solution.

$$\frac{2y}{y^2 - 25} = \frac{8}{y + 5} - \frac{1}{y - 5}$$

EXAMPLE 5 Solving an Equation with Rational Expressions

Solve, and check the proposed solution.

$$\frac{2m}{m^2 - 4} + \frac{1}{m - 2} = \frac{2}{m + 2}$$

$$\frac{2m}{(m + 2)(m - 2)} + \frac{1}{m - 2} = \frac{2}{m + 2} \qquad \begin{array}{l}\text{Factor the first denominator} \\ \text{on the left to find the LCD,} \\ (m + 2)(m - 2).\end{array}$$

Notice that -2 and 2 cannot be solutions of this equation.

$$(m + 2)(m - 2)\left(\frac{2m}{(m + 2)(m - 2)} + \frac{1}{m - 2}\right) \qquad \text{Multiply by the LCD.}$$

$$= (m + 2)(m - 2)\frac{2}{m + 2}$$

$$(m + 2)(m - 2)\frac{2m}{(m + 2)(m - 2)} + (m + 2)(m - 2)\frac{1}{m - 2}$$

$$= (m + 2)(m - 2)\frac{2}{m + 2} \qquad \text{Distributive property}$$

$$2m + m + 2 = 2(m - 2) \qquad \text{Divide out the common factors.}$$
$$3m + 2 = 2m - 4 \qquad \text{Combine like terms; distributive property}$$
$$m + 2 = -4 \qquad \text{Subtract } 2m.$$
$$m = -6 \qquad \text{Subtract 2.}$$

NOW TRY ANSWERS
4. $\{-12\}$ 5. $\{9\}$

A check verifies that $\{-6\}$ is the solution set. NOW TRY

OBJECTIVE 2 Solve problems about distance, rate, and time. Recall from **Chapter 2** the following formulas relating distance, rate, and time. You may wish to refer to **Example 5** in **Section 2.7** to review the basic use of these formulas.

Distance, Rate, and Time Relationship

$$d = rt \qquad r = \frac{d}{t} \qquad t = \frac{d}{r}$$

EXAMPLE 2 Solving a Problem about Distance, Rate, and Time

The Tickfaw River has a current of 3 mph. A motorboat takes as long to go 12 mi downstream as to go 8 mi upstream. What is the rate of the boat in still water?

Step 1   **Read** the problem again. We must find the rate (speed) of the boat in still water.

Step 2   **Assign a variable.** Let x = the rate of the boat in still water.

Because the current pushes the boat when the boat is going downstream, the rate of the boat downstream will be the *sum* of the rate of the boat and the rate of the current, $(x + 3)$ mph.

Because the current slows down the boat when the boat is going upstream, the boat's rate going upstream is given by the *difference* between the rate of the boat and the rate of the current, $(x - 3)$ mph. See **FIGURE 1**.

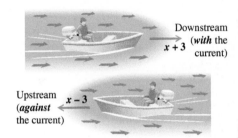

Downstream (*with* the current) $x + 3$

Upstream (*against* the current) $x - 3$

FIGURE 1

This information is summarized in the following table.

	d	r	t
Downstream	12	x + 3	
Upstream	8	x − 3	

Fill in the times by using the formula $t = \frac{d}{r}$.

The time downstream is the distance divided by the rate.

$$t = \frac{d}{r} = \frac{12}{x + 3} \qquad \text{Time downstream}$$

The time upstream is that distance divided by that rate.

$$t = \frac{d}{r} = \frac{8}{x - 3} \qquad \text{Time upstream}$$

	d	r	t	
Downstream	12	x + 3	$\dfrac{12}{x + 3}$	
Upstream	8	x − 3	$\dfrac{8}{x - 3}$	Times are equal.

NOW TRY
EXERCISE 2

In her small boat, Jennifer can travel 12 mi downstream in the same amount of time that she can travel 4 mi upstream. The rate of the current is 2 mph. Find the rate of Jennifer's boat in still water.

Step 3 **Write an equation.**

$$\frac{12}{x + 3} = \frac{8}{x - 3}$$ The time downstream equals the time upstream, so the two times from the table must be equal.

Step 4 **Solve.**

$$(x + 3)(x - 3)\frac{12}{x + 3} = (x + 3)(x - 3)\frac{8}{x - 3}$$ Multiply by the LCD, $(x + 3)(x - 3)$.

$$12(x - 3) = 8(x + 3)$$ Divide out the common factors.

$$12x - 36 = 8x + 24$$ Distributive property

$$4x = 60$$ Subtract 8x and add 36.

$$x = 15$$ Divide by 4.

Step 5 **State the answer.** The rate of the boat in still water is 15 mph.

Step 6 **Check.** First we find the rate of the boat going downstream, which is $15 + 3 = 18$ mph. Divide 12 mi by 18 mph to find the time.

$$t = \frac{d}{r} = \frac{12}{18} = \frac{2}{3} \text{ hr}$$

The rate of the boat going upstream is $15 - 3 = 12$ mph. Divide 8 mi by 12 mph to find the time.

$$t = \frac{d}{r} = \frac{8}{12} = \frac{2}{3} \text{ hr}$$

The time upstream equals the time downstream, as required.

NOW TRY

OBJECTIVE 3 **Solve problems about work.** Suppose that you can mow your lawn in 4 hr. Then after 1 hr, you will have mowed $\frac{1}{4}$ of the lawn. After 2 hr, you will have mowed $\frac{2}{4}$, or $\frac{1}{2}$, of the lawn, and so on. This idea is generalized as follows.

Rate of Work

If a job can be completed in t units of time, then the rate of work is

$$\frac{1}{t} \text{ job per unit of time.}$$

PROBLEM-SOLVING HINT

Recall that the formula $d = rt$ says that distance traveled is equal to rate of travel multiplied by time traveled. Similarly, the fractional part of a job accomplished is equal to the rate of work multiplied by the time worked. In the lawn-mowing example, after 3 hr, the fractional part of the job done is as follows.

$$\underbrace{\frac{1}{4}}_{\substack{\text{Rate of}\\\text{work}}} \cdot \underbrace{3}_{\substack{\text{Time}\\\text{worked}}} = \underbrace{\frac{3}{4}}_{\substack{\text{Fractional part}\\\text{of job done}}}$$

After 4 hr, $\frac{1}{4}(4) = 1$ whole job has been done.

NOW TRY ANSWER
2. 4 mph

**NOW TRY
EXERCISE 3**

Sarah can proofread a manuscript in 10 hr, while Joyce can proofread the same manuscript in 12 hr. How long will it take them to proofread the manuscript if they work together?

EXAMPLE 3 Solving a Problem about Work Rates

"If Joe can paint a house in 3 hr and Sam can paint the same house in 5 hr, how long does it take for them to do it together?" (*Source:* The movie *Little Big League.*)

Step 1 **Read** the problem again. We are looking for time working together.

Step 2 **Assign a variable.** Let x = the number of hours it takes Joe and Sam to paint the house, working together.

Certainly, x will be less than 3, since Joe alone can complete the job in 3 hr. We begin by making a table. Based on the preceding discussion, Joe's rate alone is $\frac{1}{3}$ job per hour, and Sam's rate is $\frac{1}{5}$ job per hour.

	Rate	Time Working Together	Fractional Part of the Job Done When Working Together	
Joe	$\frac{1}{3}$	x	$\frac{1}{3}x$	Sum is 1 whole job.
Sam	$\frac{1}{5}$	x	$\frac{1}{5}x$	

Step 3 **Write an equation.**

$$\underbrace{\frac{1}{3}x}_{\substack{\text{Fractional part} \\ \text{done by Joe}}} + \underbrace{\frac{1}{5}x}_{\substack{\text{Fractional part} \\ \text{done by Sam}}} = \underbrace{1}_{\text{1 whole job.}}$$

Together, Joe and Sam complete 1 whole job. Add their individual fractional parts and set the sum equal to 1.

Step 4 **Solve.**

$$15\left(\frac{1}{3}x + \frac{1}{5}x\right) = 15(1) \qquad \text{Multiply by the LCD, 15.}$$

$$15\left(\frac{1}{3}x\right) + 15\left(\frac{1}{5}x\right) = 15(1) \qquad \text{Distributive property}$$

$$5x + 3x = 15$$

$$8x = 15 \qquad \text{Combine like terms.}$$

$$x = \frac{15}{8} \qquad \text{Divide by 8.}$$

Step 5 **State the answer.** Working together, Joe and Sam can paint the house in $\frac{15}{8}$ hr, or $1\frac{7}{8}$ hr.

Step 6 **Check** to be sure the answer is correct.

NOW TRY

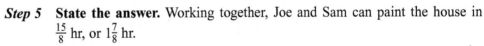

From *Little Big League*

NOTE An alternative approach in work problems is to consider the part of the job that can be done in 1 hr. For instance, in **Example 3** Joe can do the entire job in 3 hr and Sam can do it in 5 hr. Thus, their work rates, as we saw in **Example 3,** are $\frac{1}{3}$ and $\frac{1}{5}$, respectively. Since it takes them x hours to complete the job working together, in 1 hr they can paint $\frac{1}{x}$ of the house.

NOW TRY ANSWER
3. $\frac{60}{11}$ hr, or $5\frac{5}{11}$ hr

(continued)

The amount painted by Joe in 1 hr plus the amount painted by Sam in 1 hr must equal the amount they can do together. This relationship leads to the equation

Amount by Sam
↓

Amount by Joe → $\dfrac{1}{3} + \dfrac{1}{5} = \dfrac{1}{x}$. ← Amount together

Compare this equation with the one in **Example 3.** Multiplying each side by $15x$ leads to

$$5x + 3x = 15,$$

the same equation found in the third line of Step 4 in the example. The same solution results.

PROBLEM-SOLVING HINT

A common error students make when solving a work problem like that in **Example 3** is to add the two times, 3 hr and 5 hr, to get an answer of 8 hr. We reason, however, that x, the time it will take Joe and Sam working together, must be *less than* 3 hr, since Joe can complete the job by himself in 3 hr.

Another common error students make is to try to split the job in half between the two workers so that Joe would work $\frac{1}{2}(3)$, or $1\frac{1}{2}$ hr, and Sam would work $\frac{1}{2}(5)$, or $2\frac{1}{2}$ hr. In this case, Joe finishes 1 hr before Sam and they have not worked together to get the entire job done as quickly as possible. If Joe, when he finishes, helps Sam, the job should actually be completed in a time between $1\frac{1}{2}$ hr and $2\frac{1}{2}$ hr.

Based on this reasoning, does our answer of $1\frac{7}{8}$ hr in **Example 3** hold up?

6.7 EXERCISES

MyMathLab Math XL PRACTICE WATCH DOWNLOAD READ REVIEW

◉ *Complete solution available on the Video Resources on DVD*

Concept Check   Use Steps 2 and 3 of the six-step method to set up the equation you would use to solve each problem. (Remember that Step 1 is to read the problem carefully.) Do not actually solve the equation. ***See Example 1.***

1. The numerator of the fraction $\frac{5}{6}$ is increased by an amount so that the value of the resulting fraction is equivalent to $\frac{13}{3}$. By what amount was the numerator increased?

   (a) Let $x =$ _____. (*Step 2*)

   (b) Write an expression for "the numerator of the fraction $\frac{5}{6}$ is increased by an amount."

   (c) Set up an equation to solve the problem. (*Step 3*)

2. If the same number is added to the numerator and subtracted from the denominator of $\frac{23}{12}$, the resulting fraction is equivalent to $\frac{3}{2}$. What is the number?

   (a) Let $x =$ _____. (*Step 2*)

   (b) Write an expression for "a number is added to the numerator of $\frac{23}{12}$." Then write an expression for "the same number is subtracted from the denominator of $\frac{23}{12}$."

   (c) Set up an equation to solve the problem. (*Step 3*)

Solve each problem. ***See Example 1.***

3. In a certain fraction, the denominator is 6 more than the numerator. If 3 is added to both the numerator and the denominator, the resulting fraction is equivalent to $\frac{5}{7}$. What was the original fraction (*not* written in lowest terms)?

4. In a certain fraction, the denominator is 4 less than the numerator. If 3 is added to both the numerator and the denominator, the resulting fraction is equivalent to $\frac{3}{2}$. What was the original fraction?

5. The numerator of a certain fraction is four times the denominator. If 6 is added to both the numerator and the denominator, the resulting fraction is equivalent to 2. What was the original fraction (*not* written in lowest terms)?

6. The denominator of a certain fraction is three times the numerator. If 2 is added to the numerator and subtracted from the denominator, the resulting fraction is equivalent to 1. What was the original fraction (*not* written in lowest terms)?

7. One-third of a number is 2 greater than one-sixth of the same number. What is the number?

8. One-seventh of a number is 6 greater than the same number. What is the number?

9. A quantity, $\frac{2}{3}$ of it, $\frac{1}{2}$ of it, and $\frac{1}{7}$ of it, added together, equals 33. What is the quantity? (*Source:* Rhind Mathematical Papyrus.)

10. A quantity, $\frac{3}{4}$ of it, $\frac{1}{2}$ of it, and $\frac{1}{3}$ of it, added together, equals 93. What is the quantity? (*Source:* Rhind Mathematical Papyrus.)

Solve each problem. ***See Example 5 in Section 2.7 (pages 143 and 144).***

11. In 2007, British explorer and endurance swimmer Lewis Gordon Pugh became the first person to swim at the North Pole. He swam 0.6 mi at 0.0319 mi per min in waters created by melted sea ice. What was his time (to three decimal places)? (*Source: The Gazette.*)

12. In the 2008 Summer Olympics, Britta Steffen of Germany won the women's 100-m freestyle swimming event. Her rate was 1.8825 m per sec. What was her time (to two decimal places)? (*Source: World Almanac and Book of Facts.*)

13. Tirunesh Dibaba of Ethiopia won the women's 5000-m race in the 2008 Olympics with a time of 15.911 min. What was her rate (to three decimal places)? (*Source: World Almanac and Book of Facts.*)

14. The winner of the women's 1500-m run in the 2008 Olympics was Nancy Jebet Langat of Kenya with a time of 4.004 min. What was her rate (to three decimal places)? (*Source: World Almanac and Book of Facts.*)

15. The winner of the 2008 Daytona 500 (mile) race was Ryan Newman, who drove his Dodge to victory with a rate of 152.672 mph. What was his time (to the nearest thousandth of an hour)? (*Source: World Almanac and Book of Facts.*)

16. In 2008, Kasey Kahne drove his Dodge to victory in the Coca-Cola 600 (mile) race. His rate was 135.722 mph. What was his time (to the nearest thousandth of an hour)? (*Source: World Almanac and Book of Facts.*)

Concept Check Solve each problem.

17. Suppose Stephanie walks D miles at R mph in the same time that Wally walks d miles at r mph. Give an equation relating D, R, d, and r.

18. If a migrating hawk travels m mph in still air, what is its rate when it flies into a steady headwind of 6 mph?   What is its rate with a tailwind of 6 mph?

Set up the equation you would use to solve each problem. Do not actually solve the equation. **See Example 2.**

19. Mitch Levy flew his airplane 500 mi against the wind in the same time it took him to fly 600 mi with the wind. If the speed of the wind was 10 mph, what was the rate of his plane in still air? (Let x = rate of the plane in still air.)

	d	r	t
Against the Wind	500	x − 10	
With the Wind	600	x + 10	

20. Janet Sturdy can row 4 mph in still water. She takes as long to row 8 mi upstream as 24 mi downstream. How fast is the current? (Let x = rate of the current.)

	d	r	t
Upstream	8	4 − x	
Downstream	24	4 + x	

Solve each problem. **See Example 2.**

🌐 21. A boat can go 20 mi against a current in the same time that it can go 60 mi with the current. The current is 4 mph. Find the rate of the boat in still water.

22. Vince Grosso can fly his plane 200 mi against the wind in the same time it takes him to fly 300 mi with the wind. The wind blows at 30 mph. Find the rate of his plane in still air.

23. The sanderling is a small shorebird about 6.5 in. long, with a thin, dark bill and a wide, white wing stripe. If a sanderling can fly 30 mi with the wind in the same time it can fly 18 mi against the wind when the wind speed is 8 mph, what is the rate of the bird in still air? (*Source: U.S. Geological Survey.*)

24. Airplanes usually fly faster from west to east than from east to west because the prevailing winds go from west to east. The air distance between Chicago and London is about 4000 mi, while the air distance between New York and London is about 3500 mi. If a jet can fly eastbound from Chicago to London in the same time it can fly westbound from London to New York in a 35-mph wind, what is the rate of the plane in still air? (*Source: Encyclopaedia Britannica.*)

25. An airplane maintaining a constant airspeed takes as long to go 450 mi with the wind as it does to go 375 mi against the wind. If the wind is blowing at 15 mph, what is the rate of the plane in still air?

26. A river has a current of 4 km per hr. Find the rate of Jai Singh's boat in still water if it goes 40 km downstream in the same time that it takes to go 24 km upstream.

27. Connie McNair's boat goes 12 mph. Find the rate of the current of the river if she can go 6 mi upstream in the same amount of time she can go 10 mi downstream.

28. Howie Sorkin can travel 8 mi upstream in the same time it takes him to go 12 mi downstream. His boat goes 15 mph in still water. What is the rate of the current?

29. The distance from Seattle, Washington, to Victoria, British Columbia, is about 148 mi by ferry. It takes about 4 hr less to travel by the same ferry from Victoria to Vancouver, British Columbia, a distance of about 74 mi. What is the average rate of the ferry?

30. Driving from Tulsa to Detroit, Dean Loring averaged 50 mph. He figured that if he had averaged 60 mph, his driving time would have decreased 3 hr. How far is it from Tulsa to Detroit?

Concept Check *Solve each problem.*

31. If it takes Elayn 10 hr to do a job, what is her rate?

32. If it takes Clay 12 hr to do a job, how much of the job does he do in 8 hr?

In Exercises 33 and 34, set up the equation you would use to solve each problem. Do not actually solve the equation. ***See Example 3.***

33. Working alone, Edward Good can paint a room in 8 hr. Abdalla Elusta can paint the same room working alone in 6 hr. How long will it take them if they work together? (Let t represent the time they work together.)

	r	t	w
Edward		t	
Abdalla		t	

34. Donald Bridgewater can tune up his Chevy in 2 hr working alone. Jeff Bresner can do the job in 3 hr working alone. How long would it take them if they worked together? (Let t represent the time they work together.)

	r	t	w
Donald		t	
Jeff		t	

Solve each problem. ***See Example 3.***

🌐 **35.** Heather Schaefer, a high school mathematics teacher, gave a test on perimeter, area, and volume to her geometry classes. Working alone, it would take her 4 hr to grade the tests. Her student teacher, Courtney Slade, would take 6 hr to grade the same tests. How long would it take them to grade these tests if they work together?

36. Zachary and Samuel are brothers who share a bedroom. By himself, Zachary can completely mess up their room in 20 min, while it would take Samuel only 12 min to do the same thing. How long would it take them to mess up the room together?

37. A pump can pump the water out of a flooded basement in 10 hr. A smaller pump takes 12 hr. How long would it take to pump the water from the basement with both pumps?

38. Lou Viggiano's copier can do a printing job in 7 hr. Nora Demosthenes' copier can do the same job in 12 hr. How long would it take to do the job with both copiers?

39. An experienced employee can enter tax data into a computer twice as fast as a new employee. Working together, it takes the employees 2 hr. How long would it take the experienced employee working alone?

40. One roofer can put a new roof on a house three times faster than another. Working together, they can roof a house in 4 days. How long would it take the faster roofer working alone?

41. One pipe can fill a swimming pool in 6 hr, and another pipe can do it in 9 hr. How long will it take the two pipes working together to fill the pool $\frac{3}{4}$ full?

42. An inlet pipe can fill a swimming pool in 9 hr, and an outlet pipe can empty the pool in 12 hr. Through an error, both pipes are left open. How long will it take to fill the pool?

Brain Busters   *Extend the concepts of* **Example 3** *to solve each problem.*

43. A cold-water faucet can fill a sink in 12 min, and a hot-water faucet can fill it in 15 min. The drain can empty the sink in 25 min. If both faucets are on and the drain is open, how long will it take to fill the sink?

44. Refer to **Exercise 42.** Assume that the error was discovered after both pipes had been running for 3 hr and the outlet pipe was then closed. How much more time would then be required to fill the pool? (*Hint:* Consider how much of the job had been done when the error was discovered.)

PREVIEW EXERCISES

Find each quotient. ***See Section 1.6.***

45. $\dfrac{6 - 2}{5 - 3}$ **46.** $\dfrac{5 - 7}{-4 - 2}$ **47.** $\dfrac{4 - (-1)}{-3 - (-5)}$

48. $\dfrac{-6 - 0}{0 - (-3)}$ **49.** $\dfrac{-5 - (-5)}{3 - 2}$ **50.** $\dfrac{7 - (-2)}{-3 - (-3)}$

Solve each equation for y. ***See Section 2.5.***

51. $3x + 2y = 8$ **52.** $4x + 3y = 0$

CHAPTER (6) SUMMARY

KEY TERMS

6.1

rational expression
lowest terms

6.3

least common
  denominator (LCD)

6.5

complex fraction

6.6

proposed solution
extraneous solution (value)

TEST YOUR WORD POWER

See how well you have learned the vocabulary in this chapter.

1. A **rational expression** is
   A. an algebraic expression made up of a term or the sum of a finite number of terms with real coefficients and whole number exponents
   B. a polynomial equation of degree 2
   C. an expression with one or more fractions in the numerator, or denominator, or both
   D. the quotient of two polynomials with denominator not 0.

2. In a given set of fractions, the **least common denominator** is
   A. the smallest denominator of all the denominators
   B. the smallest expression that is divisible by all the denominators
   C. the largest integer that evenly divides the numerator and denominator of all the fractions
   D. the largest denominator of all the denominators.

3. A **complex fraction** is
   A. an algebraic expression made up of a term or the sum of a finite number of terms with real coefficients and whole number exponents
   B. a polynomial equation of degree 2
   C. a quotient with one or more fractions in the numerator, or denominator, or both
   D. the quotient of two polynomials with denominator not 0.

ANSWERS

1. D; *Examples:* $-\dfrac{3}{4y}, \dfrac{5x^3}{x+2}, \dfrac{a+3}{a^2-4a-5}$ 2. B; *Example:* The LCD of $\dfrac{1}{x}, \dfrac{2}{3}$, and $\dfrac{5}{x+1}$ is $3x(x+1)$.   3. C; *Examples:* $\dfrac{\frac{2}{3}}{\frac{4}{7}}, \dfrac{x-\frac{1}{y}}{x+\frac{1}{y}}, \dfrac{\frac{2}{a+1}}{a^2-1}$

QUICK REVIEW

CONCEPTS	EXAMPLES
6.1 **The Fundamental Property of Rational Expressions** To find the value(s) for which a rational expression is undefined, set the denominator equal to 0 and solve the equation.	Find the values for which the expression $\dfrac{x-4}{x^2-16}$ is undefined. $x^2 - 16 = 0$ $(x-4)(x+4) = 0$ Factor. $x - 4 = 0$ or $x + 4 = 0$ Zero-factor property $x = 4$ or $x = -4$ Solve for *x*. The rational expression is undefined for 4 and -4, so $x \neq 4$ and $x \neq -4$.

(continued)

CONCEPTS	EXAMPLES

Writing a Rational Expression in Lowest Terms

Step 1 Factor the numerator and denominator.

Step 2 Use the fundamental property to divide out common factors.

Write in lowest terms. $\dfrac{x^2 - 1}{(x - 1)^2}$

$$= \frac{(x - 1)(x + 1)}{(x - 1)(x - 1)}$$

$$= \frac{x + 1}{x - 1}$$

6.2 Multiplying and Dividing Rational Expressions

Multiplying or Dividing Rational Expressions

Step 1 Note the operation. If the operation is division, use the definition of division to rewrite as multiplication.

Step 2 Multiply numerators and multiply denominators.

Step 3 Factor numerators and denominators completely.

Step 4 Write in lowest terms, using the fundamental property.

Note: Steps 2 and 3 may be interchanged based on personal preference.

Multiply. $\dfrac{3x + 9}{x - 5} \cdot \dfrac{x^2 - 3x - 10}{x^2 - 9}$

$$= \frac{(3x + 9)(x^2 - 3x - 10)}{(x - 5)(x^2 - 9)} \quad \text{Multiply numerators and denominators.}$$

$$= \frac{3(x + 3)(x - 5)(x + 2)}{(x - 5)(x + 3)(x - 3)} \quad \text{Factor.}$$

$$= \frac{3(x + 2)}{x - 3} \quad \text{Lowest terms}$$

Divide. $\dfrac{2x + 1}{x + 5} \div \dfrac{6x^2 - x - 2}{x^2 - 25}$

$$= \frac{2x + 1}{x + 5} \cdot \frac{x^2 - 25}{6x^2 - x - 2} \quad \begin{array}{l}\text{Multiply by the}\\\text{reciprocal of the}\\\text{divisor.}\end{array}$$

$$= \frac{(2x + 1)(x^2 - 25)}{(x + 5)(6x^2 - x - 2)} \quad \begin{array}{l}\text{Multiply numerators}\\\text{and denominators.}\end{array}$$

$$= \frac{(2x + 1)(x + 5)(x - 5)}{(x + 5)(2x + 1)(3x - 2)} \quad \text{Factor.}$$

$$= \frac{x - 5}{3x - 2} \quad \text{Lowest terms}$$

6.3 Least Common Denominators

Finding the LCD

Step 1 Factor each denominator into prime factors.

Step 2 List each different factor the greatest number of times it appears.

Step 3 Multiply the factors from Step 2 to get the LCD.

Writing a Rational Expression with a Specified Denominator

Step 1 Factor both denominators.

Step 2 Decide what factor(s) the denominator must be multiplied by in order to equal the specified denominator.

Step 3 Multiply the rational expression by that factor divided by itself. (That is, multiply by 1.)

Find the LCD for $\dfrac{3}{k^2 - 8k + 16}$ and $\dfrac{1}{4k^2 - 16k}$.

$$\left.\begin{array}{l}k^2 - 8k + 16 = (k - 4)^2 \\ 4k^2 - 16k = 4k(k - 4)\end{array}\right\} \begin{array}{l}\text{Factor each}\\\text{denominator.}\end{array}$$

$$\text{LCD} = (k - 4)^2 \cdot 4 \cdot k$$

$$= 4k(k - 4)^2$$

Find the numerator. $\dfrac{5}{2z^2 - 6z} = \dfrac{?}{4z^3 - 12z^2}$

$$\frac{5}{2z(z - 3)} = \frac{?}{4z^2(z - 3)}$$

$2z(z - 3)$ must be multiplied by $2z$ in order to obtain $4z^2(z - 3)$.

$$\frac{5}{2z(z - 3)} \cdot \frac{2z}{2z} = \frac{10z}{4z^2(z - 3)} = \frac{10z}{4z^3 - 12z^2}$$

(continued)

CONCEPTS	EXAMPLES

6.4 **Adding and Subtracting Rational Expressions**

Adding Rational Expressions

Step 1 Find the LCD.

Step 2 Rewrite each rational expression with the LCD as denominator.

Step 3 Add the numerators to get the numerator of the sum. The LCD is the denominator of the sum.

Step 4 Write in lowest terms.

Subtracting Rational Expressions

Follow the same steps as for addition, but subtract in Step 3.

Add. $\dfrac{2}{3m + 6} + \dfrac{m}{m^2 - 4}$

$$3m + 6 = 3(m + 2)$$
$$m^2 - 4 = (m + 2)(m - 2)$$
The LCD is $3(m + 2)(m - 2)$.

$$= \frac{2(m - 2)}{3(m + 2)(m - 2)} + \frac{3m}{3(m + 2)(m - 2)} \quad \text{Write with the LCD.}$$

$$= \frac{2m - 4 + 3m}{3(m + 2)(m - 2)} \quad \text{Add numerators and keep the same denominator.}$$

$$= \frac{5m - 4}{3(m + 2)(m - 2)} \quad \text{Combine like terms.}$$

Subtract. $\dfrac{6}{k + 4} - \dfrac{2}{k}$ The LCD is $k(k + 4)$.

$$= \frac{6k}{(k + 4)k} - \frac{2(k + 4)}{k(k + 4)} \quad \text{Write with the LCD.}$$

$$= \frac{6k - 2(k + 4)}{k(k + 4)} \quad \text{Subtract numerators and keep the same denominator.}$$

$$= \frac{6k - 2k - 8}{k(k + 4)} \quad \text{Distributive property}$$

$$= \frac{4k - 8}{k(k + 4)} \quad \text{Combine like terms.}$$

6.5 **Complex Fractions**

Simplifying Complex Fractions

Method 1 Simplify the numerator and denominator separately. Then divide the simplified numerator by the simplified denominator.

Method 2 Multiply the numerator and denominator of the complex fraction by the LCD of all the denominators in the complex fraction. Write in lowest terms.

Simplify.

Method 1 $\dfrac{\dfrac{1}{a} - a}{1 - a} = \dfrac{\dfrac{1}{a} - \dfrac{a^2}{a}}{1 - a} = \dfrac{\dfrac{1 - a^2}{a}}{1 - a}$

$$= \frac{1 - a^2}{a} \div (1 - a)$$

$$= \frac{1 - a^2}{a} \cdot \frac{1}{1 - a} \quad \text{Multiply by the reciprocal of the divisor.}$$

$$= \frac{(1 - a)(1 + a)}{a(1 - a)} = \frac{1 + a}{a}$$

Method 2 $\dfrac{\dfrac{1}{a} - a}{1 - a} = \dfrac{\left(\dfrac{1}{a} - a\right)a}{(1 - a)a} = \dfrac{\dfrac{a}{a} - a^2}{(1 - a)a}$

$$= \frac{1 - a^2}{(1 - a)a} = \frac{(1 + a)(1 - a)}{(1 - a)a}$$

$$= \frac{1 + a}{a}$$

(continued)

CONCEPTS	EXAMPLES

6.6 Solving Equations with Rational Expressions

Solving Equations with Rational Expressions

Step 1 Multiply each side of the equation by the LCD to clear the equation of fractions. Be sure to distribute to *every* term on *both* sides.

Step 2 Solve the resulting equation.

Step 3 Check each proposed solution.

Solve.

$$\frac{x}{x-3} + \frac{4}{x+3} = \frac{18}{x^2 - 9}$$

$$\frac{x}{x-3} + \frac{4}{x+3} = \frac{18}{(x-3)(x+3)} \quad \text{Factor.}$$

The LCD is $(x-3)(x+3)$. Note that 3 and -3 cannot be solutions, as they cause a denominator to equal 0.

$$(x-3)(x+3)\left(\frac{x}{x-3} + \frac{4}{x+3}\right)$$

$$= (x-3)(x+3)\frac{18}{(x-3)(x+3)} \quad \text{Multiply by the LCD.}$$

$$x(x+3) + 4(x-3) = 18 \quad \text{Distributive property}$$

$$x^2 + 3x + 4x - 12 = 18 \quad \text{Distributive property}$$

$$x^2 + 7x - 30 = 0 \quad \text{Standard form}$$

$$(x-3)(x+10) = 0 \quad \text{Factor.}$$

$$x - 3 = 0 \quad \text{or} \quad x + 10 = 0 \quad \text{Zero-factor property}$$

Reject $\longrightarrow x = 3 \quad$ or $\quad x = -10 \quad$ Solve for x.

Since 3 causes denominators to equal 0, the only solution is -10. Thus, $\{-10\}$ is the solution set.

6.7 Applications of Rational Expressions

Solving Problems about Distance, Rate, and Time

Use the formulas relating d, r, and t.

$$d = rt, \quad r = \frac{d}{t}, \quad t = \frac{d}{r}$$

Solving Problems about Work

Step 1 Read the problem carefully.

Step 2 Assign a variable. State what the variable represents. Put the information from the problem into a table. If a job is done in t units of time, the rate is $\frac{1}{t}$.

Step 3 Write an equation. The sum of the fractional parts should equal 1 (whole job).

Step 4 Solve the equation.

Steps 5 and 6 State the answer and check the solution.

It takes the regular mail carrier 6 hr to cover her route. A substitute takes 8 hr to cover the same route. How long would it take them to cover the route together?

Let x = the number of hours required to cover the route together.

	Rate	Time	Part of the Job Done
Regular	$\frac{1}{6}$	x	$\frac{1}{6}x$
Substitute	$\frac{1}{8}$	x	$\frac{1}{8}x$

$$\frac{1}{6}x + \frac{1}{8}x = 1$$

$$24\left(\frac{1}{6}x + \frac{1}{8}x\right) = 24(1) \quad \text{The LCD is 24.}$$

$$4x + 3x = 24 \quad \text{Distributive property}$$

$$7x = 24 \quad \text{Combine like terms.}$$

$$x = \frac{24}{7} \quad \text{Divide by 7.}$$

It would take them $\frac{24}{7}$ hr, or $3\frac{3}{7}$ hr, to cover the route together.

The solution checks because $\frac{1}{6}\left(\frac{24}{7}\right) + \frac{1}{8}\left(\frac{24}{7}\right) = 1$.

CHAPTER (6)

REVIEW EXERCISES

6.1   *Find the numerical value of each rational expression for* **(a)** *and* **(b)** .

1. $\dfrac{4x - 3}{5x + 2}$

2. $\dfrac{3x}{x^2 - 4}$

Find any values of the variable for which each rational expression is undefined. Write answers with the symbol ≠.

3. $\dfrac{4}{x - 3}$

4. $\dfrac{y + 3}{2y}$

5. $\dfrac{2k + 1}{3k^2 + 17k + 10}$

6. How do you determine the values of the variable for which a rational expression is undefined?

Write each rational expression in lowest terms.

7. $\dfrac{5a^3b^3}{15a^4b^2}$

8. $\dfrac{m - 4}{4 - m}$

9. $\dfrac{4x^2 - 9}{6 - 4x}$

10. $\dfrac{4p^2 + 8pq - 5q^2}{10p^2 - 3pq - q^2}$

Write four equivalent forms for each rational expression.

11. $-\dfrac{4x - 9}{2x + 3}$

12. $-\dfrac{8 - 3x}{3 - 6x}$

6.2   *Multiply or divide, and write each answer in lowest terms.*

13. $\dfrac{18p^3}{6} \cdot \dfrac{24}{p^4}$

14. $\dfrac{8x^2}{12x^5} \cdot \dfrac{6x^4}{2x}$

15. $\dfrac{x - 3}{4} \cdot \dfrac{5}{2x - 6}$

16. $\dfrac{2r + 3}{r - 4} \cdot \dfrac{r^2 - 16}{6r + 9}$

17. $\dfrac{6a^2 + 7a - 3}{2a^2 - a - 6} \div \dfrac{a + 5}{a - 2}$

18. $\dfrac{y^2 - 6y + 8}{y^2 + 3y - 18} \div \dfrac{y - 4}{y + 6}$

19. $\dfrac{2p^2 + 13p + 20}{p^2 + p - 12} \cdot \dfrac{p^2 + 2p - 15}{2p^2 + 7p + 5}$

20. $\dfrac{3z^2 + 5z - 2}{9z^2 - 1} \cdot \dfrac{9z^2 + 6z + 1}{z^2 + 5z + 6}$

6.3   *Find the least common denominator for the fractions in each list.*

21. $\dfrac{4}{9y}, \dfrac{7}{12y^2}, \dfrac{5}{27y^4}$

22. $\dfrac{3}{x^2 + 4x + 3}, \dfrac{5}{x^2 + 5x + 4}$

Rewrite each rational expression with the given denominator.

23. $\dfrac{3}{2a^3} = \dfrac{?}{10a^4}$

24. $\dfrac{9}{x - 3} = \dfrac{?}{18 - 6x}$

25. $\dfrac{-3y}{2y - 10} = \dfrac{?}{50 - 10y}$

26. $\dfrac{4b}{b^2 + 2b - 3} = \dfrac{?}{(b + 3)(b - 1)(b + 2)}$

6.4 *Add or subtract, and write each answer in lowest terms.*

27. $\dfrac{10}{x} + \dfrac{5}{x}$

28. $\dfrac{6}{3p} - \dfrac{12}{3p}$

29. $\dfrac{9}{k} - \dfrac{5}{k-5}$

30. $\dfrac{4}{y} + \dfrac{7}{7+y}$

31. $\dfrac{m}{3} - \dfrac{2+5m}{6}$

32. $\dfrac{12}{x^2} - \dfrac{3}{4x}$

33. $\dfrac{5}{a-2b} + \dfrac{2}{a+2b}$

34. $\dfrac{4}{k^2-9} - \dfrac{k+3}{3k-9}$

35. $\dfrac{8}{z^2+6z} - \dfrac{3}{z^2+4z-12}$

36. $\dfrac{11}{2p-p^2} - \dfrac{2}{p^2-5p+6}$

6.5 *Simplify each complex fraction.*

37. $\dfrac{\dfrac{y-3}{y}}{\dfrac{y+3}{4y}}$

38. $\dfrac{\dfrac{2}{3} - \dfrac{1}{6}}{\dfrac{1}{4} + \dfrac{2}{5}}$

39. $\dfrac{x + \dfrac{1}{w}}{x - \dfrac{1}{w}}$

40. $\dfrac{\dfrac{1}{p} - \dfrac{1}{q}}{\dfrac{1}{q-p}}$

41. $\dfrac{\dfrac{x^2-25}{x+3}}{\dfrac{x+5}{x^2-9}}$

42. $\dfrac{x^{-2} - y^{-2}}{x^{-1} - y^{-1}}$

6.6 *Solve each equation, and check your solutions.*

43. $\dfrac{3x-1}{x-2} = \dfrac{5}{x-2} + 1$

44. $\dfrac{4-z}{z} + \dfrac{3}{2} = \dfrac{-4}{z}$

45. $\dfrac{3}{x+4} - \dfrac{2x}{5} = \dfrac{3}{x+4}$

46. $\dfrac{3}{m-2} + \dfrac{1}{m-1} = \dfrac{7}{m^2-3m+2}$

Solve each formula for the specified variable.

47. $m = \dfrac{Ry}{t}$ for t

48. $x = \dfrac{3y-5}{4}$ for y

49. $p^2 = \dfrac{4}{3m-q}$ for m

6.7 *Solve each problem.*

50. In a certain fraction, the denominator is 5 less than the numerator. If 5 is added to both the numerator and the denominator, the resulting fraction is equivalent to $\frac{5}{4}$. Find the original fraction (*not* written in lowest terms).

51. The denominator of a certain fraction is six times the numerator. If 3 is added to the numerator and subtracted from the denominator, the resulting fraction is equivalent to $\frac{2}{5}$. Find the original fraction (*not* written in lowest terms).

52. A plane flies 350 mi with the wind in the same time that it can fly 310 mi against the wind. The plane has a speed of 165 mph in still air. Find the speed of the wind.

53. Susan Costa can plant her garden in 5 hr working alone. A friend can do the same job in 8 hr. How long would it take them if they worked together?

54. The head gardener can mow the lawns in the city park twice as fast as his assistant. Working together, they can complete the job in $1\frac{1}{3}$ hr. How long would it take the head gardener working alone?

MIXED REVIEW EXERCISES

Perform each indicated operation.

55. $\dfrac{4}{m-1} - \dfrac{3}{m+1}$

56. $\dfrac{8p^5}{5} \div \dfrac{2p^3}{10}$

57. $\dfrac{r-3}{8} \div \dfrac{3r-9}{4}$

58. $\dfrac{t^{-2} + s^{-2}}{t^{-1} - s^{-1}}$

59. $\dfrac{\dfrac{5}{x} - 1}{\dfrac{5-x}{3x}}$

60. $\dfrac{4}{z^2 - 2z + 1} - \dfrac{3}{z^2 - 1}$

61. $\dfrac{1}{t^2 - 4} + \dfrac{1}{2-t}$

Solve.

62. $\dfrac{2}{z} - \dfrac{z}{z+3} = \dfrac{1}{z+3}$

63. $a = \dfrac{v-w}{t}$ for v

64. Rob Fusco flew his plane 400 km with the wind in the same time it took him to go 200 km against the wind. The speed of the wind is 50 km per hr. Find the rate of the plane in still air.

65. With spraying equipment, Lizette Foley can paint the woodwork in a small house in 8 hr. Seyed Sadati needs 14 hr to complete the same job painting by hand. If Lizette and Seyed work together, how long will it take them to paint the woodwork?

RELATING CONCEPTS EXERCISES 66–75

FOR INDIVIDUAL OR GROUP WORK

In these exercises, we summarize the various concepts involving rational expressions.
Work Exercises 66–75 in order.

Let P, Q, and R be rational expressions defined as follows:

$$P = \frac{6}{x+3}, \qquad Q = \frac{5}{x+1}, \qquad R = \frac{4x}{x^2 + 4x + 3}.$$

66. Find the value or values for which the expression is undefined.

    (a) P **(b)** Q **(c)** R

67. Find and express $(P \cdot Q) \div R$ in lowest terms.

68. Why is $(P \cdot Q) \div R$ not defined if $x = 0$?

69. Find the LCD for P, Q, and R.

70. Perform the operations and express $P + Q - R$ in lowest terms.

71. Simplify the complex fraction $\dfrac{P+Q}{R}$.

72. Solve the equation $P + Q = R$.

73. How does your answer to **Exercise 66** help you work **Exercise 72**?

74. Suppose that a car travels 6 miles in $(x+3)$ minutes. Explain why P represents the rate of the car (in miles per minute).

75. For what value or values of x is $R = \frac{40}{77}$?

CHAPTER  6

TEST

Step-by-step test solutions are found on the Chapter Test Prep Videos available via the Video Resources on DVD, in *MyMathLab*, or on YouTube (search "LialCombinedAlgebra").

View the complete solutions to all Chapter Test exercises on the Video Resources on DVD.

1. Find the numerical value of $\dfrac{6r + 1}{2r^2 - 3r - 20}$ for **(a)** $r = -2$ and **(b)** $r = 4$.

2. Find any values for which $\dfrac{3x - 1}{x^2 - 2x - 8}$ is undefined. Write your answer with the symbol $\neq$.

3. Write four rational expressions equivalent to $-\dfrac{6x - 5}{2x + 3}$.

Write each rational expression in lowest terms.

4. $\dfrac{-15x^6y^4}{5x^4y}$

5. $\dfrac{6a^2 + a - 2}{2a^2 - 3a + 1}$

Multiply or divide. Write each answer in lowest terms.

6. $\dfrac{5(d - 2)}{9} \div \dfrac{3(d - 2)}{5}$

7. $\dfrac{6k^2 - k - 2}{8k^2 + 10k + 3} \cdot \dfrac{4k^2 + 7k + 3}{3k^2 + 5k + 2}$

8. $\dfrac{4a^2 + 9a + 2}{3a^2 + 11a + 10} \div \dfrac{4a^2 + 17a + 4}{3a^2 + 2a - 5}$

9. $\dfrac{x^2 - 10x + 25}{9 - 6x + x^2} \cdot \dfrac{x - 3}{5 - x}$

Find the least common denominator for the fractions in each list.

10. $\dfrac{-3}{10p^2}, \dfrac{21}{25p^3}, \dfrac{-7}{30p^5}$

11. $\dfrac{r + 1}{2r^2 + 7r + 6}, \dfrac{-2r + 1}{2r^2 - 7r - 15}$

Rewrite each rational expression with the given denominator.

12. $\dfrac{15}{4p} = \dfrac{?}{64p^3}$

13. $\dfrac{3}{6m - 12} = \dfrac{?}{42m - 84}$

Add or subtract. Write each answer in lowest terms.

14. $\dfrac{4x + 2}{x + 5} + \dfrac{-2x + 8}{x + 5}$

15. $\dfrac{-4}{y + 2} + \dfrac{6}{5y + 10}$

16. $\dfrac{x + 1}{3 - x} + \dfrac{x^2}{x - 3}$

17. $\dfrac{3}{2m^2 - 9m - 5} - \dfrac{m + 1}{2m^2 - m - 1}$

Simplify each complex fraction.

18. $\dfrac{\dfrac{2p}{k^2}}{\dfrac{3p^2}{k^3}}$

19. $\dfrac{\dfrac{1}{x + 3} - 1}{1 + \dfrac{1}{x + 3}}$

20. $\dfrac{2x^{-2} + y^{-2}}{x^{-1} - y^{-1}}$

Solve.

21. $\dfrac{3x}{x + 1} = \dfrac{3}{2x}$

22. $\dfrac{2x}{x - 3} + \dfrac{1}{x + 3} = \dfrac{-6}{x^2 - 9}$

23. $F = \dfrac{k}{d - D}$ for D

Solve each problem.

24. A boat goes 7 mph in still water. It takes as long to go 20 mi upstream as 50 mi downstream. Find the rate of the current.

25. Sanford Geraci can paint a room in his house, working alone, in 5 hr. His neighbor can do the job in 4 hr. How long will it take them to paint the room if they work together?

CUMULATIVE REVIEW EXERCISES

1. Use the order of operations to evaluate $3 + 4\left(\frac{1}{2} - \frac{3}{4}\right)$.

Solve.

2. $3(2y - 5) = 2 + 5y$

3. $A = \frac{1}{2}bh$ for b

4. $\dfrac{2 + m}{2 - m} = \dfrac{3}{4}$

5. $5y \le 6y + 8$

6. Consider the graph of $4x + 3y = -12$.

    (a) What is the x-intercept?   **(b)** What is the y-intercept?

Sketch each graph.

7. $y = -3x + 2$

8. $y = -x^2 + 1$

Simplify each expression. Write with only positive exponents.

9. $\dfrac{(2x^3)^{-1} \cdot x}{2^3 x^5}$

10. $\dfrac{(m^{-2})^3 m}{m^5 m^{-4}}$

Perform each indicated operation.

11. $(2k^2 + 3k) - (k^2 + k - 1)$

12. $(2a - b)^2$

13. $(y^2 + 3y + 5)(3y - 1)$

14. $\dfrac{12p^3 + 2p^2 - 12p + 4}{2p - 2}$

Factor completely.

15. $8t^2 + 10tv + 3v^2$

16. $8r^2 - 9rs + 12s^2$

17. $16x^4 - 1$

Solve each equation.

18. $r^2 = 2r + 15$

19. $(r - 5)(2r + 1)(3r - 2) = 0$

Solve each problem.

20. One number is 4 greater than another. The product of the numbers is 2 less than the lesser number. Find the lesser number.

21. The length of a rectangle is 2 m less than twice the width. The area is 60 m². Find the width of the rectangle.

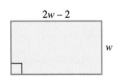

22. Which one of the following is equal to 1 for *all* real numbers?

    A. $\dfrac{k^2 + 2}{k^2 + 2}$ **B.** $\dfrac{4 - m}{4 - m}$ **C.** $\dfrac{2x + 9}{2x + 9}$ **D.** $\dfrac{x^2 - 1}{x^2 - 1}$

23. Which one of the following rational expressions is *not* equivalent to $\frac{4 - 3x}{7}$?

    A. $-\dfrac{-4 + 3x}{7}$ **B.** $-\dfrac{4 - 3x}{-7}$ **C.** $\dfrac{-4 + 3x}{-7}$ **D.** $\dfrac{-(3x + 4)}{7}$

Perform each operation and write the answer in lowest terms.

24. $\dfrac{5}{q} - \dfrac{1}{q}$

25. $\dfrac{3}{7} + \dfrac{4}{r}$

26. $\dfrac{4}{5q - 20} - \dfrac{1}{3q - 12}$

27. $\dfrac{2}{k^2 + k} - \dfrac{3}{k^2 - k}$

28. $\dfrac{7z^2 + 49z + 70}{16z^2 + 72z - 40} \div \dfrac{3z + 6}{4z^2 - 1}$

29. $\dfrac{\dfrac{4}{a} + \dfrac{5}{2a}}{\dfrac{7}{6a} - \dfrac{1}{5a}}$

Solve each equation. Check your solutions.

30. $\dfrac{r + 2}{5} = \dfrac{r - 3}{3}$

31. $\dfrac{1}{x} = \dfrac{1}{x + 1} + \dfrac{1}{2}$

32. Jody Harris can weed the yard in 3 hr. Pat Tabler can weed the same yard in 2 hr. How long will it take them if they work together?

Graphs, Linear Equations, and Functions

The two most common measures of temperature are Fahrenheit (F) and Celsius (C). It is fairly common knowledge that water freezes at 32°F, or 0°C, and boils at 212°F, or 100°C. Because there is a *linear* relationship between the Fahrenheit and Celsius temperature scales, using these two equivalences we can derive the familiar formulas for converting from one temperature scale to the other, as seen in **Section 7.2, Exercises 93–100.**

Graphs are widely used in the media because they present a great deal of information in a concise form. In this chapter, we see how information such as the relationship between the two temperature scales can be depicted by graphs.

7.1 Review of Graphs and Slopes of Lines

This section and the next review and extend some of the main topics of linear equations in two variables, first introduced in **Chapter 3.**

OBJECTIVE 1 Plot ordered pairs. Each of the pairs of numbers

$$(3, 2), \quad (-5, 6), \quad \text{and} \quad (4, -1)$$

is an example of an **ordered pair**—that is, a pair of numbers written within parentheses, consisting of a **first component** and a **second component.** We graph an ordered pair by using two perpendicular number lines that intersect at their 0 points, as shown in the plane in **FIGURE 1**. The common 0 point is called the **origin.**

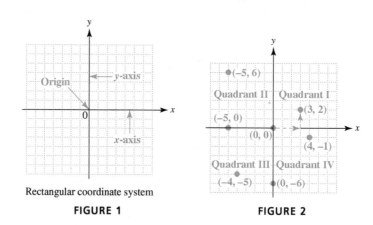

Rectangular coordinate system

FIGURE 1   **FIGURE 2**

The position of any point in this plane is determined by referring to the horizontal number line, or **x-axis,** and the vertical number line, or **y-axis.** The x-axis and y-axis make up a **rectangular coordinate system,** also called a **Cartesian coordinate system** after René Descartes, the French mathematician credited with its invention.

In an ordered pair, the first component indicates position relative to the x-axis, and the second component indicates position relative to the y-axis. For example, to locate, or **plot,** the point on the graph that corresponds to the ordered pair (3, 2), we move three units from 0 to the right along the x-axis and then two units up parallel to the y-axis. See **FIGURE 2**. The numbers in an ordered pair are called the **coordinates** of the corresponding point.

The four regions of the graph, shown in **FIGURE 2**, are called **quadrants I, II, III,** and **IV,** reading counterclockwise from the upper right quadrant. *The points on the x-axis and y-axis do not belong to any quadrant.*

OBJECTIVE 2 Graph lines and find intercepts. Each solution of an equation with two variables, such as

$$2x + 3y = 6,$$

includes two numbers, one for each variable. To keep track of which number goes with which variable, we write the solutions as ordered pairs. *(If x and y are used as the variables, the x-value is given first.)*

For example, we can show that $(6, -2)$ is a solution of the equation $2x + 3y = 6$ by substitution.

$$2x + 3y = 6$$

$$2(6) + 3(-2) \stackrel{?}{=} 6 \qquad \text{Let } x = 6, y = -2.$$

Use parentheses to avoid errors.

$$12 - 6 \stackrel{?}{=} 6 \qquad \text{Multiply.}$$

$$6 = 6 \;\checkmark\; \text{True}$$

Because the ordered pair $(6, -2)$ makes the equation true, it is a solution. On the other hand, $(5, 1)$ is *not* a solution of the equation $2x + 3y = 6$.

$$2x + 3y = 6$$

$$2(5) + 3(1) \stackrel{?}{=} 6 \qquad \text{Let } x = 5, y = 1.$$

$$10 + 3 \stackrel{?}{=} 6 \qquad \text{Multiply.}$$

$$13 = 6 \qquad \text{False}$$

To find ordered pairs that satisfy an equation, select a number for one of the variables, substitute it into the equation for that variable, and solve for the other variable. Two other ordered pairs satisfying $2x + 3y = 6$ are $(0, 2)$ and $(3, 0)$.

Since any real number could be selected for one variable and would lead to a real number for the other variable, linear equations in two variables have an infinite number of solutions.

The **graph of an equation** is the set of points corresponding to *all* ordered pairs that satisfy the equation. It gives a "picture" of the equation. The graph of the equation $2x + 3y = 6$ is shown in **FIGURE 3** along with a table of ordered pairs.

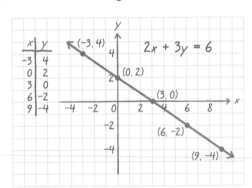

FIGURE 3

The equation $2x + 3y = 6$ is called a **first-degree equation,** because it has no term with a variable to a power greater than 1.

The graph of any first-degree equation in two variables is a straight line.

Since first-degree equations with two variables have straight-line graphs, they are called *linear equations in two variables.*

Linear Equation in Two Variables

A **linear equation in two variables** can be written in the form

$$Ax + By = C,$$

where A, B, and C are real numbers and A and B are not both 0. This form is called **standard form.**

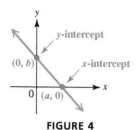

FIGURE 4

A straight line is determined if any two different points on the line are known. Two useful points for graphing are the *x*- and *y*-intercepts. The **x-intercept** is the point (if any) where the line intersects the *x*-axis. The **y-intercept** is the point (if any) where the line intersects the *y*-axis.* See **FIGURE 4**.

The *y*-value of the point where the line intersects the *x*-axis is 0. Similarly, the *x*-value of the point where the line intersects the *y*-axis is 0. This suggests a method for finding the *x*- and *y*-intercepts.

Finding Intercepts

When graphing the equation of a line, find the intercepts as follows.

Let $y = 0$ to find the *x*-intercept.

Let $x = 0$ to find the *y*-intercept.

NOW TRY
EXERCISE 1

Find the *x*- and *y*-intercepts, and graph the equation.

$$x - 2y = 4$$

EXAMPLE 1 Finding Intercepts

Find the *x*- and *y*-intercepts of $4x - y = -3$ and graph the equation.

To find the *x*-intercept, let $y = 0$. | To find the *y*-intercept, let $x = 0$.

$4x - y = -3$

$4x - 0 = -3$ Let $y = 0$.

$4x = -3$

$x = -\dfrac{3}{4}$ *x*-intercept is $\left(-\frac{3}{4}, 0\right)$.

$4x - y = -3$

$4(0) - y = -3$ Let $x = 0$.

$-y = -3$

$y = 3$ *y*-intercept is $(0, 3)$.

The intercepts of $4x - y = -3$ are the points $\left(-\frac{3}{4}, 0\right)$ and $(0, 3)$. Verify by substitution that $(-2, -5)$ also satisfies the equation. We use these ordered pairs to draw the graph in **FIGURE 5**.

x	y
$-\frac{3}{4}$	0
0	3
-2	-5

Use a third point as a check.

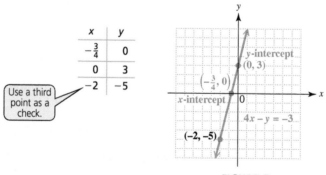

FIGURE 5

NOW TRY

NOTE While two points, such as the two intercepts in **FIGURE 5**, are sufficient to graph a straight line, *it is a good idea to use a third point to guard against errors.*

NOW TRY ANSWER

1. *x*-intercept: $(4, 0)$;
   y-intercept: $(0, -2)$

---

*Some texts define an intercept as a number, not a point. For example, "*y*-intercept $(0, 4)$" would be given as "*y*-intercept 4."

OBJECTIVE 3 **Recognize equations of horizontal and vertical lines and lines passing through the origin.** A line parallel to the x-axis will not have an x-intercept. Similarly, a line parallel to the y-axis will not have a y-intercept. We graph these types of lines in the next two examples.

*NOW TRY
EXERCISE 2*
Graph $y = -2$.

EXAMPLE 2 **Graphing a Horizontal Line**

Graph $y = 2$.

Writing $y = 2$ as $0x + 1y = 2$ shows that any value of x, including $x = 0$, gives $y = 2$. Thus, the y-intercept is $(0, 2)$. Since y is always 2, there is no value of x corresponding to $y = 0$, so the graph has no x-intercept. The graph is shown with a table of ordered pairs in **FIGURE 6**. It is a horizontal line.

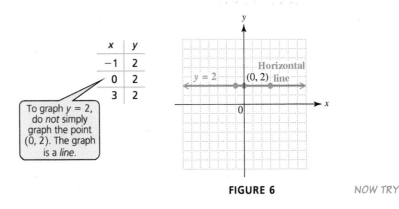

FIGURE 6   NOW TRY

NOTE The horizontal line $y = 0$ is the x-axis.

---

*NOW TRY
EXERCISE 3*
Graph $x + 3 = 0$.

EXAMPLE 3 **Graphing a Vertical Line**

Graph $x + 1 = 0$.

The form $1x + 0y = -1$ shows that every value of y leads to $x = -1$, making the x-intercept $(-1, 0)$. No value of y makes $x = 0$, so the graph has no y-intercept. A straight line that has no y-intercept is vertical. See **FIGURE 7**.

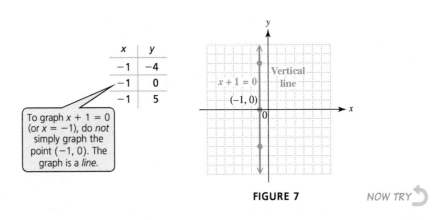

FIGURE 7   NOW TRY

NOW TRY ANSWERS

2. 3.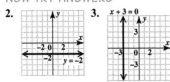

NOTE The vertical line $x = 0$ is the y-axis.

NOW TRY
EXERCISE 4
Graph $2x + 3y = 0$.

EXAMPLE 4 Graphing a Line That Passes through the Origin

Graph $x + 2y = 0$.

Find the *x*-intercept.

$$x + 2y = 0$$
$$x + 2(0) = 0 \quad \text{Let } y = 0.$$
$$x + 0 = 0 \quad \text{Multiply.}$$
$$x = 0 \quad \text{x-intercept is } (0, 0).$$

Find the *y*-intercept.

$$x + 2y = 0$$
$$0 + 2y = 0 \quad \text{Let } x = 0.$$
$$2y = 0 \quad \text{Add.}$$
$$y = 0 \quad \text{y-intercept is } (0, 0).$$

Both intercepts are the same point, $(0, 0)$, which means that the graph passes through the origin. To find another point, choose any nonzero number for *x* or *y* and solve for the other variable. We choose $x = 4$.

$$x + 2y = 0$$
$$4 + 2y = 0 \quad \text{Let } x = 4.$$
$$2y = -4 \quad \text{Subtract 4.}$$
$$y = -2 \quad \text{Divide by 2.}$$

This gives the ordered pair $(4, -2)$. As a check, verify that $(-2, 1)$ also lies on the line. The graph is shown in **FIGURE 8**.

x	y
-2	1
0	0
4	-2

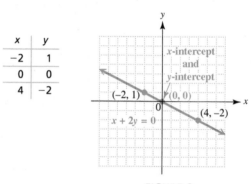

FIGURE 8

NOW TRY

OBJECTIVE 4 Use the midpoint formula. If the coordinates of the endpoints of a line segment are known, then the coordinates of the *midpoint* of the segment can be found.

FIGURE 9 shows a line segment *PQ* with endpoints $P(-8, 4)$ and $Q(3, -2)$. *R* is the point with the same *x*-coordinate as *P* and the same *y*-coordinate as *Q*. So the coordinates of *R* are $(-8, -2)$.

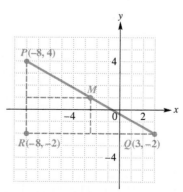

FIGURE 9

NOW TRY ANSWER
4.

The x-coordinate of the midpoint M of PQ is the same as the x-coordinate of the midpoint of RQ. Since RQ is horizontal, the x-coordinate of its midpoint is the *average* of the x-coordinates of its endpoints.

$$\frac{1}{2}(-8 + 3) = -2.5$$

The y-coordinate of M is the average of the y-coordinates of the midpoint of PR.

$$\frac{1}{2}(4 + (-2)) = 1$$

The midpoint of PQ is $M(-2.5, 1)$. This discussion leads to the *midpoint formula*.

Midpoint Formula

If the endpoints of a line segment PQ are (x_1, y_1) and (x_2, y_2), its midpoint M is

$$\left(\frac{x_1 + x_2}{2}, \frac{y_1 + y_2}{2} \right).$$

Recall that the small numbers 1 and 2 in the ordered pairs above are called **subscripts.** Read (x_1, y_1) as "**x-sub-one, y-sub-one.**"

NOW TRY
EXERCISE 5
Find the coordinates of the midpoint of the line segment PQ with endpoints $P(2, -5)$ and $Q(-4, 7)$.

EXAMPLE 5 Finding the Coordinates of a Midpoint

Find the coordinates of the midpoint of line segment PQ with endpoints $P(4, -3)$ and $Q(6, -1)$.

Use the midpoint formula with $x_1 = 4, x_2 = 6, y_1 = -3$, and $y_2 = -1$.

$$\left(\frac{4 + 6}{2}, \frac{-3 + (-1)}{2} \right) = \left(\frac{10}{2}, \frac{-4}{2} \right) = (5, -2) \longleftarrow \text{Midpoint}$$

NOW TRY

NOTE When finding the coordinates of the midpoint of a line segment, we are finding the *average* of the x-coordinates and the *average* of the y-coordinates of the endpoints of the segment. In both cases, add the corresponding coordinates and divide the sum by 2.

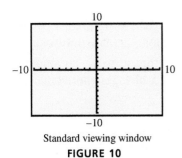
Standard viewing window
FIGURE 10

CONNECTIONS

When graphing with a graphing calculator, we must tell the calculator how to set up a rectangular coordinate system. In the screen in **FIGURE 10**, we chose minimum x- and y-values of -10 and maximum x- and y-values of 10. The **scale** on each axis determines the distance between the tick marks. In the screen shown, the scale is 1 for both axes. We refer to this screen as the **standard viewing window.**

To graph an equation such as $4x - y = 3$, we must solve the equation for y to enter it into the calculator.

$$4x - y = 3$$

$$-y = -4x + 3 \qquad \text{Subtract } 4x.$$

$$y = 4x - 3 \qquad \text{Multiply by } -1.$$

NOW TRY ANSWER
5. $(-1, 1)$

The graph of $y = 4x - 3$ in **FIGURE 11** also gives the intercepts at the bottoms of the screens. Some calculators have the capability of locating the x-intercept (called "Root" or "Zero").

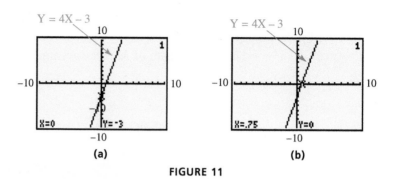

(a)   **(b)**

FIGURE 11

For Discussion or Writing

1. The graphing calculator screens in **Exercise 39** on **page 439** show the graph of a linear equation. What are the intercepts?

Graph each equation with a graphing calculator. Use the standard viewing window.

2. $4x - y = -3$ **(Example 1)**   **3.** $x + 2y = 0$ **(Example 4)**

OBJECTIVE 5 **Find the slope of a line.** Slope (steepness) is used in many practical ways. The slope of a highway (sometimes called the *grade*) is often given as a percent. For example, a 10% $\left(\text{or } \frac{10}{100} = \frac{1}{10}\right)$ slope means that the highway rises 1 unit for every 10 horizontal units. Stairs and roofs have slopes too, as shown in **FIGURE 12**.

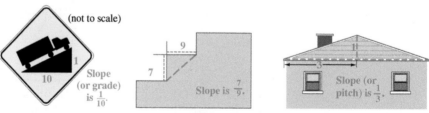

FIGURE 12

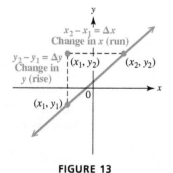

FIGURE 13

Slope is the ratio of vertical change, or **rise,** to horizontal change, or **run.** A simple way to remember this is to think, ***"Slope is rise over run."***

To get a formal definition of the slope of a line, we designate two different points (x_1, y_1) and (x_2, y_2) on the line. See **FIGURE 13**. As we move along the line in **FIGURE 13** from (x_1, y_1) to (x_2, y_2), the y-value changes (vertically) from y_1 to y_2, an amount equal to $y_2 - y_1$. As y changes from y_1 to y_2, the value of x changes (horizontally) from x_1 to x_2 by the amount $x_2 - x_1$.

NOTE The Greek letter **delta, Δ,** is used in mathematics to denote "change in," so Δy and Δx represent the change in y and the change in x, respectively.

The ratio of the change in y to the change in x (the rise over the run) is called the *slope* of the line, with the letter m traditionally used for slope.

46. *Concept Check* On the basis of the figure shown here, determine which line satisfies the given description.

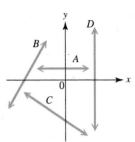

(a) The line has positive slope.

(b) The line has negative slope.

(c) The line has slope 0.

(d) The line has undefined slope.

For Exercises 47–58, (a) find the slope of the line through each pair of points, if possible, and (b) based on the slope, indicate whether the line through the points rises from left to right, falls from left to right, is horizontal, or is vertical. See Example 6 and **FIGURE 19**.

47. $(-2, -3)$ and $(-1, 5)$ **48.** $(-4, 1)$ and $(-3, 4)$ 🌐 **49.** $(-4, 1)$ and $(2, 6)$

50. $(-3, -3)$ and $(5, 6)$ **51.** $(2, 4)$ and $(-4, 4)$ **52.** $(-6, 3)$ and $(2, 3)$

53. $(-2, 2)$ and $(4, -1)$ **54.** $(-3, 1)$ and $(6, -2)$ **55.** $(5, -3)$ and $(5, 2)$

56. $(4, -1)$ and $(4, 3)$ **57.** $(1.5, 2.6)$ and $(0.5, 3.6)$ **58.** $(3.4, 4.2)$ and $(1.4, 10.2)$

Brain Busters Find the slope of the line through each pair of points. $\left(\text{Hint: } \dfrac{\frac{a}{b}}{\frac{c}{d}} = \dfrac{a}{b} \div \dfrac{c}{d} \right)$

59. $\left(\dfrac{1}{6}, \dfrac{1}{2} \right)$ and $\left(\dfrac{5}{6}, \dfrac{9}{2} \right)$ **60.** $\left(\dfrac{3}{4}, \dfrac{1}{3} \right)$ and $\left(\dfrac{5}{4}, \dfrac{10}{3} \right)$

61. $\left(-\dfrac{2}{9}, \dfrac{5}{18} \right)$ and $\left(\dfrac{1}{18}, -\dfrac{5}{9} \right)$ **62.** $\left(-\dfrac{4}{5}, \dfrac{9}{10} \right)$ and $\left(-\dfrac{3}{10}, \dfrac{1}{5} \right)$

Find the slope of each line.

63.

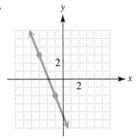

64.

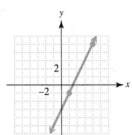

65.

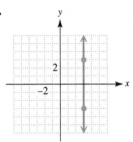

66. *Concept Check* Let k be the number of letters in your last name. Sketch the graph of $y = k$. What is the slope of this line?

Find the slope of the line and sketch the graph. See Examples 6–8.

🌐 **67.** $x + 2y = 4$ **68.** $x + 3y = -6$ 🌐 **69.** $5x - 2y = 10$

70. $4x - y = 4$ **71.** $y = 4x$ **72.** $y = -3x$

🌐 **73.** $x - 3 = 0$ **74.** $x + 2 = 0$ 🌐 **75.** $y = -5$ **76.** $y = -4$

Graph each line described. See Example 9.

77. Through $(-4, 2)$; $m = \dfrac{1}{2}$ **78.** Through $(-2, -3)$; $m = \dfrac{5}{4}$

🌐 **79.** y-intercept $(0, -2)$; $m = -\dfrac{2}{3}$ **80.** y-intercept $(0, -4)$; $m = -\dfrac{3}{2}$

81. Through $(-1, -2)$; $m = 3$ **82.** Through $(-2, -4)$; $m = 4$

83. $m = 0$; through $(2, -5)$ **84.** $m = 0$; through $(5, 3)$

85. Undefined slope; through $(-3, 1)$ **86.** Undefined slope; through $(-4, 1)$

87. *Concept Check* If a line has slope $-\frac{4}{9}$, then any line parallel to it has slope _____, and any line perpendicular to it has slope _____.

88. *Concept Check* If a line has slope 0.2, then any line parallel to it has slope _____, and any line perpendicular to it has slope _____.

Decide whether each pair of lines is parallel, perpendicular, *or* neither. ***See Example 10.***

89. The line through $(15, 9)$ and $(12, -7)$ and the line through $(8, -4)$ and $(5, -20)$

90. The line through $(4, 6)$ and $(-8, 7)$ and the line through $(-5, 5)$ and $(7, 4)$

91. $x + 4y = 7$ and $4x - y = 3$

92. $2x + 5y = -7$ and $5x - 2y = 1$

93. $4x - 3y = 6$ and $3x - 4y = 2$

94. $2x + y = 6$ and $x - y = 4$

95. $x = 6$ and $6 - x = 8$

96. $3x = y$ and $2y - 6x = 5$

97. $4x + y = 0$ and $5x - 8 = 2y$

98. $2x + 5y = -8$ and $6 + 2x = 5y$

99. $2x = y + 3$ and $2y + x = 3$

100. $4x - 3y = 8$ and $4y + 3x = 12$

Concept Check *Find and interpret the average rate of change illustrated in each graph.*

101.

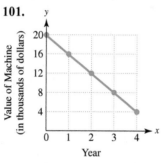

102.

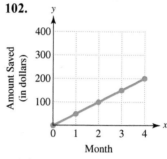

103.

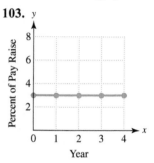

104. *Concept Check* If the graph of a linear equation rises from left to right, then the average rate of change is _____. If the graph of a linear equation falls from
(positive/negative)

left to right, then the average rate of change is _____.
(positive/negative)

Solve each problem. ***See Examples 11 and 12.***

105. The graph shows the number of cellular phone subscribers (in millions) in the United States from 2005 to 2008.

Cellular Phone Subscribers

Source: CTIA: The Wireless Association.

(a) Use the given ordered pairs to find the slope of the line.

(b) Interpret the slope in the context of this problem.

106. The graph shows spending on personal care products (in billions of dollars) in the United States from 2005 to 2008.

Spending on Personal Care Products

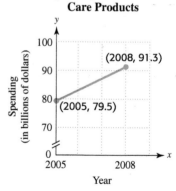

Source: U.S. Department of Commerce.

(a) Use the given ordered pairs to find the slope of the line to the nearest tenth.

(b) Interpret the slope in the context of this problem.

107. The graph provides a good approximation of the number of drive-in theaters in the United States from 2000 through 2007.

    (a) Use the given ordered pairs to find the average rate of change in the number of drive-in theaters per year during this period. Round your answer to the nearest whole number.

    (b) Explain how a negative slope is interpreted in this situation.

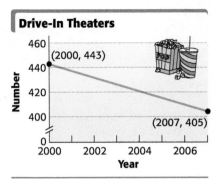

Drive-In Theaters

(2000, 443)

(2007, 405)

Source: www.drive-ins.com

108. The graph provides a good approximation of the number of mobile homes (in thousands) placed in use in the United States from 2000 through 2008.

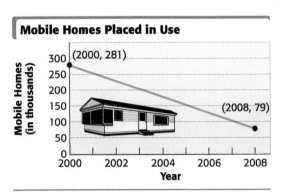

Mobile Homes Placed in Use

(2000, 281)

(2008, 79)

Source: U.S. Census Bureau.

    (a) Use the given ordered pairs to find the average rate of change in the number of mobile homes per year during this period.

    (b) Explain how a negative slope is interpreted in this situation.

109. The total amount spent on plasma TVs in the United States changed from $1590 million in 2003 to $5705 million in 2006. Find and interpret the average rate of change in sales, in millions of dollars per year. Round your answer to the nearest hundredth. (*Source:* Consumer Electronics Association.)

110. The total amount spent on analog TVs in the United States changed from $5836 million in 2003 to $1424 million in 2006. Find and interpret the average rate of change in sales, in millions of dollars per year. Round your answer to the nearest hundredth. (*Source:* Consumer Electronics Association.)

PREVIEW EXERCISES

*Write each equation in the form $Ax + By = C$. **See Section 3.4.***

111. $y - (-2) = \dfrac{3}{2}(x - 5)$

112. $y - (-1) = -\dfrac{1}{2}[x - (-2)]$

7.2 Review of Equations of Lines; Linear Models

OBJECTIVE 1 Write an equation of a line, given its slope and y-intercept. Recall that we can find the slope of a line from its equation by solving the equation for y. For example, we found that the slope of the line with equation

$$y = 4x + 8$$

is 4, the coefficient of x. What does the number 8 represent?

To find out, suppose a line has slope m and y-intercept $(0, b)$. We can find an equation of this line by choosing another point (x, y) on the line, as shown in **FIGURE 23**, and using the slope formula.

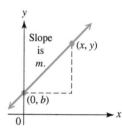

$$m = \frac{y - b}{x - 0} \quad \longleftarrow \text{Change in y-values}$$
$$\phantom{m = \frac{y - b}{x - 0}} \longleftarrow \text{Change in x-values}$$

$$m = \frac{y - b}{x} \qquad \text{Subtract in the denominator.}$$

$$mx = y - b \qquad \text{Multiply by x.}$$

$$mx + b = y \qquad \text{Add b.}$$

$$y = mx + b \qquad \text{Rewrite.}$$

FIGURE 23

This last equation is called the *slope-intercept form* of the equation of a line, because we can identify the slope m and y-intercept $(0, b)$ at a glance. Thus, in the line with equation $y = 4x + 8$, the number 8 indicates that the y-intercept is $(0, 8)$.

Slope-Intercept Form

The **slope-intercept form** of the equation of a line with slope m and y-intercept $(0, b)$ is

$$y = mx + b.$$

Slope ↑ ↑ y-intercept is $(0, b)$.

NOW TRY
EXERCISE 1

Write an equation of the line with slope $\frac{2}{3}$ and y-intercept $(0, 1)$.

EXAMPLE 1 Writing an Equation of a Line

Write an equation of the line with slope $-\frac{4}{5}$ and y-intercept $(0, -2)$.

Here, $m = -\frac{4}{5}$ and $b = -2$. Substitute these values into the slope-intercept form.

$$y = mx + b \qquad \text{Slope-intercept form}$$

$$y = -\frac{4}{5}x - 2 \qquad m = -\frac{4}{5}; b = -2 \qquad \text{NOW TRY}$$

NOTE Every linear equation (of a nonvertical line) has a *unique* (one and only one) slope-intercept form. In **Section 7.4,** we study *linear functions,* which are defined using slope-intercept form. Also, this is the form we use when graphing a line with a graphing calculator.

NOW TRY ANSWER
1. $y = \frac{2}{3}x + 1$

OBJECTIVE 2 Graph a line, using its slope and y-intercept. We first saw this approach in **Example 9(a)** of **Section 7.1.**

A summary of the various forms of linear equations follows.

Forms of Linear Equations

Equation	Description	When to Use
$y = mx + b$	**Slope-Intercept Form** Slope is m. y-intercept is $(0, b)$.	The slope and y-intercept can be easily identified and used to quickly graph the equation.
$y - y_1 = m(x - x_1)$	**Point-Slope Form** Slope is m. Line passes through (x_1, y_1).	This form is ideal for finding the equation of a line if the slope and a point on the line or two points on the line are known.
$Ax + By = C$	**Standard Form** (A, B, and C integers, $A \geq 0$) Slope is $-\frac{A}{B}$ ($B \neq 0$). x-intercept is $\left(\frac{C}{A}, 0\right)$ ($A \neq 0$). y-intercept is $\left(0, \frac{C}{B}\right)$ ($B \neq 0$).	The x- and y-intercepts can be found quickly and used to graph the equation. The slope must be calculated.
$y = b$	**Horizontal Line** Slope is 0. y-intercept is $(0, b)$.	If the graph intersects only the y-axis, then y is the only variable in the equation.
$x = a$	**Vertical Line** Slope is undefined. x-intercept is $(a, 0)$.	If the graph intersects only the x-axis, then x is the only variable in the equation.

OBJECTIVE 7 **Write an equation of a line that models real data.** If a given set of data changes at a fairly constant rate, the data may fit a linear pattern, where the rate of change is the slope of the line.

EXAMPLE 7 **Determining a Linear Equation to Describe Real Data**

A local gasoline station is selling 89-octane gas for $3.20 per gal.

(a) Write an equation that describes the cost y to buy x gallons of gas.

The total cost is determined by the number of gallons we buy multiplied by the price per gallon (in this case, $3.20). As the gas is pumped, two sets of numbers spin by: the number of gallons pumped and the cost of that number of gallons. The table illustrates this situation.

If we let x denote the number of gallons pumped, then the total cost y in dollars can be found using the following linear equation.

Number of Gallons Pumped	Cost of This Number of Gallons
0	0($3.20) = $ 0.00
1	1($3.20) = $ 3.20
2	2($3.20) = $ 6.40
3	3($3.20) = $ 9.60
4	4($3.20) = $12.80

Total cost ⌐   ⌐ Number of gallons
$$y = 3.20x$$

Theoretically, there are infinitely many ordered pairs (x, y) that satisfy this equation, but here we are limited to nonnegative values for x, since we cannot have a negative number of gallons. In this situation, there is also a practical maximum value for x that varies from one car to another. What determines this maximum value?

(b) A car wash at this gas station costs an additional $3.00. Write an equation that defines the cost of gas and a car wash.

The cost will be $3.20x + 3.00$ dollars for x gallons of gas and a car wash.

$$y = 3.2x + 3 \qquad \text{Delete unnecessary zeros.}$$

NOW TRY
EXERCISE 7

A cell phone plan costs $100 for the telephone plus $85 per month for service. Write an equation that gives the cost y in dollars for x months of cell phone service using this plan.

(c) Interpret the ordered pairs $(5, 19)$ and $(10, 35)$ in relation to the equation from part (b).

The ordered pair $(5, 19)$ indicates that 5 gal of gas and a car wash costs $19.00. Similarly, $(10, 35)$ indicates that 10 gal of gas and a car wash costs $35.00.

NOW TRY

NOTE In **Example 7(a),** the ordered pair $(0, 0)$ satisfied the equation, so the linear equation has the form $y = mx$, where $b = 0$. If a realistic situation involves an initial charge plus a charge per unit, as in **Example 7(b),** the equation has the form $y = mx + b$, where $b \neq 0$.

NOW TRY
EXERCISE 8

Refer to **Example 8.**

(a) Use the ordered pairs $(2, 183)$ and $(6, 251)$ to write an equation that models the data.

(b) Use the equation from part (a) to estimate retail spending on prescription drugs in 2011.

EXAMPLE 8 Writing an Equation of a Line That Models Data

Retail spending (in billions of dollars) on prescription drugs in the United States is shown in the graph in **FIGURE 31**.

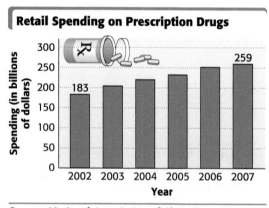

Retail Spending on Prescription Drugs

Source: National Association of Chain Drug Stores.

FIGURE 31

(a) Write an equation that models the data.

The data increase linearly—that is, a straight line through the tops of any two bars in the graph would be close to the top of each bar. To model the relationship between year x and spending on prescription drugs y, we let $x = 2$ represent 2002, $x = 3$ represent 2003, and so on. The given data for 2002 and 2007 can be written as the ordered pairs $(2, 183)$ and $(7, 259)$.

$$m = \frac{259 - 183}{7 - 2} = \frac{76}{5} = 15.2 \qquad \text{Find the slope of the line through } (2, 183) \text{ and } (7, 259).$$

Thus, spending increased by about $15.2 billion per year. To write an equation, we substitute this slope and one of the points, say, $(2, 183)$, into the point-slope form.

$$y - y_1 = m(x - x_1) \qquad \text{Point-slope form}$$
$$y - 183 = 15.2(x - 2) \qquad (x_1, y_1) = (2, 183); m = 15.2$$
$$y - 183 = 15.2x - 30.4 \qquad \text{Distributive property}$$
$$y = 15.2x + 152.6 \qquad \text{Add 183.}$$

Either point can be used here. (7, 259) provides the same answer.

NOW TRY ANSWERS
7. $y = 85x + 100$
8. (a) $y = 17x + 149$
  (b) $336 billion

Retail spending y (in billions of dollars) on prescription drugs in the United States in year x can be approximated by the equation $y = 15.2x + 152.6$.

(b) Use the equation from part (a) to estimate retail spending on prescription drugs in the United States in 2010. (Assume a constant rate of change.)

Since $x = 2$ represents 2002 and 2010 is 8 yr after 2002, $x = 10$ represents 2010.

$$y = 15.2x + 152.6 \qquad \text{Equation from part (a)}$$

$$y = 15.2(10) + 152.6 \qquad \text{Substitute 10 for } x.$$

$$y = 304.6 \qquad \text{Multiply, and then add.}$$

About $305 billion was spent on prescription drugs in 2010.   *NOW TRY*

7.2 EXERCISES

MyMathLab   Math XL PRACTICE   WATCH   DOWNLOAD   READ   REVIEW

● *Complete solution available on the Video Resources on DVD*

Concept Check   In Exercises 1–6, provide the appropriate response.

1. The following equations all represent the same line. Which one is in standard form as defined in the text?

　A. $3x - 2y = 5$　**B.** $2y = 3x - 5$　**C.** $\frac{3}{5}x - \frac{2}{5}y = 1$　**D.** $3x = 2y + 5$

2. Which equation is in point-slope form?

　A. $y = 6x + 2$　**B.** $4x + y = 9$　**C.** $y - 3 = 2(x - 1)$　**D.** $2y = 3x - 7$

3. Which equation in **Exercise 2** is in slope-intercept form?

4. Write the equation $y + 2 = -3(x - 4)$ in slope-intercept form.

5. Write the equation from **Exercise 4** in standard form.

6. Write the equation $10x - 7y = 70$ in slope-intercept form.

Concept Check   Match each equation with the graph that it most closely resembles. (Hint: Determine the signs of m and b to help you make your decision.)

7. $y = 2x + 3$

8. $y = -2x + 3$

9. $y = -2x - 3$

10. $y = 2x - 3$

11. $y = 2x$

12. $y = -2x$

13. $y = 3$

14. $y = -3$

A.

B.

C.

D.

E.

F.

G.

H.

I.

Write the equation in slope-intercept form of the line satisfying the given conditions. **See Example 1.**

15. $m = 5; b = 15$

16. $m = 2; b = 12$

17. $m = -\frac{2}{3}; b = \frac{4}{5}$

18. $m = -\frac{5}{8}; b = -\frac{1}{3}$

19. Slope 1; y-intercept $(0, -1)$

20. Slope -1; y-intercept $(0, -3)$

● **21.** Slope $\frac{2}{5}$; y-intercept $(0, 5)$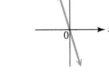

22. Slope $-\frac{3}{4}$; y-intercept $(0, 7)$

Concept Check Write an equation in slope-intercept form of the line shown in each graph. (Hint: Use the indicated points to find the slope.)

23.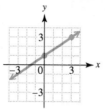

24.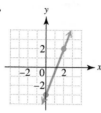

25.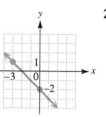

26.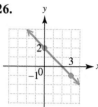

*For each equation, **(a)** write it in slope-intercept form, **(b)** give the slope of the line, **(c)** give the y-intercept, and **(d)** graph the line. **See Example 2.***

27. $-x + y = 4$ **28.** $-x + y = 6$ **29.** $6x + 5y = 30$ **30.** $3x + 4y = 12$

31. $4x - 5y = 20$ **32.** $7x - 3y = 3$ **33.** $x + 2y = -4$ **34.** $x + 3y = -9$

*Find an equation of the line that satisfies the given conditions. **(a)** Write the equation in standard form. **(b)** Write the equation in slope-intercept form. **See Example 3.***

35. Through $(5, 8)$; slope -2 **36.** Through $(12, 10)$; slope 1

37. Through $(-2, 4)$; slope $-\frac{3}{4}$ **38.** Through $(-1, 6)$; slope $-\frac{5}{6}$

39. Through $(-5, 4)$; slope $\frac{1}{2}$ **40.** Through $(7, -2)$; slope $\frac{1}{4}$

41. x-intercept $(3, 0)$; slope 4   **42.** x-intercept $(-2, 0)$; slope -5

43. Through $(2, 6.8)$; slope 1.4   **44.** Through $(6, -1.2)$; slope 0.8

*Find an equation of the line that satisfies the given conditions. **See Example 4.***

45. Through $(9, 5)$; slope 0   **46.** Through $(-4, -2)$; slope 0

47. Through $(9, 10)$; undefined slope   **48.** Through $(-2, 8)$; undefined slope

49. Through $\left(-\frac{3}{4}, -\frac{3}{2}\right)$; slope 0   **50.** Through $\left(-\frac{5}{8}, -\frac{9}{2}\right)$; slope 0

51. Through $(-7, 8)$; horizontal   **52.** Through $(2, -7)$; horizontal

53. Through $(0.5, 0.2)$; vertical   **54.** Through $(0.1, 0.4)$; vertical

*Find an equation of the line passing through the given points. **(a)** Write the equation in standard form. **(b)** Write the equation in slope-intercept form if possible. **See Example 5.***

55. $(3, 4)$ and $(5, 8)$ **56.** $(5, -2)$ and $(-3, 14)$ **57.** $(6, 1)$ and $(-2, 5)$

58. $(-2, 5)$ and $(-8, 1)$ **59.** $(2, 5)$ and $(1, 5)$ **60.** $(-2, 2)$ and $(4, 2)$

61. $(7, 6)$ and $(7, -8)$ **62.** $(13, 5)$ and $(13, -1)$ **63.** $\left(\frac{1}{2}, -3\right)$ and $\left(-\frac{2}{3}, -3\right)$

64. $\left(-\frac{4}{9}, -6\right)$ and $\left(\frac{12}{7}, -6\right)$ **65.** $\left(-\frac{2}{5}, \frac{2}{5}\right)$ and $\left(\frac{4}{3}, \frac{2}{3}\right)$ **66.** $\left(\frac{3}{4}, \frac{8}{3}\right)$ and $\left(\frac{2}{5}, \frac{2}{3}\right)$

*Find an equation of the line that satisfies the given conditions. **(a)** Write the equation in slope-intercept form. **(b)** Write the equation in standard form. **See Example 6.***

67. Through $(7, 2)$; parallel to $3x - y = 8$

68. Through $(4, 1)$; parallel to $2x + 5y = 10$

69. Through $(-2, -2)$; parallel to $-x + 2y = 10$

70. Through $(-1, 3)$; parallel to $-x + 3y = 12$

71. Through $(8, 5)$; perpendicular to $2x - y = 7$

72. Through $(2, -7)$; perpendicular to $5x + 2y = 18$

73. Through $(-2, 7)$; perpendicular to $x = 9$

74. Through $(8, 4)$; perpendicular to $x = -3$

Write an equation in the form $y = mx$ for each situation. Then give the three ordered pairs associated with the equation for x-values 0, 5, and 10. ***See Example 7(a).***

🌐 **75.** x represents the number of hours traveling at 45 mph, and y represents the distance traveled (in miles).

76. x represents the number of t-shirts sold at $26 each, and y represents the total cost of the t-shirts (in dollars).

77. x represents the number of gallons of gas sold at $3.10 per gal, and y represents the total cost of the gasoline (in dollars).

78. x represents the number of days a DVD movie is rented at $4.50 per day, and y represents the total charge for the rental (in dollars).

79. x represents the number of credit hours taken at Kirkwood Community College at $111 per credit hour, and y represents the total tuition paid for the credit hours (in dollars). (*Source:* www.kirkwood.edu)

80. x represents the number of tickets to a performance of *Jersey Boys* at the Des Moines Civic Center purchased at $125 per ticket, and y represents the total paid for the tickets (in dollars). (*Source:* Ticketmaster.)

For each situation, ***(a)*** *write an equation in the form $y = mx + b$,* ***(b)*** *find and interpret the ordered pair associated with the equation for $x = 5$, and* ***(c)*** *answer the question.* ***See Examples 7(b) and 7(c).***

81. A ticket for the 2010 Troubadour Reunion, featuring James Taylor and Carole King, costs $112.50. A parking pass costs $12. (*Source:* Ticketmaster.) Let x represent the number of tickets and y represent the cost. How much does it cost for 2 tickets and a parking pass?

82. Resident tuition at Broward College is $87.95 per credit hour. There is also a $20 health science application fee. (*Source:* www.broward.edu) Let x represent the number of credit hours and y represent the cost. How much does it cost for a student in health science to take 15 credit hours?

83. A membership in the Midwest Athletic Club costs $99, plus $41 per month. (*Source:* Midwest Athletic Club.) Let x represent the number of months and y represent the cost. How much does the first year's membership cost?

84. For a family membership, the athletic club in **Exercise 83** charges a membership fee of $159, plus $60 for each additional family member after the first. Let x represent the number of additional family members and y represent the cost. What is the membership fee for a four-person family?

85. A cell phone plan includes 900 anytime minutes for $60 per month, plus a one-time activation fee of $36. A Nokia 6650 cell phone is included at no additional charge. (*Source:* AT&T.) Let x represent the number of months of service and y represent the cost. If you sign a 1-yr contract, how much will this cell phone plan cost? (Assume that you never use more than the allotted number of minutes.)

86. Another cell phone plan includes 450 anytime minutes for $40 per month, plus $50 for a Nokia 2320 cell phone and $36 for a one-time activation fee. (*Source:* AT&T.) Let x represent the number of months of service and y represent the cost. If you sign a 1-yr contract, how much will this cell phone plan cost? (Assume that you never use more than the allotted number of minutes.)

87. There is a $30 fee to rent a chain saw, plus $6 per day. Let x represent the number of days the saw is rented and y represent the charge to the user in dollars. If the total charge is $138, for how many days is the saw rented?

88. A rental car costs $50 plus $0.20 per mile. Let x represent the number of miles driven and y represent the total charge to the renter. How many miles was the car driven if the renter paid $84.60?

Solve each problem. In part (a), give equations in slope-intercept form. (Round the slope to the nearest tenth.) **See Example 8.**

89. Total sales of digital cameras in the United States (in millions of dollars) are shown in the graph, where the year 2003 corresponds to $x = 0$.

   (a) Use the ordered pairs from the graph to write an equation that models the data. What does the slope tell us in the context of this problem?

   (b) Use the equation from part (a) to approximate the sales of digital cameras in the United States in 2007.

Digital Camera Sales

Source: Consumer Electronics Association.

90. Total sales of fax machines in the United States (in millions of dollars) are shown in the graph, where the year 2003 corresponds to $x = 0$.

   (a) Use the ordered pairs from the graph to write an equation that models the data. What does the slope tell us in the context of this problem?

   (b) Use the equation from part (a) to approximate the sales of fax machines in the United States in 2007.

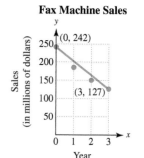

Fax Machine Sales

Source: Consumer Electronics Association.

91. Expenditures for home health care in the United States are shown in the graph.

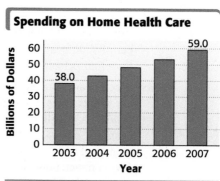

Spending on Home Health Care

Source: U.S. Centers for Medicare & Medicaid Services.

   (a) Use the information given for the years 2003 and 2007, letting $x = 3$ represent 2003, $x = 7$ represent 2007, and y represent the amount (in billions of dollars) to write an equation that models home health care spending.

   (b) Use the equation from part (a) to approximate the amount spent on home health care in 2005. How does your result compare with the actual value, $48.1 billion?

92. The number of post offices in the United States is shown in the graph.

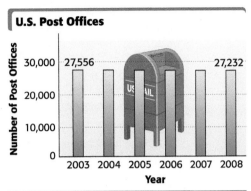

U.S. Post Offices

Source: U.S. Postal Service.

(a) Use the information given for the years 2003 and 2008, letting $x = 3$ represent 2003, $x = 8$ represent 2008, and y represent the number of post offices, to write an equation that models the data.

(b) Use the equation to approximate the number of post offices in 2006. How does this result compare with the actual value, 27,318?

RELATING CONCEPTS EXERCISES 93–100

FOR INDIVIDUAL OR GROUP WORK

*In **Section 2.5**, we worked with formulas. **Work Exercises 93–100 in order**, to see how the formula that relates Celsius and Fahrenheit temperatures is derived.*

93. There is a linear relationship between Celsius and Fahrenheit temperatures. When $C = 0°$, $F = \underline{\qquad}°$, and when $C = 100°$, $F = \underline{\qquad}°$.

94. Think of ordered pairs of temperatures (C, F), where C and F represent corresponding Celsius and Fahrenheit temperatures. The equation that relates the two scales has a straight-line graph that contains the two points determined in **Exercise 93**. What are these two points?

95. Find the slope of the line described in **Exercise 94**.

96. Use the slope found in **Exercise 95** and one of the two points determined earlier, and write an equation that gives F in terms of C. (*Hint:* Use the point-slope form, with C replacing x and F replacing y.)

97. To obtain another form of the formula, use the equation found in **Exercise 96** and solve for C in terms of F.

98. Use the equation from **Exercise 96** to find the Fahrenheit temperature when $C = 30$.

99. Use the equation from **Exercise 97** to find the Celsius temperature when $F = 50$.

100. For what temperature is $F = C$? (Use the photo to confirm your answer.)

PREVIEW EXERCISES

*Write each inequality using interval notation. **See Section 2.8.***

101. $x \geq 0$ **102.** $x \leq 0$ **103.** $-4 \leq x \leq 4$

104. Express the set of all real numbers using interval notation. **See Section 2.8.**

SUMMARY EXERCISES on Slopes and Equations of Lines

Find the slope of each line, if possible.

1. $3x + 5y = 9$ **2.** $4x + 7y = 3$ **3.** $y = 2x - 5$

4. $5x - 2y = 4$ **5.** $x - 4 = 0$ **6.** $y = 0.5$

*For each line described, write an equation of the line **(a)** in slope-intercept form and **(b)** in standard form.*

7. Through the points $(-2, 6)$ and $(4, 1)$

8. Through $(-2, 5)$ and parallel to the graph of $3x - y = 4$

9. Through the origin and perpendicular to the graph of $2x - 5y = 6$

10. Through $(5, -8)$ and parallel to the graph of $y = 4$

11. Through $\left(\frac{3}{4}, -\frac{7}{9}\right)$ and perpendicular to the graph of $x = \frac{2}{3}$

12. Through $(4, -2)$ with slope -3

13. Through $(-4, 2)$ and parallel to the line through $(3, 9)$ and $(6, 11)$

14. Through $(4, -2)$ and perpendicular to the line through $(3, 7)$ and $(5, 6)$

15. Through the points $(4, -8)$ and $(-4, 12)$

16. Through $(-3, 6)$ with slope $\frac{2}{3}$

17. Through $(0, 3)$ and the midpoint of the segment with endpoints $(2, 8)$ and $(-4, 12)$

18. *Concept Check*   Match the description in Column I with its equation in Column II.

I	II
(a) Slope -0.5, $b = -2$	**A.** $y = -\frac{1}{2}x$
(b) x-intercept $(4, 0)$, y-intercept $(0, 2)$	**B.** $y = -\frac{1}{2}x - 2$
(c) Passes through $(4, -2)$ and $(0, 0)$	**C.** $x - 2y = 2$
(d) $m = \frac{1}{2}$, passes through $(-2, -2)$	**D.** $x + 2y = 4$
(e) $m = \frac{1}{2}$, passes through the origin	**E.** $x = 2y$

7.3   Introduction to Relations and Functions

OBJECTIVES

1 Distinguish between independent and dependent variables.

2 Define and identify relations and functions.

3 Find the domain and range.

4 Identify functions defined by graphs and equations.

OBJECTIVE 1   Distinguish between independent and dependent variables.
We often describe one quantity in terms of another. Consider the following:

- The amount of a paycheck for an hourly employee depends on the number of hours worked.
- The cost at a gas station depends on the number of gallons of gas pumped.
- The distance traveled by a car moving at a constant rate depends on the time traveled.

We can use ordered pairs to represent these corresponding quantities. We indicate the relationship between hours worked and paycheck amount as follows.

$$(5, 40) \qquad \text{Working 5 hr results in a \$40 paycheck.}$$

Number of hours worked ⌐   ⌐ Paycheck amount in dollars

Similarly, the ordered pair $(10, 80)$ indicates that working 10 hr results in an $80 paycheck. In this example, what would the ordered pair $(20, 160)$ indicate?

NOTE Graphs that do not represent functions are still relations. *All equations and graphs represent relations, and all relations have a domain and range.*

Relations are often defined by equations. If a relation is defined by an equation, keep the following in mind when finding its domain.

Exclude from the domain any values that make the denominator of a fraction equal to 0.

For example, the function defined by $y = \frac{1}{x}$ has all real numbers except 0 as its domain, since division by 0 is undefined.

NOTE As we will see in **Section 10.1,** we must also **exclude from the domain any values that result in an even root of a negative number.**

In this book, we assume the following agreement on the domain of a relation.

Agreement on Domain
Unless specified otherwise, the domain of a relation is assumed to be all real numbers that produce real numbers when substituted for the independent variable.

NOW TRY
EXERCISE 5

Decide whether each relation defines y as a function of x, and give the domain.

(a) $y = 4x - 3$

(b) $y = \dfrac{1}{x - 8}$

EXAMPLE 5   Identifying Functions from Their Equations

Decide whether each relation defines y as a function of x, and give the domain.

(a) $y = x + 4$

In the defining equation (or rule) $y = x + 4$, y is always found by adding 4 to x. Thus, each value of x corresponds to just one value of y, and the relation defines a function. Since x can be any real number, the domain is

$$\{x \mid x \text{ is a real number}\}, \quad \text{or} \quad (-\infty, \infty).$$

(b) $y^2 = x$

The ordered pairs $(16, 4)$ and $(16, -4)$ both satisfy this equation. Since one value of x, 16, corresponds to two values of y, 4 and -4, this equation does not define a function. Because x is equal to the square of y, the values of x must always be nonnegative. The domain of the relation is $[0, \infty)$.

(c) $y = \dfrac{5}{x - 1}$

Given any value of x in the domain, we find y by subtracting 1 and then dividing the result into 5. This process produces exactly one value of y for each value in the domain, so the given equation defines a function.

The domain includes all real numbers except those which make the denominator 0. We find these numbers by setting the denominator equal to 0 and solving for x.

$$x - 1 = 0$$

$$x = 1 \qquad \text{Add 1.}$$

The domain includes all real numbers *except* 1, written $(-\infty, 1) \cup (1, \infty).$*

NOW TRY

NOW TRY ANSWERS
5. (a) yes; $(-\infty, \infty)$
   (b) yes; $(-\infty, 8) \cup (8, \infty)$

*For any two sets A and B, the union of A and B, symbolized $A \cup B$, consists of the elements in either A or B (or both).

In summary, we give three variations of the definition of a function.

Variations of the Definition of a Function

1. A **function** is a relation in which, for each value of the first component of the ordered pairs, there is exactly one value of the second component.

2. A **function** is a set of distinct ordered pairs in which no first component is repeated.

3. A **function** is a correspondence or rule that assigns exactly one range value to each domain value.

7.3 EXERCISES

  PRACTICE · WATCH · DOWNLOAD · READ · REVIEW

Complete solution available on the Video Resources on DVD

1. In your own words, define a function and give an example.

2. In your own words, define the domain of a function and give an example.

3. *Concept Check*   In an ordered pair of a relation, is the first element the independent or the dependent variable?

4. *Concept Check*   Give an example of a relation that is not a function and that has domain $\{-3, 2, 6\}$ and range $\{4, 6\}$. (There are many possible correct answers.)

Concept Check   Express each relation using a different form. There is more than one correct way to do this. **See Objective 2.**

5. $\{(0, 2), (2, 4), (4, 6)\}$

6.
x	y
−1	−3
0	−1
1	1
3	3

7.

8. *Concept Check*   Does the relation given in **Exercise 7** define a function? Why or why not?

Decide whether each relation defines a function, and give the domain and range. **See Examples 1–4.**

9. $\{(5, 1), (3, 2), (4, 9), (7, 6)\}$

10. $\{(8, 0), (5, 4), (9, 3), (3, 8)\}$

11. $\{(2, 4), (0, 2), (2, 5)\}$

12. $\{(9, -2), (-3, 5), (9, 2)\}$

13. $\{(-3, 1), (4, 1), (-2, 7)\}$

14. $\{(-12, 5), (-10, 3), (8, 3)\}$

15. $\{(1, 1), (1, -1), (0, 0), (2, 4), (2, -4)\}$

16. $\{(2, 5), (3, 7), (4, 9), (5, 11)\}$

17.
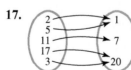

18.
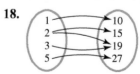

19.
x	y
1	5
1	2
1	−1
1	−4

20.
x	y
−4	−4
−4	0
−4	4
−4	8

21.
x	y
4	−3
2	−3
0	−3
−2	−3

22.
x	y
−3	−6
−1	−6
1	−6
3	−6

23.
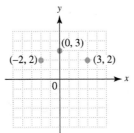

24.
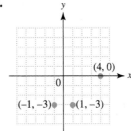

🌐 **25.**
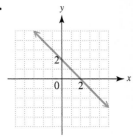

26.
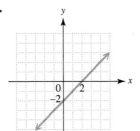

27.
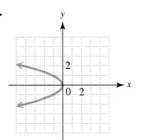

28.
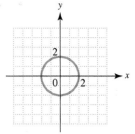

🌐 **29.**
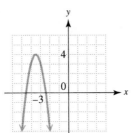

30.
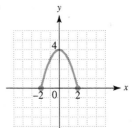

🌐 **31.**
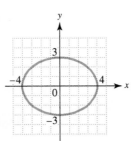

32.
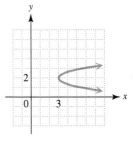

Decide whether each relation defines y as a function of x. Give the domain. ***See Example 5.***

33. $y = -6x$

34. $y = -9x$

🌐 **35.** $y = 2x - 6$

36. $y = 6x + 8$

37. $y = x^2$

38. $y = x^3$

39. $x = y^6$

40. $x = y^4$

41. $y = \dfrac{x + 4}{5}$

42. $y = \dfrac{x - 3}{2}$

43. $y = -\dfrac{2}{x}$

44. $y = -\dfrac{6}{x}$

45. $y = \dfrac{2}{x - 4}$

46. $y = \dfrac{7}{x - 2}$

47. $y = \dfrac{1}{4x + 3}$

48. $y = \dfrac{1}{2x + 9}$

49. $x = y^2 + 1$

50. $x = y^2 - 3$

51. $xy = 1$

52. $xy = 3$

Solve each problem.

53. The table shows the percentage of students at 4-year public colleges who graduated within 5 years.

(a) Does the table define a function?

(b) What are the domain and range?

(c) Call this function *f*. Give two ordered pairs that belong to *f*.

Year	Percentage
2004	42.3
2005	42.3
2006	42.8
2007	43.7
2008	43.8

Source: ACT.

54. The table shows the percentage of full-time college freshmen who said they had discussed politics in election years.

(a) Does the table define a function?

(b) What are the domain and range?

(c) Call this function *g*. Give two ordered pairs that belong to *g*.

Year	Percentage
1992	83.7
1996	73.0
2000	69.6
2004	77.4
2008	85.9

Source: Cooperative Institutional Research Program.

PREVIEW EXERCISES

Evaluate y for x = 3. ***See Section 3.1.***

55. $y = -7x + 12$ **56.** $y = -5x - 4$ **57.** $y = 3x - 8$

Solve for y. ***See Section 2.5.***

58. $3x - 7y = 8$ **59.** $2x - 4y = 7$ **60.** $\dfrac{3}{4}x + 2y = 9$

7.4   Function Notation and Linear Functions

OBJECTIVES

1. Use function notation.
2. Graph linear and constant functions.

OBJECTIVE 1 **Use function notation.** When a function *f* is defined with a rule or an equation using *x* and *y* for the independent and dependent variables, we say, "*y is a function of x*" to emphasize that *y depends on x*. We use the notation

$$y = f(x),$$

The parentheses here do *not* indicate multiplication.

called **function notation,** to express this and read $f(x)$ as "**f of x.**" The letter *f* is a name for this particular function. For example, if $y = 9x - 5$, we can name this function *f* and write

$$f(x) = 9x - 5.$$

f is the name of the function.
x is a value from the domain.
$f(x)$ is the function value (or *y*-value) that corresponds to *x*.

f(x) is just another name for the dependent variable y.

We can evaluate a function at different values of *x* by substituting *x*-values from the domain into the function.

Let $f(x) = -3x + 4$ and $g(x) = -x^2 + 4x + 1$. Find the following. **See Examples 1–3.**

3. $f(0)$ **4.** $f(-3)$ **5.** $g(-2)$ **6.** $g(10)$

7. $f\left(\dfrac{1}{3}\right)$ **8.** $f\left(\dfrac{7}{3}\right)$ **9.** $g(0.5)$ **10.** $g(1.5)$

11. $f(p)$ **12.** $g(k)$ **13.** $f(-x)$ **14.** $g(-x)$

15. $f(x + 2)$ **16.** $f(x - 2)$ **17.** $g(\pi)$ **18.** $g(e)$

19. $f(x + h)$ **20.** $f(x + h) - f(x)$ **21.** $f(4) - g(4)$ **22.** $f(10) - g(10)$

For each function, find **(a)** $f(2)$ *and* **(b)** $f(-1)$. **See Examples 4 and 5.**

23. $f = \{(-2, 2), (-1, -1), (2, -1)\}$ **24.** $f = \{(-1, -5), (0, 5), (2, -5)\}$

25. $f = \{(-1, 3), (4, 7), (0, 6), (2, 2)\}$ **26.** $f = \{(2, 5), (3, 9), (-1, 11), (5, 3)\}$

27.

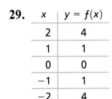

28.

29.

x	$y = f(x)$
2	4
1	1
0	0
−1	1
−2	4

30.

x	$y = f(x)$
8	6
5	3
2	0
−1	−3
−4	−6

31.

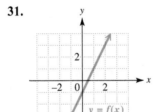

32.

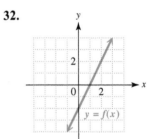

33.

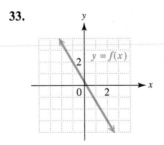

34.

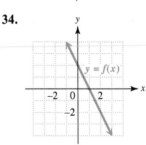

35. Refer to **Exercise 31.** Find the value of x for each value of $f(x)$. **See Example 5(c).**

   (a) $f(x) = 3$ **(b)** $f(x) = -1$ **(c)** $f(x) = -3$

36. Refer to **Exercise 32.** Find the value of x for each value of $f(x)$. **See Example 5(c).**

   (a) $f(x) = 4$ **(b)** $f(x) = -2$ **(c)** $f(x) = 0$

An equation that defines y as a function f of x is given. **(a)** *Solve for y in terms of x, and replace y with the function notation $f(x)$.* **(b)** *Find $f(3)$.* **See Example 6.**

37. $x + 3y = 12$ **38.** $x - 4y = 8$ **39.** $y + 2x^2 = 3$

40. $y - 3x^2 = 2$ **41.** $4x - 3y = 8$ **42.** $-2x + 5y = 9$

43. *Concept Check* Fill in each blank with the correct response.

The equation $2x + y = 4$ has a straight _____ as its graph. One point that lies on the graph is $(3,$ _____ $)$. If we solve the equation for y and use function notation, we obtain $f(x) =$ _____. For this function, $f(3) =$ _____, meaning that the point $($ _____ $,$ _____ $)$ lies on the graph of the function.

44. *Concept Check* Which of the following defines y as a linear function of x?

A. $y = \dfrac{1}{4}x - \dfrac{5}{4}$ **B.** $y = \dfrac{1}{x}$ **C.** $y = x^2$ **D.** $y = \sqrt{x}$

Graph each linear function. Give the domain and range. **See Example 7.**

45. $f(x) = -2x + 5$ **46.** $g(x) = 4x - 1$ **47.** $h(x) = \dfrac{1}{2}x + 2$

48. $F(x) = -\dfrac{1}{4}x + 1$ **49.** $G(x) = 2x$ **50.** $H(x) = -3x$

51. $g(x) = -4$ **52.** $f(x) = 5$ **53.** $f(x) = 0$ **54.** $f(x) = -2.5$

55. *Concept Check* What is the name that is usually given to the graph in **Exercise 53?**

56. Can the graph of a linear function have an undefined slope? Explain.

Solve each problem.

57. A package weighing x pounds costs $f(x)$ dollars to mail to a given location, where

$$f(x) = 3.75x.$$

(a) Evaluate $f(3)$.

(b) Describe what 3 and the value $f(3)$ mean in part (a), using the terminology *independent variable* and *dependent variable*.

(c) How much would it cost to mail a 5-lb package? Interpret this question and its answer, using function notation.

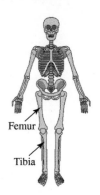

58. A taxicab driver charges $2.50 per mile.

(a) Fill in the table with the correct response for the price $f(x)$ he charges for a trip of x miles.

x	$f(x)$
0	
1	
2	
3	

(b) The linear function that gives a rule for the amount charged is $f(x) =$ _____.

(c) Graph this function for the domain $\{0, 1, 2, 3\}$.

59. Forensic scientists use the lengths of certain bones to calculate the height of a person. Two bones often used are the tibia (t), the bone from the ankle to the knee, and the femur (r), the bone from the knee to the hip socket. A person's height (h) in centimeters is determined from the lengths of these bones by using functions defined by the following formulas.

For men: $\quad h(r) = 69.09 + 2.24r \quad$ or $\quad h(t) = 81.69 + 2.39t$

For women: $\quad h(r) = 61.41 + 2.32r \quad$ or $\quad h(t) = 72.57 + 2.53t$

Femur

Tibia

(a) Find the height of a man with a femur measuring 56 cm.

(b) Find the height of a man with a tibia measuring 40 cm.

(c) Find the height of a woman with a femur measuring 50 cm.

(d) Find the height of a woman with a tibia measuring 36 cm.

60. Federal regulations set standards for the size of the quarters of marine mammals. A pool to house sea otters must have a volume of "the square of the sea otter's average adult length (in meters) multiplied by 3.14 and by 0.91 meter." If x represents the sea otter's average adult length and $f(x)$ represents the volume (in cubic meters) of the corresponding pool size, this formula can be written as

$$f(x) = 0.91(3.14)x^2.$$

Find the volume of the pool for each adult sea otter length (in meters). Round answers to the nearest hundredth.

(a) 0.8   **(b)** 1.0   **(c)** 1.2   **(d)** 1.5

61. To print t-shirts, there is a $100 set-up fee, plus a $12 charge per t-shirt. Let x represent the number of t-shirts printed and $f(x)$ represent the total charge.

(a) Write a linear function that models this situation.

(b) Find $f(125)$. Interpret your answer in the context of this problem.

(c) Find the value of x if $f(x) = 1000$. Express this situation using function notation, and interpret it in the context of this problem.

62. Rental on a car is $150, plus $0.20 per mile. Let x represent the number of miles driven and $f(x)$ represent the total cost to rent the car.

(a) Write a linear function that models this situation.

(b) How much would it cost to drive 250 mi? Interpret this question and answer, using function notation.

(c) Find the value of x if $f(x) = 230$. Interpret your answer in the context of this problem.

63. The table represents a linear function.

x	$y = f(x)$
0	3.5
1	2.3
2	1.1
3	−0.1
4	−1.3
5	−2.5

(a) What is $f(2)$?

(b) If $f(x) = -2.5$, what is the value of x?

(c) What is the slope of the line?

(d) What is the y-intercept of the line?

(e) Using your answers from parts (c) and (d), write an equation for $f(x)$.

64. The table represents a linear function.

x	$y = f(x)$
−1	−3.9
0	−2.4
1	−0.9
2	0.6
3	2.1

(a) What is $f(2)$?

(b) If $f(x) = 2.1$, what is the value of x?

(c) What is the slope of the line?

(d) What is the y-intercept of the line?

(e) Using your answers from parts (c) and (d), write an equation for $f(x)$.

65. Refer to the graph to answer each of the questions.

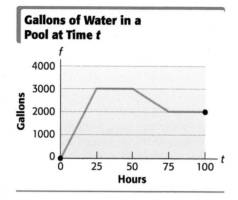

Gallons of Water in a Pool at Time _t_

(a) What numbers are possible values of the independent variable? The dependent variable?

(b) For how long is the water level increasing? Decreasing?

(c) How many gallons of water are in the pool after 90 hr?

(d) Call this function _f_. What is $f(0)$? What does it mean?

(e) What is $f(25)$? What does it mean?

66. The graph shows megawatts of electricity used on a summer day.

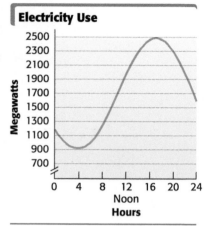

Electricity Use

Source: Sacramento Municipal Utility District.

(a) Why is this the graph of a function?

(b) What is the domain?

(c) Estimate the number of megawatts used at 8 A.M.

(d) At what time was the most electricity used? The least electricity?

(e) Call this function _f_. What is $f(12)$? What does it mean?

PREVIEW EXERCISES

*Perform each indicated operation. **See Sections 4.4, 4.5, and 4.7.***

67. $(15x^2 - 2x) + (x - 4)$ **68.** $(3r + 8) - (2r - 5)$ **69.** $(4x - 5)(3x + 1)$

70. $(3x - 4)(2x^2 + x)$ **71.** $\dfrac{27x^3 - 18x^2}{9x}$ **72.** $\dfrac{q^2 + 2q - 35}{q - 5}$

7.5 Operations on Functions and Composition

OBJECTIVES

1 Recognize and evaluate polynomial functions.

2 Perform operations on polynomial functions.

3 Find the composition of functions.

OBJECTIVE 1 Recognize and evaluate polynomial functions. In **Section 7.4,** we studied linear (first-degree polynomial) functions, defined as $f(x) = ax + b$. Now we consider more general polynomial functions.

Polynomial Function

A **polynomial function of degree _n_** is defined by

$$f(x) = a_n x^n + a_{n-1} x^{n-1} + \cdots + a_1 x + a_0,$$

for real numbers $a_n, a_{n-1}, \ldots, a_1,$ and $a_0,$ where $a_n \neq 0$ and _n_ is a whole number.

Another way of describing a polynomial function is to say that it is a function defined by a polynomial in one variable, consisting of one or more terms. It is usually written in descending powers of the variable, and its degree is the degree of the polynomial that defines it.

We can evaluate a polynomial function $f(x)$ at different values of the variable x.

⌐ *NOW TRY*
↳ *EXERCISE 1*
Let $f(x) = x^3 - 2x^2 + 7$.
Find $f(-3)$.

EXAMPLE 1 Evaluating Polynomial Functions

Let $f(x) = 4x^3 - x^2 + 5$. Find each value.

(a) $f(3)$

Read this as "f of 3," not "f times 3."		
$f(x) = 4x^3 - x^2 + 5$	Given function
$f(3) = 4(3)^3 - 3^2 + 5$	Substitute 3 for x.
$f(3) = 4(27) - 9 + 5$	Apply the exponents.
$f(3) = 108 - 9 + 5$	Multiply.
$f(3) = 104$	Subtract, and then add.

Thus, $f(3) = 104$ and the ordered pair $(3, 104)$ belongs to f.

(b) $f(-4)$

$f(x) = 4x^3 - x^2 + 5$ Use parentheses.

$f(-4) = 4 \cdot (-4)^3 - (-4)^2 + 5$ Let $x = -4$.

$f(-4) = 4 \cdot (-64) - 16 + 5$ Be careful with signs.

$f(-4) = -256 - 16 + 5$ Multiply.

$f(-4) = -267$ Subtract, and then add.

So, $f(-4) = -267$. The ordered pair $(-4, -267)$ belongs to f.   *NOW TRY*

While f is the most common letter used to represent functions, recall that other letters, such as g and h, are also used. ***The capital letter P is often used for polynomial functions.*** The function defined as

$$P(x) = 4x^3 - x^2 + 5$$

yields the same ordered pairs as the function f in **Example 1.**

OBJECTIVE 2 Perform operations on polynomial functions. The operations of addition, subtraction, multiplication, and division are also defined for functions. For example, businesses use the equation "profit equals revenue minus cost," which can be written in function notation.

$$P(x) = R(x) - C(x)$$ *x* is the number of items produced and sold.

    ↑   ↑   ↑

  Profit Revenue Cost
 function function function

NOW TRY ANSWER
1. −38

The profit function is found by subtracting the cost function from the revenue function.

We define the following **operations on functions.**

Operations on Functions

If $f(x)$ and $g(x)$ define functions, then

$$(f + g)(x) = f(x) + g(x), \qquad \text{Sum function}$$

$$(f - g)(x) = f(x) - g(x), \qquad \text{Difference function}$$

$$(fg)(x) = f(x) \cdot g(x), \qquad \text{Product function}$$

and $\quad \left(\dfrac{f}{g}\right)x = \dfrac{f(x)}{g(x)}, \quad g(x) \neq 0. \qquad$ Quotient function

In each case, the domain of the new function is the intersection of the domains of $f(x)$ and $g(x)$. Additionally, the domain of the quotient function must exclude any values of x for which $g(x) = 0$.

NOW TRY
EXERCISE 2

For $f(x) = x^3 - 3x^2 + 4$ and $g(x) = -2x^3 + x^2 - 12$, find each of the following.

(a) $(f + g)(x)$

(b) $(f - g)(x)$

EXAMPLE 2 Adding and Subtracting Polynomial Functions

Find each of the following for the polynomial functions defined by

$$f(x) = x^2 - 3x + 7 \quad \text{and} \quad g(x) = -3x^2 - 7x + 7.$$

(a) $(f + g)(x)$ — This notation does *not* indicate the distributive property.

$= f(x) + g(x) \qquad$ Use the definition.

$= (x^2 - 3x + 7) + (-3x^2 - 7x + 7) \qquad$ Substitute.

$= -2x^2 - 10x + 14 \qquad$ Add the polynomials.

(b) $(f - g)(x)$

$= f(x) - g(x) \qquad$ Use the definition.

$= (x^2 - 3x + 7) - (-3x^2 - 7x + 7) \qquad$ Substitute.

$= (x^2 - 3x + 7) + (3x^2 + 7x - 7) \qquad$ Change subtraction to addition.

$= 4x^2 + 4x \qquad$ Add. *NOW TRY*

EXAMPLE 3 Adding and Subtracting Polynomial Functions

Find each of the following for the functions defined by

$$f(x) = 10x^2 - 2x \quad \text{and} \quad g(x) = 2x.$$

(a) $\quad (f + g)(2)$

$= f(2) + g(2) \qquad$ Use the definition.

$\overbrace{f(x) = 10x^2 - 2x}^{} \quad \overbrace{g(x) = 2x}^{}$

$= [10(2)^2 - 2(2)] + 2(2) \qquad$ Substitute.

This is a key step.

$= [40 - 4] + 4 \qquad$ Order of operations

$= 40 \qquad$ Subtract, and then add.

NOW TRY ANSWERS
2. **(a)** $-x^3 - 2x^2 - 8$
   (b) $3x^3 - 4x^2 + 16$

NOW TRY
EXERCISE 3
For $f(x) = x^2 - 4$
and $g(x) = -6x^2$,
find each of the following.
(a) $(f + g)(x)$
(b) $(f - g)(-4)$

Alternatively, we could first find $(f + g)(x)$.

$$(f + g)(x)$$
$$= f(x) + g(x) \qquad \text{Use the definition.}$$
$$= (10x^2 - 2x) + 2x \quad \text{Substitute.}$$
$$= 10x^2 \qquad \text{Combine like terms.}$$

Then, $\qquad (f + g)(2)$
$$= 10(2)^2 \quad \text{Substitute.}$$
$$= 40. \qquad \text{The result is the same.}$$

(b) $(f - g)(x)$ and $(f - g)(1)$
$$(f - g)(x)$$
$$= f(x) - g(x) \qquad \text{Use the definition.}$$
$$= (10x^2 - 2x) - 2x \quad \text{Substitute.}$$
$$= 10x^2 - 4x \qquad \text{Combine like terms.}$$

Then, $\qquad (f - g)(1)$
$$= 10(1)^2 - 4(1) \quad \text{Substitute.}$$
$$= 6. \qquad \text{Simplify.}$$

Confirm that $f(1) - g(1)$ gives the same result. $\qquad$ NOW TRY

NOW TRY
EXERCISE 4
For $f(x) = 3x^2 - 1$
and $g(x) = 8x + 7$,
find $(fg)(x)$ and $(fg)(-2)$.

EXAMPLE 4 Multiplying Polynomial Functions

For $f(x) = 3x + 4$ and $g(x) = 2x^2 + x$, find $(fg)(x)$ and $(fg)(-1)$.

$$(fg)(x)$$
$$= f(x) \cdot g(x) \qquad \text{Use the definition.}$$
$$= (3x + 4)(2x^2 + x) \qquad \text{Substitute.}$$
$$= 6x^3 + 3x^2 + 8x^2 + 4x \qquad \text{FOIL}$$
$$= 6x^3 + 11x^2 + 4x \qquad \text{Combine like terms.}$$

$$(fg)(-1)$$
$$= 6(-1)^3 + 11(-1)^2 + 4(-1) \quad \text{Let } x = -1 \text{ in } (fg)(x).$$
$$= -6 + 11 - 4 \quad \boxed{\text{Be careful with signs.}}$$
$$= 1 \qquad \text{Add and subtract.}$$

Confirm that $f(-1) \cdot g(-1)$ is equal to $(fg)(-1)$. $\qquad$ NOW TRY

EXAMPLE 5 Dividing Polynomial Functions

For $f(x) = 2x^2 + x - 10$ and $g(x) = x - 2$, find $\left(\frac{f}{g}\right)(x)$ and $\left(\frac{f}{g}\right)(-3)$. What value of x is not in the domain of the quotient function?

$$\left(\frac{f}{g}\right)(x) = \frac{f(x)}{g(x)} = \frac{2x^2 + x - 10}{x - 2}$$

NOW TRY ANSWERS
3. (a) $-5x^2 - 4$ **(b)** 108
4. $24x^3 + 21x^2 - 8x - 7$; -99

**NOW TRY
EXERCISE 5**
For $f(x) = 8x^2 + 2x - 3$
and $g(x) = 2x - 1$,
find $\left(\frac{f}{g}\right)(x)$ and $\left(\frac{f}{g}\right)(8)$.

To find the quotient, divide as in **Section 4.7.**

$$
\begin{array}{r}
2x + 5 \\
x - 2\overline{)2x^2 + x - 10} \\
\end{array}
$$

To subtract, add the opposite.

$\underline{2x^2 - 4x} \qquad 2x(x - 2)$

$5x - 10 \qquad$ Subtract.

$\underline{5x - 10} \qquad 5(x - 2)$

0

The quotient here is $2x + 5$, so

$$\left(\frac{f}{g}\right)(x) = 2x + 5, \qquad x \neq 2.$$

The number 2 is not in the domain because it causes the denominator $g(x) = x - 2$ to equal 0. Then

$$\left(\frac{f}{g}\right)(-3) = 2(-3) + 5 = -1. \qquad \text{Let } x = -3.$$

Verify that the same value is found by evaluating $\frac{f(-3)}{g(-3)}$.

NOW TRY

OBJECTIVE 3 **Find the composition of functions.** The diagram in **FIGURE 41** shows a function f that assigns, to each element x of set X, some element y of set Y. Suppose that a function g takes each element of set Y and assigns a value z of set Z. Then f and g together assign an element x in X to an element z in Z. The result of this process is a new function h that takes an element x in X and assigns it an element z in Z.

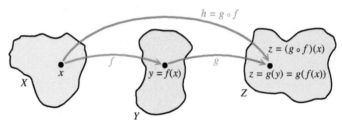

FIGURE 41

This function h is called the *composition* of functions g and f, written $\boldsymbol{g \circ f}$.

Composition of Functions

If f and g are functions, then the **composite function,** or **composition,** of g and f is defined by

$$(g \circ f)(x) = g(f(x))$$

for all x in the domain of f such that $f(x)$ is in the domain of g.

Read $g \circ f$ as "g of f".

As a real-life example of how composite functions occur, consider the following retail situation.

A \$40 pair of blue jeans is on sale for 25% off. If you purchase the jeans before noon, the retailer offers an additional 10% off. What is the final sale price of the blue jeans?

NOW TRY ANSWER
5. $4x + 3, \quad x \neq \frac{1}{2}; 35$

You might be tempted to say that the blue jeans are 25% + 10% = 35% off and calculate $40(0.35) = \$14$, giving a final sale price of

$$\$40 - \$14 = \$26. \quad \text{This is not correct.}$$

To find the correct final sale price, we must first find the price after taking 25% off, and then take an additional 10% off that price.

$40(0.25) = \$10$, giving a sale price of $40 - \$10 = \$30$.   Take 25% off original price.

$30(0.10) = \$3$, giving a *final sale price* of $30 - \$3 = \$27$.   Take additional 10% off.

This is the idea behind composition of functions.

NOW TRY
EXERCISE 6

Let $f(x) = 3x + 7$
and $g(x) = x - 2$.
Find $(f \circ g)(7)$.

EXAMPLE 6 Evaluating a Composite Function

Let $f(x) = x^2$ and $g(x) = x + 3$. Find $(f \circ g)(4)$.

$(f \circ g)(4)$ Evaluate the "inside" function value first.

$= f(g(4))$ Definition

$= f(4 + 3)$ Use the rule for $g(x)$; $g(4) = 4 + 3$.

$= f(7)$ Add.

Now evaluate the "outside" function. $= 7^2$ Use the rule for $f(x)$; $f(7) = 7^2$.

$= 49$ Square 7.   NOW TRY

If we interchange the order of the functions in **Example 6,** the composition of g and f is defined by $g(f(x))$. To find $(g \circ f)(4)$, we let $x = 4$.

$(g \circ f)(4)$

$= g(f(4))$ Definition

$= g(4^2)$ Use the rule for $f(x)$; $f(4) = 4^2$.

$= g(16)$ Square 4.

$= 16 + 3$ Use the rule for $g(x)$; $g(16) = 16 + 3$.

$= 19$ Add.

Here we see that $(f \circ g)(4) \neq (g \circ f)(4)$ because $49 \neq 19$. In general,

$$(f \circ g)(x) \neq (g \circ f)(x).$$

EXAMPLE 7 Finding Composite Functions

Let $f(x) = 4x - 1$ and $g(x) = x^2 + 5$. Find the following.

(a) $(f \circ g)(2)$

$= f(g(2))$

$= f(2^2 + 5)$ $g(x) = x^2 + 5$

$= f(9)$ Work inside the parentheses.

$= 4(9) - 1$ $f(x) = 4x - 1$

$= 35$ Multiply, and then subtract.

NOW TRY ANSWER
6. 22

NOW TRY
EXERCISE 7
Let $f(x) = x - 5$
and $g(x) = -x^2 + 2$.
Find the following.

(a) $(g \circ f)(-1)$

(b) $(f \circ g)(x)$

(b) $(f \circ g)(x)$

$= f(g(x))$ Use $g(x)$ as the input for the function f.

$= 4(g(x)) - 1$ Use the rule for $f(x)$; $f(x) = 4x - 1$.

$= 4(x^2 + 5) - 1$ $g(x) = x^2 + 5$

$= 4x^2 + 20 - 1$ Distributive property

$= 4x^2 + 19$ Combine like terms.

(c) Find $(f \circ g)(2)$ again, this time using the rule obtained in part (b).

$(f \circ g)(x) = 4x^2 + 19$ From part (b)

$(f \circ g)(2) = 4(2)^2 + 19$ Let $x = 2$.

$= 4(4) + 19$ Square 2.

$= 16 + 19$ Multiply.

Same result as in part (a) $\longrightarrow$ $= 35$ Add.   NOW TRY

NOW TRY ANSWERS
7. **(a)** -34 **(b)** $-x^2 - 3$

7.5 EXERCISES

MyMathLab   Math XL PRACTICE   WATCH   DOWNLOAD   READ   REVIEW

🌐 *Complete solution available on the Video Resources on DVD*

*For each polynomial function, find **(a)** $f(-1)$ and **(b)** $f(2)$. **See Example 1.***

1. $f(x) = 6x - 4$ **2.** $f(x) = -2x + 5$ **3.** $f(x) = x^2 - 3x + 4$

4. $f(x) = 3x^2 + x - 5$ **5.** $f(x) = 5x^4 - 3x^2 + 6$ **6.** $f(x) = -4x^4 + 2x^2 - 1$

💿 **7.** $f(x) = -x^2 + 2x^3 - 8$ **8.** $f(x) = -x^2 - x^3 + 11x$

*For each pair of functions, find **(a)** $(f + g)(x)$ and **(b)** $(f - g)(x)$. **See Example 2.***

9. $f(x) = 5x - 10$, $g(x) = 3x + 7$

10. $f(x) = -4x + 1$, $g(x) = 6x + 2$

🌐 **11.** $f(x) = 4x^2 + 8x - 3$, $g(x) = -5x^2 + 4x - 9$

12. $f(x) = 3x^2 - 9x + 10$, $g(x) = -4x^2 + 2x + 12$

*Let $f(x) = x^2 - 9, g(x) = 2x$, and $h(x) = x - 3$. Find each of the following. **See Example 3.***

🌐 **13.** $(f + g)(x)$ **14.** $(f - g)(x)$ **15.** $(f + g)(3)$ **16.** $(f - g)(-3)$

17. $(f - h)(x)$ **18.** $(f + h)(x)$ **19.** $(f - h)(-3)$

20. $(f + h)(-2)$ **21.** $(g + h)(-10)$ **22.** $(g - h)(10)$

23. $(g - h)(-3)$ **24.** $(g + h)(1)$ **25.** $(g + h)\left(\dfrac{1}{4}\right)$

26. $(g + h)\left(\dfrac{1}{3}\right)$ **27.** $(g + h)\left(-\dfrac{1}{2}\right)$ **28.** $(g + h)\left(-\dfrac{1}{4}\right)$

✏️ **29.** Construct two functions defined by $f(x)$, a polynomial of degree 3, and $g(x)$, a polynomial of degree 4. Find $(f - g)(x)$ and $(g - f)(x)$. Use your answers to decide whether subtraction of functions is a commutative operation. Explain.

30. *Concept Check*   Find two polynomial functions defined by $f(x)$ and $g(x)$ such that

$$(f + g)(x) = 3x^3 - x + 3.$$

For each pair of functions, find the product $(fg)(x)$*. See Example 4.*

31. $f(x) = 2x,\quad g(x) = 5x - 1$ **32.** $f(x) = 3x,\quad g(x) = 6x - 8$

33. $f(x) = x + 1,\quad g(x) = 2x - 3$ **34.** $f(x) = x - 7,\quad g(x) = 4x + 5$

35. $f(x) = 2x - 3,\quad g(x) = 4x^2 + 6x + 9$

36. $f(x) = 3x + 4,\quad g(x) = 9x^2 - 12x + 16$

Let $f(x) = x^2 - 9, g(x) = 2x,$ *and* $h(x) = x - 3.$ *Find each of the following. See Example 4.*

🌐 **37.** $(fg)(x)$ **38.** $(fh)(x)$ **39.** $(fg)(2)$

40. $(fh)(1)$ **41.** $(gh)(x)$ **42.** $(fh)(-1)$

43. $(gh)(-3)$ **44.** $(fg)(-2)$ **45.** $(fg)\left(-\dfrac{1}{2}\right)$

46. $(fg)\left(-\dfrac{1}{3}\right)$ **47.** $(fh)\left(-\dfrac{1}{4}\right)$ **48.** $(fh)\left(-\dfrac{1}{5}\right)$

For each pair of functions, find the quotient $\left(\dfrac{f}{g}\right)(x)$ *and give any x-values that are not in the domain of the quotient function. See Example 5.*

49. $f(x) = 10x^2 - 2x,\quad g(x) = 2x$ **50.** $f(x) = 18x^2 - 24x,\quad g(x) = 3x$

51. $f(x) = 2x^2 - x - 3,\quad g(x) = x + 1$ **52.** $f(x) = 4x^2 - 23x - 35,\quad g(x) = x - 7$

53. $f(x) = 8x^3 - 27,\quad g(x) = 2x - 3$ **54.** $f(x) = 27x^3 + 64,\quad g(x) = 3x + 4$

Let $f(x) = x^2 - 9, g(x) = 2x,$ *and* $h(x) = x - 3.$ *Find each of the following. See Example 5.*

🌐 **55.** $\left(\dfrac{f}{g}\right)(x)$ **56.** $\left(\dfrac{f}{h}\right)(x)$ **57.** $\left(\dfrac{f}{g}\right)(2)$ **58.** $\left(\dfrac{f}{h}\right)(1)$

59. $\left(\dfrac{h}{g}\right)(x)$ **60.** $\left(\dfrac{g}{h}\right)(x)$ **61.** $\left(\dfrac{h}{g}\right)(3)$ **62.** $\left(\dfrac{g}{h}\right)(-1)$

63. $\left(\dfrac{f}{g}\right)\left(\dfrac{1}{2}\right)$ **64.** $\left(\dfrac{f}{g}\right)\left(\dfrac{3}{2}\right)$ **65.** $\left(\dfrac{h}{g}\right)\left(-\dfrac{1}{2}\right)$ **66.** $\left(\dfrac{h}{g}\right)\left(-\dfrac{3}{2}\right)$

Let $f(x) = x^2 + 4, g(x) = 2x + 3,$ *and* $h(x) = x - 5.$ *Find each value or expression. See Examples 6 and 7.*

67. $(h \circ g)(4)$ **68.** $(f \circ g)(4)$ **69.** $(g \circ f)(6)$ **70.** $(h \circ f)(6)$

71. $(f \circ h)(-2)$ **72.** $(h \circ g)(-2)$ **73.** $(f \circ g)(0)$ **74.** $(f \circ h)(0)$

75. $(g \circ f)(x)$ **76.** $(g \circ h)(x)$ **77.** $(h \circ g)(x)$ **78.** $(h \circ f)(x)$

79. $(f \circ h)\left(\dfrac{1}{2}\right)$ **80.** $(h \circ f)\left(\dfrac{1}{2}\right)$ **81.** $(f \circ g)\left(-\dfrac{1}{2}\right)$ **82.** $(g \circ f)\left(-\dfrac{1}{2}\right)$

Solve each problem.

83. The function defined by $f(x) = 12x$ computes the number of inches in x feet, and the function defined by $g(x) = 5280x$ computes the number of feet in x miles. What is $(f \circ g)(x)$ and what does it compute?

84. The perimeter x of a square with sides of length s is given by the formula $x = 4s$.

(a) Solve for s in terms of x.

(b) If y represents the area of this square, write y as a function of the perimeter x.

(c) Use the composite function of part (b) to find the area of a square with perimeter 6.

85. When a thermal inversion layer is over a city (as happens often in Los Angeles), pollutants cannot rise vertically, but are trapped below the layer and must disperse horizontally. Assume that a factory smokestack begins emitting a pollutant at 8 A.M. Assume that the pollutant disperses horizontally over a circular area. Suppose that t represents the time, in hours, since the factory began emitting pollutants ($t = 0$ represents 8 A.M.), and assume that the radius of the circle of pollution is $r(t) = 2t$ miles. Let $\mathscr{A}(r) = \pi r^2$ represent the area of a circle of radius r. Find and interpret $(\mathscr{A} \circ r)(t)$.

86. An oil well is leaking, with the leak spreading oil over the surface as a circle. At any time t, in minutes, after the beginning of the leak, the radius of the circular oil slick on the surface is $r(t) = 4t$ feet. Let $\mathscr{A}(r) = \pi r^2$ represent the area of a circle of radius r. Find and interpret $(\mathscr{A} \circ r)(t)$.

PREVIEW EXERCISES

Find k, given that $y = 1$ and $x = 3$. **See Sections 2.3 and 2.5.**

87. $y = kx$ **88.** $y = kx^2$ **89.** $y = \dfrac{k}{x}$ **90.** $y = \dfrac{k}{x^2}$

7.6 Variation

OBJECTIVES

1. Write an equation expressing direct variation.
2. Find the constant of variation, and solve direct variation problems.
3. Solve inverse variation problems.
4. Solve joint variation problems.
5. Solve combined variation problems.

Functions in which *y depends on a multiple of x* or *y depends on a number divided by x* are common in business and the physical sciences.

OBJECTIVE 1 **Write an equation expressing direct variation.**
The circumference of a circle is given by the formula $C = 2\pi r$, where r is the radius of the circle. See **FIGURE 42**. The circumference is always a constant multiple of the radius. (C is always found by multiplying r by the constant 2π.)

$C = 2\pi r$

FIGURE 42

As the *radius increases*, the *circumference increases.*

As the *radius decreases*, the *circumference decreases.*

Because of these relationships, the circumference is said to *vary directly* as the radius.

Direct Variation

y **varies directly as** *x* if there exists a real number k such that

$$y = kx.$$

y is said to be **proportional to** *x*. The number k is called the **constant of variation.**

In direct variation, for $k > 0$, as the value of x increases, the value of y increases. Similarly, as x decreases, y decreases.

OBJECTIVE 2 Find the constant of variation, and solve direct variation problems. *The direct variation equation y = kx defines a linear function, where the constant of variation k is the slope of the line.* For example, we wrote the following equation to describe the cost y to buy x gallons of gasoline.

$$y = 3.20x \qquad \text{See Section 7.2, Example 7.}$$

The cost varies directly as, or is proportional to, the number of gallons of gasoline purchased.

> As the *number of gallons* of gasoline *increases,* the *cost increases.*
>
> As the *number of gallons* of gasoline *decreases,* the *cost decreases.*

The constant of variation k is 3.20, the cost of 1 gal of gasoline.

NOW TRY
EXERCISE 1
One week Morgan sold 8 dozen eggs for $20. How much does she charge for one dozen eggs?

EXAMPLE 1   Finding the Constant of Variation and the Variation Equation

Eva Lutchman is paid an hourly wage. One week she worked 43 hr and was paid $795.50. How much does she earn per hour?

Let h represent the number of hours she works and P represent her corresponding pay. Write the variation equation.

$$P = kh \qquad \text{P varies directly as h.}$$

Here, k represents Eva's hourly wage.

$$P = kh \qquad \text{P varies directly as h.}$$

$$795.50 = 43k \qquad \text{Substitute 795.50 for P and 43 for h.}$$

This is the constant of variation. $\longrightarrow$ $k = 18.50 \qquad$ Use a calculator.

Her hourly wage is $18.50, and P and h are related by

$$P = 18.50h.$$

We can use this equation to find her pay for any number of hours worked.

EXAMPLE 2   Solving a Direct Variation Problem

Hooke's law for an elastic spring states that the distance a spring stretches is directly proportional to the force applied. If a force of 150 newtons* stretches a certain spring 8 cm, how much will a force of 400 newtons stretch the spring? See **FIGURE 43.**

If d is the distance the spring stretches and f is the force applied, then $d = kf$ for some constant k. Since a force of 150 newtons stretches the spring 8 cm, we use these values to find k.

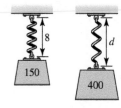

FIGURE 43

$$d = kf \qquad \text{Variation equation}$$

$$8 = k \cdot 150 \qquad \text{Let } d = 8 \text{ and } f = 150.$$

$$k = \frac{8}{150} \qquad \text{Solve for } k.$$

$$k = \frac{4}{75} \qquad \text{Lowest terms}$$

NOW TRY ANSWER
1. $2.50

*A newton is a unit of measure of force used in physics.

NOW TRY
EXERCISE 2
For a constant height, the area of a parallelogram is directly proportional to its base. If the area is 20 cm² when the base is 4 cm, find the area when the base is 7 cm.

Substitute $\frac{4}{75}$ for k in the variation equation $d = kf$.

$$d = \frac{4}{75}f \qquad \text{Here, } k = \frac{4}{75}.$$

For a force of 400 newtons, substitute 400 for f.

$$d = \frac{4}{75}(400) = \frac{64}{3} \qquad \text{Let } f = 400.$$

The spring will stretch $\frac{64}{3}$ cm, or $21\frac{1}{3}$ cm, if a force of 400 newtons is applied.

NOW TRY

Solving a Variation Problem

Step 1 Write the variation equation.

Step 2 Substitute the initial values and solve for k.

Step 3 Rewrite the variation equation with the value of k from Step 2.

Step 4 Substitute the remaining values, solve for the unknown, and find the required answer.

One variable can be proportional to a power of another variable.

Direct Variation as a Power

y* varies directly as the *n*th power of *x if there exists a real number k such that

$$y = kx^n.$$

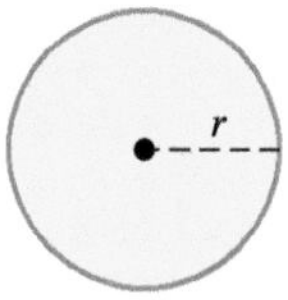

$\mathcal{A} = \pi r^2$

FIGURE 44

The formula for the area of a circle, $\mathcal{A} = \pi r^2$, is an example. See **FIGURE 44**. Here, π is the constant of variation, and the area varies directly as the *square* of the radius.

NOW TRY
EXERCISE 3
Suppose y varies directly as the square of x, and $y = 200$ when $x = 5$. Find y when $x = 7$.

EXAMPLE 3 Solving a Direct Variation Problem

The distance a body falls from rest varies directly as the square of the time it falls (disregarding air resistance). If a skydiver falls 64 ft in 2 sec, how far will she fall in 8 sec?

Step 1 If d represents the distance the skydiver falls and t the time it takes to fall, then d is a function of t for some constant k.

$$d = kt^2 \qquad \text{d varies directly as the square of t.}$$

Step 2 To find the value of k, use the fact that the skydiver falls 64 ft in 2 sec.

$$d = kt^2 \qquad \text{Variation equation}$$
$$64 = k(2)^2 \qquad \text{Let $d = 64$ and $t = 2$.}$$
$$k = 16 \qquad \text{Find k.}$$

Step 3 Now we rewrite the variation equation $d = kt^2$ using 16 for k.

$$d = 16t^2 \qquad \text{Here, $k = 16$.}$$

Step 4 Let $t = 8$ to find the number of feet the skydiver will fall in 8 sec.

$$d = 16(8)^2 = 1024 \qquad \text{Let $t = 8$.}$$

The skydiver will fall 1024 ft in 8 sec.

NOW TRY ANSWERS
2. 35 cm² **3.** 392

NOW TRY

As pressure on trash increases, volume of trash decreases.

FIGURE 45

OBJECTIVE 3   **Solve inverse variation problems.** Another type of variation is *inverse variation.* **With inverse variation, where $k > 0$, as one variable increases, the other variable decreases.**

For example, in a closed space, volume decreases as pressure increases, which can be illustrated by a trash compactor. See **FIGURE 45**. As the compactor presses down, the pressure on the trash increases, and in turn, the trash occupies a smaller space.

> ### Inverse Variation
>
> y **varies inversely as** x if there exists a real number k such that
>
> $$y = \frac{k}{x}.$$
>
> Also, y **varies inversely as the nth power of** x if there exists a real number k such that
>
> $$y = \frac{k}{x^n}.$$

The inverse variation equation defines a rational function. Another example of inverse variation comes from the distance formula.

$$d = rt \qquad \text{Distance formula}$$

$$t = \frac{d}{r} \qquad \text{Divide each side by } r.$$

Here, t (time) varies inversely as r (rate or speed), with d (distance) serving as the constant of variation. For example, if the distance between Chicago and Des Moines is 300 mi, then

$$t = \frac{300}{r},$$

and the values of r and t might be any of the following.

$$\left. \begin{array}{l} r = 50, t = 6 \\ r = 60, t = 5 \\ r = 75, t = 4 \end{array} \right\} \begin{array}{l} \text{As } r \text{ increases,} \\ t \text{ decreases.} \end{array} \qquad \left. \begin{array}{l} r = 30, t = 10 \\ r = 25, t = 12 \\ r = 20, t = 15 \end{array} \right\} \begin{array}{l} \text{As } r \text{ decreases,} \\ t \text{ increases.} \end{array}$$

If we *increase* the rate (speed) at which we drive, time *decreases.* If we *decrease* the rate (speed) at which we drive, time *increases.*

EXAMPLE 4   Solving an Inverse Variation Problem

In the manufacture of a certain medical syringe, the cost of producing the syringe varies inversely as the number produced. If 10,000 syringes are produced, the cost is $2 per syringe. Find the cost per syringe of producing 25,000 syringes.

$$\text{Let} \qquad x = \text{the number of syringes produced,}$$

$$\text{and} \qquad c = \text{the cost per syringe.}$$

Here, as production increases, cost decreases, and as production decreases, cost increases. We write a variation equation using the variables c and x and the constant k.

$$c = \frac{k}{x} \qquad c \text{ varies inversely as } x.$$

NOW TRY
EXERCISE 4

For a constant area, the height of a triangle varies inversely as the base. If the height is 7 cm when the base is 8 cm, find the height when the base is 14 cm.

To find k, we replace c with 2 and x with 10,000 in the variation equation $c = \frac{k}{x}$.

$$2 = \frac{k}{10{,}000} \qquad \text{Substitute in the variation equation.}$$

$$20{,}000 = k \qquad \text{Multiply by 10,000.}$$

Since $c = \frac{k}{x}$,

$$c = \frac{20{,}000}{25{,}000} = 0.80. \qquad \text{Here, } k = 20{,}000. \text{ Let } x = 25{,}000.$$

The cost per syringe to make 25,000 syringes is $0.80.   **NOW TRY**

NOW TRY
EXERCISE 5

The weight of an object above Earth varies inversely as the square of its distance from the center of Earth. If an object weighs 150 lb on the surface of Earth, and the radius of Earth is about 3960 mi, how much does it weigh when it is 1000 mi above Earth's surface?

EXAMPLE 5   Solving an Inverse Variation Problem

The weight of an object above Earth varies inversely as the square of its distance from the center of Earth. A space shuttle in an elliptical orbit has a maximum distance from the center of Earth (*apogee*) of 6700 mi. Its minimum distance from the center of Earth (*perigee*) is 4090 mi. See **FIGURE 46**. If an astronaut in the shuttle weighs 57 lb at its apogee, what does the astronaut weigh at its perigee?

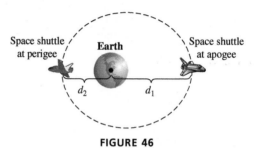

FIGURE 46

Let w = the weight and d = the distance from the center of Earth, for some constant k.

$$w = \frac{k}{d^2} \qquad w \text{ varies inversely as the square of } d.$$

At the apogee, the astronaut weighs 57 lb, and the distance from the center of Earth is 6700 mi. Use these values to find k.

$$57 = \frac{k}{(6700)^2} \qquad \text{Let } w = 57 \text{ and } d = 6700.$$

$$k = 57(6700)^2 \qquad \text{Solve for } k.$$

Substitute $k = 57(6700)^2$ and $d = 4090$ to find the weight at the perigee.

$$w = \frac{57(6700)^2}{(4090)^2} \approx 153 \text{ lb} \qquad \text{Use a calculator.} \qquad \text{NOW TRY}$$

OBJECTIVE 4   Solve joint variation problems.   If one variable varies directly as the *product* of several other variables (perhaps raised to powers), the first variable is said to *vary jointly* as the others.

Joint Variation

y **varies jointly as** *x* **and** *z* if there exists a real number *k* such that

$$y = kxz.$$

NOW TRY ANSWERS
4. 4 cm   **5.** about 96 lb

CHAPTER **7**

REVIEW EXERCISES

7.1 *Complete the table of ordered pairs for each equation. Then graph the equation.*

1. $3x + 2y = 10$

x	y
0	
	0
2	
	−2

2. $x − y = 8$

x	y
2	
	−3
3	
	−2

Find the x- and y-intercepts and then graph each equation.

3. $4x − 3y = 12$

4. $5x + 7y = 28$

5. $2x + 5y = 20$

6. $x − 4y = 8$

Use the midpoint formula to find the midpoint of each segment with the given endpoints.

7. $(−8, −12)$ and $(8, 16)$

8. $(0, −5)$ and $(−9, 8)$

Find the slope of each line.

9. Through $(−1, 2)$ and $(4, −5)$

10. Through $(0, 3)$ and $(−2, 4)$

11. $y = 2x + 3$

12. $3x − 4y = 5$

13. $x = 5$

14. Parallel to $3y = 2x + 5$

15. Perpendicular to $3x − y = 4$

16. Through $(−1, 5)$ and $(−1, −4)$

17.

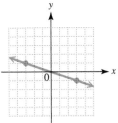

18.

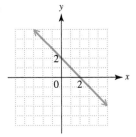

Tell whether each line has positive, negative, 0, *or* undefined *slope.*

19.

20.

21.

22.

23. *Concept Check*   If the pitch of a roof is $\frac{1}{4}$, how many feet in the horizontal direction correspond to a rise of 3 ft?

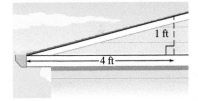

24. Family income in the United States has increased steadily for many years (primarily due to inflation). In 1980, the median family income was about $21,000 per year. In 2007, it was about $61,400 per year. Find the average rate of change of median family income to the nearest dollar over that period. (*Source:* U.S. Census Bureau.)

7.2 *Find an equation for each line.* **(a)** *Write the equation in slope-intercept form.* **(b)** *Write the equation in standard form.*

25. Slope $-\frac{1}{3}$; y-intercept $(0, -1)$

26. Slope 0; y-intercept $(0, -2)$

27. Slope $-\frac{4}{3}$; through $(2, 7)$

28. Slope 3; through $(-1, 4)$

29. Vertical; through $(2, 5)$

30. Through $(2, -5)$ and $(1, 4)$

31. Through $(-3, -1)$ and $(2, 6)$

32. The line pictured in **Exercise 18**

33. Parallel to $4x - y = 3$ and through $(7, -1)$

34. Perpendicular to $2x - 5y = 7$ and through $(4, 3)$

35. The Midwest Athletic Club offers two special membership plans. (*Source:* Midwest Athletic Club.) For each plan, write a linear equation in slope-intercept form and give the cost y in dollars of a 1-yr membership. Let x represent the number of months.

    (a) Executive VIP/Gold membership: $159 fee, plus $57 per month

    (b) Executive Regular/Silver membership: $159 fee, plus $47 per month

36. Revenue for skiing facilities in the United States is shown in the graph.

    (a) Use the information given for the years 2003 and 2007, letting $x = 3$ represent 2003, $x = 7$ represent 2007, and y represent revenue (in millions of dollars) to find a linear equation that models the data. Write the equation in slope-intercept form. Interpret the slope.

    (b) Use your equation from part (a) to estimate revenue for skiing facilities in 2008, to the nearest million.

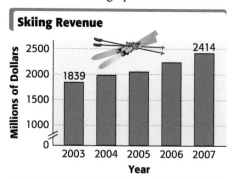

Source: U.S. Census Bureau.

7.3 *In Exercises 37–40, give the domain and range of each relation. Identify any functions.*

37. $\{(-4, 2), (-4, -2), (1, 5), (1, -5)\}$

38.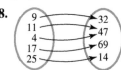

39.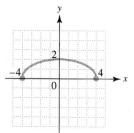

40.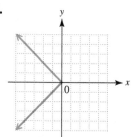

7.3–7.4 *Determine whether each equation defines y as a function of x. Give the domain in each case. Identify any linear functions.*

41. $y = 3x - 3$

42. $x = y^2$

43. $y = \dfrac{7}{x - 6}$

7.4 *Given* $f(x) = -2x^2 + 3x - 6$, *find each function value or expression.*

44. $f(0)$

45. $f(2.1)$

46. $f\left(-\dfrac{1}{2}\right)$

47. $f(k)$

48. The equation $2x^2 - y = 0$ defines y as a function f of x. Write it using function notation, and find $f(3)$.

49. *Concept Check* Suppose that $2x - 5y = 7$ defines y as a function f of x. If $y = f(x)$, which one of the following defines the same function?

A. $f(x) = -\dfrac{2}{5}x + \dfrac{7}{5}$ **B.** $f(x) = -\dfrac{2}{5}x - \dfrac{7}{5}$

C. $f(x) = \dfrac{2}{5}x - \dfrac{7}{5}$ **D.** $f(x) = \dfrac{2}{5}x + \dfrac{7}{5}$

50. The table shows life expectancy at birth in the United States for selected years.

(a) Does the table define a function?

(b) What are the domain and range?

(c) Call this function f. Give two ordered pairs that belong to f.

(d) Find $f(1980)$. What does this mean?

(e) If $f(x) = 76.8$, what does x equal?

Year	Life Expectancy at Birth (years)
1960	69.7
1970	70.8
1980	73.7
1990	75.4
2000	76.8
2009	78.1

Source: National Center for Health Statistics.

7.5

51. Find each of the following for the polynomial function defined by

$$f(x) = -2x^2 + 5x + 7.$$

(a) $f(-2)$ (b) $f(3)$

52. Find each of the following for the polynomial functions defined by

$$f(x) = 2x + 3 \quad \text{and} \quad g(x) = 5x^2 - 3x + 2.$$

(a) $(f + g)(x)$ (b) $(f - g)(x)$ (c) $(f + g)(-1)$ (d) $(f - g)(-1)$

53. Find each of the following for the polynomial functions defined by

$$f(x) = 12x^2 - 3x \quad \text{and} \quad g(x) = 3x.$$

(a) $(fg)(x)$ (b) $\left(\dfrac{f}{g}\right)(x)$ (c) $(fg)(-1)$ (d) $\left(\dfrac{f}{g}\right)(2)$

54. Find each of the following for the polynomial functions defined by

$$f(x) = 3x^2 + 2x - 1 \quad \text{and} \quad g(x) = 5x + 7.$$

(a) $(g \circ f)(3)$ (b) $(f \circ g)(3)$ (c) $(f \circ g)(-2)$

(d) $(g \circ f)(-2)$ (e) $(f \circ g)(x)$ (f) $(g \circ f)(x)$

7.6

55. *Concept Check* In which one of the following does y vary inversely as x?

A. $y = 2x$ **B.** $y = \dfrac{x}{3}$ **C.** $y = \dfrac{3}{x}$ **D.** $y = x^2$

Solve each problem.

56. For the subject in a photograph to appear in the same perspective in the photograph as in real life, the viewing distance must be properly related to the amount of enlargement. For a particular camera, the viewing distance varies directly as the amount of enlargement. A picture that is taken with this camera and enlarged 5 times should be viewed from a distance of 250 mm. Suppose a print 8.6 times the size of the negative is made. From what distance should it be viewed?

57. The frequency (number of vibrations per second) of a vibrating guitar string varies inversely as its length. That is, a longer string vibrates fewer times in a second than a shorter string. Suppose a guitar string 0.65 m long vibrates 4.3 times per sec. What frequency would a string 0.5 m long have?

58. The volume of a rectangular box of a given height is proportional to its width and length. A box with width 2 ft and length 4 ft has volume 12 ft³. Find the volume of a box with the same height, but that is 3 ft wide and 5 ft long.

CHAPTER 7

TEST

Step-by-step test solutions are found on the Chapter Test Prep Videos available via the Video Resources on DVD, in *MyMathLab*, or on YouTube (search "LialCombinedAlgebra").

View the complete solutions to all Chapter Test exercises on the Video Resources on DVD.

1. Complete the table of ordered pairs for the equation $2x - 3y = 12$.

x	y
1	
3	
	-4

Find the x- and y-intercepts, and graph each equation.

2. $3x - 2y = 20$ **3.** $y = 5$ **4.** $x = 2$

5. Find the slope of the line through the points $(6, 4)$ and $(-4, -1)$.

6. Describe how the graph of a line with undefined slope is situated in a rectangular coordinate system.

Determine whether each pair of lines is parallel, perpendicular, or neither.

7. $5x - y = 8$ and $5y = -x + 3$

8. $2y = 3x + 12$ and $3y = 2x - 5$

9. In 1980, there were 119,000 farms in Iowa. As of 2008, there were 93,000. Find and interpret the average rate of change in the number of farms per year, to the nearest whole number. (*Source:* U.S. Department of Agriculture.)

*Find an equation of each line, and write it in **(a)** slope-intercept form if possible and **(b)** standard form.*

10. Through $(4, -1)$; $m = -5$ **11.** Through $(-3, 14)$; horizontal

12. Through $(-2, 3)$ and $(6, -1)$ **13.** Through $(5, -6)$; vertical

14. Through $(-7, 2)$ and parallel to $3x + 5y = 6$

15. Through $(-7, 2)$ and perpendicular to $y = 2x$

16. *Concept Check* Which line has positive slope and negative y-coordinate for its y-intercept?

  A.   **B.**   **C.** 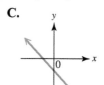   **D.**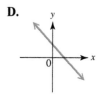

17. The bar graph shows median household income for Asians and Pacific Islanders in the United States.

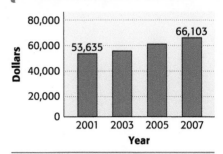

Median Household Income for Asians and Pacific Islanders

Source: U.S. Census Bureau.

   (a) Use the information for the years 2001 and 2007 to find an equation that models the data. Let $x = 1$ represent 2001, $x = 7$ represent 2007, and y represent the median income. Write the equation in slope-intercept form.

   (b) Use the equation from part (a) to approximate median household income for 2005 to the nearest dollar. How does your result compare against the actual value, \$61,094?

18. Which one of the following is the graph of a function?

A.

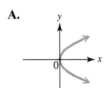

B.

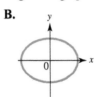

C.

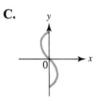

D.

19. Which of the following does not define y as a function of x?

   A. $\{(0, 1), (-2, 3), (4, 8)\}$ **B.** $y = 2x - 6$ **C.** $y = \sqrt{x + 2}$ **D.**

x	y
0	1
3	2
0	2
6	3

20. Give the domain and range of the relation shown in each of the following.

   (a) Choice A of **Exercise 18**   **(b)** Choice A of **Exercise 19**

21. For $f(x) = -x^2 + 2x - 1$, find **(a)** $f(1)$,   and   **(b)** $f(a)$.

22. Graph the linear function defined by $f(x) = \frac{2}{3}x - 1$. What is its domain and range?

23. Find each of the following for the functions defined by

$$f(x) = -2x^2 + 5x - 6 \quad \text{and} \quad g(x) = 7x - 3.$$

   (a) $f(4)$ **(b)** $(f + g)(x)$ **(c)** $(f - g)(x)$ **(d)** $(f - g)(-2)$

24. If $f(x) = x^2 + 3x + 2$ and $g(x) = x + 1$, find each of the following.

   (a) $(fg)(x)$ **(b)** $(fg)(-2)$

25. Use $f(x)$ and $g(x)$ from **Exercise 24** to find each of the following.

   (a) $\left(\dfrac{f}{g}\right)(x)$ **(b)** $\left(\dfrac{f}{g}\right)(-2)$

26. Find each of the following for the functions defined by

$$f(x) = 3x + 5 \quad \text{and} \quad g(x) = x^2 + 2.$$

   (a) $(f \circ g)(-2)$ **(b)** $(f \circ g)(x)$ **(c)** $(g \circ f)(x)$

27. The current in a simple electrical circuit is inversely proportional to the resistance. If the current is 80 amps when the resistance is 30 ohms, find the current when the resistance is 12 ohms.

28. The force of the wind blowing on a vertical surface varies jointly as the area of the surface and the square of the velocity. If a wind blowing at 40 mph exerts a force of 50 lb on a surface of 500 ft², how much force will a wind of 80 mph place on a surface of 2 ft²?

CHAPTERS (1–7)   CUMULATIVE REVIEW EXERCISES

Decide whether each statement is always true, sometimes true, *or* never true. *If the statement is* sometimes true, *give examples in which it is true and in which it is false.*

1. The absolute value of a negative number equals the additive inverse of the number.

2. The sum of two negative numbers is positive.

3. The sum of a positive number and a negative number is 0.

Simplify.

4. $-|-2| - 4 + |-3| + 7$ **5.** $-(-4m + 3)$ **6.** $\dfrac{(4^2 - 4) - (-1)7}{4 + (-6)}$

Evaluate each expression for $p = -4$, $q = \frac{1}{2}$, *and* $r = 16$.

7. $-3(2q - 3p)$ **8.** $\dfrac{r}{8p + 2r}$

Solve.

9. $2z - 5 + 3z = 2 - z$ **10.** $\dfrac{3x - 1}{5} + \dfrac{x + 2}{2} = -\dfrac{3}{10}$

Solve each problem.

11. If each side of a square were increased by 4 in., the perimeter would be 8 in. less than twice the perimeter of the original square. Find the length of a side of the original square.

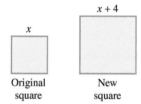

Original square   New square

12. Two planes leave the Dallas-Fort Worth airport at the same time. One travels east at 550 mph, and the other travels west at 500 mph. Assuming no wind, how long will it take for the planes to be 2100 mi apart?

West ← [airplane] Airport [airplane] → East

Solve. Write each solution set in interval notation and graph it.

13. $-4 < 3 - 2k < 9$ **14.** $-0.3x + 2.1(x - 4) \le -6.6$

15. Find the *x*- and *y*-intercepts of the line with equation $3x + 5y = 12$, and graph the line.

16. Consider the points $A(-2, 1)$ and $B(3, -5)$.

   (a) Find the slope of the line *AB*.

   (b) Find the slope of a line perpendicular to line *AB*.

*Write an equation for each line. Express the equation **(a)** in slope-intercept form if possible and **(b)** in standard form.*

17. Slope $-\dfrac{3}{4}$; *y*-intercept $(0, -1)$ **18.** Through $(4, -3)$ and $(1, 1)$

Perform the indicated operations. In Exercise 22, assume that variables represent nonzero real numbers.

19. $(3x^2y^{-1})^{-2}(2x^{-3}y)^{-1}$ **20.** $(7x + 3y)^2$

21. $(3x^3 + 4x^2 - 7) - (2x^3 - 8x^2 + 3x)$ **22.** $\dfrac{m^3 - 3m^2 + 5m - 3}{m - 1}$

Factor.

23. $16w^2 + 50wz - 21z^2$ **24.** $4x^2 - 4x + 1 - y^2$ **25.** $8p^3 + 27$

26. Solve $9x^2 = 6x - 1$.

Solve each problem.

27. A sign is to have the shape of a triangle with a height 3 ft greater than the length of the base. How long should the base be if the area is to be 14 ft²?

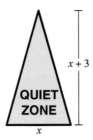

$x + 3$

QUIET ZONE

x

28. A game board has the shape of a rectangle. The longer sides are each 2 in. longer than the distance between them. The area of the board is 288 in.². Find the length of the longer sides and the distance between them.

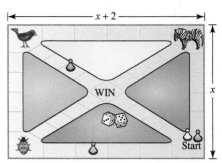

$x + 2$

WIN

x

Start

Perform each indicated operation. Write the answer in lowest terms.

29. $\dfrac{8}{x + 1} - \dfrac{2}{x + 3}$

30. $\dfrac{x^2 + 5x + 6}{3x} \div \dfrac{x^2 - 4}{x^2 + x - 6}$

31. Simplify $\dfrac{\dfrac{12}{x + 6}}{\dfrac{4}{2x + 12}}$.

32. Solve $\dfrac{2}{x - 1} = \dfrac{5}{x - 1} - \dfrac{3}{4}$.

33. Give the domain and range of the relation. Does it define a function? Explain.

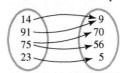

14 → 9
91 → 70
75 → 56
23 → 5

34. Consider the function defined by

$$f(x) = -4x + 10.$$

(a) Find the domain and range.

(b) Evaluate $f(-3)$.

(c) If $f(x) = 6$, find the value of x.

35. Use the information in the graph to find and interpret the average rate of change in the per capita consumption of potatoes in the United States from 2003 to 2008.

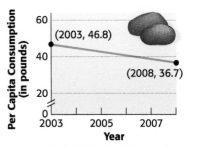

U.S. Potato Consumption

(2003, 46.8)

(2008, 36.7)

Per Capita Consumption (in pounds)

Year

Source: U.S. Department of Agriculture.

9.2 Absolute Value Equations and Inequalities

Suppose that the government of a country decides that it will comply with a certain restriction on greenhouse gas emissions *within* 3 years of 2020. This means that the *difference* between the year it will comply and 2020 is less than 3, *without regard to sign*. We state this mathematically as

$$|x - 2020| < 3, \qquad \text{\small Absolute value inequality}$$

where x represents the year in which it complies.

Reasoning tells us that the year must be between 2017 and 2023, and thus $2017 < x < 2023$ makes this inequality true. But what general procedure is used to solve such an inequality? We now investigate how to solve absolute value equations and inequalities.

OBJECTIVE 1 **Use the distance definition of absolute value.** In **Section 1.4,** we saw that the absolute value of a number x, written $|x|$, represents the distance from x to 0 on the number line. For example, the solutions of $|x| = 4$ are 4 and -4, as shown in **FIGURE 13**.

FIGURE 13

Because absolute value represents distance from 0, we interpret the solutions of $|x| > 4$ to be all numbers that are *more* than four units from 0. The set $(-\infty, -4) \cup (4, \infty)$ fits this description. **FIGURE 14** shows the graph of the solution set of $|x| > 4$. Because the graph consists of two separate intervals, the solution set is described using the word *or*: $x < -4$ or $x > 4$.

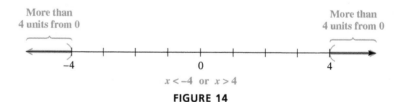

FIGURE 14

The solution set of $|x| < 4$ consists of all numbers that are *less* than 4 units from 0 on the number line. This is represented by all numbers *between* -4 and 4. This set of numbers is given by $(-4, 4)$, as shown in **FIGURE 15**. Here, the graph shows that $-4 < x < 4$, which means $x > -4$ *and* $x < 4$.

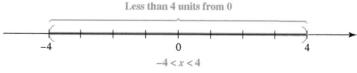

FIGURE 15

The equation and inequalities just described are examples of **absolute value equations and inequalities.** They involve the absolute value of a variable expression and generally take the form

$$|ax + b| = k, \quad |ax + b| > k, \quad \text{or} \quad |ax + b| < k,$$

where k is a positive number. From **FIGURES 13–15**, we see that

$|x| = 4$ has the same solution set as $x = -4$ or $x = 4,$

$|x| > 4$ has the same solution set as $x < -4$ or $x > 4,$

$|x| < 4$ has the same solution set as $x > -4$ and $x < 4.$

Thus, we solve an absolute value equation or inequality by solving the appropriate compound equation or inequality.

Solving Absolute Value Equations and Inequalities

Let k be a positive real number and p and q be real numbers.

Case 1 To solve $|ax + b| = k$, solve the following compound equation.

$$ax + b = k \quad \text{or} \quad ax + b = -k$$

The solution set is usually of the form $\{p, q\}$, which includes two numbers.

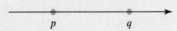

Case 2 To solve $|ax + b| > k$, solve the following compound inequality.

$$ax + b > k \quad \text{or} \quad ax + b < -k$$

The solution set is of the form $(-\infty, p) \cup (q, \infty)$, which is a disjoint interval.

Case 3 To solve $|ax + b| < k$, solve the following three-part inequality.

$$-k < ax + b < k$$

The solution set is of the form (p, q), a single interval.

NOTE Some people prefer to write the compound statements in Cases 1 and 2 of the preceding box as follows.

$$ax + b = k \quad \text{or} \quad -(ax + b) = k \qquad \text{Alternative for Case 1}$$

and $\quad ax + b > k \quad \text{or} \quad -(ax + b) > k \qquad \text{Alternative for Case 2}$

These forms produce the same results.

OBJECTIVE 2 Solve equations of the form $|ax + b| = k$, for $k > 0$. *Remember that because absolute value refers to distance from the origin, an absolute value equation will have two parts.*

⟲ NOW TRY
  EXERCISE 1
Solve $|4x - 1| = 11$.

EXAMPLE 1   Solving an Absolute Value Equation

Solve $|2x + 1| = 7$. Graph the solution set.

For $|2x + 1|$ to equal 7, $2x + 1$ must be 7 units from 0 on the number line. This can happen only when $2x + 1 = 7$ or $2x + 1 = -7$. This is Case 1 in the preceding box. Solve this compound equation as follows.

$$2x + 1 = 7 \quad \text{or} \quad 2x + 1 = -7$$
$$2x = 6 \quad \text{or} \qquad 2x = -8 \qquad \text{Subtract 1.}$$
$$x = 3 \quad \text{or} \qquad x = -4 \qquad \text{Divide by 2.}$$

Check by substituting 3 and then -4 into the original absolute value equation to verify that the solution set is $\{-4, 3\}$. The graph is shown in **FIGURE 16**.

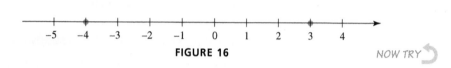

FIGURE 16   NOW TRY ⟲

OBJECTIVE 3   Solve inequalities of the form $|ax + b| < k$ and of the form $|ax + b| > k$, for $k > 0$.

⟲ NOW TRY
  EXERCISE 2
Solve $|4x - 1| > 11$.

EXAMPLE 2   Solving an Absolute Value Inequality with $>$

Solve $|2x + 1| > 7$. Graph the solution set.

By Case 2 described in the previous box, this absolute value inequality is rewritten as

$$2x + 1 > 7 \quad \text{or} \quad 2x + 1 < -7,$$

because $2x + 1$ must represent a number that is *more* than 7 units from 0 on either side of the number line. Now, solve the compound inequality.

$$2x + 1 > 7 \quad \text{or} \quad 2x + 1 < -7$$
$$2x > 6 \quad \text{or} \qquad 2x < -8 \qquad \text{Subtract 1.}$$
$$x > 3 \quad \text{or} \qquad x < -4 \qquad \text{Divide by 2.}$$

Check these solutions. The solution set is $(-\infty, -4) \cup (3, \infty)$. See **FIGURE 17**. Notice that the graph is a disjoint interval.

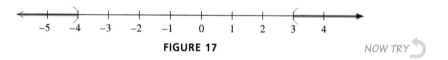

FIGURE 17   NOW TRY ⟲

EXAMPLE 3   Solving an Absolute Value Inequality with $<$

Solve $|2x + 1| < 7$. Graph the solution set.

The expression $2x + 1$ must represent a number that is less than 7 units from 0 on either side of the number line. That is, $2x + 1$ must be between -7 and 7. As Case 3 in the previous box shows, that relationship is written as a three-part inequality.

$$-7 < 2x + 1 < 7$$
$$-8 < \quad 2x \quad < 6 \qquad \text{Subtract 1 from each part.}$$
$$-4 < \quad x \quad < 3 \qquad \text{Divide each part by 2.}$$

NOW TRY ANSWERS
1. $\left\{-\frac{5}{2}, 3\right\}$
2. $\left(-\infty, -\frac{5}{2}\right) \cup (3, \infty)$

NOW TRY
EXERCISE 3
Solve $|4x - 1| < 11$.

Check that the solution set is $(-4, 3)$. The graph consists of the single interval shown in **FIGURE 18**.

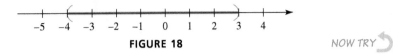

FIGURE 18

NOW TRY

Look back at **FIGURES 16, 17, AND 18**, with the graphs of

$$|2x + 1| = 7, \quad |2x + 1| > 7, \quad \text{and} \quad |2x + 1| < 7,$$

respectively. If we find the union of the three sets, we get the set of all real numbers. This is because, for any value of x, $|2x + 1|$ will satisfy one and only one of the following: It is equal to 7, greater than 7, or less than 7.

⚠ **CAUTION** When solving absolute value equations and inequalities of the types in **Examples 1, 2, and 3**, remember the following.

1. The methods described apply when the constant is alone on one side of the equation or inequality and is *positive*.

2. Absolute value equations and absolute value inequalities of the form $|ax + b| > k$ translate into "or" compound statements.

3. Absolute value inequalities of the form $|ax + b| < k$ translate into "and" compound statements, which may be written as three-part inequalities.

4. An "or" statement *cannot* be written in three parts. It would be incorrect to write $-7 > 2x + 1 > 7$ in **Example 2,** because this would imply that $-7 > 7$, which is *false.*

OBJECTIVE 4 Solve absolute value equations that involve rewriting.

NOW TRY
EXERCISE 4
Solve $|10x - 2| - 2 = 12$.

EXAMPLE 4 Solving an Absolute Value Equation That Requires Rewriting

Solve $|x + 3| + 5 = 12$.

First isolate the absolute value expression on one side of the equals symbol.

$$|x + 3| + 5 = 12$$
$$|x + 3| + 5 - 5 = 12 - 5 \qquad \text{Subtract 5.}$$
$$|x + 3| = 7 \qquad \text{Combine like terms.}$$

Now use the method shown in **Example 1** to solve $|x + 3| = 7$.

$$x + 3 = 7 \quad \text{or} \quad x + 3 = -7$$
$$x = 4 \quad \text{or} \quad x = -10 \qquad \text{Subtract 3.}$$

Check these solutions by substituting each one in the original equation.

CHECK $|x + 3| + 5 = 12$

$|4 + 3| + 5 \overset{?}{=} 12$ Let $x = 4$. $|-10 + 3| + 5 \overset{?}{=} 12$ Let $x = -10$.

$|7| + 5 \overset{?}{=} 12$ $|-7| + 5 \overset{?}{=} 12$

$12 = 12$ ✓ True $12 = 12$ ✓ True

NOW TRY ANSWERS
3. $\left(-\frac{5}{2}, 3\right)$ 4. $\left\{-\frac{6}{5}, \frac{8}{5}\right\}$

The check confirms that the solution set is $\{-10, 4\}$.

NOW TRY

NOW TRY
EXERCISE 5
Solve each inequality.

(a) $|x - 1| - 4 \leq 2$

(b) $|x - 1| - 4 \geq 2$

EXAMPLE 5 Solving Absolute Value Inequalities That Require Rewriting

Solve each inequality.

(a)
$$|x + 3| + 5 \geq 12$$
$$|x + 3| \geq 7$$
$$x + 3 \geq 7 \quad \text{or} \quad x + 3 \leq -7$$
$$x \geq 4 \quad \text{or} \quad x \leq -10$$
Solution set: $(-\infty, -10] \cup [4, \infty)$

(b)
$$|x + 3| + 5 \leq 12$$
$$|x + 3| \leq 7$$
$$-7 \leq x + 3 \leq 7$$
$$-10 \leq x \leq 4$$
Solution set: $[-10, 4]$

NOW TRY

OBJECTIVE 5 Solve equations of the form $|ax + b| = |cx + d|$. *If two expressions have the same absolute value, they must either be equal or be negatives of each other.*

Solving $|ax + b| = |cx + d|$

To solve an absolute value equation of the form
$$|ax + b| = |cx + d|,$$
solve the following compound equation.
$$ax + b = cx + d \quad \text{or} \quad ax + b = -(cx + d)$$

NOW TRY
EXERCISE 6
Solve
$$|3x - 4| = |5x + 12|.$$

EXAMPLE 6 Solving an Equation with Two Absolute Values

Solve $|x + 6| = |2x - 3|$.

This equation is satisfied either if $x + 6$ and $2x - 3$ are equal to each other or if $x + 6$ and $2x - 3$ are negatives of each other.

$$x + 6 = 2x - 3 \qquad\qquad \text{or} \quad x + 6 = -(2x - 3)$$
$$x + 9 = 2x \quad \text{Add 3.} \qquad \text{or} \quad x + 6 = -2x + 3 \quad \text{Distributive property}$$
$$9 = x \quad \text{Subtract } x. \qquad \text{or} \quad 3x = -3 \quad \text{Subtract 6.}$$
$$x = -1 \quad \text{Divide by 3.}$$

Check that the solution set is $\{-1, 9\}$.

NOW TRY

OBJECTIVE 6 Solve special cases of absolute value equations and inequalities. When an absolute value equation or inequality involves a *negative constant or 0* alone on one side, use the properties of absolute value to solve the equation or inequality.

Special Cases of Absolute Value

Case 1 The absolute value of an expression can never be negative. That is, $|a| \geq 0$ for all real numbers a.

Case 2 The absolute value of an expression equals 0 only when the expression is equal to 0.

NOW TRY ANSWERS
5. (a) $[-5, 7]$
(b) $(-\infty, -5] \cup [7, \infty)$
6. $\{-8, -1\}$

NOW TRY
EXERCISE 7

Solve each equation.

(a) $|3x - 8| = -2$

(b) $|7x + 12| = 0$

EXAMPLE 7 Solving Special Cases of Absolute Value Equations

Solve each equation.

(a) $|5x - 3| = -4$

See Case 1 in the preceding box. ***The absolute value of an expression can never be negative,*** so there are no solutions for this equation. The solution set is $\emptyset$.

(b) $|7x - 3| = 0$

See Case 2 in the preceding box. The expression $|7x - 3|$ will equal 0 *only if*

$$7x - 3 = 0$$

$$7x = 3 \quad \text{Add 3.}$$

Check by substituting in the original equation.

$$x = \frac{3}{7}. \quad \text{Divide by 7.}$$

The solution of this equation is $\frac{3}{7}$. Thus, the solution set is $\left\{\frac{3}{7}\right\}$, with just one element.

NOW TRY

NOW TRY
EXERCISE 8

Solve each inequality.

(a) $|x| > -10$

(b) $|4x + 1| + 5 < 4$

(c) $|x - 2| - 3 \le -3$

EXAMPLE 8 Solving Special Cases of Absolute Value Inequalities

Solve each inequality.

(a) $|x| \ge -4$

The absolute value of a number is always greater than or equal to 0. Thus, $|x| \ge -4$ is true for *all* real numbers. The solution set is $(-\infty, \infty)$.

(b)

$$|x + 6| - 3 < -5$$

$$|x + 6| < -2 \quad \text{Add 3 to each side.}$$

There is no number whose absolute value is less than -2, so this inequality has no solution. The solution set is $\emptyset$.

(c)

$$|x - 7| + 4 \le 4$$

$$|x - 7| \le 0 \quad \text{Subtract 4 from each side.}$$

The value of $|x - 7|$ will never be less than 0. However, $|x - 7|$ will equal 0 when $x = 7$. Therefore, the solution set is $\{7\}$.

NOW TRY

CONNECTIONS

Absolute value is used to find the *relative error* of a measurement. If x_t represents the expected measurement and x represents the actual measurement, then the relative error in x equals the absolute value of the difference between x_t and x, divided by x_t.

$$\text{relative error in } x = \left| \frac{x_t - x}{x_t} \right|$$

In quality control situations, the relative error often must be less than some predetermined amount. For example, suppose a machine filling *quart* milk cartons is set for a relative error *no greater than* 0.05. Here $x_t = 32$ oz, the relative error = 0.05 oz, and we must find x, given the following condition.

$$\left| \frac{32 - x}{32} \right| \le 0.05 \quad \text{No greater than translates as } \le.$$

For Discussion or Writing

With this tolerance level, how many *ounces* may a carton contain?

NOW TRY ANSWERS

7. (a) $\emptyset$ **(b)** $\left\{-\frac{12}{7}\right\}$

8. (a) $(-\infty, \infty)$ **(b)** $\emptyset$ **(c)** $\{2\}$

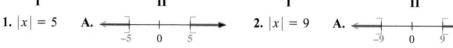

● *Complete solution available on the Video Resources on DVD*

Concept Check Match each absolute value equation or inequality in Column I with the graph of its solution set in Column II.

I	II	I	II

1. $|x| = 5$ **A.**    **2.** $|x| = 9$ **A.**

$|x| < 5$ **B.** $|x| > 9$ **B.**

$|x| > 5$ **C.**  $|x| \geq 9$ **C.**

$|x| \leq 5$ **D.**  $|x| < 9$ **D.**

$|x| \geq 5$ **E.** $|x| \leq 9$ **E.**

3. *Concept Check* How many solutions will $|ax + b| = k$ have for each situation?

(a) $k = 0$ (b) $k > 0$ (c) $k < 0$

✎ **4.** Explain when to use *and* and when to use *or* if you are solving an absolute value equation or inequality of the form $|ax + b| = k$, $|ax + b| < k$, or $|ax + b| > k$, where k is a positive number.

Solve each equation. See Example 1.

5. $|x| = 12$ **6.** $|x| = 14$ **7.** $|4x| = 20$

8. $|5x| = 30$ **9.** $|x - 3| = 9$ **10.** $|x - 5| = 13$

● **11.** $|2x - 1| = 11$ **12.** $|2x + 3| = 19$ **13.** $|4x - 5| = 17$

14. $|5x - 1| = 21$ **15.** $|2x + 5| = 14$ **16.** $|2x - 9| = 18$

17. $\left|\dfrac{1}{2}x + 3\right| = 2$ **18.** $\left|\dfrac{2}{3}x - 1\right| = 5$ **19.** $\left|1 + \dfrac{3}{4}x\right| = 7$

20. $\left|2 - \dfrac{5}{2}x\right| = 14$ **21.** $|0.02x - 1| = 2.50$ **22.** $|0.04x - 3| = 5.96$

Solve each inequality, and graph the solution set. See Example 2.

23. $|x| > 3$ **24.** $|x| > 5$ **25.** $|x| \geq 4$

26. $|x| \geq 6$ ● **27.** $|r + 5| \geq 20$ **28.** $|3r - 1| \geq 8$

29. $|x + 2| > 10$ **30.** $|4x + 1| \geq 21$ **31.** $|3 - x| > 5$

32. $|5 - x| > 3$ **33.** $|-5x + 3| \geq 12$ **34.** $|-2x - 4| \geq 5$

35. *Concept Check* The graph of the solution set of $|2x + 1| = 9$ is given here.

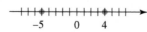

Without actually doing the algebraic work, graph the solution set of each inequality, referring to the graph shown.

(a) $|2x + 1| < 9$ (b) $|2x + 1| > 9$

36. *Concept Check*   The graph of the solution set of $|3x - 4| < 5$ is given here.

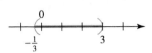

Without actually doing the algebraic work, graph the solution set of the following, referring to the graph shown.

(a) $|3x - 4| = 5$ **(b)** $|3x - 4| > 5$

Solve each inequality, and graph the solution set. ***See Example 3.*** *(Hint: Compare your answers with those in* ***Exercises 23–34.***)

37. $|x| \leq 3$
38. $|x| \leq 5$
39. $|x| < 4$

40. $|x| < 6$
41. $|r + 5| < 20$
42. $|3r - 1| < 8$

43. $|x + 2| \leq 10$
44. $|4x + 1| < 21$
45. $|3 - x| \leq 5$

46. $|5 - x| \leq 3$
47. $|-5x + 3| < 12$
48. $|-2x - 4| < 5$

In Exercises 49–66, decide which method of solution applies, and find the solution set. In Exercises 49–60, graph the solution set. ***See Examples 1–3.***

49. $|-4 + x| > 9$
50. $|-3 + x| > 8$
51. $|x + 5| > 20$

52. $|2x - 1| < 7$
53. $|7 + 2x| = 5$
54. $|9 - 3x| = 3$

55. $|3x - 1| \leq 11$
56. $|2x - 6| \leq 6$
57. $|-6x - 6| \leq 1$

58. $|-2x - 6| \leq 5$
59. $|2x - 1| \geq 7$
60. $|-4 + x| \leq 9$

61. $|x + 2| = 3$
62. $|x + 3| = 10$
63. $|x - 6| = 3$

64. $|x - 4| = 1$
65. $|2 - 0.2x| = 2$
66. $|5 - 0.5x| = 4$

Solve each equation or inequality. ***See Examples 4 and 5.***

67. $|x| - 1 = 4$
68. $|x| + 3 = 10$
69. $|x + 4| + 1 = 2$

70. $|x + 5| - 2 = 12$
71. $|2x + 1| + 3 > 8$
72. $|6x - 1| - 2 > 6$

73. $|x + 5| - 6 \leq -1$
74. $|x - 2| - 3 \leq 4$

75. $\left| \dfrac{1}{2}x + \dfrac{1}{3} \right| + \dfrac{1}{4} = \dfrac{3}{4}$
76. $\left| \dfrac{2}{3}x + \dfrac{1}{6} \right| + \dfrac{1}{2} = \dfrac{5}{2}$

77. $|0.1x - 2.5| + 0.3 \geq 0.8$
78. $|0.5x - 3.5| + 0.2 \geq 0.6$

Solve each equation. ***See Example 6.***

79. $|3x + 1| = |2x + 4|$
80. $|7x + 12| = |x - 8|$
81. $\left| x - \dfrac{1}{2} \right| = \left| \dfrac{1}{2}x - 2 \right|$

82. $\left| \dfrac{2}{3}x - 2 \right| = \left| \dfrac{1}{3}x + 3 \right|$
83. $|6x| = |9x + 1|$
84. $|13x| = |2x + 1|$

85. $|2x - 6| = |2x + 11|$
86. $|3x - 1| = |3x + 9|$

Solve each equation or inequality. ***See Examples 7 and 8.***

87. $|x| \geq -10$
88. $|x| \geq -15$
89. $|12t - 3| = -8$

90. $|13x + 1| = -3$
91. $|4x + 1| = 0$
92. $|6x - 2| = 0$

93. $|2x - 1| = -6$
94. $|8x + 4| = -4$
95. $|x + 5| > -9$

96. $|x + 9| > -3$
97. $|7x + 3| \leq 0$
98. $|4x - 1| \leq 0$

99. $|5x - 2| = 0$
100. $|7x + 4| = 0$
101. $|x - 2| + 3 \geq 2$

102. $|x - 4| + 5 \geq 4$
103. $|10x + 7| + 3 < 1$
104. $|4x + 1| - 2 < -5$

105. The recommended daily intake (RDI) of calcium for females aged 19–50 is 1000 mg. Actual needs vary from person to person. Write this statement as an absolute value inequality, with x representing the RDI, to express the RDI plus or minus 100 mg, and solve the inequality. (*Source:* National Academy of Sciences—Institute of Medicine.)

106. The average clotting time of blood is 7.45 sec, with a variation of plus or minus 3.6 sec. Write this statement as an absolute value inequality, with x representing the time, and solve the inequality.

RELATING CONCEPTS EXERCISES 107–110

FOR INDIVIDUAL OR GROUP WORK

The 10 tallest buildings in Houston, Texas, as of 2009 are listed, along with their heights.

Building	Height (in feet)
JPMorgan Chase Tower	1002
Wells Fargo Plaza	992
Williams Tower	901
Bank of America Center	780
Texaco Heritage Plaza	762
Enterprise Plaza	756
Centerpoint Energy Plaza	741
Continental Center I	732
Fulbright Tower	725
One Shell Plaza	714

Source: World Almanac and Book of Facts.

Use this information to **work Exercises 107–110 in order.**

107. To find the average of a group of numbers, we add the numbers and then divide by the number of numbers added. Use a calculator to find the average of the heights.

108. Let k represent the average height of these buildings. If a height x satisfies the inequality

$$|x - k| < t,$$

then the height is said to be within t feet of the average. Using your result from **Exercise 107**, list the buildings that are within 50 ft of the average.

109. Repeat **Exercise 108**, but list the buildings that are within 95 ft of the average.

110. **(a)** Write an absolute value inequality that describes the height of a building that is *not* within 95 ft of the average. Solve this inequality.

(b) Use the result of part (a) to list the buildings that are not within 95 ft of the average. Does your answer makes sense compared with your answer to **Exercise 109.**

PREVIEW EXERCISES

Graph each equation. **See Sections 3.2 and 7.1.**

111. $x - y = 5$　　　　**112.** $x = -5y$

Decide whether each ordered pair is a solution of the equation. **See Section 3.1.**

113. $3x - 4y = 12$;　$(-4, 3)$　　　　**114.** $x + 2y = 0$;　$(2, -1)$

SUMMARY EXERCISES on Solving Linear and Absolute Value Equations and Inequalities

Solve each equation or inequality. Give the solution set in set notation for equations and in interval notation for inequalities.

1. $4x + 1 = 49$

2. $|x - 1| = 6$

3. $6x - 9 = 12 + 3x$

4. $3x + 7 = 9 + 8x$

5. $|x + 3| = -4$

6. $2x + 1 \le x$

7. $8x + 2 \ge 5x$

8. $4(x - 11) + 3x = 20x - 31$

9. $2x - 1 = -7$

10. $|3x - 7| - 4 = 0$

11. $6x - 5 \le 3x + 10$

12. $|5x - 8| + 9 \ge 7$

13. $9x - 3(x + 1) = 8x - 7$

14. $|x| \ge 8$

15. $9x - 5 \ge 9x + 3$

16. $13x - 5 > 13x - 8$

17. $|x| < 5.5$

18. $4x - 1 = 12 + x$

19. $\dfrac{2}{3}x + 8 = \dfrac{1}{4}x$

20. $-\dfrac{5}{8}x \ge -20$

21. $\dfrac{1}{4}x < -6$

22. $7x - 3 + 2x = 9x - 8x$

23. $\dfrac{3}{5}x - \dfrac{1}{10} = 2$

24. $|x - 1| < 7$

25. $x + 9 + 7x = 4(3 + 2x) - 3$

26. $6 - 3(2 - x) < 2(1 + x) + 3$

27. $|2x - 3| > 11$

28. $\dfrac{x}{4} - \dfrac{2x}{3} = -10$

29. $|5x + 1| \le 0$

30. $5x - (3 + x) \ge 2(3x + 1)$

31. $-2 \le 3x - 1 \le 8$

32. $-1 \le 6 - x \le 5$

33. $|7x - 1| = |5x + 3|$

34. $|x + 2| = |x + 4|$

35. $|1 - 3x| \ge 4$

36. $\dfrac{1}{2} \le \dfrac{2}{3}x \le \dfrac{5}{4}$

37. $-(x + 4) + 2 = 3x + 8$

38. $\dfrac{x}{6} - \dfrac{3x}{5} = x - 86$

39. $-6 \le \dfrac{3}{2} - x \le 6$

40. $|5 - x| < 4$

41. $|x - 1| \ge -6$

42. $|2x - 5| = |x + 4|$

43. $8x - (1 - x) = 3(1 + 3x) - 4$

44. $8x - (x + 3) = -(2x + 1) - 12$

45. $|x - 5| = |x + 9|$

46. $|x + 2| < -3$

47. $2x + 1 > 5$ or $3x + 4 < 1$

48. $1 - 2x \ge 5$ and $7 + 3x \ge -2$

CHAPTER **9**

SUMMARY

9.1

intersection
compound inequality
union

9.2

absolute value equation
absolute value inequality

9.3

linear inequality in two
   variables
boundary line

$\cap$ set intersection

$\cup$ set union

See how well you have learned the vocabulary in this chapter.

1. The **intersection** of two sets A and B is the set of elements that belong
   A. to both A and B
   B. to either A or B, or both
   C. to either A or B, but not both
   D. to just A.

2. The **union** of two sets A and B is the set of elements that belong
   A. to both A and B
   B. to either A or B, or both
   C. to either A or B, but not both
   D. to just B.

3. A **linear inequality in two variables** is an inequality that can be written in the form
   A. $Ax + By < C$ or $Ax + By > C$
      ($\leq$ or $\geq$ can be used)
   B. $ax < b$
   C. $y \geq x^2$
   D. $Ax + By = C$.

ANSWERS

1. A; *Example:* If $A = \{2, 4, 6, 8\}$ and $B = \{1, 2, 3\}$, then $A \cap B = \{2\}$.   **2.** B; *Example:* Using the sets A and B from Answer 1, $A \cup B = \{1, 2, 3, 4, 6, 8\}$.   **3.** A; *Examples:* $4x + 3y < 12, x > 6y, 2x \geq 4y + 5$

CONCEPTS

EXAMPLES

9.1 Set Operations and Compound Inequalities

Solving a Compound Inequality

Step 1 Solve each inequality in the compound inequality individually.

Step 2 If the inequalities are joined with *and,* then the solution set is the intersection of the two individual solution sets.

If the inequalities are joined with *or,* then the solution set is the union of the two individual solution sets.

Solve $x + 1 > 2$ and $2x < 6$.

$$x + 1 > 2 \quad \text{and} \quad 2x < 6$$
$$x > 1 \quad \text{and} \quad x < 3$$

The solution set is $(1, 3)$.

Solve $x \geq 4$ or $x \leq 0$.

The solution set is $(-\infty, 0] \cup [4, \infty)$.

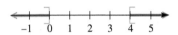

9.2 Absolute Value Equations and Inequalities

Solving Absolute Value Equations and Inequalities
Let k be a positive number.

To solve $|ax + b| = k$, solve the following compound equation.

$$ax + b = k \quad \text{or} \quad ax + b = -k$$

Solve $|x - 7| = 3$.

$$x - 7 = 3 \quad \text{or} \quad x - 7 = -3$$
$$x = 10 \quad \text{or} \quad x = 4 \qquad \text{Add 7.}$$

The solution set is $\{4, 10\}$.

To solve $|ax + b| > k$, solve the following compound inequality.

$$ax + b > k \quad \text{or} \quad ax + b < -k$$

Solve $|x - 7| > 3$.

$$x - 7 > 3 \quad \text{or} \quad x - 7 < -3$$
$$x > 10 \quad \text{or} \quad x < 4 \qquad \text{Add 7.}$$

The solution set is $(-\infty, 4) \cup (10, \infty)$.

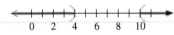

To solve $|ax + b| < k$, solve the following compound inequality.

$$-k < ax + b < k$$

Solve $|x - 7| < 3$.

$$-3 < x - 7 < 3$$
$$4 < x < 10 \qquad \text{Add 7.}$$

The solution set is $(4, 10)$.

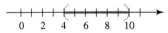

To solve an absolute value equation of the form

$$|ax + b| = |cx + d|,$$

solve the following compound equation.

$$ax + b = cx + d \quad \text{or} \quad ax + b = -(cx + d)$$

Solve $|x + 2| = |2x - 6|$.

$$x + 2 = 2x - 6 \quad \text{or} \quad x + 2 = -(2x - 6)$$
$$x = 8 \qquad\qquad x + 2 = -2x + 6$$
$$3x = 4$$
$$x = \frac{4}{3}$$

The solution set is $\left\{\frac{4}{3}, 8\right\}$.

(continued)

CONCEPTS	EXAMPLES

9.3   Linear Inequalities in Two Variables

Graphing a Linear Inequality

Step 1   Draw the graph of the line that is the boundary. Make the line solid if the inequality involves $\leq$ or $\geq$. Make the line dashed if the inequality involves $<$ or $>$.

Step 2   Choose any point not on the line as a test point. Substitute the coordinates into the inequality.

Step 3   Shade the region that includes the test point if the test point satisfies the original inequality. Otherwise, shade the region on the other side of the boundary line.

Graph $2x - 3y \leq 6$.

Draw the graph of $2x - 3y = 6$. Use a solid line because of the inclusion of equality in the symbol $\leq$.

Choose $(0, 0)$ as a test point.

$$2(0) - 3(0) \overset{?}{\leq} 6$$

$$0 \leq 6 \quad \text{True}$$

Shade the side of the line that includes $(0, 0)$.

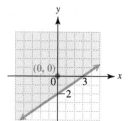

CHAPTER 9

REVIEW EXERCISES

9.1   *Let* $A = \{a, b, c, d\}$, $B = \{a, c, e, f\}$, *and* $C = \{a, e, f, g\}$. *Find each set.*

1. $A \cap B$ **2.** $A \cap C$ **3.** $B \cup C$ **4.** $A \cup C$

Solve each compound inequality. Give the solution set in both interval and graph form.

5. $x > 6$ and $x < 9$ **6.** $x + 4 > 12$ and $x - 2 < 12$

7. $x > 5$ or $x \leq -3$ **8.** $x \geq -2$ or $x < 2$

9. $x - 4 > 6$ and $x + 3 \leq 10$ **10.** $-5x + 1 \geq 11$ or $3x + 5 \geq 26$

Express each union or intersection in simplest interval form.

11. $(-3, \infty) \cap (-\infty, 4)$ **12.** $(-\infty, 6) \cap (-\infty, 2)$

13. $(4, \infty) \cup (9, \infty)$ **14.** $(1, 2) \cup (1, \infty)$

9.2   *Solve each absolute value equation.*

15. $|x| = 7$ **16.** $|x + 2| = 9$

17. $|3x - 7| = 8$ **18.** $|x - 4| = -12$

19. $|2x - 7| + 4 = 11$ **20.** $|4x + 2| - 7 = -3$

21. $|3x + 1| = |x + 2|$ **22.** $|2x - 1| = |2x + 3|$

Solve each absolute value inequality. Give the solution set in interval form.

23. $|x| < 14$ **24.** $|-x + 6| \leq 7$ **25.** $|2x + 5| \leq 1$

26. $|x + 1| \geq -3$ **27.** $|5x - 1| > 9$ **28.** $|11x - 3| \leq -2$

29. $|11x - 3| \geq -2$ **30.** $|11x - 3| \leq 0$

9.3   *Graph the solution set of each inequality or compound inequality.*

31. $3x - 2y \leq 12$ **32.** $5x - y > 6$ **33.** $3x + 2y < 0$

34. $2x + y \leq 1$ and $x \geq 2y$ **35.** $x \geq 2$ or $y \geq 2$

36. *Concept Check*   Which one of the following has as its graph a dashed boundary line and shading below the line?

   A. $y \geq 4x + 3$ **B.** $y > 4x + 3$ **C.** $y \leq 4x + 3$ **D.** $y < 4x + 3$

MIXED REVIEW EXERCISES

Solve.

37. $x < 3$ and $x \geq -2$ **38.** $|3x + 6| \geq 0$ **39.** $|3x + 2| + 4 = 9$

40. $|x + 3| \leq 13$ **41.** $|5x - 1| > 14$ **42.** $x \geq -2$ or $x < 4$

43. $|x - 1| = |2x + 3|$ **44.** $|x + 3| \leq 1$ **45.** $|3x - 7| = 4$

46. *Concept Check*   If $k < 0$, what is the solution set of each of the following?

   (a) $|2x - 5| = k$ **(b)** $|2x - 5| < k$ **(c)** $|2x - 5| > k$

Solve. Give the solution set in both interval and graph form.

47. $x > 6$ and $x < 8$ **48.** $-5x + 1 \geq 11$ or $3x + 5 \geq 26$

Graph the solution set of each inequality.

49. $2x - 3y > -6$ **50.** $3x + 5y > 9$

51. The numbers of civilian workers (to the nearest thousand) for several states in 2008 are shown in the table.

Number of Workers

State	Female	Male
Illinois	2,918,000	3,345,000
Maine	320,000	349,000
North Carolina	2,016,000	2,242,000
Oregon	869,000	976,000
Utah	571,000	755,000
Wisconsin	1,427,000	1,526,000

Source: U.S. Bureau of Labor Statistics.

List the elements of each set.

   (a) The set of states with less than 3 million female workers *and* more than 3 million male workers

   (b) The set of states with less than 1 million female workers *or* more than 2 million male workers

   (c) The set of states with a total of more than 7 million civilian workers

52. *Concept Check*   The solution set of $|3x + 4| = 7$ is shown on the number line.

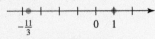

   (a) What is the solution set of $|3x + 4| \geq 7$?

   (b) What is the solution set of $|3x + 4| \leq 7$?

CHAPTER **9**

TEST

Step-by-step test solutions are found on the Chapter Test Prep Videos available via the Video Resources on DVD, in *MyMathLab*, or on You Tube (search "LialCombinedAlgebra").

View the complete solutions to all Chapter Test exercises on the Video Resources on DVD.

The median weekly earnings of full-time workers by occupation for a recent year were as shown in the table.

Weekly Earnings of Full-Time Workers (in dollars)

Occupation	Men	Women
Managerial/Professional	994	709
Technical/Sales/Administrative Support	655	452
Service	357	316
Operators/Fabricators/Laborers	487	351

Source: U.S. Bureau of Labor Statistics.

List the elements of each set.

1. The set of occupations with median earnings for men less than $900 and for women greater than $500

2. The set of occupations with median earnings for men greater than $600 or for women less than $400

Let $A = \{1, 2, 5, 7\}$ and $B = \{1, 5, 9, 12\}$. Write each of the following sets.

3. $A \cap B$

4. $A \cup B$

Solve each compound inequality. Give the solution set in both interval and graph form.

5. $3k \geq 6$ and $k - 4 < 5$

6. $-4x \leq -24$ or $4x - 2 < 10$

Solve each absolute value equation or inequality. Give the solution set in interval form.

7. $|4x - 3| = 7$

8. $|5 - 6x| > 12$

9. $|7 - x| \leq -1$

10. $|3 - 5x| = |2x + 8|$

11. $|-3x + 4| - 4 < -1$

12. $|12t + 7| \geq 0$

13. *Concept Check* If $k < 0$, what is the solution set of each of the following?

    (a) $|5x + 3| < k$ (b) $|5x + 3| > k$ (c) $|5x + 3| = k$

Graph the solution set of each inequality or compound inequality.

14. $3x - 2y > 6$

15. $3x - y > 0$

16. $y < 2x - 1$ and $x - y < 3$

17. $x - 2 \geq y$ or $y \geq 3$

CHAPTERS **1–9**

CUMULATIVE REVIEW EXERCISES

1. Match each number in Column I with the choice or choices of sets of numbers in Column II to which the number belongs.

<table>
<tr><td colspan="2" align="center">I</td><td colspan="2" align="center">II</td></tr>
<tr><td>(a) 34</td><td>(b) 0</td><td>A. Natural numbers</td><td>B. Whole numbers</td></tr>
<tr><td>(c) 2.16</td><td>(d) $-\sqrt{36}$</td><td>C. Integers</td><td>D. Rational numbers</td></tr>
<tr><td>(e) $\sqrt{13}$</td><td>(f) $-\dfrac{4}{5}$</td><td>E. Irrational numbers</td><td>F. Real numbers</td></tr>
</table>

Evaluate.

2. $9 \cdot 4 - 16 \div 4$

3. $-|8 - 13| - |-4| + |-9|$

We summarize our discussion of square roots as follows.

Square Roots of _a_

If a is a positive real number, then

$$\sqrt{a} \text{ is the positive or principal square root of } a,$$

and $\quad -\sqrt{a}$ is the negative square root of a.

For nonnegative a,

$$\sqrt{a} \cdot \sqrt{a} = \left(\sqrt{a}\right)^2 = a \quad \text{and} \quad -\sqrt{a} \cdot \left(-\sqrt{a}\right) = \left(-\sqrt{a}\right)^2 = a.$$

Also, $\sqrt{0} = 0$.

NOW TRY
EXERCISE 2

Find each square root.

(a) $\sqrt{400}$ **(b)** $-\sqrt{169}$

(c) $\sqrt{\dfrac{100}{121}}$

EXAMPLE 2 Finding Square Roots

Find each square root.

(a) $\sqrt{144}$

The radical $\sqrt{144}$ represents the positive or principal square root of 144. Think of a positive number whose square is 144.

$$12^2 = 144, \quad \text{so} \quad \sqrt{144} = 12.$$

(b) $-\sqrt{1024}$

This symbol represents the negative square root of 1024. A calculator with a square root key can be used to find $\sqrt{1024} = 32$. Therefore,

$$-\sqrt{1024} = -32.$$

(c) $\sqrt{\dfrac{4}{9}} = \dfrac{2}{3}$ **(d)** $-\sqrt{\dfrac{16}{49}} = -\dfrac{4}{7}$ **(e)** $\sqrt{0.81} = 0.9$ NOW TRY

As shown in the preceding definition, when the square root of a positive real number is squared, the result is that positive real number. $\left(\text{Also, } \left(\sqrt{0}\right)^2 = 0.\right)$

NOW TRY
EXERCISE 3

Find the square of each radical expression.

(a) $\sqrt{15}$ **(b)** $-\sqrt{23}$

(c) $\sqrt{2k^2 + 5}$

EXAMPLE 3 Squaring Radical Expressions

Find the *square* of each radical expression.

(a) $\sqrt{13}$

$$\left(\sqrt{13}\right)^2 = 13 \qquad \text{Definition of square root}$$

(b) $-\sqrt{29}$

$$\left(-\sqrt{29}\right)^2 = 29 \qquad \text{The square of a } \textit{negative} \text{ number is positive.}$$

(c) $\sqrt{p^2 + 1}$

$$\left(\sqrt{p^2 + 1}\right)^2 = p^2 + 1$$

NOW TRY

NOW TRY ANSWERS
2. **(a)** 20 **(b)** -13 **(c)** $\frac{10}{11}$
3. **(a)** 15 **(b)** 23 **(c)** $2k^2 + 5$

OBJECTIVE 2 **Decide whether a given root is rational, irrational, or not a real number.** Numbers with square roots that are rational are called **perfect squares.**

Perfect squares		Rational square roots
↓		↓
25		$\sqrt{25} = 5$
144	are perfect squares since	$\sqrt{144} = 12$
$\dfrac{4}{9}$		$\sqrt{\dfrac{4}{9}} = \dfrac{2}{3}$

A number that is not a perfect square has a square root that is not a rational number. For example, $\sqrt{5}$ is not a rational number because it cannot be written as the ratio of two integers. Its decimal equivalent neither terminates nor repeats. However, $\sqrt{5}$ is a real number and corresponds to a point on the number line.

A real number that is not rational is called an **irrational number.** The number $\sqrt{5}$ is irrational. *Many square roots of integers are irrational.*

> If a is a positive real number that is *not* a perfect square, then $\sqrt{a}$ is irrational.

Not every number has a real number square root. For example, there is no real number that can be squared to get -36. (The square of a real number can never be negative.) Because of this, $\sqrt{-36}$ *is not a real number.*

> If a is a *negative* real number, then $\sqrt{a}$ is *not* a real number.

⚠ **CAUTION** $\sqrt{-36}$ is *not* a real number, since there is no real number that can be squared to obtain -36. However, $-\sqrt{36}$ is the negative square root of 36, or -6.

**NOW TRY
EXERCISE 4**

Tell whether each square root is *rational, irrational,* or *not a real number.*

(a) $\sqrt{31}$ (b) $\sqrt{900}$
(c) $\sqrt{-16}$

EXAMPLE 4 Identifying Types of Square Roots

Tell whether each square root is *rational, irrational,* or *not a real number.*

(a) $\sqrt{17}$ Because 17 is not a perfect square, $\sqrt{17}$ is irrational.

(b) $\sqrt{64}$ The number 64 is a perfect square, 8^2, so $\sqrt{64} = 8$, a rational number.

(c) $\sqrt{-25}$ There is no real number whose square is -25. Therefore, $\sqrt{-25}$ is not a real number.

NOW TRY

NOTE Not all irrational numbers are square roots of integers. For example, π (approximately 3.14159) is an irrational number that is not a square root of any integer.

OBJECTIVE 3 **Find cube, fourth, and other roots.** Finding the square root of a number is the opposite (inverse) of squaring a number. In a similar way, there are inverses to finding the cube of a number or to finding the fourth or greater power of a number. These inverses are, respectively, the **cube root,** written $\sqrt[3]{a}$, and the **fourth root,** written $\sqrt[4]{a}$. Similar symbols are used for other roots.

NOW TRY ANSWERS
4. (a) irrational (b) rational
   (c) not a real number

$\sqrt[n]{a}$

The *n*th root of *a*, written $\sqrt[n]{a}$, is a number whose *n*th power equals *a*. That is,

$$\sqrt[n]{a} = b \quad \text{means} \quad b^n = a.$$

In $\sqrt[n]{a}$, the number *n* is the **index** or **order** of the radical.

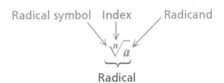

Radical symbol   Index   Radicand

Radical

We could write $\sqrt[2]{a}$ instead of $\sqrt{a}$, but the simpler symbol $\sqrt{a}$ is customary, since the square root is the most commonly used root.

NOTE When working with cube roots or fourth roots, it is helpful to memorize the first few **perfect cubes** $(2^3 = 8, 3^3 = 27,$ and so on$)$ and the first few **perfect fourth powers** $(2^4 = 16, 3^4 = 81,$ and so on$)$. See **Exercises 63 and 64.**

NOW TRY
EXERCISE 5

Find each cube root.

(a) $\sqrt[3]{343}$ (b) $\sqrt[3]{-1000}$

(c) $\sqrt[3]{27}$

EXAMPLE 5 Finding Cube Roots

Find each cube root.

(a) $\sqrt[3]{8}$ What number can be cubed to give 8? Because $2^3 = 8$, $\sqrt[3]{8} = 2$.

(b) $\sqrt[3]{-8} = -2$, because $(-2)^3 = -8$.

(c) $\sqrt[3]{216} = 6$, because $6^3 = 216$.   NOW TRY

Notice in **Example 5(b)** that we can find the cube root of a negative number. (Contrast this with the square root of a negative number, which is not real.) In fact, the cube root of a positive number is positive, and the cube root of a negative number is negative. *There is only one real number cube root for each real number.*

When a radical has an *even index* (square root, fourth root, and so on), *the radicand must be nonnegative* to yield a real number root. Also, for $a > 0$,

$$\sqrt{a}, \ \sqrt[4]{a}, \ \sqrt[6]{a}, \text{ and so on are positive (principal) roots.}$$

$$-\sqrt{a}, \ -\sqrt[4]{a}, \ -\sqrt[6]{a}, \text{ and so on are negative roots.}$$

NOW TRY
EXERCISE 6

Find each root.

(a) $\sqrt[4]{625}$ (b) $\sqrt[4]{-625}$

(c) $\sqrt[5]{3125}$ (d) $\sqrt[5]{-3125}$

EXAMPLE 6 Finding Other Roots

Find each root.

(a) $\sqrt[4]{16} = 2$, because 2 is positive and $2^4 = 16$.

(b) $-\sqrt[4]{16}$ From part (a), $\sqrt[4]{16} = 2$, so the negative root is $-\sqrt[4]{16} = -2$.

(c) $\sqrt[4]{-16}$ For a fourth root to be a real number, the radicand must be non-negative. There is no real number that equals $\sqrt[4]{-16}$.

(d) $-\sqrt[5]{32}$
First find $\sqrt[5]{32}$. Because 2 is the number whose fifth power is 32, $\sqrt[5]{32} = 2$. Since $\sqrt[5]{32} = 2$, it follows that

$$-\sqrt[5]{32} = -2.$$

(e) $\sqrt[5]{-32} = -2$, because $(-2)^5 = -32$.   NOW TRY

NOW TRY ANSWERS

5. (a) 7 (b) −10 (c) 3
6. (a) 5 (b) not a real number
   (c) 5 (d) −5

OBJECTIVE 4 Graph functions defined by radical expressions. A **radical expression** is an algebraic expression that contains radicals.

$$3 - \sqrt{x}, \quad \sqrt[3]{x}, \quad \text{and} \quad \sqrt{2x - 1} \qquad \text{Examples of radical expressions}$$

In earlier chapters, we graphed functions defined by polynomial and rational expressions. Now we examine the graphs of functions defined by the basic radical expressions $f(x) = \sqrt{x}$ and $f(x) = \sqrt[3]{x}$.

FIGURE 1 shows the graph of the **square root function,** together with a table of selected points. Only nonnegative values can be used for x, so the domain is $[0, \infty)$. Because $\sqrt{x}$ is the principal square root of x, it always has a nonnegative value, so the range is also $[0, \infty)$.

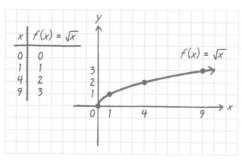

Square root function

$$f(x) = \sqrt{x}$$

Domain: $[0, \infty)$
Range: $[0, \infty)$

FIGURE 1

FIGURE 2 shows the graph of the **cube root function.** Since any real number (positive, negative, or 0) can be used for x in the cube root function, $\sqrt[3]{x}$ can be positive, negative, or 0. Thus, both the domain and the range of the cube root function are $(-\infty, \infty)$.

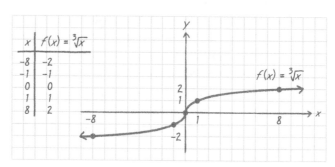

Cube root function

$$f(x) = \sqrt[3]{x}$$

Domain: $(-\infty, \infty)$
Range: $(-\infty, \infty)$

FIGURE 2

EXAMPLE 7 Graphing Functions Defined with Radicals

Graph each function by creating a table of values. Give the domain and range.

(a) $f(x) = \sqrt{x - 3}$

A table of values is given with the graph in **FIGURE 3** on the next page. The x-values were chosen in such a way that the function values are all integers. For the radicand to be nonnegative, we must have

$$x - 3 \geq 0, \quad \text{or} \quad x \geq 3.$$

Therefore, the domain of this function is $[3, \infty)$. Function values are positive or 0, so the range is $[0, \infty)$.

NOW TRY
EXERCISE 7

Graph each function. Give the domain and range.

(a) $f(x) = \sqrt{x + 1}$

(b) $f(x) = \sqrt[3]{x} - 1$

x	$f(x) = \sqrt{x - 3}$
3	$\sqrt{3 - 3} = 0$
4	$\sqrt{4 - 3} = 1$
7	$\sqrt{7 - 3} = 2$

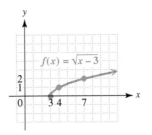

FIGURE 3

(b) $f(x) = \sqrt[3]{x} + 2$

See **FIGURE 4**. Both the domain and range are $(-\infty, \infty)$.

x	$f(x) = \sqrt[3]{x} + 2$
-8	$\sqrt[3]{-8} + 2 = 0$
-1	$\sqrt[3]{-1} + 2 = 1$
0	$\sqrt[3]{0} + 2 = 2$
1	$\sqrt[3]{1} + 2 = 3$
8	$\sqrt[3]{8} + 2 = 4$

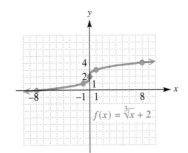

FIGURE 4

NOW TRY

OBJECTIVE 5 Find *n*th roots of *n*th powers. Consider the expression $\sqrt{a^2}$. At first glance, you may think that it is equivalent to a. However, this is not necessarily true. For example, consider the following.

NOW TRY
EXERCISE 8

Find each square root.

(a) $\sqrt{11^2}$ **(b)** $\sqrt{(-11)^2}$

(c) $\sqrt{z^2}$ **(d)** $\sqrt{(-z)^2}$

If $a = 6$,   then $\sqrt{a^2} = \sqrt{6^2} = \sqrt{36} = 6$.

If $a = -6$,   then $\sqrt{a^2} = \sqrt{(-6)^2} = \sqrt{36} = 6$. ← Instead of −6, we get 6, the *absolute value* of −6.

Since the symbol $\sqrt{a^2}$ represents the *nonnegative* square root, we express $\sqrt{a^2}$ with absolute value bars, as $|a|$, because a may be a negative number.

$\sqrt{a^2}$

For any real number a, $\sqrt{a^2} = |a|$.

That is, the principal square root of a^2 is the absolute value of a.

NOW TRY ANSWERS
7. (a)

domain: $[-1, \infty)$;
range: $[0, \infty)$

(b)

domain: $(-\infty, \infty)$;
range: $(-\infty, \infty)$

8. (a) 11   **(b)** 11   **(c)** $|z|$
    (d) $|z|$

EXAMPLE 8 Simplifying Square Roots by Using Absolute Value

Find each square root.

(a) $\sqrt{7^2} = |7| = 7$

(b) $\sqrt{(-7)^2} = |-7| = 7$

(c) $\sqrt{k^2} = |k|$

(d) $\sqrt{(-k)^2} = |-k| = |k|$

NOW TRY

We can generalize this idea to any nth root.

$$\sqrt[n]{a^n}$$

If n is an *even* positive integer, then $\sqrt[n]{a^n} = |a|$.

If n is an *odd* positive integer, then $\sqrt[n]{a^n} = a$.

That is, use the absolute value symbol when n is even. Absolute value is not used when n is odd.

NOW TRY
EXERCISE 9

Simplify each root.

(a) $\sqrt[8]{(-2)^8}$ (b) $\sqrt[3]{(-9)^3}$

(c) $-\sqrt[4]{(-10)^4}$ (d) $-\sqrt{m^8}$

(e) $\sqrt[3]{x^{18}}$ (f) $\sqrt[4]{t^{20}}$

EXAMPLE 9 Simplifying Higher Roots by Using Absolute Value

Simplify each root.

(a) $\sqrt[6]{(-3)^6} = |-3| = 3$ n is even. Use absolute value.

(b) $\sqrt[5]{(-4)^5} = -4$ n is odd.

(c) $-\sqrt[4]{(-9)^4} = -|-9| = -9$ n is even. Use absolute value.

(d) $-\sqrt{m^4} = -|m^2| = -m^2$ For all m, $|m^2| = m^2$.

No absolute value bars are needed here, because m^2 is nonnegative for any real number value of m.

(e) $\sqrt[3]{a^{12}} = a^4$, because $a^{12} = (a^4)^3$.

(f) $\sqrt[4]{x^{12}} = |x^3|$

We use absolute value to guarantee that the result is not negative (because x^3 is negative when x is negative). If desired $|x^3|$ can be written as $x^2 \cdot |x|$.   **NOW TRY**

OBJECTIVE 6 Use a calculator to find roots. While numbers such as $\sqrt{9}$ and $\sqrt[3]{-8}$ are rational, radicals are often irrational numbers. To find approximations of such radicals, we usually use a scientific or graphing calculator. For example,

$$\sqrt{15} \approx 3.872983346, \quad \sqrt[3]{10} \approx 2.15443469, \quad \text{and} \quad \sqrt[4]{2} \approx 1.189207115,$$

where the symbol $\approx$ means "is approximately equal to." In this book, we often show approximations rounded to three decimal places. Thus,

$$\sqrt{15} \approx 3.873, \quad \sqrt[3]{10} \approx 2.154, \quad \text{and} \quad \sqrt[4]{2} \approx 1.189.$$

FIGURE 5 shows how the preceding approximations are displayed on a TI-83/84 Plus graphing calculator.

There is a simple way to check that a calculator approximation is "in the ballpark." For example, because 16 is a little larger than 15, $\sqrt{16} = 4$ should be a little larger than $\sqrt{15}$. Thus, 3.873 is reasonable as an approximation for $\sqrt{15}$.

```
√(15)
              3.873
³√(10)
              2.154
4 ×√2
              1.189
```

FIGURE 5

NOTE The methods for finding approximations differ among makes and models of calculators. *You should always consult your owner's manual for keystroke instructions.* Be aware that graphing calculators often differ from scientific calculators in the order in which keystrokes are made.

NOW TRY ANSWERS

9. (a) 2   (b) −9   (c) −10
   (d) $-m^4$ (e) x^6 (f) $|t^5|$

150. The Vietnam Veterans Memorial in Washington, DC, is in the shape of an unenclosed isosceles triangle with equal sides of length 246.75 ft. If the triangle were enclosed, the third side would have length 438.14 ft. Use Heron's formula from **Exercise 147** to find the area of this enclosure to the nearest hundred square feet. (*Source:* Information pamphlet obtained at the Vietnam Veterans Memorial.)

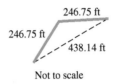

246.75 ft

246.75 ft

438.14 ft

Not to scale

PREVIEW EXERCISES

Apply the rules for exponents. Write each result with only positive exponents. Assume that all variables represent nonzero real numbers. **See Sections 4.1 and 4.2.**

151. $x^5 \cdot x^{-1} \cdot x^{-3}$ **152.** $(4x^2y^3)(2^3x^5y)$ **153.** $\left(\dfrac{2}{3}\right)^{-3}$ **154.** $\dfrac{5}{5^{-1}}$

(10.2) Rational Exponents

OBJECTIVES

1. Use exponential notation for *n*th roots.
2. Define and use expressions of the form $a^{m/n}$.
3. Convert between radicals and rational exponents.
4. Use the rules for exponents with rational exponents.

OBJECTIVE 1 Use exponential notation for *n*th roots. Consider the product $(3^{1/2})^2 = 3^{1/2} \cdot 3^{1/2}$. Using the rules of exponents from **Section 4.1,** we can simplify this product as follows.

$$(3^{1/2})^2 = 3^{1/2} \cdot 3^{1/2}$$
$$= 3^{1/2+1/2} \qquad \text{Product rule: } a^m \cdot a^n = a^{m+n}$$
$$= 3^1 \qquad \text{Add exponents.}$$
$$= 3 \qquad a^1 = a$$

Also, by definition,

$$\left(\sqrt{3}\right)^2 = \sqrt{3} \cdot \sqrt{3} = 3.$$

Since both $(3^{1/2})^2$ and $\left(\sqrt{3}\right)^2$ are equal to 3, it seems reasonable to define

$$3^{1/2} = \sqrt{3}.$$

This suggests the following generalization.

$a^{1/n}$

If $\sqrt[n]{a}$ is a real number, then $\quad a^{1/n} = \sqrt[n]{a}.$

$$4^{1/2} = \sqrt{4}, \quad 8^{1/3} = \sqrt[3]{8}, \quad \text{and} \quad 16^{1/4} = \sqrt[4]{16} \qquad \text{Examples of } a^{1/n}$$

Notice that the denominator of the rational exponent is the index of the radical.

NOW TRY
EXERCISE 1

Evaluate each exponential.

(a) $81^{1/2}$ **(b)** $125^{1/3}$

(c) $-625^{1/4}$ **(d)** $(-625)^{1/4}$

(e) $(-125)^{1/3}$ **(f)** $\left(\dfrac{1}{16}\right)^{1/4}$

EXAMPLE 1 Evaluating Exponentials of the Form $a^{1/n}$

Evaluate each exponential.

The denominator is the index.

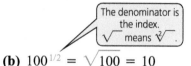
The denominator is the index. $\sqrt{\ }$ means $\sqrt[2]{\ }$.

(a) $64^{1/3} = \sqrt[3]{64} = 4$ **(b)** $100^{1/2} = \sqrt{100} = 10$

(c) $-256^{1/4} = -\sqrt[4]{256} = -4$

(d) $(-256)^{1/4} = \sqrt[4]{-256}$ is not a real number, because the radicand, -256, is negative and the index is even.

(e) $(-32)^{1/5} = \sqrt[5]{-32} = -2$ **(f)** $\left(\dfrac{1}{8}\right)^{1/3} = \sqrt[3]{\dfrac{1}{8}} = \dfrac{1}{2}$ NOW TRY

⚠ **CAUTION** Notice the difference between **Examples 1(c) and (d).** The radical in part (c) is the *negative fourth root of a positive number,* while the radical in part (d) is the *principal fourth root of a negative number, which is not a real number.*

OBJECTIVE 2 Define and use expressions of the form $a^{m/n}$. We know that $8^{1/3} = \sqrt[3]{8}$. We can define a number like $8^{2/3}$, where the numerator of the exponent is not 1. For past rules of exponents to be valid,

$$8^{2/3} = 8^{(1/3)2} = (8^{1/3})^2.$$

Since $8^{1/3} = \sqrt[3]{8}$,

$$8^{2/3} = \left(\sqrt[3]{8}\right)^2 = 2^2 = 4.$$

Generalizing from this example, we define $a^{m/n}$ as follows.

$a^{m/n}$

If m and n are positive integers with m/n in lowest terms, then

$$a^{m/n} = (a^{1/n})^m,$$

provided that $a^{1/n}$ is a real number. If $a^{1/n}$ is not a real number, then $a^{m/n}$ is not a real number.

EXAMPLE 2 Evaluating Exponentials of the Form $a^{m/n}$

Evaluate each exponential.

Think:
$36^{1/2} = \sqrt{36} = 6$

Think:
$125^{1/3} = \sqrt[3]{125} = 5$

(a) $36^{3/2} = (36^{1/2})^3 = 6^3 = 216$ **(b)** $125^{2/3} = (125^{1/3})^2 = 5^2 = 25$

Be careful.
The base is 4.

(c) $-4^{5/2} = -(4^{5/2}) = -(4^{1/2})^5 = -(2)^5 = -32$

Because the base here is 4, the negative sign is *not* affected by the exponent.

NOW TRY ANSWERS
1. **(a)** 9 **(b)** 5 **(c)** -5
   (d) It is not a real number.
   (e) -5 **(f)** $\frac{1}{2}$

NOW TRY
EXERCISE 2

Evaluate each exponential.

(a) $32^{2/5}$ **(b)** $8^{5/3}$

(c) $-100^{3/2}$ **(d)** $(-121)^{3/2}$

(e) $(-125)^{4/3}$

(d) $(-27)^{2/3} = [(-27)^{1/3}]^2 = (-3)^2 = 9$

Notice in part (c) that we first evaluate the exponential and then find its negative. In part (d), the $-$ sign is part of the base, -27.

(e) $(-100)^{3/2} = [(-100)^{1/2}]^3$, which is not a real number, since $(-100)^{1/2}$, or $\sqrt{-100}$, is not a real number.

NOW TRY

When a rational exponent is negative, the earlier interpretation of negative exponents is applied.

$a^{-m/n}$

If $a^{m/n}$ is a real number, then

$$a^{-m/n} = \frac{1}{a^{m/n}} \quad (a \neq 0).$$

NOW TRY
EXERCISE 3

Evaluate each exponential.

(a) $243^{-3/5}$ **(b)** $4^{-5/2}$

(c) $\left(\dfrac{216}{125}\right)^{-2/3}$

EXAMPLE 3 Evaluating Exponentials with Negative Rational Exponents

Evaluate each exponential.

(a) $16^{-3/4} = \dfrac{1}{16^{3/4}} = \dfrac{1}{(16^{1/4})^3} = \dfrac{1}{(\sqrt[4]{16})^3} = \dfrac{1}{2^3} = \dfrac{1}{8}$

> The denominator of 3/4 is the index and the numerator is the exponent.

(b) $25^{-3/2} = \dfrac{1}{25^{3/2}} = \dfrac{1}{(25^{1/2})^3} = \dfrac{1}{(\sqrt{25})^3} = \dfrac{1}{5^3} = \dfrac{1}{125}$

(c) $\left(\dfrac{8}{27}\right)^{-2/3} = \dfrac{1}{\left(\dfrac{8}{27}\right)^{2/3}} = \dfrac{1}{\left(\sqrt[3]{\dfrac{8}{27}}\right)^2} = \dfrac{1}{\left(\dfrac{2}{3}\right)^2} = \dfrac{1}{\dfrac{4}{9}} = \dfrac{9}{4}$

> $\dfrac{1}{\frac{4}{9}} = 1 \div \dfrac{4}{9} = 1 \cdot \dfrac{9}{4}$

We can also use the rule $\left(\dfrac{b}{a}\right)^{-m} = \left(\dfrac{a}{b}\right)^m$ here, as follows.

$$\left(\dfrac{8}{27}\right)^{-2/3} = \left(\dfrac{27}{8}\right)^{2/3} = \left(\sqrt[3]{\dfrac{27}{8}}\right)^2 = \left(\dfrac{3}{2}\right)^2 = \dfrac{9}{4}$$

> Take the reciprocal only of the base, **not** the exponent.

NOW TRY

⚠ **CAUTION** Be careful to distinguish between exponential expressions like the following.

$16^{-1/4}$, which equals $\dfrac{1}{2}$, $-16^{1/4}$, which equals -2, and $-16^{-1/4}$, which equals $-\dfrac{1}{2}$

A negative exponent does not necessarily lead to a negative result. Negative exponents lead to reciprocals, which may be positive.

NOW TRY ANSWERS
2. **(a)** 4 **(b)** 32 **(c)** -1000
   (d) It is not a real number.
   (e) 625
3. **(a)** $\frac{1}{27}$ **(b)** $\frac{1}{32}$ **(c)** $\frac{25}{36}$

We obtain an alternative definition of $a^{m/n}$ by using the power rule for exponents differently than in the earlier definition. If all indicated roots are real numbers,

then $\qquad a^{m/n} = a^{m(1/n)} = (a^m)^{1/n}, \quad \text{so} \quad a^{m/n} = (a^m)^{1/n}.$

$a^{m/n}$

If all indicated roots are real numbers, then

$$a^{m/n} = (a^{1/n})^m = (a^m)^{1/n}.$$

We can now evaluate an expression such as $27^{2/3}$ in two ways.

$$27^{2/3} = (27^{1/3})^2 = 3^2 = 9$$

The result is the same.

or $\qquad 27^{2/3} = (27^2)^{1/3} = 729^{1/3} = 9$

In most cases, it is easier to use $(a^{1/n})^m$.

Radical Form of $a^{m/n}$

If all indicated roots are real numbers, then

$$a^{m/n} = \sqrt[n]{a^m} = (\sqrt[n]{a})^m.$$

That is, raise a to the mth power and then take the nth root, or take the nth root of a and then raise to the mth power.

For example,

$$8^{2/3} = \sqrt[3]{8^2} = \sqrt[3]{64} = 4, \quad \text{and} \quad 8^{2/3} = (\sqrt[3]{8})^2 = 2^2 = 4,$$

so $\qquad 8^{2/3} = \sqrt[3]{8^2} = (\sqrt[3]{8})^2.$

OBJECTIVE 3 **Convert between radicals and rational exponents.** Using the definition of rational exponents, we can simplify many problems involving radicals by converting the radicals to numbers with rational exponents. After simplifying, we can convert the answer back to radical form if required.

EXAMPLE 4 **Converting between Rational Exponents and Radicals**

Write each exponential as a radical. Assume that all variables represent positive real numbers. Use the definition that takes the root first.

(a) $13^{1/2} = \sqrt{13}$ $\qquad$ **(b)** $6^{3/4} = (\sqrt[4]{6})^3$ $\qquad$ **(c)** $9m^{5/8} = 9(\sqrt[8]{m})^5$

(d) $6x^{2/3} - (4x)^{3/5} = 6(\sqrt[3]{x})^2 - (\sqrt[5]{4x})^3$

(e) $r^{-2/3} = \dfrac{1}{r^{2/3}} = \dfrac{1}{(\sqrt[3]{r})^2}$

(f) $(a^2 + b^2)^{1/2} = \sqrt{a^2 + b^2}$ $\qquad$ $\boxed{\sqrt{a^2 + b^2} \neq a + b}$

NOW TRY
EXERCISE 4

Write each exponential as a radical. Assume that all variables represent positive real numbers.

(a) $21^{1/2}$ **(b)** $17^{5/4}$

(c) $4t^{3/5} + (4t)^{2/3}$

(d) $w^{-2/5}$ **(e)** $(a^2 - b^2)^{1/4}$

In parts (f)–(h), write each radical as an exponential. Simplify. Assume that all variables represent positive real numbers.

(f) $\sqrt[3]{15}$ **(g)** $\sqrt[4]{4^2}$

(h) $\sqrt[4]{x^4}$

In parts (g)–(i), write each radical as an exponential. Simplify. Assume that all variables represent positive real numbers.

(g) $\sqrt{10} = 10^{1/2}$

(h) $\sqrt[4]{3^8} = 3^{8/4} = 3^2 = 9$

(i) $\sqrt[6]{z^6} = z$, since z is positive.

 NOW TRY

NOTE In **Example 4(i),** it is not necessary to use absolute value bars, since the directions specifically state that the variable represents a positive real number. Because the absolute value of the positive real number z is z itself, the answer is simply z.

OBJECTIVE 4 **Use the rules for exponents with rational exponents.** The definition of rational exponents allows us to apply the rules for exponents from **Sections 4.1 and 4.2.**

Rules for Rational Exponents

Let r and s be rational numbers. For all real numbers a and b for which the indicated expressions exist, the following are true.

$$a^r \cdot a^s = a^{r+s} \qquad a^{-r} = \frac{1}{a^r} \qquad \frac{a^r}{a^s} = a^{r-s} \qquad \left(\frac{a}{b}\right)^{-r} = \frac{b^r}{a^r}$$

$$(a^r)^s = a^{rs} \qquad (ab)^r = a^r b^r \qquad \left(\frac{a}{b}\right)^r = \frac{a^r}{b^r} \qquad a^{-r} = \left(\frac{1}{a}\right)^r$$

EXAMPLE 5 **Applying Rules for Rational Exponents**

Write with only positive exponents. Assume that all variables represent positive real numbers.

(a) $2^{1/2} \cdot 2^{1/4}$

$= 2^{1/2+1/4}$ Product rule

$= 2^{3/4}$ Add exponents.

(b) $\dfrac{5^{2/3}}{5^{7/3}}$

$= 5^{2/3 - 7/3}$ Quotient rule

$= 5^{-5/3}$ Subtract exponents.

$= \dfrac{1}{5^{5/3}}$ $a^{-r} = \frac{1}{a^r}$

(c) $\dfrac{(x^{1/2}y^{2/3})^4}{y}$

$= \dfrac{(x^{1/2})^4(y^{2/3})^4}{y}$ Power rule

$= \dfrac{x^2 y^{8/3}}{y^1}$ Power rule

$= x^2 y^{8/3-1}$ Quotient rule

$= x^2 y^{5/3}$ $\frac{8}{3} - 1 = \frac{8}{3} - \frac{3}{3} = \frac{5}{3}$

NOW TRY ANSWERS

4. (a) $\sqrt{21}$ **(b)** $\left(\sqrt[4]{17}\right)^5$

(c) $4\left(\sqrt[5]{t}\right)^3 + \left(\sqrt[3]{4t}\right)^2$

(d) $\dfrac{1}{\left(\sqrt[5]{w}\right)^2}$ **(e)** $\sqrt[4]{a^2 - b^2}$

(f) $15^{1/3}$ **(g)** 2   **(h)** x

NOW TRY
EXERCISE 5

Write with only positive exponents. Assume that all variables represent positive real numbers.

(a) $5^{1/4} \cdot 5^{2/3}$ **(b)** $\dfrac{9^{3/5}}{9^{7/5}}$

(c) $\dfrac{(r^{2/3}t^{1/4})^8}{t}$

(d) $\left(\dfrac{2x^{1/2}y^{-2/3}}{x^{-3/5}y^{-1/5}}\right)^{-3}$

(e) $y^{2/3}(y^{1/3} + y^{5/3})$

(d) $\left(\dfrac{x^4 y^{-6}}{x^{-2}y^{1/3}}\right)^{-2/3}$

$= \dfrac{(x^4)^{-2/3}(y^{-6})^{-2/3}}{(x^{-2})^{-2/3}(y^{1/3})^{-2/3}}$ Power rule

$= \dfrac{x^{-8/3}y^4}{x^{4/3}y^{-2/9}}$ Power rule

$= x^{-8/3-4/3}y^{4-(-2/9)}$ Quotient rule

$= x^{-4}y^{38/9}$ Use parentheses to avoid errors. $4 - \left(-\frac{2}{9}\right) = \frac{36}{9} + \frac{2}{9} = \frac{38}{9}$

$= \dfrac{y^{38/9}}{x^4}$ Definition of negative exponent

The same result is obtained if we simplify within the parentheses first.

$\left(\dfrac{x^4 y^{-6}}{x^{-2}y^{1/3}}\right)^{-2/3}$

$= (x^{4-(-2)}y^{-6-1/3})^{-2/3}$ Quotient rule

$= (x^6 y^{-19/3})^{-2/3}$ $-6 - \frac{1}{3} = -\frac{18}{3} - \frac{1}{3} = -\frac{19}{3}$

$= (x^6)^{-2/3}(y^{-19/3})^{-2/3}$ Power rule

$= x^{-4}y^{38/9}$ Power rule

$= \dfrac{y^{38/9}}{x^4}$ Definition of negative exponent

(e) $\qquad m^{3/4}(m^{5/4} - m^{1/4})$

$= m^{3/4}(m^{5/4}) - m^{3/4}(m^{1/4})$ Distributive property

Do not make the common mistake of multiplying exponents in the first step.

$= m^{3/4+5/4} - m^{3/4+1/4}$ Product rule

$= m^{8/4} - m^{4/4}$ Add exponents.

$= m^2 - m$ Lowest terms in exponents

NOW TRY

⚠ **CAUTION** Use the rules of exponents in problems like those in **Example 5.** Do not convert the expressions to radical form.

EXAMPLE 6 Applying Rules for Rational Exponents

Write all radicals as exponentials, and then apply the rules for rational exponents. Leave answers in exponential form. Assume that all variables represent positive real numbers.

(a) $\sqrt[3]{x^2} \cdot \sqrt[4]{x}$

$= x^{2/3} \cdot x^{1/4}$ Convert to rational exponents.

$= x^{2/3+1/4}$ Product rule

$= x^{8/12+3/12}$ Write exponents with a common denominator.

$= x^{11/12}$ Add exponents.

NOW TRY
EXERCISE 6

Write all radicals as exponentials, and then apply the rules for rational exponents. Leave answers in exponential form. Assume that all variables represent positive real numbers.

(a) $\sqrt[5]{y^3} \cdot \sqrt[3]{y}$ **(b)** $\dfrac{\sqrt[4]{y^3}}{\sqrt{y^5}}$

(c) $\sqrt{\sqrt[3]{y}}$

NOW TRY ANSWERS

6. **(a)** $y^{14/15}$ **(b)** $\dfrac{1}{y^{7/4}}$ **(c)** $y^{1/6}$

(b) $\dfrac{\sqrt{x^3}}{\sqrt[3]{x^2}}$

$= \dfrac{x^{3/2}}{x^{2/3}}$ Convert to rational exponents.

$= x^{3/2 - 2/3}$ Quotient rule

$= x^{5/6}$ $\dfrac{3}{2} - \dfrac{2}{3} = \dfrac{9}{6} - \dfrac{4}{6} = \dfrac{5}{6}$

(c) $\sqrt{\sqrt[4]{z}}$

$= \sqrt{z^{1/4}}$ Convert the inside radical to rational exponents.

$= (z^{1/4})^{1/2}$ Convert to rational exponents.

$= z^{1/8}$ Power rule

NOW TRY

NOTE The ability to convert between radicals and rational exponents is important in the study of exponential and logarithmic functions in **Chapter 12.**

10.2 EXERCISES

MyMathLab   Math XL PRACTICE   WATCH   DOWNLOAD   READ   REVIEW

🌐 *Complete solution available on the Video Resources on DVD*

Concept Check Match each expression from Column I with the equivalent choice from Column II.

I

1. $3^{1/2}$ 2. $(-27)^{1/3}$
3. $-16^{1/2}$ 4. $(-25)^{1/2}$
5. $(-32)^{1/5}$ 6. $(-32)^{2/5}$
7. $4^{3/2}$ 8. $6^{2/4}$
9. $-6^{2/4}$ 10. $36^{0.5}$

II

A. -4 B. 8
C. $\sqrt{3}$ D. $-\sqrt{6}$
E. -3 F. $\sqrt{6}$
G. 4 H. -2
I. 6 J. Not a real number

Evaluate each exponential. See Examples 1–3.

🌐 11. $169^{1/2}$ 12. $121^{1/2}$ 13. $729^{1/3}$ 14. $512^{1/3}$

15. $16^{1/4}$ 16. $625^{1/4}$ 17. $\left(\dfrac{64}{81}\right)^{1/2}$ 18. $\left(\dfrac{8}{27}\right)^{1/3}$

19. $(-27)^{1/3}$ 20. $(-32)^{1/5}$ 🌐 21. $(-144)^{1/2}$ 22. $(-36)^{1/2}$

🌐 23. $100^{3/2}$ 24. $64^{3/2}$ 25. $81^{3/4}$ 26. $216^{2/3}$

27. $-16^{5/2}$ 28. $-32^{3/5}$ 29. $(-8)^{4/3}$ 30. $(-243)^{2/5}$

🌐 31. $32^{-3/5}$ 32. $27^{-4/3}$ 33. $64^{-3/2}$ 34. $81^{-3/2}$

35. $\left(\dfrac{125}{27}\right)^{-2/3}$ 36. $\left(\dfrac{64}{125}\right)^{-2/3}$ 37. $\left(\dfrac{16}{81}\right)^{-3/4}$ 38. $\left(\dfrac{729}{64}\right)^{-5/6}$

Write with radicals. Assume that all variables represent positive real numbers. See Example 4.

🌐 39. $10^{1/2}$ 40. $3^{1/2}$ 41. $8^{3/4}$

42. $7^{2/3}$ 🌐 43. $(9q)^{5/8} - (2x)^{2/3}$ 44. $(3p)^{3/4} + (4x)^{1/3}$

45. $(2m)^{-3/2}$ 46. $(5y)^{-3/5}$ 47. $(2y + x)^{2/3}$

48. $(r + 2z)^{3/2}$ 49. $(3m^4 + 2k^2)^{-2/3}$ 50. $(5x^2 + 3z^3)^{-5/6}$

Simplify by first converting to rational exponents. Assume that all variables represent positive real numbers. See Example 4.

51. $\sqrt{2^{12}}$ 52. $\sqrt{5^{10}}$ 53. $\sqrt[3]{4^9}$ 54. $\sqrt[4]{6^8}$ 🌐 55. $\sqrt{x^{20}}$

56. $\sqrt{r^{50}}$ 57. $\sqrt[3]{x} \cdot \sqrt{x}$ 58. $\sqrt[4]{y} \cdot \sqrt[5]{y^2}$ 59. $\dfrac{\sqrt[3]{t^4}}{\sqrt[5]{t^4}}$ 60. $\dfrac{\sqrt[4]{w^3}}{\sqrt[6]{w}}$

Simplify each expression. Write all answers with positive exponents. Assume that all variables represent positive real numbers. **See Example 5.**

61. $3^{1/2} \cdot 3^{3/2}$

62. $6^{4/3} \cdot 6^{2/3}$

63. $\dfrac{64^{5/3}}{64^{4/3}}$

64. $\dfrac{125^{7/3}}{125^{5/3}}$

65. $y^{7/3} \cdot y^{-4/3}$

66. $r^{-8/9} \cdot r^{17/9}$

67. $x^{2/3} \cdot x^{-1/4}$

68. $x^{2/5} \cdot x^{-1/3}$

69. $\dfrac{k^{1/3}}{k^{2/3} \cdot k^{-1}}$

70. $\dfrac{z^{3/4}}{z^{5/4} \cdot z^{-2}}$

71. $\dfrac{(x^{1/4}y^{2/5})^{20}}{x^2}$

72. $\dfrac{(r^{1/5}s^{2/3})^{15}}{r^2}$

73. $\dfrac{(x^{2/3})^2}{(x^2)^{7/3}}$

74. $\dfrac{(p^3)^{1/4}}{(p^{5/4})^2}$

75. $\dfrac{m^{3/4}n^{-1/4}}{(m^2n)^{1/2}}$

76. $\dfrac{(a^2b^5)^{-1/4}}{(a^{-3}b^2)^{1/6}}$

77. $\dfrac{p^{1/5}p^{7/10}p^{1/2}}{(p^3)^{-1/5}}$

78. $\dfrac{z^{1/3}z^{-2/3}z^{1/6}}{(z^{-1/6})^3}$

79. $\left(\dfrac{b^{-3/2}}{c^{-5/3}}\right)^2 (b^{-1/4}c^{-1/3})^{-1}$

80. $\left(\dfrac{m^{-2/3}}{a^{-3/4}}\right)^4 (m^{-3/8}a^{1/4})^{-2}$

81. $\left(\dfrac{p^{-1/4}q^{-3/2}}{3^{-1}p^{-2}q^{-2/3}}\right)^{-2}$

82. $\left(\dfrac{2^{-2}w^{-3/4}x^{-5/8}}{w^{3/4}x^{-1/2}}\right)^{-3}$

83. $p^{2/3}(p^{1/3} + 2p^{4/3})$

84. $z^{5/8}(3z^{5/8} + 5z^{11/8})$

85. $k^{1/4}(k^{3/2} - k^{1/2})$

86. $r^{3/5}(r^{1/2} + r^{3/4})$

87. $6a^{7/4}(a^{-7/4} + 3a^{-3/4})$

88. $4m^{5/3}(m^{-2/3} - 4m^{-5/3})$

89. $-5x^{7/6}(x^{5/6} - x^{-1/6})$

90. $-8y^{11/7}(y^{3/7} - y^{-4/7})$

Write with rational exponents, and then apply the properties of exponents. Assume that all radicands represent positive real numbers. Give answers in exponential form. **See Example 6.**

91. $\sqrt[5]{x^3} \cdot \sqrt[4]{x}$

92. $\sqrt[6]{y^5} \cdot \sqrt[3]{y^2}$

93. $\dfrac{\sqrt{x^5}}{\sqrt{x^8}}$

94. $\dfrac{\sqrt[3]{k^5}}{\sqrt[3]{k^7}}$

95. $\sqrt{y} \cdot \sqrt[3]{yz}$

96. $\sqrt[3]{xz} \cdot \sqrt{z}$

97. $\sqrt[4]{\sqrt[3]{m}}$

98. $\sqrt[3]{\sqrt{k}}$

99. $\sqrt{\sqrt{\sqrt{x}}}$

100. $\sqrt{\sqrt{\sqrt{\sqrt{x}}}}$

101. $\sqrt{\sqrt[3]{\sqrt[4]{x}}}$

102. $\sqrt[3]{\sqrt[5]{\sqrt{y}}}$

103. Show that, in general, $\sqrt{a^2 + b^2} \neq a + b$ by replacing a with 3 and b with 4.

104. Suppose someone claims that $\sqrt[n]{a^n + b^n}$ must equal $a + b$, since, when $a = 1$ and $b = 0$, a true statement results:

$$\sqrt[n]{a^n + b^n} = \sqrt[n]{1^n + 0^n} = \sqrt[n]{1^n} = 1 = 1 + 0 = a + b.$$

Explain why this is faulty reasoning.

Solve each problem.

105. Meteorologists can determine the duration of a storm by using the function defined by

$$T(D) = 0.07D^{3/2},$$

where D is the diameter of the storm in miles and T is the time in hours. Find the duration of a storm with a diameter of 16 mi. Round your answer to the nearest tenth of an hour.

106. The threshold weight T, in pounds, for a person is the weight above which the risk of death increases greatly. The threshold weight in pounds for men aged 40–49 is related to height h in inches by the function defined by

$$h(T) = (1860.867T)^{1/3}.$$

What height corresponds to a threshold weight of 200 lb for a 46-yr-old man? Round your answer to the nearest inch and then to the nearest tenth of a foot.

*The **windchill factor** is a measure of the cooling effect that the wind has on a person's skin. It calculates the equivalent cooling temperature if there were no wind. The National Weather Service uses the formula*

$$\text{Windchill temperature} = 35.74 + 0.6215T - 35.75V^{4/25} + 0.4275TV^{4/25},$$

where T is the temperature in °F and V is the wind speed in miles per hour, to calculate windchill. The chart gives the windchill factor for various wind speeds and temperatures at which frostbite is a risk, and how quickly it may occur.

Temperature (°F)

Calm	40	30	20	10	0	−10	−20	−30	−40
5	36	25	13	1	−11	−22	−34	−46	−57
10	34	21	9	−4	−16	−28	−41	−53	−66
15	32	19	6	−7	−19	−32	−45	−58	−71
20	30	17	4	−9	−22	−35	−48	−61	−74
25	29	16	3	−11	−24	−37	−51	−64	−78
30	28	15	1	−12	−26	−39	−53	−67	−80
35	28	14	0	−14	−27	−41	−55	−69	−82
40	27	13	−1	−15	−29	−43	−57	−71	−84

Wind speed (mph)

Frostbites times: ☐ 30 minutes ■ 10 minutes ■ 5 minutes

Source: National Oceanic and Atmospheric Administration, National Weather Service.

Use the formula and a calculator to determine the windchill to the nearest tenth of a degree, given the following conditions. Compare your answers with the appropriate entries in the table.

107. 30°F, 15-mph wind

108. 10°F, 30-mph wind

109. 20°F, 20-mph wind

110. 40°F, 10-mph wind

PREVIEW EXERCISES

*Simplify each pair of expressions, and then compare the results. **See Section 10.1.***

111. $\sqrt{25} \cdot \sqrt{36}, \quad \sqrt{25 \cdot 36}$

112. $\dfrac{\sqrt[3]{27}}{\sqrt[3]{729}}, \quad \sqrt[3]{\dfrac{27}{729}}$

10.3 Simplifying Radical Expressions

OBJECTIVES

1 Use the product rule for radicals.

2 Use the quotient rule for radicals.

3 Simplify radicals.

4 Simplify products and quotients of radicals with different indexes.

5 Use the Pythagorean theorem.

6 Use the distance formula.

OBJECTIVE 1 Use the product rule for radicals. Consider the expressions $\sqrt{36 \cdot 4}$ and $\sqrt{36} \cdot \sqrt{4}$. Are they equal?

$$\sqrt{36 \cdot 4} = \sqrt{144} = 12$$
$$\sqrt{36} \cdot \sqrt{4} = 6 \cdot 2 = 12$$

The result is the same.

This is an example of the **product rule for radicals.**

Product Rule for Radicals

If $\sqrt[n]{a}$ and $\sqrt[n]{b}$ are real numbers and n is a natural number, then

$$\sqrt[n]{a} \cdot \sqrt[n]{b} = \sqrt[n]{ab}.$$

That is, the product of two *n*th roots is the *n*th root of the product.

We justify the product rule by using the rules for rational exponents. Since $\sqrt[n]{a} = a^{1/n}$ and $\sqrt[n]{b} = b^{1/n}$,

$$\sqrt[n]{a} \cdot \sqrt[n]{b} = a^{1/n} \cdot b^{1/n} = (ab)^{1/n} = \sqrt[n]{ab}.$$

> ⚠ **CAUTION** *Use the product rule only when the radicals have the same index.*

NOW TRY
EXERCISE 1

Multiply. Assume that all variables represent positive real numbers.

(a) $\sqrt{7} \cdot \sqrt{11}$

(b) $\sqrt{2mn} \cdot \sqrt{15}$

EXAMPLE 1 Using the Product Rule

Multiply. Assume that all variables represent positive real numbers.

(a) $\sqrt{5} \cdot \sqrt{7}$
$= \sqrt{5 \cdot 7}$
$= \sqrt{35}$

(b) $\sqrt{11} \cdot \sqrt{p}$
$= \sqrt{11p}$

(c) $\sqrt{7} \cdot \sqrt{11xyz}$
$= \sqrt{77xyz}$

NOW TRY ↻

NOW TRY
EXERCISE 2

Multiply. Assume that all variables represent positive real numbers.

(a) $\sqrt[3]{4} \cdot \sqrt[3]{5}$

(b) $\sqrt[4]{5t} \cdot \sqrt[4]{6r^3}$

(c) $\sqrt[7]{20x} \cdot \sqrt[7]{3xy^3}$

(d) $\sqrt[3]{5} \cdot \sqrt[4]{9}$

EXAMPLE 2 Using the Product Rule

Multiply. Assume that all variables represent positive real numbers.

(a) $\sqrt[3]{3} \cdot \sqrt[3]{12}$
$= \sqrt[3]{3 \cdot 12}$
$= \sqrt[3]{36}$ ← Remember to write the index.

(b) $\sqrt[4]{8y} \cdot \sqrt[4]{3r^2}$
$= \sqrt[4]{24yr^2}$

(c) $\sqrt[6]{10m^4} \cdot \sqrt[6]{5m}$
$= \sqrt[6]{50m^5}$

(d) $\sqrt[4]{2} \cdot \sqrt[5]{2}$ cannot be simplified using the product rule for radicals, because the indexes (4 and 5) are different.

NOW TRY ↻

OBJECTIVE 2 Use the quotient rule for radicals. The **quotient rule for radicals** is similar to the product rule.

> **Quotient Rule for Radicals**
>
> If $\sqrt[n]{a}$ and $\sqrt[n]{b}$ are real numbers, $b \neq 0$, and n is a natural number, then
>
> $$\sqrt[n]{\frac{a}{b}} = \frac{\sqrt[n]{a}}{\sqrt[n]{b}}.$$
>
> That is, the *n*th root of a quotient is the quotient of the *n*th roots.

EXAMPLE 3 Using the Quotient Rule

Simplify. Assume that all variables represent positive real numbers.

NOW TRY ANSWERS
1. (a) $\sqrt{77}$ (b) $\sqrt{30mn}$
2. (a) $\sqrt[3]{20}$ (b) $\sqrt[4]{30tr^3}$
   (c) $\sqrt[7]{60x^2y^3}$
   (d) This expression cannot be simplified by the product rule.

(a) $\sqrt{\frac{16}{25}} = \frac{\sqrt{16}}{\sqrt{25}} = \frac{4}{5}$

(b) $\sqrt{\frac{7}{36}} = \frac{\sqrt{7}}{\sqrt{36}} = \frac{\sqrt{7}}{6}$

(c) $\sqrt[3]{-\frac{8}{125}} = \sqrt[3]{\frac{-8}{125}} = \frac{\sqrt[3]{-8}}{\sqrt[3]{125}} = \frac{-2}{5} = -\frac{2}{5}$ $\quad \frac{-a}{b} = -\frac{a}{b}$

NOW TRY
EXERCISE 3

Simplify. Assume that all variables represent positive real numbers.

(a) $\sqrt{\dfrac{49}{36}}$ **(b)** $\sqrt{\dfrac{5}{144}}$

(c) $\sqrt[3]{-\dfrac{27}{1000}}$ **(d)** $\sqrt[4]{\dfrac{t}{16}}$

(e) $-\sqrt[5]{\dfrac{m^{15}}{243}}$

(d) $\sqrt[3]{\dfrac{7}{216}} = \dfrac{\sqrt[3]{7}}{\sqrt[3]{216}} = \dfrac{\sqrt[3]{7}}{6}$

(e) $\sqrt[5]{\dfrac{x}{32}} = \dfrac{\sqrt[5]{x}}{\sqrt[5]{32}} = \dfrac{\sqrt[5]{x}}{2}$

(f) $-\sqrt[3]{\dfrac{m^6}{125}} = -\dfrac{\sqrt[3]{m^6}}{\sqrt[3]{125}} = -\dfrac{m^2}{5}$ ◁ Think: $\sqrt[3]{m^6} = m^{6/3} = m^2$

NOW TRY

OBJECTIVE 3 **Simplify radicals.** We use the product and quotient rules to simplify radicals. A radical is **simplified** if the following four conditions are met.

Conditions for a Simplified Radical

1. The radicand has no factor raised to a power greater than or equal to the index.
2. The radicand has no fractions.
3. No denominator contains a radical.
4. Exponents in the radicand and the index of the radical have greatest common factor 1.

EXAMPLE 4 **Simplifying Roots of Numbers**

Simplify.

(a) $\sqrt{24}$

Check to see whether 24 is divisible by a perfect square (the square of a natural number) such as 4, 9, 16, ... The greatest perfect square that divides into 24 is 4.

$$\sqrt{24}$$
$$= \sqrt{4 \cdot 6} \qquad \text{Factor; 4 is a perfect square.}$$
$$= \sqrt{4} \cdot \sqrt{6} \qquad \text{Product rule}$$
$$= 2\sqrt{6} \qquad \sqrt{4} = 2$$

(b) $\sqrt{108}$

As shown on the left, the number 108 is divisible by the perfect square 36. If this perfect square is not immediately clear, try factoring 108 into its prime factors, as shown on the right.

$$\sqrt{108}$$
$$= \sqrt{36 \cdot 3} \qquad \text{Factor.}$$
$$= \sqrt{36} \cdot \sqrt{3} \qquad \text{Product rule}$$
$$= 6\sqrt{3} \qquad \sqrt{36} = 6$$

$$\sqrt{108}$$
$$= \sqrt{2^2 \cdot 3^3}$$
$$= \sqrt{2^2 \cdot 3^2 \cdot 3} \qquad a^3 = a^2 \cdot a$$
$$= \sqrt{2^2} \cdot \sqrt{3^2} \cdot \sqrt{3} \qquad \text{Product rule}$$
$$= 2 \cdot 3 \cdot \sqrt{3} \qquad \sqrt{2^2} = 2, \sqrt{3^2} = 3$$
$$= 6\sqrt{3} \qquad \text{Multiply.}$$

NOW TRY ANSWERS
3. **(a)** $\dfrac{7}{6}$ **(b)** $\dfrac{\sqrt{5}}{12}$ **(c)** $-\dfrac{3}{10}$
(d) $\dfrac{\sqrt[4]{t}}{2}$ **(e)** $-\dfrac{m^3}{3}$

(c) $\sqrt{10}$

No perfect square (other than 1) divides into 10, so $\sqrt{10}$ cannot be simplified further.

NOW TRY
EXERCISE 4

Simplify.

(a) $\sqrt{50}$ **(b)** $\sqrt{192}$

(c) $\sqrt{42}$ **(d)** $\sqrt[3]{108}$

(e) $-\sqrt[4]{80}$

(d) $\sqrt[3]{16}$

The greatest perfect *cube* that divides into 16 is 8, so factor 16 as $8 \cdot 2$.

$\sqrt[3]{16}$ — Remember to write the index.

$= \sqrt[3]{8 \cdot 2}$ 8 is a perfect cube.

$= \sqrt[3]{8} \cdot \sqrt[3]{2}$ Product rule

$= 2\sqrt[3]{2}$ $\sqrt[3]{8} = 2$

(e) $-\sqrt[4]{162}$

$= -\sqrt[4]{81 \cdot 2}$ 81 is a perfect 4th power.

Remember the negative sign in each line.

$= -\sqrt[4]{81} \cdot \sqrt[4]{2}$ Product rule

$= -3\sqrt[4]{2}$ $\sqrt[4]{81} = 3$ NOW TRY

⚠ CAUTION *Be careful with which factors belong outside the radical sign and which belong inside.* Note in **Example 4(b)** how $2 \cdot 3$ is written outside because $\sqrt{2^2} = 2$ and $\sqrt{3^2} = 3$, while the remaining 3 is left inside the radical.

NOW TRY
EXERCISE 5

Simplify. Assume that all variables represent positive real numbers.

(a) $\sqrt{36x^5}$ **(b)** $\sqrt{32m^5n^4}$

(c) $\sqrt[3]{-125k^3p^7}$

(d) $-\sqrt[4]{162x^7y^8}$

EXAMPLE 5 Simplifying Radicals Involving Variables

Simplify. Assume that all variables represent positive real numbers.

(a) $\sqrt{16m^3}$

$= \sqrt{16m^2 \cdot m}$ Factor.

$= \sqrt{16m^2} \cdot \sqrt{m}$ Product rule

$= 4m\sqrt{m}$ Take the square root.

Absolute value bars are not needed around the *m* in color because all the variables represent *positive* real numbers.

(b) $\sqrt{200k^7q^8}$

$= \sqrt{10^2 \cdot 2 \cdot (k^3)^2 \cdot k \cdot (q^4)^2}$ Factor.

$= 10k^3q^4\sqrt{2k}$ Remove perfect square factors.

(c) $\sqrt[3]{-8x^4y^5}$

$= \sqrt[3]{(-8x^3y^3)(xy^2)}$ Choose $-8x^3y^3$ as the perfect cube that divides into $-8x^4y^5$.

$= \sqrt[3]{-8x^3y^3} \cdot \sqrt[3]{xy^2}$ Product rule

$= -2xy\sqrt[3]{xy^2}$ Take the cube root.

(d) $-\sqrt[4]{32y^9}$

$= -\sqrt[4]{(16y^8)(2y)}$ $16y^8$ is the greatest 4th power that divides $32y^9$.

$= -\sqrt[4]{16y^8} \cdot \sqrt[4]{2y}$ Product rule

$= -2y^2\sqrt[4]{2y}$ Take the fourth root. NOW TRY

NOW TRY ANSWERS
4. (a) $5\sqrt{2}$ (b) $8\sqrt{3}$
   (c) $\sqrt{42}$ cannot be simplified
   further.
   (d) $3\sqrt[3]{4}$ (e) $-2\sqrt[4]{5}$
5. (a) $6x^2\sqrt{x}$ (b) $4m^2n^2\sqrt{2m}$
   (c) $-5kp^2\sqrt[3]{p}$ (d) $-3xy^2\sqrt[4]{2x^3}$

NOTE From **Example 5,** we see that if a variable is raised to a power with an exponent divisible by 2, it is a perfect square. If it is raised to a power with an exponent divisible by 3, it is a perfect cube. *In general, if it is raised to a power with an exponent divisible by n, it is a perfect nth power.*

The conditions for a simplified radical given earlier state that an exponent in the radicand and the index of the radical should have greatest common factor 1.

EXAMPLE 6 Simplifying Radicals by Using Smaller Indexes

Simplify. Assume that all variables represent positive real numbers.

(a) $\sqrt[9]{5^6}$

We write this radical by using rational exponents and then write the exponent in lowest terms. We then express the answer as a radical.

$$\sqrt[9]{5^6} = (5^6)^{1/9} = 5^{6/9} = 5^{2/3} = \sqrt[3]{5^2}, \quad \text{or} \quad \sqrt[3]{25}$$

(b) $\sqrt[4]{p^2} = (p^2)^{1/4} = p^{2/4} = p^{1/2} = \sqrt{p}$ (Recall the assumption that $p > 0$.)

NOW TRY

These examples suggest the following rule.

> $\sqrt[kn]{a^{km}}$
>
> If m is an integer, n and k are natural numbers, and all indicated roots exist, then
>
> $$\sqrt[kn]{a^{km}} = \sqrt[n]{a^m}.$$

OBJECTIVE 4 Simplify products and quotients of radicals with different indexes. We multiply and divide radicals with different indexes by using rational exponents.

EXAMPLE 7 Multiplying Radicals with Different Indexes

Simplify $\sqrt{7} \cdot \sqrt[3]{2}$.

Because the different indexes, 2 and 3, have a least common multiple of 6, use rational exponents to write each radical as a sixth root.

$$\sqrt{7} = 7^{1/2} = 7^{3/6} = \sqrt[6]{7^3} = \sqrt[6]{343}$$

$$\sqrt[3]{2} = 2^{1/3} = 2^{2/6} = \sqrt[6]{2^2} = \sqrt[6]{4}$$

Now we can multiply.

$$\sqrt{7} \cdot \sqrt[3]{2} = \sqrt[6]{343} \cdot \sqrt[6]{4} \quad \text{Substitute; } \sqrt{7} = \sqrt[6]{343}, \sqrt[3]{2} = \sqrt[6]{4}$$

$$= \sqrt[6]{1372} \quad \text{Product rule} \qquad \text{NOW TRY}$$

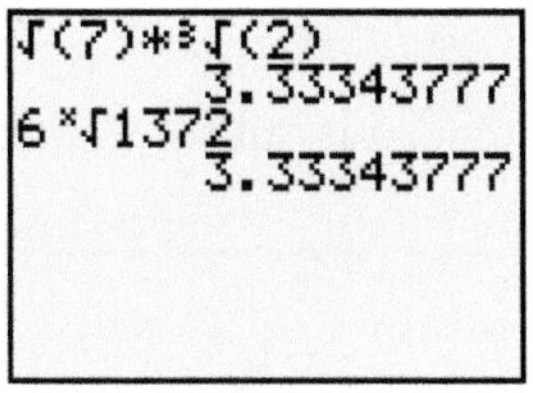

Results such as the one in **Example 7** can be supported with a calculator, as shown in **FIGURE 6.** Notice that the calculator gives the same approximation for the initial product and the final radical that we obtained.

⚠ **CAUTION** The computation in **FIGURE 6** is not *proof* that the two expressions are equal. The algebra in **Example 7,** however, is valid proof of their equality.

NOW TRY
EXERCISE 6

Simplify. Assume that all variables represent positive real numbers.

(a) $\sqrt[6]{7^2}$ **(b)** $\sqrt[6]{y^4}$

NOW TRY
EXERCISE 7

Simplify $\sqrt[3]{3} \cdot \sqrt{6}$.

```
√(7)*³√(2)
           3.33343777
6ˣ√1372
           3.33343777
```

FIGURE 6

NOW TRY ANSWERS
6. (a) $\sqrt[3]{7}$ **(b)** $\sqrt[3]{y^2}$
7. (a) $\sqrt[6]{1944}$

OBJECTIVE 5 Use the Pythagorean theorem. The **Pythagorean theorem** provides an equation that relates the lengths of the three sides of a right triangle.

Pythagorean Theorem

If a and b are the lengths of the shorter sides of a right triangle and c is the length of the longest side, then

$$a^2 + b^2 = c^2.$$

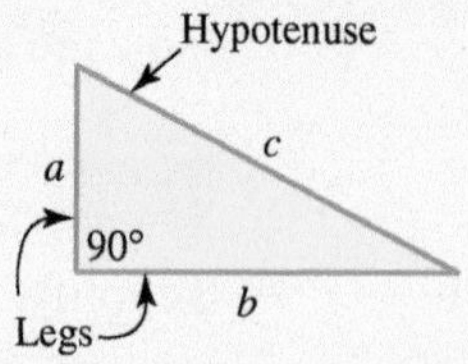

The two shorter sides are the **legs** of the triangle, and the longest side is the **hypotenuse.** The hypotenuse is the side opposite the right angle.

In **Section 11.1** we will see that an equation such as $x^2 = 7$ has two solutions: $\sqrt{7}$ (the principal, or positive, square root of 7) and $-\sqrt{7}$. Similarly, $c^2 = 52$ has two solutions, $\pm\sqrt{52} = \pm 2\sqrt{13}$. In applications we often choose only the principal square root.

NOW TRY
EXERCISE 8

Find the length of the unknown side in each triangle.

(a)
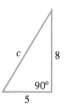

(b)
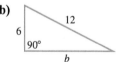

EXAMPLE 8 Using the Pythagorean Theorem

Use the Pythagorean theorem to find the length of the unknown side of the triangle in **FIGURE 7**.

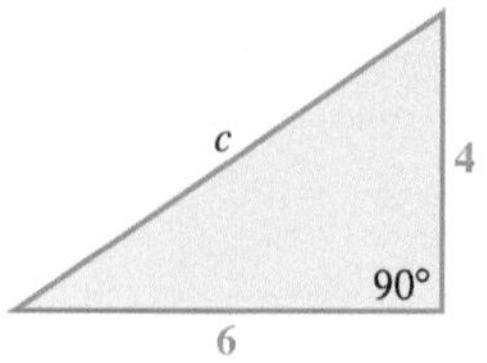

Substitute carefully. $a^2 + b^2 = c^2$	Pythagorean theorem
$4^2 + 6^2 = c^2$	Let $a = 4$ and $b = 6$.
$16 + 36 = c^2$	Apply the exponents.
$c^2 = 52$	Add. Interchange sides.
$c = \sqrt{52}$	Choose the principal root.
$c = \sqrt{4 \cdot 13}$	Factor.
$c = \sqrt{4} \cdot \sqrt{13}$	Product rule
$c = 2\sqrt{13}$	Simplify.

FIGURE 7

The length of the hypotenuse is $2\sqrt{13}$. *NOW TRY*

⚠ **CAUTION** When substituting in the equation $a^2 + b^2 = c^2$, of the Pythagorean theorem, be sure that the length of the hypotenuse is substituted for c and that the lengths of the legs are substituted for a and b.

OBJECTIVE 6 Use the distance formula. The *distance formula* allows us to find the distance between two points in the coordinate plane, or the length of the line segment joining those two points.

FIGURE 8 on the next page shows the points $(3, -4)$ and $(-5, 3)$. The vertical line through $(-5, 3)$ and the horizontal line through $(3, -4)$ intersect at the point $(-5, -4)$. Thus, the point $(-5, -4)$ becomes the vertex of the right angle in a right triangle.

NOW TRY ANSWERS
8. (a) $\sqrt{89}$ **(b)** $6\sqrt{3}$

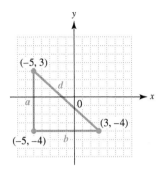

FIGURE 8

By the Pythagorean theorem, the square of the length of the hypotenuse d of the right triangle in **FIGURE 8** is equal to the sum of the squares of the lengths of the two legs a and b.

$$a^2 + b^2 = d^2$$

The length a is the difference between the y-coordinates of the endpoints. Since the x-coordinate of both points in **FIGURE 8** is -5, the side is vertical, and we can find a by finding the difference between the y-coordinates. We subtract -4 from 3 to get a positive value for a.

$$a = 3 - (-4) = 7$$

Similarly, we find b by subtracting -5 from 3.

$$b = 3 - (-5) = 8$$

Now substitute these values into the equation.

$$d^2 = a^2 + b^2$$
$$d^2 = 7^2 + 8^2 \qquad \text{Let } a = 7 \text{ and } b = 8.$$
$$d^2 = 49 + 64 \qquad \text{Apply the exponents.}$$
$$d^2 = 113 \qquad \text{Add.}$$
$$d = \sqrt{113} \qquad \text{Choose the principal root.}$$

We choose the principal root, since distance cannot be negative. Therefore, the distance between $(-5, 3)$ and $(3, -4)$ is $\sqrt{113}$.

NOTE It is customary to leave the distance in simplified radical form. Do not use a calculator to get an approximation, unless you are specifically directed to do so.

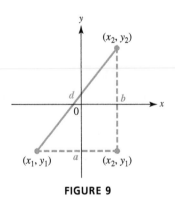

FIGURE 9

This result can be generalized. **FIGURE 9** shows the two points (x_1, y_1) and (x_2, y_2). The distance a between (x_1, y_1) and (x_2, y_1) is given by

$$a = |x_2 - x_1|,$$

and the distance b between (x_2, y_2) and (x_2, y_1) is given by

$$b = |y_2 - y_1|.$$

From the Pythagorean theorem, we obtain the following.

$$d^2 = a^2 + b^2$$
$$d^2 = (x_2 - x_1)^2 + (y_2 - y_1)^2$$

Choosing the principal square root gives the **distance formula.**

Distance Formula

The distance d between the points (x_1, y_1) and (x_2, y_2) is

$$d = \sqrt{(x_2 - x_1)^2 + (y_2 - y_1)^2}.$$

NOW TRY
EXERCISE 9

Find the distance between the points $(-4, -3)$ and $(-8, 6)$.

EXAMPLE 9 Using the Distance Formula

Find the distance between the points $(-3, 5)$ and $(6, 4)$.

Designating the points as (x_1, y_1) and (x_2, y_2) is arbitrary. We choose $(x_1, y_1) = (-3, 5)$ and $(x_2, y_2) = (6, 4)$.

$$d = \sqrt{(x_2 - x_1)^2 + (y_2 - y_1)^2}$$
$$= \sqrt{[6 - (-3)]^2 + (4 - 5)^2} \quad x_2 = 6,\ y_2 = 4,\ x_1 = -3,\ y_1 = 5$$
$$= \sqrt{9^2 + (-1)^2} \quad \text{Substitute carefully.}$$
$$= \sqrt{82} \quad \text{Leave in radical form.} \quad \textit{NOW TRY}$$

NOW TRY ANSWER
9. $\sqrt{97}$

10.3 EXERCISES

MyMathLab Math XL PRACTICE WATCH DOWNLOAD READ REVIEW

🌐 *Complete solution available on the Video Resources on DVD*

Multiply, if possible, using the product rule. Assume that all variables represent positive real numbers. ***See Examples 1 and 2.***

1. $\sqrt{3} \cdot \sqrt{3}$ **2.** $\sqrt{5} \cdot \sqrt{5}$ **3.** $\sqrt{18} \cdot \sqrt{2}$ **4.** $\sqrt{12} \cdot \sqrt{3}$

🌐 **5.** $\sqrt{5} \cdot \sqrt{6}$ **6.** $\sqrt{10} \cdot \sqrt{3}$ **7.** $\sqrt{14} \cdot \sqrt{x}$ **8.** $\sqrt{23} \cdot \sqrt{t}$

9. $\sqrt{14} \cdot \sqrt{3pqr}$ **10.** $\sqrt{7} \cdot \sqrt{5xt}$ **11.** $\sqrt[3]{2} \cdot \sqrt[3]{5}$ **12.** $\sqrt[3]{3} \cdot \sqrt[3]{6}$

🌐 **13.** $\sqrt[3]{7x} \cdot \sqrt[3]{2y}$ **14.** $\sqrt[3]{9x} \cdot \sqrt[3]{4y}$ **15.** $\sqrt[4]{11} \cdot \sqrt[4]{3}$ **16.** $\sqrt[4]{6} \cdot \sqrt[4]{9}$

17. $\sqrt[4]{2x} \cdot \sqrt[4]{3x^2}$ **18.** $\sqrt[4]{3y^2} \cdot \sqrt[4]{6y}$ **19.** $\sqrt[3]{7} \cdot \sqrt[3]{3}$ **20.** $\sqrt[5]{8} \cdot \sqrt[6]{12}$

Simplify each radical. Assume that all variables represent positive real numbers. ***See Example 3.***

🌐 **21.** $\sqrt{\dfrac{64}{121}}$ **22.** $\sqrt{\dfrac{16}{49}}$ **23.** $\sqrt{\dfrac{3}{25}}$ **24.** $\sqrt{\dfrac{13}{49}}$

25. $\sqrt{\dfrac{x}{25}}$ **26.** $\sqrt{\dfrac{k}{100}}$ **27.** $\sqrt{\dfrac{p^6}{81}}$ **28.** $\sqrt{\dfrac{w^{10}}{36}}$

29. $\sqrt[3]{-\dfrac{27}{64}}$ **30.** $\sqrt[3]{-\dfrac{216}{125}}$ **31.** $\sqrt[3]{\dfrac{r^2}{8}}$ **32.** $\sqrt[3]{\dfrac{t}{125}}$

33. $-\sqrt[4]{\dfrac{81}{x^4}}$ **34.** $-\sqrt[4]{\dfrac{625}{y^4}}$ **35.** $\sqrt[5]{\dfrac{1}{x^{15}}}$ **36.** $\sqrt[5]{\dfrac{32}{y^{20}}}$

Express each radical in simplified form. ***See Example 4.***

🌐 **37.** $\sqrt{12}$ **38.** $\sqrt{18}$ **39.** $\sqrt{288}$ **40.** $\sqrt{72}$ **41.** $-\sqrt{32}$

42. $-\sqrt{48}$ **43.** $-\sqrt{28}$ **44.** $-\sqrt{24}$ **45.** $\sqrt{30}$ **46.** $\sqrt{46}$

47. $\sqrt[3]{128}$ **48.** $\sqrt[3]{24}$ **49.** $\sqrt[3]{-16}$ **50.** $\sqrt[3]{-250}$ **51.** $\sqrt[3]{40}$

52. $\sqrt[3]{375}$ **53.** $-\sqrt[4]{512}$ **54.** $-\sqrt[4]{1250}$ **55.** $\sqrt[5]{64}$ **56.** $\sqrt[5]{128}$

57. $-\sqrt[5]{486}$ **58.** $-\sqrt[5]{2048}$ **59.** $\sqrt[6]{128}$ **60.** $\sqrt[6]{1458}$

📝 **61.** A student claimed that $\sqrt[3]{14}$ is not in simplified form, since $14 = 8 + 6$, and 8 is a perfect cube. Was his reasoning correct? Why or why not?

📝 **62.** Explain in your own words why $\sqrt[3]{k^4}$ is not a simplified radical.

Express each radical in simplified form. Assume that all variables represent positive real numbers. ***See Example 5.***

63. $\sqrt{72k^2}$ **64.** $\sqrt{18m^2}$ **65.** $\sqrt{144x^3y^9}$

66. $\sqrt{169s^5t^{10}}$ **67.** $\sqrt{121x^6}$ **68.** $\sqrt{256z^{12}}$

69. $-\sqrt[3]{27t^{12}}$ **70.** $-\sqrt[3]{64y^{18}}$ **71.** $-\sqrt{100m^8z^4}$

72. $-\sqrt{25t^6s^{20}}$ **73.** $-\sqrt[3]{-125a^6b^9c^{12}}$ **74.** $-\sqrt[3]{-216y^{15}x^6z^3}$

75. $\sqrt[4]{\dfrac{1}{16}r^8t^{20}}$ **76.** $\sqrt[4]{\dfrac{81}{256}t^{12}u^8}$ **77.** $\sqrt{50x^3}$ **78.** $\sqrt{300z^3}$

79. $-\sqrt{500r^{11}}$ **80.** $-\sqrt{200p^{13}}$ **81.** $\sqrt{13x^7y^8}$ **82.** $\sqrt{23k^9p^{14}}$

83. $\sqrt[3]{8z^6w^9}$ **84.** $\sqrt[3]{64a^{15}b^{12}}$ **85.** $\sqrt[3]{-16z^5t^7}$ **86.** $\sqrt[3]{-81m^4n^{10}}$

87. $\sqrt[4]{81x^{12}y^{16}}$ **88.** $\sqrt[4]{81t^8u^{28}}$ **89.** $-\sqrt[4]{162r^{15}s^{10}}$ **90.** $-\sqrt[4]{32k^5m^{10}}$

91. $\sqrt{\dfrac{y^{11}}{36}}$ **92.** $\sqrt{\dfrac{v^{13}}{49}}$ **93.** $\sqrt[3]{\dfrac{x^{16}}{27}}$ **94.** $\sqrt[3]{\dfrac{y^{17}}{125}}$

Simplify each radical. Assume that $x \geq 0$. ***See Example 6.***

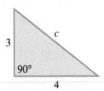 **95.** $\sqrt[4]{48^2}$ **96.** $\sqrt[4]{50^2}$ **97.** $\sqrt[4]{25}$

98. $\sqrt[6]{8}$ **99.** $\sqrt[10]{x^{25}}$ **100.** $\sqrt[12]{x^{44}}$

Simplify by first writing the radicals as radicals with the same index. Then multiply. Assume that all variables represent positive real numbers. ***See Example 7.***

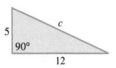 **101.** $\sqrt[3]{4} \cdot \sqrt{3}$ **102.** $\sqrt[3]{5} \cdot \sqrt{6}$ **103.** $\sqrt[4]{3} \cdot \sqrt[3]{4}$

104. $\sqrt[5]{7} \cdot \sqrt[7]{5}$ **105.** $\sqrt{x} \cdot \sqrt[3]{x}$ **106.** $\sqrt[3]{y} \cdot \sqrt[4]{y}$

Find the unknown length in each right triangle. Simplify the answer if possible. ***See Example 8.***

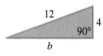 **107.** **108.** **109.**

110. **111.** **112.**

Find the distance between each pair of points. ***See Example 9.***

113. $(6, 13)$ and $(1, 1)$ **114.** $(8, 13)$ and $(2, 5)$

 115. $(-6, 5)$ and $(3, -4)$ **116.** $(-1, 5)$ and $(-7, 7)$

117. $(-8, 2)$ and $(-4, 1)$ **118.** $(-1, 2)$ and $(5, 3)$

119. $(4.7, 2.3)$ and $(1.7, -1.7)$ **120.** $(-2.9, 18.2)$ and $(2.1, 6.2)$

121. $\left(\sqrt{2}, \sqrt{6}\right)$ and $\left(-2\sqrt{2}, 4\sqrt{6}\right)$ **122.** $\left(\sqrt{7}, 9\sqrt{3}\right)$ and $\left(-\sqrt{7}, 4\sqrt{3}\right)$

123. $(x + y, y)$ and $(x - y, x)$ **124.** $(c, c - d)$ and $(d, c + d)$

Find the perimeter of each triangle. $\left(\text{Hint: For Exercise 125, use } \sqrt{k} + \sqrt{k} = 2\sqrt{k}.\right)$

125.

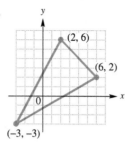

(2, 6)
(6, 2)
(−3, −3)

126.

(1, 3)
(1, −2)
(−2, −4)

Solve each problem.

127. The following letter appeared in the column "Ask Tom Why," written by Tom Skilling of the *Chicago Tribune*:

> *Dear Tom,*
>
> *I cannot remember the formula to calculate the distance to the horizon. I have a stunning view from my 14th-floor condo, 150 ft above the ground. How far can I see?*
>
> *Ted Fleischaker; Indianapolis, Ind.*

Skilling's answer was as follows:

> To find the distance to the horizon in miles, take the square root of the height of your view in feet and multiply that result by 1.224. Your answer will be the number of miles to the horizon. (*Source: Chicago Tribune.*)

Assuming that Ted's eyes are 6 ft above the ground, the total height from the ground is $150 + 6 = 156$ ft. To the nearest tenth of a mile, how far can he see to the horizon?

128. The length of the diagonal of a box is given by

$$D = \sqrt{L^2 + W^2 + H^2},$$

where *L*, *W*, and *H* are, respectively, the length, width, and height of the box. Find the length of the diagonal *D* of a box that is 4 ft long, 2 ft wide, and 3 ft high. Give the exact value, and then round to the nearest tenth of a foot.

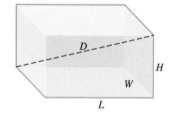

129. A Sanyo color television, model AVM-2755, has a rectangular screen with a 21.7-in. width. Its height is 16 in. What is the measure of the diagonal of the screen, to the nearest tenth of an inch? (*Source:* Actual measurements of the author's television.)

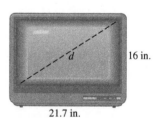

130. A formula from electronics dealing with the impedance of parallel resonant circuits is

$$I = \frac{E}{\sqrt{R^2 + \omega^2 L^2}},$$

where the variables are in appropriate units. Find *I* if $E = 282$, $R = 100$, $L = 264$, and $\omega = 120\pi$. Give your answer to the nearest thousandth.

131. In the study of sound, one version of the law of tensions is

$$f_1 = f_2 \sqrt{\frac{F_1}{F_2}}.$$

If $F_1 = 300$, $F_2 = 60$, and $f_2 = 260$, find f_1 to the nearest unit.

132. The illumination I, in foot-candles, produced by a light source is related to the distance d, in feet, from the light source by the equation

$$d = \sqrt{\frac{k}{I}},$$

where k is a constant. If $k = 640$, how far from the light source will the illumination be 2 foot-candles? Give the exact value, and then round to the nearest tenth of a foot.

*Refer to the Chapter Opener on **page 599**. Recall that an **isosceles triangle** is a triangle that has two sides of equal length.*

133. The statement made by the Scarecrow in *The Wizard of Oz* can be proved false by providing at least one situation in which it leads to a false statement. Use the isosceles triangle shown here to prove that the statement is false.

134. Use the same style of wording as the Scarecrow to state the Pythagorean theorem correctly.

The table gives data on three different solar modules available for roofing.

Model	Watts	Volts	Amps	Size (in inches)	Cost (in dollars)
MSX-77	77	16.9	4.56	44 × 26	475
MSX-83	83	17.1	4.85	44 × 24	490
MSX-60	60	17.1	3.5	44 × 20	382

Source: Solarex table in Jade Mountain catalog.

You must determine the size of frame needed to support each panel on a roof. (Note: The sides of each frame will form a right triangle, and the hypotenuse of the triangle will be the width of the panel.) In Exercises 135–136, use the Pythagorean theorem to find the dimensions of the legs for each frame under the given conditions. Round answers to the nearest tenth.

135. The legs have equal length.

136. One leg is twice the length of the other.

PREVIEW EXERCISES

*Combine like terms. **See Section 4.4.***

137. $13x^4 - 12x^3 + 9x^4 + 2x^3$

138. $-15z^3 - z^2 + 4z^4 + 12z^8$

139. $9q^2 + 2q - 5q - q^2$

140. $7m^5 - 2m^3 + 8m^5 - m^3$

(10.4) Adding and Subtracting Radical Expressions

OBJECTIVE

1 Simplify radical expressions involving addition and subtraction.

OBJECTIVE 1 Simplify radical expressions involving addition and subtraction. Expressions such as $4\sqrt{2} + 3\sqrt{2}$ and $2\sqrt{3} - 5\sqrt{3}$ can be simplified using the distributive property.

$$4\sqrt{2} + 3\sqrt{2}$$
$$= (4 + 3)\sqrt{2} = 7\sqrt{2}$$

This is similar to simplifying $4x + 3x$ to $7x$.

$$2\sqrt{3} - 5\sqrt{3}$$
$$= (2 - 5)\sqrt{3} = -3\sqrt{3}$$

This is similar to simplifying $2x - 5x$ to $-3x$.

NOW TRY
EXERCISE 1
Add or subtract to simplify
each radical expression.

(a) $\sqrt{12} + \sqrt{75}$

(b) $-\sqrt{63t} + 3\sqrt{28t}, \quad t \geq 0$

(c) $6\sqrt{7} - 2\sqrt{3}$

⚠ **CAUTION**   *Only radical expressions with the same index and the same radicand may be combined.*

EXAMPLE 1   Adding and Subtracting Radicals

Add or subtract to simplify each radical expression.

(a) $3\sqrt{24} + \sqrt{54}$

$\quad = 3\sqrt{4} \cdot \sqrt{6} + \sqrt{9} \cdot \sqrt{6}$ Product rule

$\quad = 3 \cdot 2\sqrt{6} + 3\sqrt{6}$ $\sqrt{4} = 2; \sqrt{9} = 3$

$\quad = 6\sqrt{6} + 3\sqrt{6}$ Multiply.

$\quad = 9\sqrt{6}$ $6\sqrt{6} + 3\sqrt{6} = (6 + 3)\sqrt{6}$

(b) $2\sqrt{20x} - \sqrt{45x}, \quad x \geq 0$

$\quad = 2\sqrt{4} \cdot \sqrt{5x} - \sqrt{9} \cdot \sqrt{5x}$ Product rule

$\quad = 2 \cdot 2\sqrt{5x} - 3\sqrt{5x}$ $\sqrt{4} = 2; \sqrt{9} = 3$

$\quad = 4\sqrt{5x} - 3\sqrt{5x}$ Multiply.

$\quad = \sqrt{5x}$ Combine like terms.

(c) $2\sqrt{3} - 4\sqrt{5}$ The radicands differ and are already simplified, so $2\sqrt{3} - 4\sqrt{5}$ cannot be simplified further.

NOW TRY

⚠ **CAUTION**   *The root of a sum does not equal the sum of the roots.* For example,

$$\sqrt{9 + 16} \neq \sqrt{9} + \sqrt{16}$$

since $\sqrt{9 + 16} = \sqrt{25} = 5, \quad$ but $\quad \sqrt{9} + \sqrt{16} = 3 + 4 = 7.$

EXAMPLE 2   Adding and Subtracting Radicals with Higher Indexes

Add or subtract to simplify each radical expression. Assume that all variables represent positive real numbers.

(a) $2\sqrt[3]{16} - 5\sqrt[3]{54}$ [Remember to write the index with each radical.]

$\quad = 2\sqrt[3]{8 \cdot 2} - 5\sqrt[3]{27 \cdot 2}$ Factor.

$\quad = 2\sqrt[3]{8} \cdot \sqrt[3]{2} - 5\sqrt[3]{27} \cdot \sqrt[3]{2}$ Product rule

$\quad = 2 \cdot 2 \cdot \sqrt[3]{2} - 5 \cdot 3 \cdot \sqrt[3]{2}$ Find the cube roots.

$\quad = 4\sqrt[3]{2} - 15\sqrt[3]{2}$ Multiply.

$\quad = (4 - 15)\sqrt[3]{2}$ Distributive property

$\quad = -11\sqrt[3]{2}$ Combine like terms.

(b) $2\sqrt[3]{x^2y} + \sqrt[3]{8x^5y^4}$

$\quad = 2\sqrt[3]{x^2y} + \sqrt[3]{(8x^3y^3)x^2y}$ Factor.

$\quad = 2\sqrt[3]{x^2y} + \sqrt[3]{8x^3y^3} \cdot \sqrt[3]{x^2y}$ Product rule

$\quad = 2\sqrt[3]{x^2y} + 2xy\sqrt[3]{x^2y}$ Find the cube root.

$\quad = (2 + 2xy)\sqrt[3]{x^2y}$ Distributive property

[This result cannot be simplified further.]

NOW TRY ANSWERS
1. (a) $7\sqrt{3}$ (b) $3\sqrt{7t}$
   (c) The expression cannot
     be simplified further.

NOW TRY
EXERCISE 1

Multiply, using the FOIL method.

(a) $\left(8 - \sqrt{5}\right)\left(9 - \sqrt{2}\right)$

(b) $\left(\sqrt{7} + \sqrt{5}\right)\left(\sqrt{7} - \sqrt{5}\right)$

(c) $\left(\sqrt{15} - 4\right)^2$

(d) $\left(8 + \sqrt[3]{5}\right)\left(8 - \sqrt[3]{5}\right)$

(e) $\left(\sqrt{m} - \sqrt{n}\right)\left(\sqrt{m} + \sqrt{n}\right)$,
    $m \geq 0$ and $n \geq 0$

(f) $\left(\sqrt{k} + \sqrt{y}\right)\left(\sqrt{k} - \sqrt{y}\right)$

$= \left(\sqrt{k}\right)^2 - \left(\sqrt{y}\right)^2$ Difference of squares

$= k - y, \quad k \geq 0 \text{ and } y \geq 0$ NOW TRY

NOTE In **Example 1(d),** we could have used the formula for the square of a binomial to obtain the same result.

$\left(\sqrt{7} - 3\right)^2$

$= \left(\sqrt{7}\right)^2 - 2\left(\sqrt{7}\right)(3) + 3^2$ $(x - y)^2 = x^2 - 2xy + y^2$

$= 7 - 6\sqrt{7} + 9$ Apply the exponents. Multiply.

$= 16 - 6\sqrt{7}$ Add.

OBJECTIVE 2 **Rationalize denominators with one radical term.** As defined earlier, a simplified radical expression has no radical in the denominator. The origin of this agreement no doubt occurred before the days of high-speed calculation, when computation was a tedious process performed by hand.

For example, consider the radical expression $\dfrac{1}{\sqrt{2}}$. To find a decimal approximation by hand, it is necessary to divide 1 by a decimal approximation for $\sqrt{2}$, such as 1.414. It is much easier if the divisor is a whole number. This can be accomplished by multiplying $\dfrac{1}{\sqrt{2}}$ by 1 in the form $\dfrac{\sqrt{2}}{\sqrt{2}}$. *Multiplying by 1 in any form does not change the value of the original expression.*

$$\frac{1}{\sqrt{2}} \cdot \frac{\sqrt{2}}{\sqrt{2}} = \frac{\sqrt{2}}{2} \qquad \text{Multiply by 1; } \frac{\sqrt{2}}{\sqrt{2}} = 1$$

Now the computation requires dividing 1.414 by 2 to obtain 0.707, a much easier task.

With current technology, either form of this fraction can be approximated with the same number of keystrokes. See **FIGURE 10**, which shows how a calculator gives the same approximation for both forms of the expression.

```
1/√(2)
          .7071067812
√(2)/2
          .7071067812
```

FIGURE 10

Rationalizing the Denominator

A common way of "standardizing" the form of a radical expression is to have the denominator contain no radicals. The process of removing radicals from a denominator so that the denominator contains only rational numbers is called **rationalizing the denominator.** This is done by multiplying by a form of 1.

EXAMPLE 2 **Rationalizing Denominators with Square Roots**

Rationalize each denominator.

(a) $\dfrac{3}{\sqrt{7}}$

Multiply the numerator and denominator by $\sqrt{7}$. This is, in effect, multiplying by 1.

$$\frac{3}{\sqrt{7}} = \frac{3 \cdot \sqrt{7}}{\sqrt{7} \cdot \sqrt{7}} = \frac{3\sqrt{7}}{7}$$

In the denominator,
$\sqrt{7} \cdot \sqrt{7} = \sqrt{7 \cdot 7} = \sqrt{49} = 7.$
The final denominator is now a rational number.

NOW TRY ANSWERS

1. (a) $72 - 8\sqrt{2} - 9\sqrt{5} + \sqrt{10}$
   (b) 2   (c) $31 - 8\sqrt{15}$
   (d) $64 - \sqrt[3]{25}$ (e) $m - n$

NOW TRY
EXERCISE 2

Rationalize each denominator.

(a) $\dfrac{8}{\sqrt{13}}$ **(b)** $\dfrac{9\sqrt{7}}{\sqrt{3}}$

(c) $\dfrac{-10}{\sqrt{20}}$

(b) $\dfrac{5\sqrt{2}}{\sqrt{5}} = \dfrac{5\sqrt{2} \cdot \sqrt{5}}{\sqrt{5} \cdot \sqrt{5}} = \dfrac{5\sqrt{10}}{5} = \sqrt{10}$

(c) $\dfrac{-6}{\sqrt{12}}$

Less work is involved if we simplify the radical in the denominator first.

$$\dfrac{-6}{\sqrt{12}} = \dfrac{-6}{\sqrt{4 \cdot 3}} = \dfrac{-6}{2\sqrt{3}} = \dfrac{-3}{\sqrt{3}}$$

Now we rationalize the denominator.

$$\dfrac{-3}{\sqrt{3}} = \dfrac{-3 \cdot \sqrt{3}}{\sqrt{3} \cdot \sqrt{3}} = \dfrac{-3\sqrt{3}}{3} = -\sqrt{3} \qquad \text{NOW TRY}$$

NOW TRY
EXERCISE 3

Simplify each radical.

(a) $-\sqrt{\dfrac{27}{80}}$

(b) $\sqrt{\dfrac{48x^8}{y^3}}, \quad y > 0$

EXAMPLE 3 Rationalizing Denominators in Roots of Fractions

Simplify each radical. In part (b), $p > 0$.

(a) $-\sqrt{\dfrac{18}{125}}$

$= -\dfrac{\sqrt{18}}{\sqrt{125}}$ Quotient rule

$= -\dfrac{\sqrt{9 \cdot 2}}{\sqrt{25 \cdot 5}}$ Factor.

$= -\dfrac{3\sqrt{2}}{5\sqrt{5}}$ Product rule

$= -\dfrac{3\sqrt{2} \cdot \sqrt{5}}{5\sqrt{5} \cdot \sqrt{5}}$ Multiply by $\frac{\sqrt{5}}{\sqrt{5}}$.

$= -\dfrac{3\sqrt{10}}{5 \cdot 5}$ Product rule

$= -\dfrac{3\sqrt{10}}{25}$ Multiply.

(b) $\sqrt{\dfrac{50m^4}{p^5}}$

$= \dfrac{\sqrt{50m^4}}{\sqrt{p^5}}$ Quotient rule

$= \dfrac{5m^2\sqrt{2}}{p^2\sqrt{p}}$ Product rule

$= \dfrac{5m^2\sqrt{2} \cdot \sqrt{p}}{p^2\sqrt{p} \cdot \sqrt{p}}$ Multiply by $\frac{\sqrt{p}}{\sqrt{p}}$.

$= \dfrac{5m^2\sqrt{2p}}{p^2 \cdot p}$ Product rule

$= \dfrac{5m^2\sqrt{2p}}{p^3}$ Multiply. NOW TRY

EXAMPLE 4 Rationalizing Denominators with Cube and Fourth Roots

Simplify.

(a) $\sqrt[3]{\dfrac{27}{16}}$

Use the quotient rule, and simplify the numerator and denominator.

$$\sqrt[3]{\dfrac{27}{16}} = \dfrac{\sqrt[3]{27}}{\sqrt[3]{16}} = \dfrac{3}{\sqrt[3]{8} \cdot \sqrt[3]{2}} = \dfrac{3}{2\sqrt[3]{2}}$$

Since $2 \cdot 4 = 8$, a perfect cube, multiply the numerator and denominator by $\sqrt[3]{4}$.

NOW TRY
EXERCISE 4
Simplify.

(a) $\sqrt[3]{\dfrac{8}{81}}$

(b) $\sqrt[4]{\dfrac{7x}{y}}, \quad x \geq 0, y > 0$

$$\dfrac{3}{2\sqrt[3]{2}}$$

$\sqrt[3]{\dfrac{27}{16}} = \dfrac{3}{2\sqrt[3]{2}}$ from **page 636**

$$= \dfrac{3 \cdot \sqrt[3]{4}}{2\sqrt[3]{2} \cdot \sqrt[3]{4}}$$
Multiply by $\sqrt[3]{4}$ in numerator and denominator. This will give $\sqrt[3]{8} = 2$ in the denominator.

$$= \dfrac{3\sqrt[3]{4}}{2\sqrt[3]{8}}$$
Multiply.

$$= \dfrac{3\sqrt[3]{4}}{2 \cdot 2}$$
$\sqrt[3]{8} = 2$

$$= \dfrac{3\sqrt[3]{4}}{4}$$
Multiply.

(b) $$\sqrt[4]{\dfrac{5x}{z}}$$

$$= \dfrac{\sqrt[4]{5x}}{\sqrt[4]{z}}$$
Quotient rule

$$= \dfrac{\sqrt[4]{5x}}{\sqrt[4]{z}} \cdot \dfrac{\sqrt[4]{z^3}}{\sqrt[4]{z^3}}$$
Multiply by 1.

$\sqrt[4]{z} \cdot \sqrt[4]{z^3}$ will give $\sqrt[4]{z^4}$.

$$= \dfrac{\sqrt[4]{5xz^3}}{\sqrt[4]{z^4}}$$
Product rule

$$= \dfrac{\sqrt[4]{5xz^3}}{z}, \quad x \geq 0, z > 0$$

NOW TRY

⚠ CAUTION In **Example 4(a),** a typical error is to multiply the numerator and denominator by $\sqrt[3]{2}$, forgetting that $\sqrt[3]{2} \cdot \sqrt[3]{2} = \sqrt[3]{2^2}$, which does **not** equal 2. We need *three* factors of 2 to obtain 2^3 under the radical.

$$\sqrt[3]{2} \cdot \sqrt[3]{2} \cdot \sqrt[3]{2} = \sqrt[3]{2^3} \quad \text{which does equal} \quad 2.$$

OBJECTIVE 3 Rationalize denominators with binomials involving radicals.
Recall the special product $(x + y)(x - y) = x^2 - y^2$. To rationalize a denominator that contains a binomial expression (one that contains exactly two terms) involving radicals, such as

$$\dfrac{3}{1 + \sqrt{2}},$$

we must use *conjugates*. The conjugate of $1 + \sqrt{2}$ is $1 - \sqrt{2}$. In general, $x + y$ and $x - y$ are **conjugates.**

Rationalizing a Binomial Denominator

Whenever a radical expression has a sum or difference with square root radicals in the denominator, rationalize the denominator by multiplying both the numerator and denominator by the conjugate of the denominator.

NOW TRY ANSWERS

4. (a) $\dfrac{2\sqrt[3]{9}}{9}$ (b) $\dfrac{\sqrt[4]{7xy^3}}{y}$

NOW TRY
EXERCISE 5

Rationalize each denominator.

(a) $\dfrac{4}{1 + \sqrt{3}}$ **(b)** $\dfrac{4}{5 + \sqrt{7}}$

(c) $\dfrac{\sqrt{3} + \sqrt{7}}{\sqrt{5} - \sqrt{2}}$

(d) $\dfrac{8}{\sqrt{3x} - \sqrt{y}}$,
$3x \neq y, x > 0, y > 0$

EXAMPLE 5   Rationalizing Binomial Denominators

Rationalize each denominator.

(a) $\dfrac{3}{1 + \sqrt{2}}$

> Again, we are multiplying by a form of 1.

$$= \dfrac{3\left(1 - \sqrt{2}\right)}{\left(1 + \sqrt{2}\right)\left(1 - \sqrt{2}\right)}$$

Multiply the numerator and denominator by $1 - \sqrt{2}$, the conjugate of the denominator.

$$\left(1 + \sqrt{2}\right)\left(1 - \sqrt{2}\right)$$
$$= 1^2 - \left(\sqrt{2}\right)^2$$
$$= 1 - 2, \text{ or } -1$$

$$= \dfrac{3\left(1 - \sqrt{2}\right)}{-1}$$

> The denominator is now a rational number.

$$= \dfrac{3}{-1}\left(1 - \sqrt{2}\right)$$

$$= -3\left(1 - \sqrt{2}\right), \quad \text{or} \quad -3 + 3\sqrt{2} \qquad \text{Distributive property}$$

(b) $\dfrac{5}{4 - \sqrt{3}}$

$$= \dfrac{5\left(4 + \sqrt{3}\right)}{\left(4 - \sqrt{3}\right)\left(4 + \sqrt{3}\right)}$$ Multiply the numerator and denominator by $4 + \sqrt{3}$.

$$= \dfrac{5\left(4 + \sqrt{3}\right)}{16 - 3}$$ Multiply in the denominator.

$$= \dfrac{5\left(4 + \sqrt{3}\right)}{13}$$ Subtract in the denominator.

Notice that the numerator is left in factored form. This makes it easier to determine whether the expression is written in lowest terms.

(c) $\dfrac{\sqrt{2} - \sqrt{3}}{\sqrt{5} + \sqrt{3}}$

$$= \dfrac{\left(\sqrt{2} - \sqrt{3}\right)\left(\sqrt{5} - \sqrt{3}\right)}{\left(\sqrt{5} + \sqrt{3}\right)\left(\sqrt{5} - \sqrt{3}\right)}$$ Multiply the numerator and denominator by $\sqrt{5} - \sqrt{3}$.

$$= \dfrac{\sqrt{10} - \sqrt{6} - \sqrt{15} + 3}{5 - 3}$$ Multiply.

$$= \dfrac{\sqrt{10} - \sqrt{6} - \sqrt{15} + 3}{2}$$ Subtract in the denominator.

(d) $\dfrac{3}{\sqrt{5m} - \sqrt{p}}$, $5m \neq p, m > 0, p > 0$

$$= \dfrac{3\left(\sqrt{5m} + \sqrt{p}\right)}{\left(\sqrt{5m} - \sqrt{p}\right)\left(\sqrt{5m} + \sqrt{p}\right)}$$ Multiply the numerator and denominator by $\sqrt{5m} + \sqrt{p}$.

$$= \dfrac{3\left(\sqrt{5m} + \sqrt{p}\right)}{5m - p}$$ Multiply in the denominator.

NOW TRY

NOW TRY ANSWERS

5. (a) $-2\left(1 - \sqrt{3}\right), \text{ or } -2 + 2\sqrt{3}$

(b) $\dfrac{2\left(5 - \sqrt{7}\right)}{9}$

(c) $\dfrac{\sqrt{15} + \sqrt{6} + \sqrt{35} + \sqrt{14}}{3}$

(d) $\dfrac{8\left(\sqrt{3x} + \sqrt{y}\right)}{3x - y}$

7. $\dfrac{8}{\sqrt{7} + \sqrt{5}}$

8. $\dfrac{1 - \sqrt{2}}{1 + \sqrt{2}}$

9. $\left(\sqrt{5} + 7\right)\left(\sqrt{5} - 7\right)$

10. $\dfrac{1}{\sqrt{x} - \sqrt{5}}, \quad x \neq 5$

11. $\sqrt[3]{8a^3b^5c^9}$

12. $\dfrac{15}{\sqrt[3]{9}}$

13. $\dfrac{3}{\sqrt{5} + 2}$

14. $\sqrt{\dfrac{3}{5x}}$

15. $\dfrac{16\sqrt{3}}{5\sqrt{12}}$

16. $\dfrac{2\sqrt{25}}{8\sqrt{50}}$

17. $\dfrac{-10}{\sqrt[3]{10}}$

18. $\dfrac{\sqrt{6} + \sqrt{5}}{\sqrt{6} - \sqrt{5}}$

19. $\sqrt{12x} - \sqrt{75x}$

20. $\left(5 - 3\sqrt{3}\right)^2$

21. $\sqrt[3]{\dfrac{13}{81}}$

22. $\dfrac{\sqrt{3} + \sqrt{7}}{\sqrt{6} - \sqrt{5}}$

23. $\dfrac{6}{\sqrt[4]{3}}$

24. $\dfrac{1}{1 - \sqrt[3]{3}}$

25. $\sqrt[3]{\dfrac{x^2y}{x^{-3}y^4}}$

26. $\sqrt{12} - \sqrt{108} - \sqrt[3]{27}$

27. $\dfrac{x^{-2/3}y^{4/5}}{x^{-5/3}y^{-2/5}}$

28. $\left(\dfrac{x^{3/4}y^{2/3}}{x^{1/3}y^{5/8}}\right)^{24}$

29. $(125x^3)^{-2/3}$

30. $\dfrac{4^{1/2} + 3^{1/2}}{4^{1/2} - 3^{1/2}}$

31. $\sqrt[3]{16x^2} - \sqrt[3]{54x^2} + \sqrt[3]{128x^2}$

32. $\left(1 - \sqrt[3]{3}\right)\left(1 + \sqrt[3]{3} + \sqrt[3]{9}\right)$

Students often have trouble distinguishing between the following two types of problems:

Simplifying a Radical Involving a Square Root	**Solving an Equation Using Square Roots**
Exercise: Simplify $\sqrt{25}$.	*Exercise:* Solve $x^2 = 25$.
Answer: 5	*Answer:* $\{-5, 5\}$
In this situation, $\sqrt{25}$ represents the positive square root of 25, namely 5.	In this situation, $x^2 = 25$ has two solutions, the negative square root of 25 or the positive square root of 25: $-5, 5$.

In Exercises 33–40, provide the appropriate responses.

33. **(a)** Simplify $\sqrt{64}$.
    (b) Solve $x^2 = 64$.

34. **(a)** Simplify $\sqrt{100}$.
    (b) Solve $x^2 = 100$.

35. **(a)** Solve $x^2 = 16$.
    (b) Simplify $-\sqrt{16}$.

36. **(a)** Solve $x^2 = 25$.
    (b) Simplify $-\sqrt{25}$.

37. **(a)** Simplify $-\sqrt{\dfrac{81}{121}}$.
    (b) Solve $x^2 = \dfrac{81}{121}$.

38. **(a)** Simplify $-\sqrt{\dfrac{49}{100}}$.
    (b) Solve $x^2 = \dfrac{49}{100}$.

39. **(a)** Solve $x^2 = 0.04$.
    (b) Simplify $\sqrt{0.04}$.

40. **(a)** Solve $x^2 = 0.09$.
    (b) Simplify $\sqrt{0.09}$.

OBJECTIVES

1 Solve radical equations by using the power rule.

2 Solve radical equations that require additional steps.

3 Solve radical equations with indexes greater than 2.

4 Use the power rule to solve a formula for a specified variable.

An equation that includes one or more radical expressions with a variable is called a **radical equation**.

$$\sqrt{x-4} = 8, \quad \sqrt{5x+12} = 3\sqrt{2x-1}, \quad \text{and} \quad \sqrt[3]{6+x} = 27 \qquad \text{Examples of radical equations}$$

OBJECTIVE 1 Solve radical equations by using the power rule. The equation $x = 1$ has only one solution. Its solution set is $\{1\}$. If we square both sides of this equation, we get $x^2 = 1$. This new equation has *two* solutions: -1 and 1. Notice that the solution of the original equation is also a solution of the equation following squaring. However, that equation has another solution, -1, that is *not* a solution of the original equation.

When solving equations with radicals, we use this idea of raising both sides to a power. It is an application of the **power rule.**

Power Rule for Solving an Equation with Radicals

If both sides of an equation are raised to the same power, all solutions of the original equation are also solutions of the new equation.

The power rule does not say that all solutions of the new equation are solutions of the original equation. They may or may not be. Solutions that do not satisfy the original equation are called **extraneous solutions.** They must be rejected.

⚠ **CAUTION** When the power rule is used to solve an equation, *every solution of the new equation must be checked in the original equation.*

NOW TRY EXERCISE 1

Solve $\sqrt{9x+7} = 5$.

EXAMPLE 1 Using the Power Rule

Solve $\sqrt{3x+4} = 8$.

$$\left(\sqrt{3x+4}\right)^2 = 8^2 \qquad \text{Use the power rule and square each side.}$$

$\boxed{\left(\sqrt{a}\right)^2 = \sqrt{a} \cdot \sqrt{a} = a}$

$$3x + 4 = 64 \qquad \text{Apply the exponents.}$$
$$3x = 60 \qquad \text{Subtract 4.}$$
$$x = 20 \qquad \text{Divide by 3.}$$

CHECK

$$\sqrt{3x+4} = 8 \qquad \text{Original equation}$$
$$\sqrt{3 \cdot 20 + 4} \overset{?}{=} 8 \qquad \text{Let } x = 20.$$
$$\sqrt{64} \overset{?}{=} 8 \qquad \text{Simplify.}$$
$$8 = 8 \checkmark \qquad \text{True}$$

NOW TRY ANSWER
1. $\{2\}$

Since 20 satisfies the *original* equation, the solution set is $\{20\}$. NOW TRY ⟳

Use the following steps to solve equations with radicals.

Solving an Equation with Radicals

Step 1 **Isolate the radical.** Make sure that one radical term is alone on one side of the equation.

Step 2 **Apply the power rule.** Raise each side of the equation to a power that is the same as the index of the radical.

Step 3 **Solve** the resulting equation. If it still contains a radical, repeat Steps 1 and 2.

Step 4 **Check** all proposed solutions in the original equation.

NOW TRY
EXERCISE 2

Solve $\sqrt{3x + 4} + 5 = 0$.

EXAMPLE 2 Using the Power Rule

Solve $\sqrt{5x - 1} + 3 = 0$.

Step 1 $\sqrt{5x - 1} = -3$ To isolate the radical on one side, subtract 3 from each side.

Step 2 $\left(\sqrt{5x - 1}\right)^2 = (-3)^2$ Square each side.

Step 3 $5x - 1 = 9$ Apply the exponents.

$5x = 10$ Add 1.

$x = 2$ Divide by 5.

Step 4 CHECK $\sqrt{5x - 1} + 3 = 0$ Original equation

$\sqrt{5 \cdot 2 - 1} + 3 \stackrel{?}{=} 0$ Let $x = 2$.

$3 + 3 = 0$ False

Be sure to check the proposed solution.

This false result shows that the *proposed* solution 2 is *not* a solution of the original equation. It is extraneous. The solution set is $\emptyset$. *NOW TRY*

NOTE We could have determined after Step 1 that the equation in **Example 2** has no solution because the expression on the left cannot be negative. (Why?)

OBJECTIVE 2 **Solve radical equations that require additional steps.** The next examples involve finding the square of a binomial. Recall the rule from **Section 4.6.**

$$(x + y)^2 = x^2 + 2xy + y^2$$

EXAMPLE 3 Using the Power Rule (Squaring a Binomial)

Solve $\sqrt{4 - x} = x + 2$.

Step 1 The radical is alone on the left side of the equation.

Step 2 Square each side. The square of $x + 2$ is $(x + 2)^2 = x^2 + 2(x)(2) + 4$.

$$\left(\sqrt{4 - x}\right)^2 = (x + 2)^2$$ Remember the middle term.

$4 - x = x^2 + 4x + 4$

↑ Twice the product of 2 and x

NOW TRY ANSWER
2. $\emptyset$

NOW TRY
EXERCISE 3

Solve $\sqrt{16 - x} = x + 4$.

Step 3 The new equation is quadratic, so write it in standard form.

$$4 - x = x^2 + 4x + 4 \quad \text{Equation from Step 2}$$
$$x^2 + 5x = 0 \quad \text{Subtract 4. Add } x.$$
$$x(x + 5) = 0 \quad \text{Factor.}$$

Set each factor equal to 0. → $\quad x = 0 \quad \text{or} \quad x + 5 = 0 \quad \text{Zero-factor property}$
$$x = -5 \quad \text{Solve for } x.$$

Step 4 Check each proposed solution in the original equation.

CHECK
$$\sqrt{4 - x} = x + 2 \qquad\qquad \sqrt{4 - x} = x + 2$$
$$\sqrt{4 - 0} \stackrel{?}{=} 0 + 2 \quad \text{Let } x = 0. \qquad \sqrt{4 - (-5)} \stackrel{?}{=} -5 + 2 \quad \text{Let } x = -5.$$
$$\sqrt{4} \stackrel{?}{=} 2 \qquad\qquad\qquad \sqrt{9} \stackrel{?}{=} -3$$
$$2 = 2 \; \checkmark \quad \text{True} \qquad\qquad\quad 3 = -3 \qquad \text{False}$$

The solution set is $\{0\}$. The other proposed solution, -5, is extraneous. **NOW TRY**

NOW TRY
EXERCISE 4

Solve
$$\sqrt{x^2 - 3x + 18} = x + 3.$$

EXAMPLE 4 Using the Power Rule (Squaring a Binomial)

Solve $\sqrt{x^2 - 4x + 9} = x - 1$.

Squaring gives $(x - 1)^2 = x^2 - 2(x)(1) + 1^2$ on the right.

$$\left(\sqrt{x^2 - 4x + 9}\right)^2 = (x - 1)^2 \quad \boxed{\text{Remember the middle term.}}$$
$$x^2 - 4x + 9 = x^2 - 2x + 1$$

↑ Twice the product of x and -1

$$-2x = -8 \quad \text{Subtract } x^2 \text{ and 9. Add } 2x.$$
$$x = 4 \quad \text{Divide by } -2.$$

CHECK
$$\sqrt{x^2 - 4x + 9} = x - 1 \quad \text{Original equation}$$
$$\sqrt{4^2 - 4 \cdot 4 + 9} \stackrel{?}{=} 4 - 1 \quad \text{Let } x = 4.$$
$$3 = 3 \; \checkmark \quad \text{True}$$

The solution set is $\{4\}$. **NOW TRY**

EXAMPLE 5 Using the Power Rule (Squaring Twice)

Solve $\sqrt{5x + 6} + \sqrt{3x + 4} = 2$.

Isolate one radical on one side of the equation by subtracting $\sqrt{3x + 4}$ from each side.

$$\sqrt{5x + 6} = 2 - \sqrt{3x + 4} \quad \text{Subtract } \sqrt{3x + 4}.$$
$$\left(\sqrt{5x + 6}\right)^2 = \left(2 - \sqrt{3x + 4}\right)^2 \quad \text{Square each side.}$$
$$5x + 6 = 4 - 4\sqrt{3x + 4} + (3x + 4) \quad \boxed{\text{Be careful here.}}$$

$\boxed{\text{Remember the middle term.}}$ ↑ Twice the product of 2 and $-\sqrt{3x + 4}$

NOW TRY
EXERCISE 5

Solve

$\sqrt{3x + 1} - \sqrt{x + 4} = 1.$

The equation still contains a radical, so isolate the radical term on the right and square both sides again.

$$5x + 6 = 4 - 4\sqrt{3x + 4} + 3x + 4 \qquad \text{Result after squaring}$$

$$5x + 6 = 8 - 4\sqrt{3x + 4} + 3x \qquad \text{Combine like terms.}$$

$$2x - 2 = -4\sqrt{3x + 4} \qquad \text{Subtract 8 and } 3x.$$

Divide each term by 2. $\qquad x - 1 = -2\sqrt{3x + 4} \qquad \text{Divide by 2.}$

$$(x - 1)^2 = \left(-2\sqrt{3x + 4}\right)^2 \qquad \text{Square each side again.}$$

$$x^2 - 2x + 1 = (-2)^2\left(\sqrt{3x + 4}\right)^2 \qquad \text{On the right, } (ab)^2 = a^2b^2.$$

$$x^2 - 2x + 1 = 4(3x + 4) \qquad \text{Apply the exponents.}$$

$$x^2 - 2x + 1 = 12x + 16 \qquad \text{Distributive property}$$

$$x^2 - 14x - 15 = 0 \qquad \text{Standard form}$$

$$(x - 15)(x + 1) = 0 \qquad \text{Factor.}$$

$$x - 15 = 0 \quad \text{or} \quad x + 1 = 0 \qquad \text{Zero-factor property}$$

$$x = 15 \quad \text{or} \qquad x = -1 \qquad \text{Solve each equation.}$$

CHECK $\qquad \sqrt{5x + 6} + \sqrt{3x + 4} = 2 \qquad \text{Original equation}$

$$\sqrt{5(15) + 6} + \sqrt{3(15) + 4} \stackrel{?}{=} 2 \qquad \text{Let } x = 15.$$

$$\sqrt{81} + \sqrt{49} \stackrel{?}{=} 2 \qquad \text{Simplify.}$$

$$9 + 7 \stackrel{?}{=} 2 \qquad \text{Take square roots.}$$

$$16 = 2 \qquad \text{False}$$

Thus, 15 is an extraneous solution and must be rejected. Confirm that the proposed solution -1 checks, so the solution set is $\{-1\}$. NOW TRY

OBJECTIVE 3 Solve radical equations with indexes greater than 2.

NOW TRY
EXERCISE 6

Solve $\sqrt[3]{4x - 5} = \sqrt[3]{3x + 2}.$

EXAMPLE 6 Using the Power Rule for a Power Greater Than 2

Solve $\sqrt[3]{z + 5} = \sqrt[3]{2z - 6}.$

$$\left(\sqrt[3]{z + 5}\right)^3 = \left(\sqrt[3]{2z - 6}\right)^3 \qquad \text{Cube each side.}$$

$$z + 5 = 2z - 6$$

$$11 = z \qquad \text{Subtract } z. \text{ Add 6.}$$

CHECK $\qquad \sqrt[3]{z + 5} = \sqrt[3]{2z - 6} \qquad \text{Original equation}$

$$\sqrt[3]{11 + 5} \stackrel{?}{=} \sqrt[3]{2 \cdot 11 - 6} \qquad \text{Let } z = 11.$$

$$\sqrt[3]{16} = \sqrt[3]{16} \checkmark \qquad \text{True}$$

The solution set is $\{11\}$. NOW TRY

NOW TRY ANSWERS
5. $\{5\}$ **6.** $\{7\}$

OBJECTIVE 4 Use the power rule to solve a formula for a specified variable.

NOW TRY
EXERCISE 7

Solve the formula for a.

$$x = \sqrt{\frac{y + 2}{a}}$$

EXAMPLE 7 Solving a Formula from Electronics for a Variable

An important property of a radio-frequency transmission line is its **characteristic impedance**, represented by Z and measured in ohms. If L and C are the inductance and capacitance, respectively, per unit of length of the line, then these quantities are related by the formula $Z = \sqrt{\frac{L}{C}}$. Solve this formula for C.

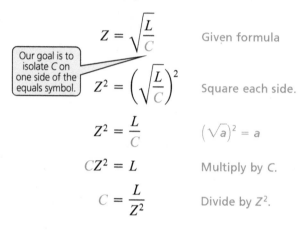

$$Z = \sqrt{\frac{L}{C}} \qquad \text{Given formula}$$

Our goal is to isolate C on one side of the equals symbol.

$$Z^2 = \left(\sqrt{\frac{L}{C}}\right)^2 \qquad \text{Square each side.}$$

$$Z^2 = \frac{L}{C} \qquad (\sqrt{a})^2 = a$$

$$CZ^2 = L \qquad \text{Multiply by } C.$$

$$C = \frac{L}{Z^2} \qquad \text{Divide by } Z^2.$$

NOW TRY

NOW TRY ANSWER

7. $a = \dfrac{y + 2}{x^2}$

10.6 EXERCISES

MyMathLab MathXL PRACTICE WATCH DOWNLOAD READ REVIEW

🌐 *Complete solution available on the Video Resources on DVD*

Concept Check *Check each equation to see if the given value for x is a solution.*

1. $\sqrt{3x + 18} - x = 0$

   (a) 6   **(b)** -3

2. $\sqrt{3x - 3} - x + 1 = 0$

   (a) 1   **(b)** 4

3. $\sqrt{x + 2} - \sqrt{9x - 2} = -2\sqrt{x - 1}$

   (a) 2   **(b)** 7

4. $\sqrt{8x - 3} - 2x = 0$

   (a) $\dfrac{3}{2}$ **(b)** $\dfrac{1}{2}$

📝 **5.** Is 9 a solution of the equation $\sqrt{x} = -3$? If not, what is the solution of this equation? Explain.

📝 **6.** Before even attempting to solve $\sqrt{3x + 18} = x$, how can you be sure that the equation cannot have a negative solution?

Solve each equation. See Examples 1–4.

7. $\sqrt{x - 2} = 3$

8. $\sqrt{x + 1} = 7$

🌐 **9.** $\sqrt{6k - 1} = 1$

10. $\sqrt{7x - 3} = 6$

🌐 **11.** $\sqrt{4r + 3} + 1 = 0$

12. $\sqrt{5k - 3} + 2 = 0$

13. $\sqrt{3x + 1} - 4 = 0$

14. $\sqrt{5x + 1} - 11 = 0$

15. $4 - \sqrt{x - 2} = 0$

16. $9 - \sqrt{4x + 1} = 0$

17. $\sqrt{9x - 4} = \sqrt{8x + 1}$

18. $\sqrt{4x - 2} = \sqrt{3x + 5}$

19. $2\sqrt{x} = \sqrt{3x + 4}$

20. $2\sqrt{x} = \sqrt{5x - 16}$

21. $3\sqrt{x - 1} = 2\sqrt{2x + 2}$

22. $5\sqrt{4x + 1} = 3\sqrt{10x + 25}$

23. $x = \sqrt{x^2 + 4x - 20}$

24. $x = \sqrt{x^2 - 3x + 18}$

25. $x = \sqrt{x^2 + 3x + 9}$

26. $x = \sqrt{x^2 - 4x - 8}$

27. $\sqrt{9 - x} = x + 3$

28. $\sqrt{5 - x} = x + 1$

29. $\sqrt{k^2 + 2k + 9} = k + 3$

30. $\sqrt{x^2 - 3x + 3} = x - 1$

31. $\sqrt{x^2 + 12x - 4} = x - 4$

32. $\sqrt{x^2 - 15x + 15} = x - 5$

33. $\sqrt{r^2 + 9r + 15} - r - 4 = 0$

34. $\sqrt{m^2 + 3m + 12} - m - 2 = 0$

35. *Concept Check* In solving the equation $\sqrt{3x + 4} = 8 - x$, a student wrote the following for her first step. *WHAT WENT WRONG?* Solve the given equation correctly.

$$3x + 4 = 64 + x^2$$

36. *Concept Check* In solving the equation $\sqrt{5x + 6} - \sqrt{x + 3} = 3$, a student wrote the following for his first step. *WHAT WENT WRONG?* Solve the given equation correctly.

$$(5x + 6) + (x + 3) = 9$$

Solve each equation. ***See Examples 5 and 6.***

37. $\sqrt[3]{2x + 5} = \sqrt[3]{6x + 1}$

38. $\sqrt[3]{p + 5} = \sqrt[3]{2p - 4}$

39. $\sqrt[3]{x^2 + 5x + 1} = \sqrt[3]{x^2 + 4x}$

40. $\sqrt[3]{r^2 + 2r + 8} = \sqrt[3]{r^2 + 3r + 12}$

41. $\sqrt[3]{2m - 1} = \sqrt[3]{m + 13}$

42. $\sqrt[3]{2k - 11} = \sqrt[3]{5k + 1}$

43. $\sqrt[4]{x + 12} = \sqrt[4]{3x - 4}$

44. $\sqrt[4]{z + 11} = \sqrt[4]{2z + 6}$

45. $\sqrt[3]{x - 8} + 2 = 0$

46. $\sqrt[3]{r + 1} + 1 = 0$

47. $\sqrt[4]{2k - 5} + 4 = 0$

48. $\sqrt[4]{8z - 3} + 2 = 0$

49. $\sqrt{k + 2} - \sqrt{k - 3} = 1$

50. $\sqrt{r + 6} - \sqrt{r - 2} = 2$

51. $\sqrt{2r + 11} - \sqrt{5r + 1} = -1$

52. $\sqrt{3x - 2} - \sqrt{x + 3} = 1$

53. $\sqrt{3p + 4} - \sqrt{2p - 4} = 2$

54. $\sqrt{4x + 5} - \sqrt{2x + 2} = 1$

55. $\sqrt{3 - 3p} - 3 = \sqrt{3p + 2}$

56. $\sqrt{4x + 7} - 4 = \sqrt{4x - 1}$

57. $\sqrt{2\sqrt{x + 11}} = \sqrt{4x + 2}$

58. $\sqrt{1 + \sqrt{24 - 10x}} = \sqrt{3x + 5}$

For each equation, write the expressions with rational exponents as radical expressions, and then solve, using the procedures explained in this section.

59. $(2x - 9)^{1/2} = 2 + (x - 8)^{1/2}$

60. $(3w + 7)^{1/2} = 1 + (w + 2)^{1/2}$

61. $(2w - 1)^{2/3} - w^{1/3} = 0$

62. $(x^2 - 2x)^{1/3} - x^{1/3} = 0$

Solve each formula for the indicated variable. **See Example 7.** (*Source: Cooke, Nelson M., and Joseph B. Orleans,* Mathematics Essential to Electricity and Radio, *McGraw-Hill.*)

63. $Z = \sqrt{\dfrac{L}{C}}$ for L

64. $r = \sqrt{\dfrac{\mathcal{A}}{\pi}}$ for $\mathcal{A}$

🌐 **65.** $V = \sqrt{\dfrac{2K}{m}}$ for K

66. $V = \sqrt{\dfrac{2K}{m}}$ for m

67. $r = \sqrt{\dfrac{Mm}{F}}$ for M

68. $r = \sqrt{\dfrac{Mm}{F}}$ for F

The formula

$$N = \frac{1}{2\pi}\sqrt{\frac{a}{r}}$$

is used to find the rotational rate N of a space station. Here, a is the acceleration and r represents the radius of the space station, in meters. To find the value of r that will make N simulate the effect of gravity on Earth, the equation must be solved for r, using the required value of N. (Source: Kastner, Bernice, Space Mathematics, *NASA.)*

69. Solve the equation for r.

70. (a) Approximate the value of r so that $N = 0.063$ rotation per sec if $a = 9.8$ m per sec^2.

(b) Approximate the value of r so that $N = 0.04$ rotation per sec if $a = 9.8$ m per sec^2.

PREVIEW EXERCISES

Perform the indicated operations. **See Sections 4.4 and 4.5.**

71. $(5 + 9x) + (-4 - 8x)$ **72.** $(12 + 7y) - (-3 + 2y)$ **73.** $(x + 3)(2x - 5)$

Simplify each radical. **See Section 10.5.**

74. $\dfrac{2}{4 + \sqrt{3}}$

75. $\dfrac{-7}{5 - \sqrt{2}}$

76. $\dfrac{\sqrt{2} + \sqrt{7}}{\sqrt{5} + \sqrt{3}}$

(10.7) Complex Numbers

OBJECTIVE 1 Simplify numbers of the form $\sqrt{-b}$, where $b > 0$. The equation $x^2 + 1 = 0$ has no real number solution, since any solution must be a number whose square is -1. In the set of real numbers, all squares are nonnegative numbers because the product of two positive numbers or two negative numbers is positive and $0^2 = 0$. To provide a solution of the equation $x^2 + 1 = 0$, we introduce a new number i.

Imaginary Unit i

The **imaginary unit i** is defined as

$$i = \sqrt{-1}, \quad \text{where} \quad i^2 = -1.$$

That is, i is the principal square root of -1.

CONCEPTS	EXAMPLES
10.6 Solving Equations with Radicals **Solving an Equation with Radicals** **Step 1** Isolate one radical on one side of the equation. **Step 2** Raise both sides of the equation to a power that is the same as the index of the radical. **Step 3** Solve the resulting equation. If it still contains a radical, repeat Steps 1 and 2. **Step 4** Check all proposed solutions in the *original* equation.	Solve $\sqrt{2x+3} - x = 0$. $\sqrt{2x+3} = x$ Subtract x. $\left(\sqrt{2x+3}\right)^2 = x^2$ Square each side. $2x + 3 = x^2$ Apply the exponents. $x^2 - 2x - 3 = 0$ Standard form $(x-3)(x+1) = 0$ Factor. $x - 3 = 0$ or $x + 1 = 0$ Zero-factor property $x = 3$ or $x = -1$ Solve each equation. A check shows that 3 is a solution, but -1 is extraneous. The solution set is $\{3\}$.
10.7 Complex Numbers $i = \sqrt{-1}$, where $i^2 = -1$. For any positive number b, $\sqrt{-b} = i\sqrt{b}$. *To multiply radicals with negative radicands, first change each factor to the form $i\sqrt{b}$ and then multiply. The same procedure applies to quotients.*	$\sqrt{-25} = i\sqrt{25} = 5i$ $\sqrt{-3} \cdot \sqrt{-27}$ $= i\sqrt{3} \cdot i\sqrt{27}$ $\sqrt{-b} = i\sqrt{b}$ $= i^2\sqrt{81}$ $= -1 \cdot 9$ $i^2 = -1$ $= -9$ $\dfrac{\sqrt{-18}}{\sqrt{-2}} = \dfrac{i\sqrt{18}}{i\sqrt{2}} = \sqrt{\dfrac{18}{2}} = \sqrt{9} = 3$
Adding and Subtracting Complex Numbers Add (or subtract) the real parts and add (or subtract) the imaginary parts.	$(5 + 3i) + (8 - 7i)$ $\bigg|$ $(5 + 3i) - (8 - 7i)$ $= 13 - 4i$ $= -3 + 10i$
Multiplying Complex Numbers Multiply complex numbers by using the FOIL method.	$(2 + i)(5 - 3i)$ $= 10 - 6i + 5i - 3i^2$ FOIL $= 10 - i - 3(-1)$ $i^2 = -1$ $= 10 - i + 3$ Multiply. $= 13 - i$ Combine real terms.
Dividing Complex Numbers Divide complex numbers by multiplying the numerator and the denominator by the conjugate of the denominator.	$\dfrac{20}{3+i}$ $= \dfrac{20(3-i)}{(3+i)(3-i)}$ Multiply by the conjugate. $= \dfrac{20(3-i)}{9 - i^2}$ $(a+b)(a-b) = a^2 - b^2$ $= \dfrac{20(3-i)}{10}$ $i^2 = -1$ $= 2(3-i)$, or $6 - 2i$

10.1 *Find each root.*

1. $\sqrt{1764}$

2. $-\sqrt{289}$

3. $\sqrt[3]{216}$

4. $\sqrt[3]{-125}$

5. $-\sqrt[3]{27}$

6. $\sqrt[5]{-32}$

7. *Concept Check* Under what conditions is $\sqrt[n]{a}$ not a real number?

8. Simplify each radical so that no radicals appear. Assume that x represents any real number.

(a) $\sqrt{x^2}$ **(b)** $-\sqrt{x^2}$ **(c)** $\sqrt[3]{x^3}$

Use a calculator to find a decimal approximation for each number. Give the answer to the nearest thousandth.

9. $-\sqrt{47}$

10. $\sqrt[3]{-129}$

11. $\sqrt[4]{605}$

12. $\sqrt[4]{500^{-3}}$

13. $-\sqrt[3]{500^4}$

14. $-\sqrt{28^{-1}}$

Graph each function. Give the domain and range.

15. $f(x) = \sqrt{x - 1}$

16. $f(x) = \sqrt[3]{x} + 4$

17. What is the best estimate of the area of the triangle shown here?

A. 3600   **B.** 30   **C.** 60   **D.** 360

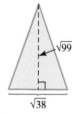

10.2

18. *Concept Check* Fill in the blanks with the correct responses: One way to evaluate $8^{2/3}$ is to first find the _____ root of _____, which is _____. Then raise that result to the _____ power, to get an answer of _____. Therefore, $8^{2/3} =$ _____.

19. *Concept Check* Which one of the following is a positive number?

A. $(-27)^{2/3}$ **B.** $(-64)^{5/3}$ **C.** $(-100)^{1/2}$ **D.** $(-32)^{1/5}$

20. *Concept Check* If a is a negative number and n is odd, then what must be true about m for $a^{m/n}$ to be   **(a)** positive   **(b)** negative?

21. *Concept Check* If a is negative and n is even, is $a^{1/n}$ a real number?

Simplify. If the expression does not represent a real number, say so.

22. $49^{1/2}$

23. $-121^{1/2}$

24. $16^{5/4}$

25. $-8^{2/3}$

26. $-\left(\dfrac{36}{25}\right)^{3/2}$

27. $\left(-\dfrac{1}{8}\right)^{-5/3}$

28. $\left(\dfrac{81}{10,000}\right)^{-3/4}$

29. $(-16)^{3/4}$

30. *Concept Check* Illustrate two different ways of writing $8^{2/3}$ as a radical expression.

31. Explain the relationship between the expressions $a^{m/n}$ and $\sqrt[n]{a^m}$. Give an example.

Write each expression as a radical.

32. $(m + 3n)^{1/2}$

33. $(3a + b)^{-5/3}$

Write each expression with a rational exponent.

34. $\sqrt{7^9}$

35. $\sqrt[5]{p^4}$

Use the rules for exponents to simplify each expression. Write the answer with only positive exponents. Assume that all variables represent positive real numbers.

36. $5^{1/4} \cdot 5^{7/4}$

37. $\dfrac{96^{2/3}}{96^{-1/3}}$

38. $\dfrac{(a^{1/3})^4}{a^{2/3}}$

39. $\dfrac{y^{-1/3} \cdot y^{5/6}}{y}$

40. $\left(\dfrac{z^{-1}x^{-3/5}}{2^{-2}z^{-1/2}x}\right)^{-1}$

41. $r^{-1/2}(r + r^{3/2})$

Simplify by first writing each radical in exponential form. Leave the answer in exponential form. Assume that all variables represent positive real numbers.

42. $\sqrt[8]{s^4}$

43. $\sqrt[6]{r^9}$

44. $\dfrac{\sqrt{p^5}}{p^2}$

45. $\sqrt[4]{k^3} \cdot \sqrt{k^3}$

46. $\sqrt[3]{m^5} \cdot \sqrt[3]{m^8}$

47. $\sqrt[4]{\sqrt[3]{z}}$

48. $\sqrt{\sqrt{\sqrt{x}}}$

49. $\sqrt[3]{\sqrt[5]{x}}$

50. $\sqrt{\sqrt[6]{\sqrt[3]{x}}}$

51. The product rule does not apply to $3^{1/4} \cdot 2^{1/5}$. Why?

10.3   *Simplify each radical. Assume that all variables represent positive real numbers.*

52. $\sqrt{6} \cdot \sqrt{11}$

53. $\sqrt{5} \cdot \sqrt{r}$

54. $\sqrt[3]{6} \cdot \sqrt[3]{5}$

55. $\sqrt[4]{7} \cdot \sqrt[4]{3}$

56. $\sqrt{20}$

57. $\sqrt{75}$

58. $-\sqrt{125}$

59. $\sqrt[3]{-108}$

60. $\sqrt{100y^7}$

61. $\sqrt[3]{64p^4q^6}$

62. $\sqrt[3]{108a^8b^5}$

63. $\sqrt[3]{632r^8t^4}$

64. $\sqrt{\dfrac{y^3}{144}}$

65. $\sqrt[3]{\dfrac{m^{15}}{27}}$

66. $\sqrt[3]{\dfrac{r^2}{8}}$

67. $\sqrt[4]{\dfrac{a^9}{81}}$

Simplify each radical expression.

68. $\sqrt[6]{15^3}$

69. $\sqrt[4]{p^6}$

70. $\sqrt[3]{2} \cdot \sqrt[4]{5}$

71. $\sqrt{x} \cdot \sqrt[5]{x}$

72. Find the unknown length in the right triangle. Simplify the answer if applicable.

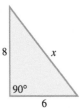

73. Find the distance between the points $(-4, 7)$ and $(10, 6)$.

10.4   *Perform the indicated operations. Assume that all variables represent positive real numbers.*

74. $2\sqrt{8} - 3\sqrt{50}$

75. $8\sqrt{80} - 3\sqrt{45}$

76. $-\sqrt{27y} + 2\sqrt{75y}$

77. $2\sqrt{54m^3} + 5\sqrt{96m^3}$

78. $3\sqrt[3]{54} + 5\sqrt[3]{16}$

79. $-6\sqrt[4]{32} + \sqrt[4]{512}$

In Exercises 80 and 81, leave answers as simplified radicals.

80. Find the perimeter of a rectangular electronic billboard having sides of lengths shown in the figure.

81. Find the perimeter of a triangular electronic highway road sign having the dimensions shown in the figure.

10.5 *Multiply.*

82. $\left(\sqrt{3} + 1\right)\left(\sqrt{3} - 2\right)$

83. $\left(\sqrt{7} + \sqrt{5}\right)\left(\sqrt{7} - \sqrt{5}\right)$

84. $\left(3\sqrt{2} + 1\right)\left(2\sqrt{2} - 3\right)$

85. $\left(\sqrt{13} - \sqrt{2}\right)^2$

86. $\left(\sqrt[3]{2} + 3\right)\left(\sqrt[3]{4} - 3\sqrt[3]{2} + 9\right)$

87. $\left(\sqrt[3]{4y} - 1\right)\left(\sqrt[3]{4y} + 3\right)$

88. Use a calculator to show that the answer to **Exercise 85**, $15 - 2\sqrt{26}$, is not equal to $13\sqrt{26}$.

89. *Concept Check* A friend tried to rationalize the denominator of $\dfrac{5}{\sqrt[3]{6}}$, by multiplying the numerator and denominator by $\sqrt[3]{6}$. **WHAT WENT WRONG?**

Rationalize each denominator. Assume that all variables represent positive real numbers.

90. $\dfrac{\sqrt{6}}{\sqrt{5}}$

91. $\dfrac{-6\sqrt{3}}{\sqrt{2}}$

92. $\dfrac{3\sqrt{7p}}{\sqrt{y}}$

93. $\sqrt{\dfrac{11}{8}}$

94. $-\sqrt[3]{\dfrac{9}{25}}$

95. $\sqrt[3]{\dfrac{108m^3}{n^5}}$

96. $\dfrac{1}{\sqrt{2} + \sqrt{7}}$

97. $\dfrac{-5}{\sqrt{6} - 3}$

Write in lowest terms.

98. $\dfrac{2 - 2\sqrt{5}}{8}$

99. $\dfrac{4 - 8\sqrt{8}}{12}$

100. $\dfrac{-18 + \sqrt{27}}{6}$

10.6 *Solve each equation.*

101. $\sqrt{8x + 9} = 5$

102. $\sqrt{2x - 3} - 3 = 0$

103. $\sqrt{3x + 1} - 2 = -3$

104. $\sqrt{7x + 1} = x + 1$

105. $3\sqrt{x} = \sqrt{10x - 9}$

106. $\sqrt{x^2 + 3x + 7} = x + 2$

107. $\sqrt{x + 2} - \sqrt{x - 3} = 1$

108. $\sqrt[3]{5x - 1} = \sqrt[3]{3x - 2}$

109. $\sqrt[3]{2x^2 + 3x - 7} = \sqrt[3]{2x^2 + 4x + 6}$

110. $\sqrt[3]{3x^2 - 4x + 6} = \sqrt[3]{3x^2 - 2x + 8}$

111. $\sqrt[3]{1 - 2x} - \sqrt[3]{-x - 13} = 0$

112. $\sqrt[3]{11 - 2x} - \sqrt[3]{-1 - 5x} = 0$

113. $\sqrt[4]{x - 1} + 2 = 0$

114. $\sqrt[4]{2x + 3} + 1 = 0$

115. $\sqrt[4]{x + 7} = \sqrt[4]{2x}$

116. $\sqrt[4]{x + 8} = \sqrt[4]{3x}$

117. Carpenters stabilize wall frames with a diagonal brace, as shown in the figure. The length of the brace is given by $L = \sqrt{H^2 + W^2}$.

(a) Solve this formula for H.

(b) If the bottom of the brace is attached 9 ft from the corner and the brace is 12 ft long, how far up the corner post should it be nailed? Give your answer to the nearest tenth of a foot.

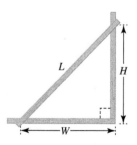

10.7 *Write each expression as a product of a real number and i.*

118. $\sqrt{-25}$

119. $\sqrt{-200}$

120. *Concept Check* If a is a positive real number, is $-\sqrt{-a}$ a real number?

Perform the indicated operations. Give answers in standard form.

121. $(-2 + 5i) + (-8 - 7i)$ **122.** $(5 + 4i) - (-9 - 3i)$ **123.** $\sqrt{-5} \cdot \sqrt{-7}$

124. $\sqrt{-25} \cdot \sqrt{-81}$ **125.** $\dfrac{\sqrt{-72}}{\sqrt{-8}}$ **126.** $(2 + 3i)(1 - i)$

127. $(6 - 2i)^2$ **128.** $\dfrac{3 - i}{2 + i}$ **129.** $\dfrac{5 + 14i}{2 + 3i}$

Find each power of i.

130. i^{11} **131.** i^{36} **132.** i^{-10} **133.** i^{-8}

MIXED REVIEW EXERCISES

Simplify. Assume that all variables represent positive real numbers.

134. $-\sqrt[4]{256}$ **135.** $1000^{-2/3}$ **136.** $\dfrac{z^{-1/5} \cdot z^{3/10}}{z^{7/10}}$

137. $\sqrt[4]{k^{24}}$ **138.** $\sqrt[3]{54z^9t^8}$ **139.** $-5\sqrt{18} + 12\sqrt{72}$

140. $\dfrac{-1}{\sqrt{12}}$ **141.** $\sqrt[3]{\dfrac{12}{25}}$ **142.** i^{-1000}

143. $\sqrt{-49}$ **144.** $(4 - 9i) + (-1 + 2i)$ **145.** $\dfrac{\sqrt{50}}{\sqrt{-2}}$

146. $\dfrac{3 + \sqrt{54}}{6}$ **147.** $(3 + 2i)^2$ **148.** $8\sqrt[3]{x^3y^2} - 2x\sqrt[3]{y^2}$

149. $9\sqrt{5} - 4\sqrt{15}$ **150.** $\left(\sqrt{5} - \sqrt{3}\right)\left(\sqrt{7} + \sqrt{3}\right)$

Solve each equation.

151. $\sqrt{x + 4} = x - 2$ **152.** $\sqrt[3]{2x - 9} = \sqrt[3]{5x + 3}$

153. $\sqrt{6 + 2x} - 1 = \sqrt{7 - 2x}$ **154.** $\sqrt{7x + 11} - 5 = 0$

155. $\sqrt{6x + 2} - \sqrt{5x + 3} = 0$ **156.** $\sqrt{3 + 5x} - \sqrt{x + 11} = 0$

157. $3\sqrt{x} = \sqrt{8x + 9}$ **158.** $6\sqrt{x} = \sqrt{30x + 24}$

159. $\sqrt{11 + 2x} + 1 = \sqrt{5x + 1}$ **160.** $\sqrt{5x + 6} - \sqrt{x + 3} = 3$

CHAPTER (10)

TEST

Step-by-step test solutions are found on the Chapter Test Prep Videos available via the Video Resources on DVD, in *MyMathLab*, or on **You Tube** (search "LialCombinedAlgebra").

View the complete solutions to all Chapter Test exercises on the Video Resources on DVD.

Evaluate.

1. $-\sqrt{841}$ **2.** $\sqrt[3]{-512}$ **3.** $125^{1/3}$

4. *Concept Check*   For $\sqrt{146.25}$, which choice gives the best estimate?

   A. 10   **B.** 11   **C.** 12   **D.** 13

Use a calculator to approximate each root to the nearest thousandth.

5. $\sqrt{478}$ **6.** $\sqrt[3]{-832}$

7. Graph the function defined by $f(x) = \sqrt{x + 6}$, and give the domain and range.

Simplify each expression. Assume that all variables represent positive real numbers.

8. $\left(\dfrac{16}{25}\right)^{-3/2}$

9. $(-64)^{-4/3}$

10. $\dfrac{3^{2/5}x^{-1/4}y^{2/5}}{3^{-8/5}x^{7/4}y^{1/10}}$

11. $\left(\dfrac{x^{-4}y^{-6}}{x^{-2}y^3}\right)^{-2/3}$

12. $7^{3/4} \cdot 7^{-1/4}$

13. $\sqrt[3]{a^4} \cdot \sqrt[3]{a^7}$

14. Use the Pythagorean theorem to find the exact length of side b in the figure.

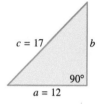

$c = 17$, b, $90°$, $a = 12$

15. Find the distance between the points $(-4, 2)$ and $(2, 10)$.

Simplify each expression. Assume that all variables represent positive real numbers.

16. $\sqrt{54x^5y^6}$

17. $\sqrt[4]{32a^7b^{13}}$

18. $\sqrt{2} \cdot \sqrt[3]{5}$ (Express as a radical.)

19. $3\sqrt{20} - 5\sqrt{80} + 4\sqrt{500}$

20. $\sqrt[3]{16t^3s^5} - \sqrt[3]{54t^6s^2}$

21. $\left(7\sqrt{5} + 4\right)\left(2\sqrt{5} - 1\right)$

22. $\left(\sqrt{3} - 2\sqrt{5}\right)^2$

23. $\dfrac{-5}{\sqrt{40}}$

24. $\dfrac{2}{\sqrt[3]{5}}$

25. $\dfrac{-4}{\sqrt{7} + \sqrt{5}}$

26. Write $\dfrac{6 + \sqrt{24}}{2}$ in lowest terms.

27. The following formula is used in physics, relating the velocity V of sound to the temperature T.

$$V = \dfrac{V_0}{\sqrt{1 - kT}}$$

(a) Find an approximation of V to the nearest tenth if $V_0 = 50$, $k = 0.01$, and $T = 30$. Use a calculator.

(b) Solve the formula for T.

Solve each equation.

28. $\sqrt[3]{5x} = \sqrt[3]{2x - 3}$

29. $x + \sqrt{x + 6} = 9 - x$

30. $\sqrt{x + 4} - \sqrt{1 - x} = -1$

In Exercises 31–33, perform the indicated operations. Give the answers in standard form.

31. $(-2 + 5i) - (3 + 6i) - 7i$

32. $(1 + 5i)(3 + i)$

33. $\dfrac{7 + i}{1 - i}$

34. Simplify i^{37}.

35. *Concept Check* Answer *true* or *false* to each of the following.

(a) $i^2 = -1$ **(b)** $i = \sqrt{-1}$ **(c)** $i = -1$ **(d)** $\sqrt{-3} = i\sqrt{3}$

> ### Square Root Property
>
> If k is a positive number and if $x^2 = k$, then
>
> $$x = \sqrt{k} \quad \text{or} \quad x = -\sqrt{k}.$$
>
> The solution set is $\{-\sqrt{k}, \sqrt{k}\}$, which can be written $\{\pm\sqrt{k}\}$. ($\pm$ is read "positive or negative" or "plus or minus.")

NOTE When we solve an equation, we must find *all* values of the variable that satisfy the equation. Therefore, we want both the positive and negative square roots of k.

NOW TRY
EXERCISE 2

Solve each equation. Write radicals in simplified form.

(a) $t^2 = 25$

(b) $x^2 = 13$

(c) $3x^2 - 54 = 0$

(d) $2x^2 - 5 = 35$

EXAMPLE 2   **Solving Quadratic Equations of the Form $x^2 = k$**

Solve each equation. Write radicals in simplified form.

(a) $x^2 = 16$

By the square root property, if $x^2 = 16$, then

$$x = \sqrt{16} = 4 \quad \text{or} \quad x = -\sqrt{16} = -4.$$

Check each solution by substituting it for x in the original equation. The solution set is

$$\{-4, 4\}, \quad \text{or} \quad \{\pm 4\}.$$

> This notation indicates *two* solutions, one positive and one negative.

(b) $x^2 = 5$

By the square root property, if $x^2 = 5$, then

$$x = \sqrt{5} \quad \text{or} \quad x = -\sqrt{5}.$$

> Don't forget the negative solution.

The solution set is $\{\sqrt{5}, -\sqrt{5}\}$, or $\{\pm\sqrt{5}\}$.

(c)
$$4x^2 - 48 = 0$$
$$4x^2 = 48 \qquad \text{Add 48.}$$
$$x^2 = 12 \qquad \text{Divide by 4.}$$

> Don't stop here. Simplify the radicals.

$$x = \sqrt{12} \quad \text{or} \quad x = -\sqrt{12} \qquad \text{Square root property}$$
$$x = 2\sqrt{3} \quad \text{or} \quad x = -2\sqrt{3} \qquad \sqrt{12} = \sqrt{4}\cdot\sqrt{3} = 2\sqrt{3}$$

The solutions are $2\sqrt{3}$ and $-2\sqrt{3}$. Check each in the original equation.

CHECK $4x^2 - 48 = 0$ Original equation

$$4\left(2\sqrt{3}\right)^2 - 48 \overset{?}{=} 0 \quad \text{Let } x = 2\sqrt{3}. \qquad 4\left(-2\sqrt{3}\right)^2 - 48 \overset{?}{=} 0 \quad \text{Let } x = -2\sqrt{3}.$$
$$4(12) - 48 \overset{?}{=} 0 \qquad\qquad\qquad 4(12) - 48 \overset{?}{=} 0$$
$$48 - 48 \overset{?}{=} 0 \qquad\qquad\qquad 48 - 48 \overset{?}{=} 0$$
$$0 = 0 \checkmark \text{ True} \qquad\qquad\qquad 0 = 0 \checkmark \text{ True}$$

> $(2\sqrt{3})^2$
> $= 2^2 \cdot (\sqrt{3})^2$

The solution set is $\{2\sqrt{3}, -2\sqrt{3}\}$, or $\{\pm 2\sqrt{3}\}$.

(d)
$$3x^2 + 5 = 11$$
$$3x^2 = 6 \qquad \text{Subtract 5.}$$
$$x^2 = 2 \qquad \text{Divide by 3.}$$
$$x = \sqrt{2} \quad \text{or} \quad x = -\sqrt{2} \qquad \text{Square root property}$$

The solution set is $\{\sqrt{2}, -\sqrt{2}\}$, or $\{\pm\sqrt{2}\}$.

NOW TRY

NOW TRY ANSWERS

2. (a) $\{\pm 5\}$ **(b)** $\{\pm\sqrt{13}\}$

(c) $\{\pm 3\sqrt{2}\}$ **(d)** $\{\pm 2\sqrt{5}\}$

NOW TRY
EXERCISE 3

Tim is dropping roofing nails from the top of a roof 25 ft high into a large bucket on the ground. Use the formula in **Example 3** to determine how long it will take a nail dropped from 25 ft to hit the bottom of the bucket.

EXAMPLE 3 Using the Square Root Property in an Application

Galileo Galilei developed a formula for freely falling objects described by

$$d = 16t^2,$$

where d is the distance in feet that an object falls (disregarding air resistance) in t seconds, regardless of weight. Galileo dropped objects from the Leaning Tower of Pisa. If the Leaning Tower is about 180 ft tall, use Galileo's formula to determine how long it would take an object dropped from the top of the tower to fall to the ground. (*Source:* www.brittanica.com)

Galileo Galilei (1564–1642)

$d = 16t^2$	Galileo's formula
$180 = 16t^2$	Let $d = 180$.
$11.25 = t^2$	Divide by 16.
$t = \sqrt{11.25}$ or $t = -\sqrt{11.25}$	Square root property

Time cannot be negative, so we discard the negative solution. Since $\sqrt{11.25} \approx 3.4$, $t \approx 3.4$. The object would fall to the ground in about 3.4 sec.   *NOW TRY*

OBJECTIVE 3 Solve equations of the form $(ax + b)^2 = k$, where $k > 0$.

In each equation in **Example 2,** the exponent 2 had a single variable as its base. We can extend the square root property to solve equations in which the base is a binomial.

NOW TRY
EXERCISE 4

Solve $(x - 2)^2 = 32$.

EXAMPLE 4 Solving Quadratic Equations of the Form $(x + b)^2 = k$

Solve each equation.

(a) Use $(x - 3)$ as the base. $(x - 3)^2 = 16$

$x - 3 = \sqrt{16}$	or	$x - 3 = -\sqrt{16}$	Square root property
$x - 3 = 4$	or	$x - 3 = -4$	$\sqrt{16} = 4$
$x = 7$	or	$x = -1$	Add 3.

CHECK Substitute each solution in the original equation.

$$(x - 3)^2 = 16$$
$$(7 - 3)^2 \overset{?}{=} 16 \qquad \text{Let } x = 7.$$
$$4^2 \overset{?}{=} 16 \qquad \text{Subtract.}$$
$$16 = 16 \checkmark \text{ True}$$

$$(x - 3)^2 = 16$$
$$(-1 - 3)^2 \overset{?}{=} 16 \qquad \text{Let } x = -1.$$
$$(-4)^2 \overset{?}{=} 16 \qquad \text{Subtract.}$$
$$16 = 16 \checkmark \text{ True}$$

The solution set is $\{-1, 7\}$.

(b) $(x - 1)^2 = 6$

$x - 1 = \sqrt{6}$	or	$x - 1 = -\sqrt{6}$	Square root property
$x = 1 + \sqrt{6}$	or	$x = 1 - \sqrt{6}$	Add 1.

CHECK $\left(1 + \sqrt{6} - 1\right)^2 = \left(\sqrt{6}\right)^2 = 6$ ✓   Let $x = 1 + \sqrt{6}$.

$\left(1 - \sqrt{6} - 1\right)^2 = \left(-\sqrt{6}\right)^2 = 6$ ✓   Let $x = 1 - \sqrt{6}$.

NOW TRY ANSWERS
3. 1.25 sec **4.** $\left\{2 \pm 4\sqrt{2}\right\}$

The solution set is $\left\{1 + \sqrt{6}, 1 - \sqrt{6}\right\}$, or $\left\{1 \pm \sqrt{6}\right\}$.   *NOW TRY*

NOW TRY
EXERCISE 5
Solve $(2t - 4)^2 = 50$.

EXAMPLE 5   Solving a Quadratic Equation of the Form $(ax + b)^2 = k$

Solve $(3r - 2)^2 = 27$.

$$(3r - 2)^2 = 27$$

$3r - 2 = \sqrt{27}$ or $3r - 2 = -\sqrt{27}$ Square root property

$3r - 2 = 3\sqrt{3}$ or $3r - 2 = -3\sqrt{3}$ $\sqrt{27} = \sqrt{9} \cdot \sqrt{3} = 3\sqrt{3}$

$3r = 2 + 3\sqrt{3}$ or $3r = 2 - 3\sqrt{3}$ Add 2.

$r = \dfrac{2 + 3\sqrt{3}}{3}$ or $r = \dfrac{2 - 3\sqrt{3}}{3}$ Divide by 3.

CHECK $\left(3 \cdot \dfrac{2 + 3\sqrt{3}}{3} - 2\right)^2 \overset{?}{=} 27$ Let $r = \frac{2 + 3\sqrt{3}}{3}$.

$$\left(2 + 3\sqrt{3} - 2\right)^2 \overset{?}{=} 27 \qquad \text{Multiply.}$$

$$\left(3\sqrt{3}\right)^2 \overset{?}{=} 27 \qquad \text{Subtract.}$$

$\boxed{(ab)^2 = a^2 b^2}$ $27 = 27$ ✓   True

The check of the other solution is similar. The solution set is $\left\{\dfrac{2 \pm 3\sqrt{3}}{3}\right\}$.

NOW TRY

⚠ **CAUTION**   The solutions in **Example 5** are fractions that cannot be simplified, since 3 is *not* a common factor in the numerator.

OBJECTIVE 4   Solve quadratic equations with solutions that are not real numbers.   In $x^2 = k$, if $k < 0$, there will be two nonreal complex solutions.

NOW TRY
EXERCISE 6
Solve each equation.
(a) $t^2 = -24$
(b) $(x + 4)^2 = -36$

EXAMPLE 6   Solving for Nonreal Complex Solutions

Solve each equation.

(a) $x^2 = -15$

$x = \sqrt{-15}$ or $x = -\sqrt{-15}$ Square root property

$x = i\sqrt{15}$ or $x = -i\sqrt{15}$ $\sqrt{-1} = i$ (See **Section 10.7**.)

The solution set is $\left\{i\sqrt{15}, -i\sqrt{15}\right\}$, or $\left\{\pm i\sqrt{15}\right\}$.

(b) $(x + 2)^2 = -16$

$x + 2 = \sqrt{-16}$ or $x + 2 = -\sqrt{-16}$ Square root property

$x + 2 = 4i$ or $x + 2 = -4i$ $\sqrt{-16} = 4i$

$x = -2 + 4i$ or $x = -2 - 4i$ Add -2.

The solution set is $\{-2 + 4i, -2 - 4i\}$, or $\{-2 \pm 4i\}$.   **NOW TRY**

NOW TRY ANSWERS

5. $\left\{\dfrac{4 \pm 5\sqrt{2}}{2}\right\}$

6. (a) $\left\{\pm 2i\sqrt{6}\right\}$
    (b) $\{-4 \pm 6i\}$

11.1 EXERCISES   *MyMathLab*   Math XL PRACTICE   WATCH   DOWNLOAD   READ   REVIEW

⊕ *Complete solution available on the Video Resources on DVD*

1. *Concept Check*   Which of the following are quadratic equations?

    A. $x + 2y = 0$ **B.** $x^2 - 8x + 16 = 0$ **C.** $2t^2 - 5t = 3$ **D.** $x^3 + x^2 + 4 = 0$

2. *Concept Check*   Which quadratic equation identified in **Exercise 1** is in standard form?

3. *Concept Check*   A student incorrectly solved the equation $x^2 - x - 2 = 5$ as follows. *WHAT WENT WRONG?*

$$x^2 - x - 2 = 5$$
$$(x - 2)(x + 1) = 5 \qquad \text{Factor.}$$
$$x - 2 = 5 \quad \text{or} \quad x + 1 = 5 \qquad \text{Zero-factor property}$$
$$x = 7 \quad \text{or} \qquad x = 4 \qquad \text{Solve each equation.}$$

4. *Concept Check*   A student was asked to solve the quadratic equation $x^2 = 16$ and did not get full credit for the solution set $\{4\}$. *WHAT WENT WRONG?*

*Solve each equation by the zero-factor property. **See Example 1.***

5. $x^2 - x - 56 = 0$ **6.** $x^2 - 2x - 99 = 0$ **7.** $x^2 = 121$

8. $x^2 = 144$ **9.** $3x^2 - 13x = 30$ **10.** $5x^2 - 14x = 3$

*Solve each equation by using the square root property. Simplify all radicals. **See Example 2.***

⊕ **11.** $x^2 = 81$ **12.** $z^2 = 169$ **13.** $x^2 = 14$

14. $m^2 = 22$ **15.** $t^2 = 48$ **16.** $x^2 = 54$

17. $x^2 = \dfrac{25}{4}$ **18.** $m^2 = \dfrac{36}{121}$ **19.** $x^2 = 2.25$

20. $w^2 = 56.25$ **21.** $r^2 - 3 = 0$ **22.** $x^2 - 13 = 0$

23. $x^2 - 20 = 0$ **24.** $p^2 - 50 = 0$ **25.** $7x^2 = 4$

26. $3p^2 = 10$ **27.** $3n^2 - 72 = 0$ **28.** $5z^2 - 200 = 0$

29. $5x^2 + 4 = 8$ **30.** $4p^2 - 3 = 7$ **31.** $2t^2 + 7 = 61$

32. $3x^2 + 8 = 80$ **33.** $-8x^2 = -64$ **34.** $-12x^2 = -144$

*Solve each equation by using the square root property. Simplify all radicals. **See Examples 4 and 5.***

⊕ **35.** $(x - 3)^2 = 25$ **36.** $(x - 7)^2 = 16$ **37.** $(x - 4)^2 = 3$

38. $(x + 3)^2 = 11$ **39.** $(x - 8)^2 = 27$ **40.** $(p - 5)^2 = 40$

41. $(3x + 2)^2 = 49$ **42.** $(5t + 3)^2 = 36$ **43.** $(4x - 3)^2 = 9$

44. $(7z - 5)^2 = 25$ **45.** $(3x - 1)^2 = 7$ **46.** $(2x - 5)^2 = 10$

⊕ **47.** $(3k + 1)^2 = 18$ **48.** $(5z + 6)^2 = 75$ **49.** $(5 - 2x)^2 = 30$

50. $(3 - 2x)^2 = 70$ **51.** $\left(\dfrac{1}{2}x + 5\right)^2 = 12$ **52.** $\left(\dfrac{1}{3}m + 4\right)^2 = 27$

53. $(4x - 1)^2 - 48 = 0$ **54.** $(2x - 5)^2 - 180 = 0$

Use a calculator with a square root key to solve each equation. Round your answers to the nearest hundredth.

55. $(k + 2.14)^2 = 5.46$ **56.** $(r - 3.91)^2 = 9.28$

57. $(2.11p + 3.42)^2 = 9.58$ **58.** $(1.71m - 6.20)^2 = 5.41$

*Find the nonreal complex solutions of each equation. **See Example 6.***

59. $x^2 = -12$ **60.** $x^2 = -18$ **61.** $(r - 5)^2 = -4$

62. $(t + 6)^2 = -9$ **63.** $(6x - 1)^2 = -8$ **64.** $(4m - 7)^2 = -27$

*In Exercises 65 and 66, round answers to the nearest tenth. **See Example 3.***

65. The sculpture of American presidents at Mount Rushmore National Memorial is 500 ft above the valley floor. How long would it take a rock dropped from the top of the sculpture to fall to the ground? (*Source:* www.travelsd.com)

66. The Gateway Arch in St. Louis, Missouri, is 630 ft tall. How long would it take an object dropped from the top of the arch to fall to the ground? (*Source:* www.gatewayarch.com)

*Solve each problem. **See Example 3.***

67. The area $\mathcal{A}$ of a circle with radius r is given by the formula

$$\mathcal{A} = \pi r^2.$$

If a circle has area 81π in.^{2}, what is its radius?

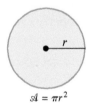

$\mathcal{A} = \pi r^2$

68. The surface area S of a sphere with radius r is given by the formula

$$S = 4\pi r^2.$$

If a sphere has surface area 36π ft^2, what is its radius?

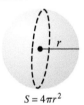

$S = 4\pi r^2$

The amount A that P dollars invested at an annual rate of interest r will grow to in 2 yr is

$$A = P(1 + r)^2.$$

69. At what interest rate will $100 grow to $104.04 in 2 yr?

70. At what interest rate will $500 grow to $530.45 in 2 yr?

PREVIEW EXERCISES

*Simplify all radicals, and combine like terms. Express fractions in lowest terms. **See Sections 10.3–10.5.***

71. $\dfrac{4}{5} + \sqrt{\dfrac{48}{25}}$ **72.** $\dfrac{12 - \sqrt{27}}{9}$ **73.** $\dfrac{6 + \sqrt{24}}{8}$

*Factor each perfect square trinomial. **See Section 5.4.***

74. $z^2 + 4z + 4$ **75.** $x^2 - 10x + 25$ **76.** $z^2 + z + \dfrac{1}{4}$

11.2 Solving Quadratic Equations by Completing the Square

OBJECTIVE 1 Solve quadratic equations by completing the square when the coefficient of the second-degree term is 1. The methods we have studied so far are not enough to solve an equation such as

$$x^2 + 6x + 7 = 0.$$

If we could write the equation in the form $(x + 3)^2$ equals a constant, we could solve it with the square root property discussed in **Section 11.1.** To do that, we need to have a perfect square trinomial on one side of the equation.

Recall from **Section 5.4** that the perfect square trinomial

$$x^2 + 6x + 9 \quad \text{can be factored as} \quad (x + 3)^2.$$

If we take half of 6, the coefficient of x (the first-degree term), and square it, we get the constant term, 9.

$$\left[\frac{1}{2}\overset{\text{Coefficient of } x}{(6)}\right]^2 = 3^2 = \overset{\text{Constant}}{9}$$

Similarly, in $\quad x^2 + 12x + 36, \quad \left[\frac{1}{2}(12)\right]^2 = 6^2 = 36,$

and in $\quad m^2 - 6m + 9, \quad \left[\frac{1}{2}(-6)\right]^2 = (-3)^2 = 9.$

This relationship is true in general and is the idea behind writing a quadratic equation so that the square root property can be applied.

EXAMPLE 1 Rewriting an Equation to Use the Square Root Property

Solve $x^2 + 6x + 7 = 0$.

This quadratic equation cannot be solved by factoring, and it is not in the correct form to solve using the square root property. To obtain this form, we need a perfect square trinomial on the left side of the equation.

$$x^2 + 6x + 7 = 0 \qquad \text{Original equation}$$
$$x^2 + 6x = -7 \qquad \text{Subtract 7.}$$

We must add a constant to get a perfect square trinomial on the left.

$$\underbrace{x^2 + 6x + \underline{\quad ? \quad}}_{\substack{\text{Needs to be a perfect} \\ \text{square trinomial}}}$$

As above, take half the coefficient of the first-degree term, $6x$, and square the result.

$$\left[\frac{1}{2}(6)\right]^2 = 3^2 = 9 \longleftarrow \text{Desired constant}$$

If we add 9 to each side of $x^2 + 6x = -7$, the equation will have a perfect square trinomial on the left side, as needed.

$$x^2 + 6x = -7$$
$$\overset{\text{This is a key step.}}{\longrightarrow} x^2 + 6x + 9 = -7 + 9 \qquad \text{Add 9.}$$
$$(x + 3)^2 = 2 \qquad \text{Factor. Add.}$$

NOW TRY
EXERCISE 1
Solve $x^2 + 10x + 8 = 0$.

Now use the square root property to complete the solution.

$$x + 3 = \sqrt{2} \qquad \text{or} \qquad x + 3 = -\sqrt{2}$$
$$x = -3 + \sqrt{2} \qquad \text{or} \qquad x = -3 - \sqrt{2}$$

Check by substituting $-3 + \sqrt{2}$ and $-3 - \sqrt{2}$ for x in the original equation. The solution set is $\left\{-3 \pm \sqrt{2}\right\}$.

NOW TRY

The process of changing the form of the equation in **Example 1** from

$$x^2 + 6x + 7 = 0 \qquad \text{to} \qquad (x + 3)^2 = 2$$

is called **completing the square.** Completing the square changes only the form of the equation. To see this, multiply out the left side of $(x + 3)^2 = 2$ and combine like terms. Then subtract 2 from each side to see that the result is $x^2 + 6x + 7 = 0$.

NOW TRY
EXERCISE 2
Solve $x^2 - 6x = 9$.

EXAMPLE 2 Completing the Square to Solve a Quadratic Equation

Solve $x^2 - 8x = 5$.

To complete the square on $x^2 - 8x$, take half the coefficient of x and square it.

$$\frac{1}{2}(-8) = -4 \qquad \text{and} \qquad (-4)^2 = 16$$

Coefficient of x

Add the result, 16, to each side of the equation.

$x^2 - 8x = 5$	Given equation
$x^2 - 8x + 16 = 5 + 16$	Add 16.
$(x - 4)^2 = 21$	Factor on the left. Add on the right.
$x - 4 = \sqrt{21} \quad \text{or} \quad x - 4 = -\sqrt{21}$	Square root property
$x = 4 + \sqrt{21} \quad \text{or} \quad x = 4 - \sqrt{21}$	Add 4.

A check indicates that the solution set is $\left\{4 \pm \sqrt{21}\right\}$.

NOW TRY

Completing the Square

To solve $ax^2 + bx + c = 0$ $(a \neq 0)$ by completing the square, use these steps.

Step 1 **Be sure the second-degree (squared) term has coefficient 1.** If the coefficient of the second-degree term is 1, proceed to Step 2. If the coefficient of the second-degree term is not 1 but some other nonzero number a, divide each side of the equation by a.

Step 2 **Write the equation in correct form** so that terms with variables are on one side of the equals symbol and the constant is on the other side.

Step 3 **Square half the coefficient of the first-degree (linear) term.**

Step 4 **Add the square to each side.**

Step 5 **Factor the perfect square trinomial.** One side should now be a perfect square trinomial. Factor it as the square of a binomial. Simplify the other side.

Step 6 **Solve the equation.** Apply the square root property to complete the solution.

NOW TRY ANSWERS
1. $\left\{-5 \pm \sqrt{17}\right\}$
2. $\left\{3 \pm 3\sqrt{2}\right\}$

NOW TRY
EXERCISE 3

Solve $x^2 + x - 3 = 0$.

EXAMPLE 3 Solving a Quadratic Equation by Completing the Square ($a = 1$)

Solve $x^2 + 5x - 1 = 0$.

Since the coefficient of the squared term is 1, begin with Step 2.

Step 2 $\qquad\qquad x^2 + 5x = 1 \qquad$ Add 1 to each side.

Step 3 Take half the coefficient of the first-degree term and square the result.

$$\left[\frac{1}{2}(5)\right]^2 = \left(\frac{5}{2}\right)^2 = \frac{25}{4}$$

Step 4 $\qquad\qquad x^2 + 5x + \frac{25}{4} = 1 + \frac{25}{4} \qquad$ Add the square to each side of the equation.

Step 5 $\qquad\qquad \left(x + \frac{5}{2}\right)^2 = \frac{29}{4} \qquad$ Factor on the left.
Add on the right.

Step 6 $\quad x + \frac{5}{2} = \sqrt{\frac{29}{4}} \qquad$ or $\qquad x + \frac{5}{2} = -\sqrt{\frac{29}{4}} \qquad$ Square root property

$\qquad x + \frac{5}{2} = \frac{\sqrt{29}}{2} \qquad$ or $\qquad x + \frac{5}{2} = -\frac{\sqrt{29}}{2} \qquad \sqrt{\frac{a}{b}} = \frac{\sqrt{a}}{\sqrt{b}}$

$\qquad x = -\frac{5}{2} + \frac{\sqrt{29}}{2} \qquad$ or $\qquad x = -\frac{5}{2} - \frac{\sqrt{29}}{2} \qquad$ Add $-\frac{5}{2}$.

$\qquad x = \frac{-5 + \sqrt{29}}{2} \qquad$ or $\qquad x = \frac{-5 - \sqrt{29}}{2} \qquad \frac{a}{c} \pm \frac{b}{c} = \frac{a \pm b}{c}$

Check that the solution set is $\left\{\dfrac{-5 \pm \sqrt{29}}{2}\right\}$.

NOW TRY

OBJECTIVE 2 Solve quadratic equations by completing the square when the coefficient of the second-degree term is not 1. If a quadratic equation has the form

$$ax^2 + bx + c = 0, \quad \text{where} \quad a \neq 1,$$

we obtain 1 as the coefficient of x^2 by dividing each side of the equation by a.

EXAMPLE 4 Solving a Quadratic Equation by Completing the Square ($a \neq 1$)

Solve $4x^2 + 16x - 9 = 0$.

Step 1 *Before completing the square, the coefficient of x^2 must be 1,* not 4. We get 1 as the coefficient of x^2 here by dividing each side by 4.

$$4x^2 + 16x - 9 = 0 \qquad \text{Given equation}$$

The coefficient of x^2 must be 1. $\longrightarrow x^2 + 4x - \frac{9}{4} = 0 \qquad$ Divide by 4.

Step 2 Write the equation so that all variable terms are on one side of the equation and all constant terms are on the other side.

$$x^2 + 4x = \frac{9}{4} \qquad \text{Add } \frac{9}{4}.$$

NOW TRY ANSWER
3. $\left\{\dfrac{-1 \pm \sqrt{13}}{2}\right\}$

NOW TRY
EXERCISE 4
Solve $4t^2 - 4t - 3 = 0$.

Step 3 Complete the square by taking half the coefficient of x, and squaring it.

$$\frac{1}{2}(4) = 2 \quad \text{and} \quad 2^2 = 4$$

Step 4 We add the result, 4, to each side of the equation.

$$x^2 + 4x + 4 = \frac{9}{4} + 4 \qquad \text{Add 4.}$$

Step 5 $$(x + 2)^2 = \frac{25}{4} \qquad \text{Factor; } \tfrac{9}{4} + 4 = \tfrac{9}{4} + \tfrac{16}{4} = \tfrac{25}{4}.$$

Step 6 Solve the equation by using the square root property.

$$x + 2 = \sqrt{\frac{25}{4}} \quad \text{or} \quad x + 2 = -\sqrt{\frac{25}{4}} \qquad \text{Square root property}$$

$$x + 2 = \frac{5}{2} \quad \text{or} \quad x + 2 = -\frac{5}{2} \qquad \text{Take square roots.}$$

$$x = -2 + \frac{5}{2} \quad \text{or} \quad x = -2 - \frac{5}{2} \qquad \text{Add } -2.$$

$$x = \frac{1}{2} \quad \text{or} \quad x = -\frac{9}{2} \qquad -2 = -\tfrac{4}{2}$$

CHECK

$$4x^2 + 16x - 9 = 0$$

$$4\left(\frac{1}{2}\right)^2 + 16\left(\frac{1}{2}\right) - 9 \stackrel{?}{=} 0 \qquad \text{Let } x = \tfrac{1}{2}.$$

$$4\left(\frac{1}{4}\right) + 8 - 9 \stackrel{?}{=} 0$$

$$1 + 8 - 9 \stackrel{?}{=} 0$$

$$0 = 0 \ \checkmark \ \text{True}$$

$$4x^2 + 16x - 9 = 0$$

$$4\left(-\frac{9}{2}\right)^2 + 16\left(-\frac{9}{2}\right) - 9 \stackrel{?}{=} 0 \qquad \text{Let } x = -\tfrac{9}{2}.$$

$$4\left(\frac{81}{4}\right) - 72 - 9 \stackrel{?}{=} 0$$

$$81 - 72 - 9 \stackrel{?}{=} 0$$

$$0 = 0 \ \checkmark \ \text{True}$$

The two solutions, $\frac{1}{2}$ and $-\frac{9}{2}$, check, so the solution set is $\left\{-\frac{9}{2}, \frac{1}{2}\right\}$. NOW TRY

EXAMPLE 5 Solving a Quadratic Equation by Completing the Square ($a \neq 1$)
Solve $2x^2 - 4x - 5 = 0$.

Divide each side by 2 to get 1 as the coefficient of the second-degree term.

$$x^2 - 2x - \frac{5}{2} = 0 \qquad \text{Step 1}$$

$$x^2 - 2x = \frac{5}{2} \qquad \text{Step 2}$$

$$\left[\frac{1}{2}(-2)\right]^2 = (-1)^2 = 1 \qquad \text{Step 3}$$

$$x^2 - 2x + 1 = \frac{5}{2} + 1 \qquad \text{Step 4}$$

NOW TRY ANSWER
4. $\left\{-\frac{1}{2}, \frac{3}{2}\right\}$

NOW TRY
EXERCISE 5
Solve $3x^2 + 12x - 5 = 0$.

$$(x - 1)^2 = \frac{7}{2} \qquad \text{Step 5}$$

$$x - 1 = \sqrt{\frac{7}{2}} \qquad \text{or} \quad x - 1 = -\sqrt{\frac{7}{2}} \qquad \text{Step 6}$$

$$x = 1 + \sqrt{\frac{7}{2}} \qquad \text{or} \qquad x = 1 - \sqrt{\frac{7}{2}} \qquad \text{Add 1.}$$

$$x = 1 + \frac{\sqrt{14}}{2} \qquad \text{or} \qquad x = 1 - \frac{\sqrt{14}}{2} \qquad \sqrt{\frac{7}{2}} = \frac{\sqrt{7}}{\sqrt{2}} = \frac{\sqrt{7}}{\sqrt{2}} \cdot \frac{\sqrt{2}}{\sqrt{2}} = \frac{\sqrt{14}}{2}$$

Add the two terms in each solution as follows.

$$1 + \frac{\sqrt{14}}{2} = \frac{2}{2} + \frac{\sqrt{14}}{2} = \frac{2 + \sqrt{14}}{2} \qquad 1 = \frac{2}{2}$$

$$1 - \frac{\sqrt{14}}{2} = \frac{2}{2} - \frac{\sqrt{14}}{2} = \frac{2 - \sqrt{14}}{2}$$

Check that the solution set is $\left\{ \dfrac{2 \pm \sqrt{14}}{2} \right\}$. **NOW TRY**

NOW TRY
EXERCISE 6
Solve $x^2 + 8x + 21 = 0$.

EXAMPLE 6 Solving a Quadratic Equation with Nonreal Complex Solutions

Solve $4p^2 + 8p + 5 = 0$.

$$4p^2 + 8p + 5 = 0$$

$$\boxed{\text{The coefficient of the second-degree term must be 1.}} \longrightarrow p^2 + 2p + \frac{5}{4} = 0 \qquad \text{Divide by 4.}$$

$$p^2 + 2p = -\frac{5}{4} \qquad \text{Add } -\frac{5}{4} \text{ to each side.}$$

The coefficient of p is 2. Take half of 2, square the result, and add it to each side.

$$p^2 + 2p + 1 = -\frac{5}{4} + 1 \qquad \left[\frac{1}{2}(2)\right]^2 = 1^2 = 1; \text{ Add 1.}$$

$$(p + 1)^2 = -\frac{1}{4} \qquad \begin{array}{l}\text{Factor on the left.}\\ \text{Add on the right.}\end{array}$$

$$p + 1 = \sqrt{-\frac{1}{4}} \qquad \text{or} \quad p + 1 = -\sqrt{-\frac{1}{4}} \qquad \text{Square root property}$$

$$p + 1 = \frac{1}{2}i \qquad \text{or} \quad p + 1 = -\frac{1}{2}i \qquad \sqrt{-\frac{1}{4}} = \frac{1}{2}i$$

$$p = -1 + \frac{1}{2}i \quad \text{or} \qquad p = -1 - \frac{1}{2}i \qquad \text{Add } -1.$$

The solution set is $\left\{ -1 \pm \frac{1}{2}i \right\}$. **NOW TRY**

NOW TRY ANSWERS
5. $\left\{ \dfrac{-6 \pm \sqrt{51}}{3} \right\}$

6. $\left\{ -4 \pm i\sqrt{5} \right\}$

OBJECTIVE 3 **Simplify the terms of an equation before solving.**

NOW TRY
EXERCISE 7
Solve $(x - 5)(x + 1) = 2$.

EXAMPLE 7 Simplifying the Terms of an Equation before Solving

Solve $(x + 3)(x - 1) = 2$.

$$(x + 3)(x - 1) = 2$$

$$x^2 + 2x - 3 = 2 \qquad \text{Multiply by using the FOIL method.}$$

$$x^2 + 2x = 5 \qquad \text{Add 3.}$$

$$x^2 + 2x + 1 = 5 + 1 \qquad \text{Complete the square. Add } \left[\tfrac{1}{2}(2)\right]^2 = 1^2 = 1.$$

$$(x + 1)^2 = 6 \qquad \text{Factor on the left. Add on the right.}$$

$$x + 1 = \sqrt{6} \qquad \text{or} \qquad x + 1 = -\sqrt{6} \qquad \text{Square root property}$$

$$x = -1 + \sqrt{6} \qquad \text{or} \qquad x = -1 - \sqrt{6} \qquad \text{Subtract 1.}$$

NOW TRY ANSWER
7. $\{2 \pm \sqrt{11}\}$

The solution set is $\{-1 \pm \sqrt{6}\}$. NOW TRY

11.2 EXERCISES

MyMathLab Math XL PRACTICE WATCH DOWNLOAD READ REVIEW

🌐 *Complete solution available on the Video Resources on DVD*

1. *Concept Check* Which one of the two equations
$$(2x + 1)^2 = 5 \quad \text{and} \quad x^2 + 4x = 12,$$
is more suitable for solving by the square root property? Which one is more suitable for solving by completing the square?

✎ 2. Why would most students find the equation $x^2 + 4x = 20$ easier to solve by completing the square than the equation $5x^2 + 2x = 3$?

Concept Check Decide what number must be added to make each expression a perfect square trinomial. Then factor the trinomial.

3. $x^2 + 6x + \underline{\quad}$ 4. $x^2 + 14x + \underline{\quad}$ 5. $p^2 - 12p + \underline{\quad}$

6. $x^2 - 20x + \underline{\quad}$ 7. $q^2 + 9q + \underline{\quad}$ 8. $t^2 + 13t + \underline{\quad}$

9. $x^2 + \dfrac{1}{4}x + \underline{\quad}$ 10. $x^2 + \dfrac{1}{2}x + \underline{\quad}$ 11. $x^2 - 0.8x + \underline{\quad}$

12. *Concept Check* What would be the first step in solving $2x^2 + 8x = 9$ by completing the square?

Determine the number that will complete the square to solve each equation, after the constant term has been written on the right side and the coefficient of the second-degree term is 1. Do not actually solve. **See Examples 1–5.**

13. $x^2 + 4x - 2 = 0$ 14. $t^2 + 2t - 1 = 0$ 15. $x^2 + 10x + 18 = 0$

16. $x^2 + 8x + 11 = 0$ 17. $3w^2 - w - 24 = 0$ 18. $4z^2 - z - 39 = 0$

Solve each equation by completing the square. Use the results of **Exercises 13–16** *to solve Exercises 23–26.* **See Examples 1–3.**

🌐 19. $x^2 - 4x = -3$ 20. $p^2 - 2p = 8$ 🌐 21. $x^2 + 2x - 5 = 0$

22. $r^2 + 4r + 1 = 0$ 🌐 23. $x^2 + 4x - 2 = 0$ 24. $t^2 + 2t - 1 = 0$

25. $x^2 + 10x + 18 = 0$ **26.** $x^2 + 8x + 11 = 0$ **27.** $x^2 - 8x = -4$

28. $m^2 - 4m = 14$ 🌐 **29.** $x^2 + 7x - 1 = 0$ **30.** $x^2 + 13x - 3 = 0$

*Solve each equation by completing the square. Use the results of **Exercises 17 and 18** to solve Exercises 33 and 34. **See Examples 4, 5, and 7.***

🌐 **31.** $4x^2 + 4x = 3$ **32.** $9x^2 + 3x = 2$ **33.** $3w^2 - w = 24$

34. $4z^2 - z = 39$ **35.** $2k^2 + 5k - 2 = 0$ **36.** $3r^2 + 2r - 2 = 0$

🌐 **37.** $5x^2 - 10x + 2 = 0$ **38.** $2x^2 - 16x + 25 = 0$ **39.** $9x^2 - 24x = -13$

40. $25n^2 - 20n = 1$ 🌐 **41.** $(x + 3)(x - 1) = 5$ **42.** $(x - 8)(x + 2) = 24$

43. $(r - 3)(r - 5) = 2$ **44.** $(x - 1)(x - 7) = 1$ **45.** $-x^2 + 2x = -5$

46. $-x^2 + 4x = 1$ **47.** $z^2 - \dfrac{4}{3}z = -\dfrac{1}{9}$ **48.** $p^2 - \dfrac{8}{3}p = -1$

49. $0.1x^2 - 0.2x - 0.1 = 0$ **50.** $0.1p^2 - 0.4p + 0.1 = 0$
(*Hint:* First clear the decimals.)   (*Hint:* First clear the decimals.)

*Solve each equation by completing the square. Give **(a)** exact solutions and **(b)** solutions rounded to the nearest thousandth.*

51. $3r^2 - 2 = 6r + 3$ **52.** $4p + 3 = 2p^2 + 2p$

53. $(x + 1)(x + 3) = 2$ **54.** $(x - 3)(x + 1) = 1$

*Find the nonreal complex solutions of each equation. **See Example 6.***

55. $m^2 + 4m + 13 = 0$ **56.** $t^2 + 6t + 10 = 0$ **57.** $3r^2 + 4r + 4 = 0$

58. $4x^2 + 5x + 5 = 0$ **59.** $-m^2 - 6m - 12 = 0$ **60.** $-x^2 - 5x - 10 = 0$

RELATING CONCEPTS EXERCISES 61–66

FOR INDIVIDUAL OR GROUP WORK

The Greeks had a method of completing the square geometrically in which they literally changed a figure into a square. For example, to complete the square for $x^2 + 6x$, we begin with a square of side x, as in the figure on the left. We add three rectangles of width 1 to the right side and the bottom to get a region with area $x^2 + 6x$. To fill in the corner (complete the square), we must add nine 1-by-1 squares as shown.

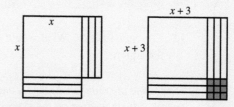

Work Exercises 61–66 in order.

61. What is the area of the original square?

62. What is the area of each strip?

63. What is the total area of the six strips?

64. What is the area of each small square in the corner of the second figure?

65. What is the total area of the small squares?

66. What is the area of the new "complete" square?

Brain Busters   Solve for x. Assume that a and b represent positive real numbers.

67. $x^2 - b = 0$ **68.** $x^2 = 4b$ **69.** $4x^2 = b^2 + 16$

70. $9x^2 - 25a = 0$ **71.** $(5x - 2b)^2 = 3a$ **72.** $x^2 - a^2 - 36 = 0$

PREVIEW EXERCISES

Evaluate $\sqrt{b^2 - 4ac}$ for the given values of a, b, and c. ***See Sections 1.3 and 10.1.***

73. $a = 3, b = 1, c = -1$ **74.** $a = 4, b = 11, c = -3$

75. $a = 6, b = 7, c = 2$ **76.** $a = 1, b = -6, c = 9$

11.3 Solving Quadratic Equations by the Quadratic Formula

OBJECTIVES

1 Derive the quadratic formula.

2 Solve quadratic equations by using the quadratic formula.

3 Use the discriminant to determine the number and type of solutions.

In this section, we complete the square to solve the general quadratic equation

$$ax^2 + bx + c = 0,$$

where a, b, and c are complex numbers and $a \neq 0$. The solution of this general equation gives a formula for finding the solution of *any* specific quadratic equation.

OBJECTIVE 1   **Derive the quadratic formula.**   To solve $ax^2 + bx + c = 0$ by completing the square (assuming $a > 0$), we follow the steps given in **Section 11.2.**

$$ax^2 + bx + c = 0$$

$$x^2 + \frac{b}{a}x + \frac{c}{a} = 0 \qquad \text{Divide by } a. \text{ (Step 1)}$$

$$x^2 + \frac{b}{a}x = -\frac{c}{a} \qquad \text{Subtract } \tfrac{c}{a}. \text{(Step 2)}$$

$$\left[\frac{1}{2}\left(\frac{b}{a}\right)\right]^2 = \left(\frac{b}{2a}\right)^2 = \frac{b^2}{4a^2} \qquad \text{(Step 3)}$$

$$x^2 + \frac{b}{a}x + \frac{b^2}{4a^2} = -\frac{c}{a} + \frac{b^2}{4a^2} \qquad \text{Add } \tfrac{b^2}{4a^2} \text{ to each side. (Step 4)}$$

$$\left(x + \frac{b}{2a}\right)^2 = \frac{b^2}{4a^2} + \frac{-c}{a} \qquad \begin{array}{l}\text{Write the left side as a perfect square.}\\\text{Rearrange the right side. (Step 5)}\end{array}$$

$$\left(x + \frac{b}{2a}\right)^2 = \frac{b^2}{4a^2} + \frac{-4ac}{4a^2} \qquad \text{Write with a common denominator.}$$

$$\left(x + \frac{b}{2a}\right)^2 = \frac{b^2 - 4ac}{4a^2} \qquad \text{Add fractions.}$$

$$x + \frac{b}{2a} = \sqrt{\frac{b^2 - 4ac}{4a^2}} \quad \text{or} \quad x + \frac{b}{2a} = -\sqrt{\frac{b^2 - 4ac}{4a^2}} \qquad \begin{array}{l}\text{Square root property}\\\text{(Step 6)}\end{array}$$

We can simplify $\sqrt{\dfrac{b^2 - 4ac}{4a^2}}$ as $\dfrac{\sqrt{b^2 - 4ac}}{\sqrt{4a^2}}$, or $\dfrac{\sqrt{b^2 - 4ac}}{2a}$.

The right side of each equation can be expressed as follows.

$$x + \frac{b}{2a} = \frac{\sqrt{b^2 - 4ac}}{2a} \quad \text{or} \quad x + \frac{b}{2a} = \frac{-\sqrt{b^2 - 4ac}}{2a}$$

$$x = \frac{-b}{2a} + \frac{\sqrt{b^2 - 4ac}}{2a} \quad \text{or} \quad x = \frac{-b}{2a} - \frac{\sqrt{b^2 - 4ac}}{2a}$$

If $a < 0$, the same two solutions are obtained.

$$x = \frac{-b + \sqrt{b^2 - 4ac}}{2a} \quad \text{or} \quad x = \frac{-b - \sqrt{b^2 - 4ac}}{2a}$$

The result is the **quadratic formula,** which is abbreviated as follows.

Quadratic Formula

The solutions of the equation $ax^2 + bx + c = 0$ (with $a \neq 0$) are given by

$$x = \frac{-b \pm \sqrt{b^2 - 4ac}}{2a}.$$

⚠ **CAUTION**   In the quadratic formula, *the square root is added to or subtracted from the value of $-b$ before dividing by $2a$.*

OBJECTIVE 2   Solve quadratic equations by using the quadratic formula.

NOW TRY
EXERCISE 1
Solve $2x^2 + 3x - 20 = 0$.

EXAMPLE 1   Using the Quadratic Formula (Rational Solutions)

Solve $6x^2 - 5x - 4 = 0$.

This equation is in standard form, so we identify the values of a, b, and c. Here a, the coefficient of the second-degree term, is 6, and b, the coefficient of the first-degree term, is -5. The constant c is -4. Now substitute into the quadratic formula.

$$x = \frac{-b \pm \sqrt{b^2 - 4ac}}{2a} \qquad \text{Quadratic formula}$$

$$x = \frac{-(-5) \pm \sqrt{(-5)^2 - 4(6)(-4)}}{2(6)} \qquad a = 6, b = -5, c = -4$$

Use parentheses and substitute carefully to avoid errors.

$$x = \frac{5 \pm \sqrt{25 + 96}}{12}$$

$$x = \frac{5 \pm \sqrt{121}}{12} \qquad \text{Simplify the radical.}$$

$$x = \frac{5 \pm 11}{12} \qquad \text{Take the square root.}$$

There are two solutions, one from the $+$ sign and one from the $-$ sign.

$$x = \frac{5 + 11}{12} = \frac{16}{12} = \frac{4}{3} \quad \text{or} \quad x = \frac{5 - 11}{12} = \frac{-6}{12} = -\frac{1}{2}$$

NOW TRY ANSWER
1. $\left\{-4, \frac{5}{2}\right\}$

Check each solution in the original equation. The solution set is $\left\{-\frac{1}{2}, \frac{4}{3}\right\}$.

NOW TRY

NOTE We could have used factoring to solve the equation in **Example 1.**

$$6x^2 - 5x - 4 = 0$$

$$(3x - 4)(2x + 1) = 0 \qquad \text{Factor.}$$

$$3x - 4 = 0 \quad \text{or} \quad 2x + 1 = 0 \qquad \text{Zero-factor property}$$

$$3x = 4 \quad \text{or} \qquad 2x = -1 \qquad \text{Solve each equation.}$$

$$x = \frac{4}{3} \quad \text{or} \qquad x = -\frac{1}{2} \qquad \text{Same solutions as in \textbf{Example 1}}$$

When solving quadratic equations, it is a good idea to try factoring first. If the polynomial cannot be factored or if factoring is difficult, then use the quadratic formula.

NOW TRY
EXERCISE 2

Solve $3x^2 + 1 = -5x$.

EXAMPLE 2   Using the Quadratic Formula (Irrational Solutions)

Solve $4x^2 = 8x - 1$.

Write the equation in standard form as $4x^2 - 8x + 1 = 0$. ⟵ This is a key step.

$$x = \frac{-b \pm \sqrt{b^2 - 4ac}}{2a} \qquad \text{Quadratic formula}$$

$$x = \frac{-(-8) \pm \sqrt{(-8)^2 - 4(4)(1)}}{2(4)} \qquad a = 4, b = -8, c = 1$$

$$x = \frac{8 \pm \sqrt{64 - 16}}{8} \qquad \text{Simplify.}$$

$$x = \frac{8 \pm \sqrt{48}}{8}$$

$$x = \frac{8 \pm 4\sqrt{3}}{8} \qquad \sqrt{48} = \sqrt{16} \cdot \sqrt{3} = 4\sqrt{3}$$

$$x = \frac{4\left(2 \pm \sqrt{3}\right)}{4(2)} \qquad \text{Factor.}$$

Factor first. Then divide out the common factor.

$$x = \frac{2 \pm \sqrt{3}}{2} \qquad \text{Lowest terms}$$

The solution set is $\left\{ \dfrac{2 \pm \sqrt{3}}{2} \right\}$.

NOW TRY

⚠ **CAUTION**

1. *Every quadratic equation must be expressed in standard form* $ax^2 + bx + c = 0$ *before we begin to solve it,* whether we use factoring or the quadratic formula.

2. *When writing solutions in lowest terms, be sure to FACTOR FIRST. Then divide out the common factor,* as shown in the last two steps in **Example 2.**

NOW TRY ANSWER

2. $\left\{ \dfrac{-5 \pm \sqrt{13}}{6} \right\}$

NOW TRY
EXERCISE 3
Solve $(x + 5)(x - 1) = -18$.

EXAMPLE 3   Using the Quadratic Formula (Nonreal Complex Solutions)

Solve $(9x + 3)(x - 1) = -8$.

$$(9x + 3)(x - 1) = -8$$

$$9x^2 - 6x - 3 = -8 \qquad \text{Multiply.}$$

Standard form $\longrightarrow$ $9x^2 - 6x + 5 = 0 \qquad$ Add 8.

From the equation $9x^2 - 6x + 5 = 0$, we identify $a = 9$, $b = -6$, and $c = 5$.

$$x = \frac{-b \pm \sqrt{b^2 - 4ac}}{2a} \qquad \text{Quadratic formula}$$

$$x = \frac{-(-6) \pm \sqrt{(-6)^2 - 4(9)(5)}}{2(9)} \qquad \text{Substitute.}$$

$$x = \frac{6 \pm \sqrt{-144}}{18} \qquad \text{Simplify.}$$

$$x = \frac{6 \pm 12i}{18} \qquad \sqrt{-144} = 12i$$

$$x = \frac{6(1 \pm 2i)}{6(3)} \qquad \text{Factor.}$$

$$x = \frac{1 \pm 2i}{3} \qquad \text{Lowest terms}$$

$$x = \frac{1}{3} \pm \frac{2}{3}i \qquad \text{Standard form } a + bi \text{ for a complex number}$$

The solution set is $\left\{ \frac{1}{3} \pm \frac{2}{3}i \right\}$.   *NOW TRY* ↩

OBJECTIVE 3 **Use the discriminant to determine the number and type of solutions.** The solutions of the quadratic equation $ax^2 + bx + c = 0$ are given by

$$x = \frac{-b \pm \sqrt{b^2 - 4ac}}{2a}. \quad \leftarrow \text{Discriminant}$$

If a, b, and c are integers, the type of solutions of a quadratic equation—that is, rational, irrational, or nonreal complex—is determined by the expression under the radical symbol, $b^2 - 4ac$, called the *discriminant* (because it distinguishes among the three types of solutions). By calculating the discriminant, we can predict the number and type of solutions of a quadratic equation.

Discriminant

The **discriminant** of $ax^2 + bx + c = 0$ is $b^2 - 4ac$. If a, b, and c are integers, then the number and type of solutions are determined as follows.

Discriminant	Number and Type of Solutions
Positive, and the square of an integer	Two rational solutions
Positive, but not the square of an integer	Two irrational solutions
Zero	One rational solution
Negative	Two nonreal complex solutions

NOW TRY ANSWER
3. $\{-2 \pm 3i\}$

Calculating the discriminant can also help you decide how to solve a quadratic equation. *If the discriminant is a perfect square (including 0), then the equation can be solved by factoring. Otherwise, the quadratic formula should be used.*

**NOW TRY
EXERCISE 4**

Find each discriminant. Use it to predict the number and type of solutions for each equation. Tell whether the equation can be solved by factoring or whether the quadratic formula should be used.

(a) $8x^2 - 6x - 5 = 0$

(b) $9x^2 = 24x - 16$

(c) $3x^2 + 2x = -1$

EXAMPLE 4 Using the Discriminant

Find the discriminant. Use it to predict the number and type of solutions for each equation. Tell whether the equation can be solved by factoring or whether the quadratic formula should be used.

(a) $6x^2 - x - 15 = 0$

We find the discriminant by evaluating $b^2 - 4ac$. Because $-x = -1x$, the value of b in this equation is -1.

$$b^2 - 4ac$$

Use parentheses and substitute carefully.

$$= (-1)^2 - 4(6)(-15) \qquad a = 6, b = -1, c = -15$$

$$= 1 + 360 \qquad \text{Apply the exponent. Multiply.}$$

$$= 361, \quad \text{or} \quad 19^2, \quad \text{which is a perfect square.}$$

Since a, b, and c are integers and the discriminant 361 is a perfect square, there will be two rational solutions. The equation can be solved by factoring.

(b) $3x^2 - 4x = 5$ Write in standard form as $3x^2 - 4x - 5 = 0$.

$$b^2 - 4ac$$

$$= (-4)^2 - 4(3)(-5) \qquad a = 3, b = -4, c = -5$$

$$= 16 + 60 \qquad \text{Apply the exponent. Multiply.}$$

$$= 76 \qquad \text{Add.}$$

Because 76 is positive but *not* the square of an integer and a, b, and c are integers, the equation will have two irrational solutions and is best solved using the quadratic formula.

(c) $4x^2 + x + 1 = 0$

$x = 1x$, so $b = 1$.

$$b^2 - 4ac$$

$$= 1^2 - 4(4)(1) \qquad a = 4, b = 1, c = 1$$

$$= 1 - 16 \qquad \text{Apply the exponent. Multiply.}$$

$$= -15 \qquad \text{Subtract.}$$

Because the discriminant is negative and a, b, and c are integers, this equation will have two nonreal complex solutions. The quadratic formula should be used to solve it.

(d) $4x^2 + 9 = 12x$ Write in standard form as $4x^2 - 12x + 9 = 0$.

$$b^2 - 4ac$$

$$= (-12)^2 - 4(4)(9) \qquad a = 4, b = -12, c = 9$$

$$= 144 - 144 \qquad \text{Apply the exponent. Multiply.}$$

$$= 0 \qquad \text{Subtract.}$$

NOW TRY ANSWERS
4. (a) 196; two rational solutions; factoring
(b) 0; one rational solution; factoring
(c) -8; two nonreal complex solutions; quadratic formula

The discriminant is 0, so the quantity under the radical in the quadratic formula is 0, and there is only one rational solution. The equation can be solved by factoring.

NOW TRY

⟲ NOW TRY
EXERCISE 5

Find k so that the equation
will have exactly one rational
solution.

$$4x^2 + kx + 25 = 0$$

EXAMPLE 5 Using the Discriminant

Find k so that $9x^2 + kx + 4 = 0$ will have exactly one rational solution.

The equation will have only one rational solution if the discriminant is 0.

$$b^2 - 4ac$$

$$= k^2 - 4(9)(4) \qquad \text{Here, } a = 9, b = k, \text{and } c = 4.$$

$$= k^2 - 144 \longleftarrow \text{Value of the discriminant}$$

Set the discriminant equal to 0 and solve for k.

$$k^2 - 144 = 0$$

$$k^2 = 144 \qquad \text{Add 144.}$$

$$k = 12 \quad \text{or} \quad k = -12 \qquad \text{Square root property}$$

NOW TRY ANSWER
5. 20, −20

The equation will have only one rational solution if $k = 12$ or $k = -12$.

NOW TRY ⟲

11.3 EXERCISES

 MyMathLab | Math XL PRACTICE | WATCH | DOWNLOAD | READ | REVIEW

🌐 *Complete solution available
on the Video Resources on DVD*

Concept Check   Answer each question in Exercises 1–4.

1. An early version of Microsoft *Word* for Windows included the 1.0 edition of *Equation Editor*. The documentation used the following for the quadratic formula. Was this correct? If not, correct it.

$$x = -b \pm \frac{\sqrt{b^2 - 4ac}}{2a}$$

2. The Cadillac Bar in Houston, Texas, encourages patrons to write (tasteful) messages on the walls. One person wrote the quadratic formula, as shown here. Was this correct? If not, correct it.

$$x = \frac{-b\sqrt{b^2 - 4ac}}{2a}$$

3. A student incorrectly solved $5x^2 - 5x + 1 = 0$ as follows. *WHAT WENT WRONG?*

$$x = \frac{-(-5) \pm \sqrt{(-5)^2 - 4(5)(1)}}{2(5)}$$

$$x = \frac{5 \pm \sqrt{5}}{10}$$

$$x = \frac{1}{2} \pm \sqrt{5}$$

Solution set: $\left\{ \dfrac{1}{2} \pm \sqrt{5} \right\}$

4. A student claimed that the equation $2x^2 - 5 = 0$ cannot be solved using the quadratic formula because there is no first-degree x-term. Was the student correct? If not, give the values of a, b, and c.

Use the quadratic formula to solve each equation. (All solutions for these equations are real numbers.) See Examples 1 and 2.

5. $x^2 - 8x + 15 = 0$

6. $x^2 + 3x - 28 = 0$

7. $2x^2 + 4x + 1 = 0$

8. $2x^2 + 3x - 1 = 0$

9. $2x^2 - 2x = 1$

10. $9x^2 + 6x = 1$

11. $x^2 + 18 = 10x$

12. $x^2 - 4 = 2x$

13. $4x^2 + 4x - 1 = 0$

14. $4r^2 - 4r - 19 = 0$

15. $2 - 2x = 3x^2$

16. $26r - 2 = 3r^2$

17. $\dfrac{x^2}{4} - \dfrac{x}{2} = 1$

18. $p^2 + \dfrac{p}{3} = \dfrac{1}{6}$

19. $-2t(t + 2) = -3$

20. $-3x(x + 2) = -4$

21. $(r - 3)(r + 5) = 2$

22. $(x + 1)(x - 7) = 1$

23. $(x + 2)(x - 3) = 1$

24. $(x - 5)(x + 2) = 6$

25. $p = \dfrac{5(5 - p)}{3(p + 1)}$

26. $x = \dfrac{2(x + 3)}{x + 5}$

27. $(2x + 1)^2 = x + 4$

28. $(2x - 1)^2 = x + 2$

Use the quadratic formula to solve each equation. (All solutions for these equations are non-real complex numbers.) See Example 3.

29. $x^2 - 3x + 6 = 0$

30. $x^2 - 5x + 20 = 0$

31. $r^2 - 6r + 14 = 0$

32. $t^2 + 4t + 11 = 0$

33. $4x^2 - 4x = -7$

34. $9x^2 - 6x = -7$

35. $x(3x + 4) = -2$

36. $z(2z + 3) = -2$

37. $(2x - 1)(8x - 4) = -1$

38. $(x - 1)(9x - 3) = -2$

Use the discriminant to determine whether the solutions for each equation are
    A. *two rational numbers*   **B.** *one rational number*
    C. *two irrational numbers*   **D.** *two nonreal complex numbers.*

Tell whether the equation can be solved by factoring or whether the quadratic formula should be used. Do not actually solve. See Example 4.

39. $25x^2 + 70x + 49 = 0$

40. $4x^2 - 28x + 49 = 0$

41. $x^2 + 4x + 2 = 0$

42. $9x^2 - 12x - 1 = 0$

43. $3x^2 = 5x + 2$

44. $4x^2 = 4x + 3$

45. $3m^2 - 10m + 15 = 0$

46. $18x^2 + 60x + 82 = 0$

Based on your answers in Exercises 39–46, solve the equation given in each exercise.

47. Exercise 39   **48. Exercise 40**   **49. Exercise 43**   **50. Exercise 44**

51. Find the discriminant for each quadratic equation. Use it to tell whether the equation can be solved by factoring or whether the quadratic formula should be used. Then solve each equation.

    (a) $3x^2 + 13x = -12$ **(b)** $2x^2 + 19 = 14x$

52. *Concept Check* Is it possible for the solution of a quadratic equation with integer coefficients to include just one irrational number? Why or why not?

Find the value of a, b, or c so that each equation will have exactly one rational solution. See Example 5.

53. $p^2 + bp + 25 = 0$

54. $r^2 - br + 49 = 0$

55. $am^2 + 8m + 1 = 0$

56. $at^2 + 24t + 16 = 0$

57. $9x^2 - 30x + c = 0$

58. $4m^2 + 12m + c = 0$

59. One solution of $4x^2 + bx - 3 = 0$ is $-\frac{5}{2}$. Find b and the other solution.

60. One solution of $3x^2 - 7x + c = 0$ is $\frac{1}{3}$. Find c and the other solution.

PREVIEW EXERCISES

Solve each equation. **See Section 2.3.**

61. $\frac{3}{4}x + \frac{1}{2}x = -10$

62. $\frac{x}{5} + \frac{3x}{4} = -19$

Solve each equation. **See Section 10.6.**

63. $\sqrt{2x + 6} = x - 1$

64. $\sqrt{2x + 1} + \sqrt{x + 3} = 0$

(11.4) Equations Quadratic in Form

OBJECTIVES

1. Solve an equation with fractions by writing it in quadratic form.
2. Use quadratic equations to solve applied problems.
3. Solve an equation with radicals by writing it in quadratic form.
4. Solve an equation that is quadratic in form by substitution.

OBJECTIVE 1 **Solve an equation with fractions by writing it in quadratic form.** A variety of nonquadratic equations can be written in the form of a quadratic equation and solved by using the methods of this chapter.

EXAMPLE 1 **Solving an Equation with Fractions that Leads to a Quadratic Equation**

Solve $\frac{1}{x} + \frac{1}{x - 1} = \frac{7}{12}$.

Clear fractions by multiplying each term by the least common denominator, $12x(x - 1)$. (Note that the domain must be restricted to $x \neq 0$, $x \neq 1$.)

$$12x(x - 1)\left(\frac{1}{x} + \frac{1}{x - 1}\right) = 12x(x - 1)\left(\frac{7}{12}\right)$$ Multiply by the LCD.

$$12x(x - 1)\frac{1}{x} + 12x(x - 1)\frac{1}{x - 1} = 12x(x - 1)\frac{7}{12}$$ Distributive property

$$12(x - 1) + 12x = 7x(x - 1)$$

$$12x - 12 + 12x = 7x^2 - 7x$$ Distributive property

$$24x - 12 = 7x^2 - 7x$$ Combine like terms.

$$7x^2 - 31x + 12 = 0$$ Standard form

$$(7x - 3)(x - 4) = 0$$ Factor.

$$7x - 3 = 0 \quad \text{or} \quad x - 4 = 0$$ Zero-factor property

$$7x = 3 \quad \text{or} \quad x = 4$$ Solve for x.

$$x = \frac{3}{7}$$

The solution set is $\left\{\frac{3}{7}, 4\right\}$.

NOW TRY

NOW TRY
EXERCISE 1

Solve $\frac{2}{x} + \frac{3}{x + 2} = 1$.

NOW TRY ANSWER
1. $\{-1, 4\}$

OBJECTIVE 2 **Use quadratic equations to solve applied problems.** Some distance-rate-time (or motion) problems lead to quadratic equations. We continue to use the six-step problem-solving method from **Section 2.4.**

NOW TRY
EXERCISE 2

A small fishing boat averages 18 mph in still water. It takes the boat $\frac{9}{10}$ hr to travel 8 mi upstream and return. Find the rate of the current.

Riverboat traveling upstream—the current slows it down.

FIGURE 1

EXAMPLE 2   Solving a Motion Problem

A riverboat for tourists averages 12 mph in still water. It takes the boat 1 hr, 4 min to go 6 mi upstream and return. Find the rate of the current.

Step 1   **Read** the problem carefully.

Step 2   **Assign a variable.** Let $x =$ the rate of the current.

The current slows down the boat when it is going upstream, so the rate of the boat going upstream is its rate in still water *less* the rate of the current, or $(12 - x)$ mph. See **FIGURE 1**.

Similarly, the current speeds up the boat as it travels downstream, so its rate downstream is $(12 + x)$ mph. Thus,

$$12 - x = \text{the rate upstream in miles per hour,}$$

and $$12 + x = \text{the rate downstream in miles per hour.}$$

	d	r	t
Upstream	6	$12 - x$	$\dfrac{6}{12 - x}$
Downstream	6	$12 + x$	$\dfrac{6}{12 + x}$

Complete a table. Use the distance formula, $d = rt$, solved for time t, $t = \frac{d}{r}$, to write expressions for t.

Times in hours

Step 3   **Write an equation.** We use the total time of 1 hr, 4 min written as a fraction.

$$1 + \frac{4}{60} = 1 + \frac{1}{15} = \frac{16}{15} \text{ hr} \qquad \text{Total time}$$

The time upstream plus the time downstream equals $\frac{16}{15}$ hr.

$$
\begin{array}{ccccc}
\text{Time upstream} & + & \text{Time downstream} & = & \text{Total time} \\
\downarrow & & \downarrow & & \downarrow \\
\dfrac{6}{12 - x} & + & \dfrac{6}{12 + x} & = & \dfrac{16}{15}
\end{array}
$$

Step 4   **Solve** the equation. The LCD is $15(12 - x)(12 + x)$.

$$15(12 - x)(12 + x)\left(\frac{6}{12 - x} + \frac{6}{12 + x}\right)$$

$$= 15(12 - x)(12 + x)\left(\frac{16}{15}\right)$$

Multiply by the LCD.

$$15(12 + x) \cdot 6 + 15(12 - x) \cdot 6 = 16(12 - x)(12 + x)$$

Distributive property; multiply.

$$90(12 + x) + 90(12 - x) = 16(144 - x^2) \qquad \text{Multiply.}$$

$$1080 + 90x + 1080 - 90x = 2304 - 16x^2 \qquad \text{Distributive property}$$

$$2160 = 2304 - 16x^2 \qquad \text{Combine like terms.}$$

$$16x^2 = 144 \qquad \text{Add } 16x^2. \text{ Subtract 2160.}$$

$$x^2 = 9 \qquad \text{Divide by 16.}$$

$$x = 3 \quad \text{or} \quad x = -3 \qquad \text{Square root property}$$

Step 5   **State the answer.** The current rate cannot be -3, so the answer is 3 mph.

Step 6   **Check** that this value satisfies the original problem.

NOW TRY

NOW TRY ANSWER
2. 2 mph

> **PROBLEM-SOLVING HINT**
>
> Recall from **Section 6.7** that a person's work rate is $\frac{1}{t}$ part of the job per hour, where t is the time in hours required to do the complete job. Thus, the part of the job the person will do in x hours is $\frac{1}{t}x$.

EXAMPLE 3 Solving a Work Problem

It takes two carpet layers 4 hr to carpet a room. If each worked alone, one of them could do the job in 1 hr less time than the other. How long would it take each carpet layer to complete the job alone?

Step 1 **Read** the problem again. There will be two answers.

Step 2 **Assign a variable.** Let x = the number of hours for the slower carpet layer to complete the job alone. Then the faster carpet layer could do the entire job in $(x - 1)$ hours. The slower person's rate is $\frac{1}{x}$, and the faster person's rate is $\frac{1}{x-1}$. Together, they do the job in 4 hr.

	Rate	Time Working Together	Fractional Part of the Job Done
Slower Worker	$\frac{1}{x}$	4	$\frac{1}{x}(4)$
Faster Worker	$\frac{1}{x-1}$	4	$\frac{1}{x-1}(4)$

Complete a table.

Sum is 1 whole job.

Step 3 **Write an equation.**

Part done by slower worker $+$ Part done by faster worker $=$ 1 whole job

$$\frac{4}{x} \quad + \quad \frac{4}{x-1} \quad = \quad 1$$

Step 4 **Solve** the equation from Step 3.

$$x(x-1)\left(\frac{4}{x} + \frac{4}{x-1}\right) = x(x-1)(1) \qquad \text{Multiply by the LCD, } x(x-1).$$

$$4(x-1) + 4x = x(x-1) \qquad \text{Distributive property}$$

$$4x - 4 + 4x = x^2 - x \qquad \text{Distributive property}$$

$$x^2 - 9x + 4 = 0 \qquad \text{Standard form}$$

This equation cannot be solved by factoring, so use the quadratic formula.

$$x = \frac{-b \pm \sqrt{b^2 - 4ac}}{2a} \qquad \text{Quadratic formula}$$

$$x = \frac{-(-9) \pm \sqrt{(-9)^2 - 4(1)(4)}}{2(1)} \qquad a = 1, b = -9, c = 4$$

$$x = \frac{9 \pm \sqrt{65}}{2} \qquad \text{Simplify.}$$

$$x = \frac{9 + \sqrt{65}}{2} \approx 8.5 \quad \text{or} \quad x = \frac{9 - \sqrt{65}}{2} \approx 0.5 \qquad \text{Use a calculator.}$$

NOW TRY
EXERCISE 3

Two electricians are running wire to finish a basement. One electrician could finish the job in 2 hr less time than the other. Together, they complete the job in 6 hr. How long (to the nearest tenth) would it take the slower electrician to complete the job alone?

NOW TRY
EXERCISE 4

Solve each equation.

(a) $x = \sqrt{9x - 20}$

(b) $x + \sqrt{x} = 20$

Step 5   **State the answer.** Only the solution 8.5 makes sense in the original problem, because if $x = 0.5$, then

$$x - 1 = 0.5 - 1 = -0.5,$$

which cannot represent the time for the faster worker. The slower worker could do the job in about 8.5 hr and the faster in about $8.5 - 1 = 7.5$ hr.

Step 6   **Check** that these results satisfy the original problem.   NOW TRY

OBJECTIVE 3   Solve an equation with radicals by writing it in quadratic form.

EXAMPLE 4   Solving Radical Equations That Lead to Quadratic Equations

Solve each equation.

(a) $x = \sqrt{6x - 8}$

This equation is not quadratic. However, squaring each side of the equation gives a quadratic equation that can be solved by factoring.

$$
\begin{array}{ll}
x^2 = \left(\sqrt{6x - 8}\right)^2 & \text{Square each side.} \\
x^2 = 6x - 8 & \left(\sqrt{a}\right)^2 = a \\
x^2 - 6x + 8 = 0 & \text{Standard form} \\
(x - 4)(x - 2) = 0 & \text{Factor.} \\
x - 4 = 0 \quad \text{or} \quad x - 2 = 0 & \text{Zero-factor property} \\
x = 4 \quad \text{or} \quad x = 2 & \text{Proposed solutions}
\end{array}
$$

Squaring each side of an equation can introduce extraneous solutions. *All proposed solutions must be checked in the original (not the squared) equation.*

CHECK
$$
\begin{array}{ll}
x = \sqrt{6x - 8} & \\
4 \stackrel{?}{=} \sqrt{6(4) - 8} & \text{Let } x = 4. \\
4 \stackrel{?}{=} \sqrt{16} & \\
4 = 4 \ \checkmark & \text{True}
\end{array}
$$
$$
\begin{array}{ll}
x = \sqrt{6x - 8} & \\
2 \stackrel{?}{=} \sqrt{6(2) - 8} & \text{Let } x = 2. \\
2 \stackrel{?}{=} \sqrt{4} & \\
2 = 2 \ \checkmark & \text{True}
\end{array}
$$

Both solutions check, so the solution set is $\{2, 4\}$.

(b)
$$
\begin{array}{ll}
x + \sqrt{x} = 6 & \boxed{(a - b)^2 = a^2 - 2ab + b^2} \\
\sqrt{x} = 6 - x & \text{Isolate the radical on one side.} \\
x = 36 - 12x + x^2 & \text{Square each side.} \\
x^2 - 13x + 36 = 0 & \text{Standard form} \\
(x - 4)(x - 9) = 0 & \text{Factor.} \\
x - 4 = 0 \quad \text{or} \quad x - 9 = 0 & \text{Zero-factor property} \\
x = 4 \quad \text{or} \quad x = 9 & \text{Proposed solutions}
\end{array}
$$

CHECK
$$
\begin{array}{ll}
x + \sqrt{x} = 6 & \\
4 + \sqrt{4} \stackrel{?}{=} 6 & \text{Let } x = 4. \\
6 = 6 \ \checkmark \quad \text{True}
\end{array}
$$
$$
\begin{array}{ll}
x + \sqrt{x} = 6 & \\
9 + \sqrt{9} \stackrel{?}{=} 6 & \text{Let } x = 9. \\
12 = 6 \quad \text{False}
\end{array}
$$

NOW TRY ANSWERS
3. 13.1 hr
4. (a) $\{4, 5\}$ **(b)** $\{16\}$

Only the solution 4 checks, so the solution set is $\{4\}$.   NOW TRY

OBJECTIVE 4 Solve an equation that is quadratic in form by substitution.
A nonquadratic equation that can be written in the form

$$au^2 + bu + c = 0,$$

for $a \neq 0$ and an algebraic expression u, is called **quadratic in form.**

Many equations that are quadratic in form can be solved more easily by defining and substituting a "temporary" variable u for an expression involving the variable in the original equation.

**NOW TRY
EXERCISE 5**
Define a variable u, and write each equation in the form $au^2 + bu + c = 0$.
(a) $x^4 - 10x^2 + 9 = 0$
(b) $6(x + 2)^2$
$\quad - 11(x + 2) + 4 = 0$

EXAMPLE 5 Defining Substitution Variables

Define a variable u, and write each equation in the form $au^2 + bu + c = 0$.

(a) $x^4 - 13x^2 + 36 = 0$

Look at the two terms involving the variable x, ignoring their coefficients. Try to find one variable expression that is the square of the other. Since $x^4 = (x^2)^2$, we can define $u = x^2$, and rewrite the original equation as a quadratic equation.

$$u^2 - 13u + 36 = 0 \qquad \text{Here, } u = x^2.$$

(b) $2(4x - 3)^2 + 7(4x - 3) + 5 = 0$

Because this equation involves both $(4x - 3)^2$ and $(4x - 3)$, we choose $u = 4x - 3$. Substituting u for $4x - 3$ gives the quadratic equation

$$2u^2 + 7u + 5 = 0. \qquad \text{Here, } u = 4x - 3.$$

(c) $2x^{2/3} - 11x^{1/3} + 12 = 0$

We apply a power rule for exponents **(Section 4.1)**, $(a^m)^n = a^{mn}$. Because $(x^{1/3})^2 = x^{2/3}$, we define $u = x^{1/3}$. The original equation becomes

$$2u^2 - 11u + 12 = 0. \qquad \text{Here, } u = x^{1/3}. \qquad \text{NOW TRY}$$

EXAMPLE 6 Solving Equations That Are Quadratic in Form

Solve each equation.

(a) $x^4 - 13x^2 + 36 = 0$

We can write this equation in quadratic form by substituting u for x^2. (See **Example 5(a)**.)

$$x^4 - 13x^2 + 36 = 0$$
$$(x^2)^2 - 13x^2 + 36 = 0 \qquad x^4 = (x^2)^2$$
$$u^2 - 13u + 36 = 0 \qquad \text{Let } u = x^2.$$
$$(u - 4)(u - 9) = 0 \qquad \text{Factor.}$$
$$u - 4 = 0 \quad \text{or} \quad u - 9 = 0 \qquad \text{Zero-factor property}$$

(Don't stop here.) $\quad u = 4 \quad \text{or} \quad u = 9 \qquad$ Solve.

$$x^2 = 4 \quad \text{or} \quad x^2 = 9 \qquad \text{Substitute } x^2 \text{ for } u.$$
$$x = \pm 2 \quad \text{or} \quad x = \pm 3 \qquad \text{Square root property}$$

The equation $x^4 - 13x^2 + 36 = 0$, a fourth-degree equation, has four solutions, $-3, -2, 2, 3$.* The solution set is abbreviated $\{\pm 2, \pm 3\}$. Each solution can be verified by substituting it into the original equation for x.

NOW TRY ANSWERS
5. (a) $u = x^2; u^2 - 10u + 9 = 0$
(b) $u = x + 2;$
$\quad 6u^2 - 11u + 4 = 0$

---

*In general, an equation in which an nth-degree polynomial equals 0 has n complex solutions, although some of them may be repeated.

NOW TRY
EXERCISE 6

Solve each equation.

(a) $x^4 - 17x^2 + 16 = 0$

(b) $x^4 + 4 = 8x^2$

(b)

$$4x^4 + 1 = 5x^2$$

$$4(x^2)^2 + 1 = 5x^2 \qquad x^4 = (x^2)^2$$

$$4u^2 + 1 = 5u \qquad \text{Let } u = x^2.$$

$$4u^2 - 5u + 1 = 0 \qquad \text{Standard form}$$

$$(4u - 1)(u - 1) = 0 \qquad \text{Factor.}$$

$$4u - 1 = 0 \quad \text{or} \quad u - 1 = 0 \qquad \text{Zero-factor property}$$

$$u = \frac{1}{4} \quad \text{or} \quad u = 1 \qquad \text{Solve.}$$

> This is a key step.

$$x^2 = \frac{1}{4} \quad \text{or} \quad x^2 = 1 \qquad \text{Substitute } x^2 \text{ for } u.$$

$$x = \pm\frac{1}{2} \quad \text{or} \quad x = \pm 1 \qquad \text{Square root property}$$

Check that the solution set is $\left\{ \pm\frac{1}{2}, \pm 1 \right\}$.

(c)

$$x^4 = 6x^2 - 3$$

$$x^4 - 6x^2 + 3 = 0 \qquad \text{Standard form}$$

$$(x^2)^2 - 6x^2 + 3 = 0 \qquad x^4 = (x^2)^2$$

$$u^2 - 6u + 3 = 0 \qquad \text{Let } u = x^2.$$

Since this equation cannot be solved by factoring, use the quadratic formula.

$$u = \frac{-(-6) \pm \sqrt{(-6)^2 - 4(1)(3)}}{2(1)} \qquad a = 1, b = -6, c = 3$$

$$u = \frac{6 \pm \sqrt{24}}{2} \qquad \text{Simplify.}$$

$$u = \frac{6 \pm 2\sqrt{6}}{2} \qquad \sqrt{24} = \sqrt{4} \cdot \sqrt{6} = 2\sqrt{6}$$

$$u = \frac{2(3 \pm \sqrt{6})}{2} \qquad \text{Factor.}$$

$$u = 3 \pm \sqrt{6} \qquad \text{Lowest terms}$$

> Find *both* square roots in each case.

$$x^2 = 3 + \sqrt{6} \quad \text{or} \quad x^2 = 3 - \sqrt{6} \qquad u = x^2$$

$$x = \pm\sqrt{3 + \sqrt{6}} \quad \text{or} \quad x = \pm\sqrt{3 - \sqrt{6}}$$

The solution set $\left\{ \pm\sqrt{3 + \sqrt{6}}, \pm\sqrt{3 - \sqrt{6}} \right\}$ contains four numbers. NOW TRY

NOTE Equations like those in **Examples 6(a) and (b)** can be solved by factoring.

$$x^4 - 13x^2 + 36 = 0 \qquad \text{Example 6(a) equation}$$

$$(x^2 - 9)(x^2 - 4) = 0 \qquad \text{Factor.}$$

$$(x + 3)(x - 3)(x + 2)(x - 2) = 0 \qquad \text{Factor again.}$$

Using the zero-factor property gives the same solutions obtained in **Example 6(a).** Equations that cannot be solved by factoring (as in **Example 6(c)**) must be solved by substitution and the quadratic formula.

NOW TRY ANSWERS
6. (a) $\{\pm 1, \pm 4\}$

(b) $\left\{ \pm\sqrt{4 + 2\sqrt{3}}, \pm\sqrt{4 - 2\sqrt{3}} \right\}$

Solving an Equation That Is Quadratic in Form by Substitution

Step 1   **Define a temporary variable u,** based on the relationship between the variable expressions in the given equation. Substitute u in the original equation and rewrite the equation in the form $au^2 + bu + c = 0$.

Step 2   **Solve the quadratic equation** obtained in **Step 1** by factoring or the quadratic formula.

Step 3   **Replace u with the expression it defined in Step 1.**

Step 4   **Solve the resulting equations for the original variable.**

Step 5   **Check** all solutions by substituting them in the original equation.

**NOW TRY
EXERCISE 7**

Solve each equation.

(a) $6(x - 4)^2 + 11(x - 4) - 10 = 0$

(b) $2x^{2/3} - 7x^{1/3} + 3 = 0$

EXAMPLE 7   Solving Equations That Are Quadratic in Form

Solve each equation.

(a) $2(4x - 3)^2 + 7(4x - 3) + 5 = 0$

Step 1   Because of the repeated quantity $4x - 3$, substitute u for $4x - 3$. (See **Example 5(b).**)

$$2(4x - 3)^2 + 7(4x - 3) + 5 = 0$$
$$2u^2 + 7u + 5 = 0 \qquad \text{Let } u = 4x - 3.$$

Step 2 $$(2u + 5)(u + 1) = 0 \qquad \text{Factor.}$$

$$2u + 5 = 0 \quad \text{or} \quad u + 1 = 0 \qquad \text{Zero-factor property}$$

$\boxed{\text{Don't stop here.}} \rightarrow$ $u = -\dfrac{5}{2}$ or $u = -1$ Solve for u.

Step 3 $4x - 3 = -\dfrac{5}{2}$ or $4x - 3 = -1$ Substitute $4x - 3$ for u.

Step 4 $4x = \dfrac{1}{2}$ or $4x = 2$ Solve for x.

$$x = \dfrac{1}{8} \quad \text{or} \quad x = \dfrac{1}{2}$$

Step 5   Check that the solution set of the original equation is $\left\{\frac{1}{8}, \frac{1}{2}\right\}$.

(b) $2x^{2/3} - 11x^{1/3} + 12 = 0$

Substitute u for $x^{1/3}$. (See **Example 5(c).**)

$$2u^2 - 11u + 12 = 0 \qquad \text{Let } x^{1/3} = u; x^{2/3} = u^2.$$
$$(2u - 3)(u - 4) = 0 \qquad \text{Factor.}$$

$$2u - 3 = 0 \quad \text{or} \quad u - 4 = 0 \qquad \text{Zero-factor property}$$

$$u = \dfrac{3}{2} \quad \text{or} \quad u = 4 \qquad \text{Solve for } u.$$

$$x^{1/3} = \dfrac{3}{2} \quad \text{or} \quad x^{1/3} = 4 \qquad u = x^{1/3}$$

$$(x^{1/3})^3 = \left(\dfrac{3}{2}\right)^3 \quad \text{or} \quad (x^{1/3})^3 = 4^3 \qquad \text{Cube each side.}$$

$$x = \dfrac{27}{8} \quad \text{or} \quad x = 64$$

Check that the solution set is $\left\{\frac{27}{8}, 64\right\}$.

NOW TRY ANSWERS

7. (a) $\left\{\frac{3}{2}, \frac{14}{3}\right\}$ **(b)** $\left\{\frac{1}{8}, 27\right\}$

NOW TRY

⚠ **CAUTION** A common error when solving problems like those in **Examples 6 and 7** is to stop too soon. *Once you have solved for u, remember to substitute and solve for the values of the original variable.*

11.4 EXERCISES

⊙ *Complete solution available on the Video Resources on DVD*

Concept Check Write a sentence describing the first step you would take to solve each equation. Do not actually solve.

1. $\dfrac{14}{x} = x - 5$

2. $\sqrt{1 + x} + x = 5$

3. $(x^2 + x)^2 - 8(x^2 + x) + 12 = 0$

4. $3x = \sqrt{16 - 10x}$

5. *Concept Check* Study this incorrect "solution." *WHAT WENT WRONG?*

$$x = \sqrt{3x + 4}$$
$$x^2 = 3x + 4 \qquad \text{Square each side.}$$
$$x^2 - 3x - 4 = 0$$
$$(x - 4)(x + 1) = 0$$
$$x - 4 = 0 \quad \text{or} \quad x + 1 = 0$$
$$x = 4 \quad \text{or} \qquad x = -1$$

Solution set: $\{4, -1\}$

6. *Concept Check* Study this incorrect "solution." *WHAT WENT WRONG?*

$$2(x - 1)^2 - 3(x - 1) + 1 = 0$$
$$2u^2 - 3u + 1 = 0 \qquad \text{Let } u = x - 1.$$
$$(2u - 1)(u - 1) = 0$$
$$2u - 1 = 0 \quad \text{or} \quad u - 1 = 0$$
$$u = \frac{1}{2} \quad \text{or} \qquad u = 1$$

Solution set: $\left\{\frac{1}{2}, 1\right\}$

---

*Solve each equation. Check your solutions. **See Example 1.***

7. $\dfrac{14}{x} = x - 5$

8. $\dfrac{-12}{x} = x + 8$

9. $1 - \dfrac{3}{x} - \dfrac{28}{x^2} = 0$

10. $4 - \dfrac{7}{r} - \dfrac{2}{r^2} = 0$

11. $3 - \dfrac{1}{t} = \dfrac{2}{t^2}$

12. $1 + \dfrac{2}{x} = \dfrac{3}{x^2}$

⊙ **13.** $\dfrac{1}{x} + \dfrac{2}{x + 2} = \dfrac{17}{35}$

14. $\dfrac{2}{m} + \dfrac{3}{m + 9} = \dfrac{11}{4}$

15. $\dfrac{2}{x + 1} + \dfrac{3}{x + 2} = \dfrac{7}{2}$

16. $\dfrac{4}{3 - p} + \dfrac{2}{5 - p} = \dfrac{26}{15}$

17. $\dfrac{3}{2x} - \dfrac{1}{2(x + 2)} = 1$

18. $\dfrac{4}{3x} - \dfrac{1}{2(x + 1)} = 1$

19. $3 = \dfrac{1}{t + 2} + \dfrac{2}{(t + 2)^2}$

20. $1 + \dfrac{2}{3z + 2} = \dfrac{15}{(3z + 2)^2}$

21. $\dfrac{6}{p} = 2 + \dfrac{p}{p + 1}$

22. $\dfrac{x}{2 - x} + \dfrac{2}{x} = 5$

23. $1 - \dfrac{1}{2x + 1} - \dfrac{1}{(2x + 1)^2} = 0$

24. $1 - \dfrac{1}{3x - 2} - \dfrac{1}{(3x - 2)^2} = 0$

Concept Check   *Answer each question.*

25. A boat goes 20 mph in still water, and the rate of the current is t mph.

 (a) What is the rate of the boat when it travels upstream?

 (b) What is the rate of the boat when it travels downstream?

26. (a) If it takes m hours to grade a set of papers, what is the grader's rate (in job per hour)?

 (b) How much of the job will the grader do in 2 hr?

*Solve each problem. **See Examples 2 and 3.***

27. On a windy day William Kunz found that he could go 16 mi downstream and then 4 mi back upstream at top speed in a total of 48 min. What was the top speed of William's boat if the rate of the current was 15 mph?

	d	r	t
Upstream	4	$x - 15$	
Downstream	16		

28. Vera Koutsoyannis flew her plane for 6 hr at a constant rate. She traveled 810 mi with the wind, then turned around and traveled 720 mi against the wind. The wind speed was a constant 15 mph. Find the rate of the plane.

	d	r	t
With Wind	810		
Against Wind	720		

29. The distance from Jackson to Lodi is about 40 mi, as is the distance from Lodi to Manteca. Adrian Iorgoni drove from Jackson to Lodi, stopped in Lodi for a high-energy drink, and then drove on to Manteca at 10 mph faster. Driving time for the entire trip was 88 min. Find the rate from Jackson to Lodi. (*Source: State Farm Road Atlas.*)

30. Medicine Hat and Cranbrook are 300 km apart. Steve Roig-Watnik rides his Harley 20 km per hr faster than Mohammad Shakil rides his Yamaha. Find Steve's average rate if he travels from Cranbrook to Medicine Hat in $1\frac{1}{4}$ hr less time than Mohammad. (*Source: State Farm Road Atlas.*)

31. Working together, two people can cut a large lawn in 2 hr. One person can do the job alone in 1 hr less time than the other. How long (to the nearest tenth) would it take the faster worker to do the job? (*Hint: x is the time of the faster worker.*)

	Rate	Time Working Together	Fractional Part of the Job Done
Faster Worker	$\dfrac{1}{x}$	2	
Slower Worker		2	

32. Working together, two people can clean an office building in 5 hr. One person is new to the job and would take 2 hr longer than the other person to clean the building alone. How long (to the nearest tenth) would it take the new worker to clean the building alone?

	Rate	Time Working Together	Fractional Part of the Job Done
Faster Worker			
Slower Worker			

33. Rusty and Nancy Brauner are planting flats of spring flowers. Working alone, Rusty would take 2 hr longer than Nancy to plant the flowers. Working together, they do the job in 12 hr. How long (to the nearest tenth) would it have taken each person working alone?

34. Joel Spring can work through a stack of invoices in 1 hr less time than Noel White can. Working together they take $1\frac{1}{2}$ hr. How long (to the nearest tenth) would it take each person working alone?

35. Two pipes together can fill a tank in 2 hr. One of the pipes, used alone, takes 3 hr longer than the other to fill the tank. How long would each pipe take to fill the tank alone?

36. A washing machine can be filled in 6 min if both the hot and cold water taps are fully opened. Filling the washer with hot water alone takes 9 min longer than filling it with cold water alone. How long does it take to fill the washer with cold water?

Solve each equation. Check your solutions. ***See Example 4.***

37. $x = \sqrt{7x - 10}$ **38.** $z = \sqrt{5z - 4}$ **39.** $2x = \sqrt{11x + 3}$

40. $4x = \sqrt{6x + 1}$ **41.** $3x = \sqrt{16 - 10x}$ **42.** $4t = \sqrt{8t + 3}$

43. $t + \sqrt{t} = 12$ **44.** $p - 2\sqrt{p} = 8$ **45.** $x = \sqrt{\dfrac{6 - 13x}{5}}$

46. $r = \sqrt{\dfrac{20 - 19r}{6}}$ **47.** $-x = \sqrt{\dfrac{8 - 2x}{3}}$ **48.** $-x = \sqrt{\dfrac{3x + 7}{4}}$

Solve each equation. Check your solutions. ***See Examples 5–7.***

49. $x^4 - 29x^2 + 100 = 0$ **50.** $x^4 - 37x^2 + 36 = 0$

51. $4q^4 - 13q^2 + 9 = 0$ **52.** $9x^4 - 25x^2 + 16 = 0$

53. $x^4 + 48 = 16x^2$ **54.** $z^4 + 72 = 17z^2$

55. $(x + 3)^2 + 5(x + 3) + 6 = 0$ **56.** $(x - 4)^2 + (x - 4) - 20 = 0$

57. $3(m + 4)^2 - 8 = 2(m + 4)$ **58.** $(t + 5)^2 + 6 = 7(t + 5)$

59. $x^{2/3} + x^{1/3} - 2 = 0$ **60.** $x^{2/3} - 2x^{1/3} - 3 = 0$

61. $r^{2/3} + r^{1/3} - 12 = 0$ **62.** $3x^{2/3} - x^{1/3} - 24 = 0$

63. $4x^{4/3} - 13x^{2/3} + 9 = 0$ **64.** $9t^{4/3} - 25t^{2/3} + 16 = 0$

65. $2 + \dfrac{5}{3x - 1} = \dfrac{-2}{(3x - 1)^2}$ **66.** $3 - \dfrac{7}{2p + 2} = \dfrac{6}{(2p + 2)^2}$

67. $2 - 6(z - 1)^{-2} = (z - 1)^{-1}$ **68.** $3 - 2(x - 1)^{-1} = (x - 1)^{-2}$

The equations in Exercises 69–82 are not grouped by type. Solve each equation. Exercises 81 and 82 require knowledge of complex numbers. ***See Examples 1 and 4–7.***

69. $12x^4 - 11x^2 + 2 = 0$ **70.** $\left(x - \dfrac{1}{2}\right)^2 + 5\left(x - \dfrac{1}{2}\right) - 4 = 0$

71. $\sqrt{2x + 3} = 2 + \sqrt{x - 2}$ **72.** $\sqrt{m + 1} = -1 + \sqrt{2m}$

73. $2\left(1 + \sqrt{r}\right)^2 = 13\left(1 + \sqrt{r}\right) - 6$ **74.** $(x^2 + x)^2 + 12 = 8(x^2 + x)$

75. $2m^6 + 11m^3 + 5 = 0$ **76.** $8x^6 + 513x^3 + 64 = 0$

77. $6 = 7(2w - 3)^{-1} + 3(2w - 3)^{-2}$ **78.** $x^6 - 10x^3 = -9$

79. $2x^4 - 9x^2 = -2$ **80.** $8x^4 + 1 = 11x^2$

81. $2x^4 + x^2 - 3 = 0$ **82.** $4x^4 + 5x^2 + 1 = 0$

Solve each equation for the specified variable. ***See Section 2.5.***

83. $P = 2L + 2W$ for W **84.** $A = \dfrac{1}{2}bh$ for h **85.** $F = \dfrac{9}{5}C + 32$ for C

SUMMARY EXERCISES on Solving Quadratic Equations

We have introduced four methods for solving quadratic equations written in standard form $ax^2 + bx + c = 0.$

Method	Advantages	Disadvantages
Factoring	This is usually the fastest method.	Not all polynomials are factorable. Some factorable polynomials are difficult to factor.
Square root property	This is the simplest method for solving equations of the form $(ax + b)^2 = c.$	Few equations are given in this form.
Completing the square	This method can always be used, although most people prefer the quadratic formula.	It requires more steps than other methods.
Quadratic formula	This method can always be used.	Sign errors are common when evaluating $\sqrt{b^2 - 4ac}.$

Concept Check *Decide whether* factoring, *the* square root property, *or the* quadratic formula *is most appropriate for solving each quadratic equation. Do not actually solve.*

1. $(2x + 3)^2 = 4$ **2.** $4x^2 - 3x = 1$ **3.** $x^2 + 5x - 8 = 0$

4. $2x^2 + 3x = 1$ **5.** $3x^2 = 2 - 5x$ **6.** $x^2 = 5$

Solve each quadratic equation by the method of your choice.

7. $p^2 = 7$ **8.** $6x^2 - x - 15 = 0$ **9.** $n^2 + 6n + 4 = 0$

10. $(x - 3)^2 = 25$ **11.** $\dfrac{5}{x} + \dfrac{12}{x^2} = 2$ **12.** $3x^2 = 3 - 8x$

13. $2r^2 - 4r + 1 = 0$ ***14.** $x^2 = -12$ **15.** $x\sqrt{2} = \sqrt{5x - 2}$

16. $x^4 - 10x^2 + 9 = 0$ **17.** $(2x + 3)^2 = 8$ **18.** $\dfrac{2}{x} + \dfrac{1}{x - 2} = \dfrac{5}{3}$

19. $t^4 + 14 = 9t^2$ **20.** $8x^2 - 4x = 2$ ***21.** $z^2 + z + 1 = 0$

22. $5x^6 + 2x^3 - 7 = 0$ **23.** $4t^2 - 12t + 9 = 0$ **24.** $x\sqrt{3} = \sqrt{2 - x}$

25. $r^2 - 72 = 0$ **26.** $-3x^2 + 4x = -4$ **27.** $x^2 - 5x - 36 = 0$

28. $w^2 = 169$ ***29.** $3p^2 = 6p - 4$ **30.** $z = \sqrt{\dfrac{5z + 3}{2}}$

*31. $\dfrac{4}{r^2} + 3 = \dfrac{1}{r}$ **32.** $2(3x - 1)^2 + 5(3x - 1) = -2$

---

*This exercise requires knowledge of complex numbers.

Formulas and Further Applications

OBJECTIVE 1 Solve formulas for variables involving squares and square roots.

EXAMPLE 1 Solving for Variables Involving Squares or Square Roots

Solve each formula for the given variable. Keep $\pm$ in the answer in part (a).

(a) $w = \dfrac{kFr}{v^2}$ for v

$$w = \frac{kFr}{v^2} \quad \text{The goal is to isolate } v \text{ on one side.}$$

$$v^2 w = kFr \qquad \text{Multiply by } v^2.$$

$$v^2 = \frac{kFr}{w} \qquad \text{Divide by } w.$$

$$v = \pm\sqrt{\frac{kFr}{w}} \qquad \text{Square root property}$$

$$v = \frac{\pm\sqrt{kFr}}{\sqrt{w}} \cdot \frac{\sqrt{w}}{\sqrt{w}} \qquad \text{Rationalize the denominator.}$$

$$v = \frac{\pm\sqrt{kFrw}}{w} \qquad \begin{array}{l}\sqrt{a}\cdot\sqrt{b}=\sqrt{ab};\\ \sqrt{a}\cdot\sqrt{a}=a\end{array}$$

(b) $d = \sqrt{\dfrac{4\mathscr{A}}{\pi}}$ for $\mathscr{A}$

$$d = \sqrt{\frac{4\mathscr{A}}{\pi}} \quad \text{The goal is to isolate } \mathscr{A} \text{ on one side.}$$

$$d^2 = \frac{4\mathscr{A}}{\pi} \qquad \text{Square both sides.}$$

$$\pi d^2 = 4\mathscr{A} \qquad \text{Multiply by } \pi.$$

$$\frac{\pi d^2}{4} = \mathscr{A}, \quad \text{or} \quad \mathscr{A} = \frac{\pi d^2}{4} \qquad \text{Divide by 4.} \qquad \textit{NOW TRY}$$

NOTE In formulas like $v = \dfrac{\pm\sqrt{kFrw}}{w}$ in **Example 1(a)**, we include both positive and negative values.

EXAMPLE 2 Solving for a Variable That Appears in First- and Second-Degree Terms

Solve $s = 2t^2 + kt$ for t.

Since the given equation has terms with t^2 and t, write it in standard form $ax^2 + bx + c = 0$, with t as the variable instead of x.

$$s = 2t^2 + kt$$

$$0 = 2t^2 + kt - s \qquad \text{Subtract } s.$$

$$2t^2 + kt - s = 0 \qquad \text{Standard form}$$

NOW TRY
EXERCISE 1

Solve each formula for the given variable. Keep $\pm$ in the answer in part (a).

(a) $n = \dfrac{ab}{E^2}$ for E

(b) $S = \sqrt{\dfrac{pq}{n}}$ for p

NOW TRY
EXERCISE 2
Solve for r.

$$r^2 + 9r = -c$$

To solve $2t^2 + kt - s = 0$, use the quadratic formula with $a = 2$, $b = k$, and $c = -s$.

$$t = \frac{-k \pm \sqrt{k^2 - 4(2)(-s)}}{2(2)} \qquad \text{Substitute.}$$

$$t = \frac{-k \pm \sqrt{k^2 + 8s}}{4} \qquad \text{Solve for } t.$$

The solutions are $t = \dfrac{-k + \sqrt{k^2 + 8s}}{4}$ and $t = \dfrac{-k - \sqrt{k^2 + 8s}}{4}$.   *NOW TRY*

OBJECTIVE 2 Solve applied problems using the Pythagorean theorem. The Pythagorean theorem, represented by the equation

$$a^2 + b^2 = c^2,$$

is illustrated in **FIGURE 2** and was introduced in **Sections 5.6 and 10.3.** It is used to solve applications involving right triangles.

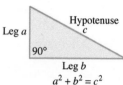

FIGURE 2

NOW TRY
EXERCISE 3
Matt Porter is building a new barn, with length 10 ft more than width. While determining the footprint of the barn, he measured the diagonal as 50 ft. What will be the dimensions of the barn?

EXAMPLE 3   Using the Pythagorean Theorem

Two cars left an intersection at the same time, one heading due north, the other due west. Some time later, they were exactly 100 mi apart. The car headed north had gone 20 mi farther than the car headed west. How far had each car traveled?

Step 1   **Read** the problem carefully.

Step 2   **Assign a variable.**

Let $x =$ the distance traveled by the car headed west.

Then $x + 20 =$ the distance traveled by the car headed north.

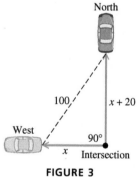

See **FIGURE 3**. The cars are 100 mi apart, so the hypotenuse of the right triangle equals 100.

FIGURE 3

Step 3   **Write an equation.** Use the Pythagorean theorem.

$$a^2 + b^2 = c^2$$

$$x^2 + (x + 20)^2 = 100^2$$

$(x + y)^2 = x^2 + 2xy + y^2$

Step 4   **Solve.** $x^2 + x^2 + 40x + 400 = 10{,}000$ Square the binomial.

$$2x^2 + 40x - 9600 = 0 \qquad \text{Standard form}$$

$$x^2 + 20x - 4800 = 0 \qquad \text{Divide by 2.}$$

$$(x + 80)(x - 60) = 0 \qquad \text{Factor.}$$

$$x + 80 = 0 \quad \text{or} \quad x - 60 = 0 \qquad \text{Zero-factor property}$$

$$x = -80 \quad \text{or} \qquad x = 60 \qquad \text{Solve for } x.$$

NOW TRY ANSWERS

2. $r = \dfrac{-9 \pm \sqrt{81 - 4c}}{2}$

3. 30 ft by 40 ft

Step 5   **State the answer.** Since distance cannot be negative, discard the negative solution. The required distances are 60 mi and $60 + 20 = 80$ mi.

Step 6   **Check.** Since $60^2 + 80^2 = 100^2$, the answer is correct.   *NOW TRY*

41. A rectangular piece of sheet metal has a length that is 4 in. less than twice the width. A square piece 2 in. on a side is cut from each corner. The sides are then turned up to form an uncovered box of volume 256 in.³. Find the length and width of the original piece of metal.

42. Another rectangular piece of sheet metal is 2 in. longer than it is wide. A square piece 3 in. on a side is cut from each corner. The sides are then turned up to form an uncovered box of volume 765 in.³. Find the dimensions of the original piece of metal.

Solve each problem. When appropriate, round answers to the nearest tenth. ***See Example 5.***

43. An object is projected directly upward from the ground. After t seconds its distance in feet above the ground is

$$s(t) = 144t - 16t^2.$$

After how many seconds will the object be 128 ft above the ground? (*Hint:* Look for a common factor before solving the equation.)

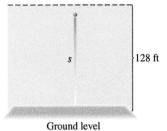

Ground level

44. When does the object in **Exercise 43** strike the ground?

45. A ball is projected upward from the ground. Its distance in feet from the ground in t seconds is given by

$$s(t) = -16t^2 + 128t.$$

At what times will the ball be 213 ft from the ground?

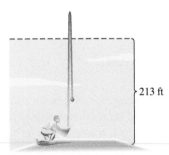

213 ft

46. A toy rocket is launched from ground level. Its distance in feet from the ground in t seconds is given by

$$s(t) = -16t^2 + 208t.$$

At what times will the rocket be 550 ft from the ground?

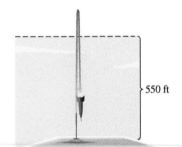

550 ft

47. The function defined by

$$D(t) = 13t^2 - 100t$$

gives the distance in feet a car going approximately 68 mph will skid in t seconds. Find the time it would take for the car to skid 180 ft.

48. The function given in **Exercise 47** becomes $D(t) = 13t^2 - 73t$ for a car going 50 mph. Find the time it takes for this car to skid 218 ft.

A ball is projected upward from ground level, and its distance in feet from the ground in t seconds is given by $s(t) = -16t^2 + 160t$.

49. After how many seconds does the ball reach a height of 400 ft? How would you describe in words its position at this height?

50. After how many seconds does the ball reach a height of 425 ft? How would you interpret the mathematical result here?

Solve each problem using a quadratic equation.

51. A certain bakery has found that the daily demand for blueberry muffins is $\frac{3200}{p}$, where p is the price of a muffin in cents. The daily supply is $3p - 200$. Find the price at which supply and demand are equal.

52. In one area the demand for compact discs is $\frac{700}{P}$ per day, where P is the price in dollars per disc. The supply is $5P - 1$ per day. At what price, to the nearest cent, does supply equal demand?

53. The formula

$$A = P(1 + r)^2$$

gives the amount A in dollars that P dollars will grow to in 2 yr at interest rate r (where r is given as a decimal), using compound interest. What interest rate will cause $2000 to grow to $2142.45 in 2 yr?

54. Use the formula $A = P(1 + r)^2$ to find the interest rate r at which a principal P of $10,000 will increase to $10,920.25 in 2 yr.

William Froude was a 19th century naval architect who used the expression

$$\frac{v^2}{g\ell}$$

in shipbuilding. This expression, known as the Froude number, was also used by R. McNeill Alexander in his research on dinosaurs. (Source: "How Dinosaurs Ran," Scientific American, April 1991.) In Exercises 55 and 56, find the value of v (in meters per second), given $g = 9.8$ m per sec². (Round to the nearest tenth.)

55. Rhinoceros: $\ell = 1.2$;
    Froude number $= 2.57$

56. Triceratops: $\ell = 2.8$;
    Froude number $= 0.16$

Recall that corresponding sides of similar triangles are proportional. Use this fact to find the lengths of the indicated sides of each pair of similar triangles. Check all possible solutions in both triangles. Sides of a triangle cannot be negative (and are not drawn to scale here).

57. Side AC

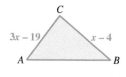

58. Side RQ

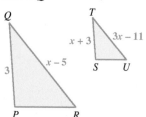

Total spending (in billions of dollars) in the United States from all sources on physician and clinical services for the years 2000–2007 are shown in the bar graph on the next page and can be modeled by the quadratic function defined by

$$f(x) = 0.3214x^2 + 25.06x + 288.2.$$

*Here, $x = 0$ represents 2000, $x = 1$ represents 2001, and so on. Use the graph and the model to work Exercises 59–62. **See Example 6.***

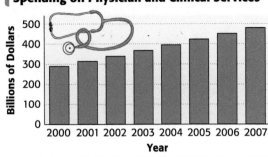

Spending on Physician and Clinical Services

Source: U.S. Centers for Medicare and Medicaid Services.

59. (a) Use the graph to estimate spending on physician and clinical services in 2005 to the nearest $10 billion.

(b) Use the model to approximate spending to the nearest $10 billion. How does this result compare to your estimate in part (a)?

60. Based on the model, in what year did spending on physician and clinical services first exceed $350 billion? (Round down for the year.) How does this result compare to the amount of spending shown in the graph?

61. Based on the model, in what year did spending on physician and clinical services first exceed $400 billion? (Round down for the year.) How does this result compare to the amount of spending shown in the graph?

62. If these data were modeled by a *linear* function defined by $f(x) = ax + b$, would the value of a be positive or negative? Explain.

PREVIEW EXERCISES

Find each function value. See Section 7.4.

63. $f(x) = x^2 + 4x - 3$. Find $f(2)$.　　**64.** $f(x) = 2(x - 3)^2 + 5$. Find $f(3)$.

65. Graph $f(x) = 2x^2$. Give the domain and range. **See Sections 4.4 and 7.3.**

11.6 Graphs of Quadratic Functions

OBJECTIVES

1 Graph a quadratic function.

2 Graph parabolas with horizontal and vertical shifts.

3 Use the coefficient of x^2 to predict the shape and direction in which a parabola opens.

4 Find a quadratic function to model data.

OBJECTIVE 1 **Graph a quadratic function.** **FIGURE 5** gives a graph of the simplest *quadratic function,* defined by $y = x^2$. This graph is called a **parabola.** (See **Section 4.4.**) The point $(0, 0)$, the lowest point on the curve, is the **vertex** of this parabola. The vertical line through the vertex is the **axis** of the parabola, here $x = 0$. A parabola is **symmetric about its axis**—if the graph were folded along the axis, the two portions of the curve would coincide.

As **FIGURE 5** suggests, x can be any real number, so the domain of the function defined by $y = x^2$ is $(-\infty, \infty)$. Since y is always nonnegative, the range is $[0, \infty)$.

x	y
−2	4
−1	1
0	0
1	1
2	4

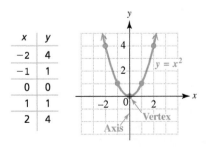

FIGURE 5

Quadratic Function

A function that can be written in the form

$$f(x) = ax^2 + bx + c$$

for real numbers a, b, and c, with $a \neq 0$, is a **quadratic function.**

The graph of any quadratic function is a parabola with a vertical axis.

NOTE We use the variable y and function notation $f(x)$ interchangeably. Although we use the letter f most often to name quadratic functions, other letters can be used. We use the capital letter F to distinguish between different parabolas graphed on the same coordinate axes.

Parabolas have a special reflecting property that makes them useful in the design of telescopes, radar equipment, solar furnaces, and automobile headlights. (See the figure.)

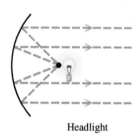

Headlight

OBJECTIVE 2 Graph parabolas with horizontal and vertical shifts. Parabolas need not have their vertices at the origin, as does the graph of $f(x) = x^2$.

NOW TRY EXERCISE 1

Graph $f(x) = x^2 - 3$. Give the vertex, axis, domain, and range.

EXAMPLE 1 Graphing a Parabola (Vertical Shift)

Graph $F(x) = x^2 - 2$.

The graph of $F(x) = x^2 - 2$ has the same shape as that of $f(x) = x^2$ but is *shifted*, or *translated*, 2 units down, with vertex $(0, -2)$. Every function value is 2 less than the corresponding function value of $f(x) = x^2$. Plotting points on both sides of the vertex gives the graph in **FIGURE 6**.

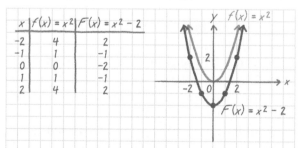

x	$f(x) = x^2$	$F(x) = x^2 - 2$
-2	4	2
-1	1	-1
0	0	-2
1	1	-1
2	4	2

$F(x) = x^2 - 2$
Vertex: $(0, -2)$
Axis: $x = 0$
Domain: $(-\infty, \infty)$
Range: $[-2, \infty)$
The graph of $f(x) = x^2$ is shown for comparison.

FIGURE 6

 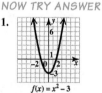
This parabola is symmetric about its axis $x = 0$, so the plotted points are "mirror images" of each other. Since x can be any real number, the domain is still $(-\infty, \infty)$. The value of y (or $F(x)$) is always greater than or equal to -2, so the range is $[-2, \infty)$.

NOW TRY

Vertical Shift

The graph of $F(x) = x^2 + k$ is a parabola.

- The graph has the same shape as the graph of $f(x) = x^2$.
- The parabola is shifted k units up if $k > 0$, and $|k|$ units down if $k < 0$.
- The vertex of the parabola is $(0, k)$.

NOW TRY
EXERCISE 2

Graph $f(x) = (x + 1)^2$. Give the vertex, axis, domain, and range.

EXAMPLE 2 Graphing a Parabola (Horizontal Shift)

Graph $F(x) = (x - 2)^2$.

If $x = 2$, then $F(x) = 0$, giving the vertex $(2, 0)$. The graph of $F(x) = (x - 2)^2$ has the same shape as that of $f(x) = x^2$ but is shifted 2 units to the right. Plotting points on one side of the vertex, and using symmetry about the axis $x = 2$ to find corresponding points on the other side, gives the graph in **FIGURE 7**.

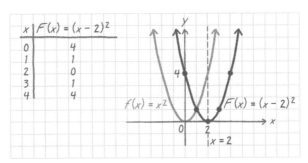

$F(x) = (x - 2)^2$
Vertex: $(2, 0)$
Axis: $x = 2$
Domain: $(-\infty, \infty)$
Range: $[0, \infty)$

FIGURE 7

NOW TRY

Horizontal Shift

The graph of $F(x) = (x - h)^2$ is a parabola.

- The graph has the same shape as the graph of $f(x) = x^2$.
- The parabola is shifted h units to the right if $h > 0$, and $|h|$ units to the left if $h < 0$.
- The vertex of the parabola is $(h, 0)$.

⚠ **CAUTION** *Errors frequently occur when horizontal shifts are involved.* To determine the direction and magnitude of a horizontal shift, find the value that causes the expression $x - h$ to equal 0, as shown below.

$$F(x) = (x - 5)^2$$

Shift the graph of $F(x)$ **5 units to the right,** because $+5$ causes $x - 5$ to equal 0.

$$F(x) = (x + 5)^2$$

Shift the graph of $F(x)$ **5 units to the left,** because -5 causes $x + 5$ to equal 0.

NOW TRY ANSWER

2.

vertex: $(-1, 0)$; axis: $x = -1$;
domain: $(-\infty, \infty)$; range: $[0, \infty)$

EXAMPLE 3 Graphing a Parabola (Horizontal and Vertical Shifts)

Graph $F(x) = (x + 3)^2 - 2$.

This graph has the same shape as that of $f(x) = x^2$, but is shifted 3 units to the left (since $x + 3 = 0$ if $x = -3$) and 2 units down (because of the -2). See **FIGURE 8** on the next page.

NOW TRY
EXERCISE 3

Graph $f(x) = (x + 1)^2 - 2$.
Give the vertex, axis, domain,
and range.

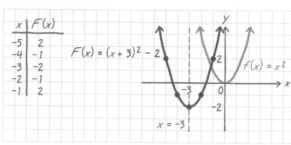

$F(x) = (x + 3)^2 - 2$
Vertex: $(-3, -2)$
Axis: $x = -3$
Domain: $(-\infty, \infty)$
Range: $[-2, \infty)$

FIGURE 8

NOW TRY

Vertex and Axis of a Parabola

The graph of $F(x) = (x - h)^2 + k$ is a parabola.

- The graph has the same shape as the graph of $f(x) = x^2$.
- The vertex of the parabola is (h, k).
- The axis is the vertical line $x = h$.

OBJECTIVE 3 Use the coefficient of x^2 to predict the shape and direction in which a parabola opens. Not all parabolas open up, and not all parabolas have the same shape as the graph of $f(x) = x^2$.

NOW TRY
EXERCISE 4

Graph $f(x) = -3x^2$. Give
the vertex, axis, domain,
and range.

EXAMPLE 4 Graphing a Parabola That Opens Down

Graph $f(x) = -\frac{1}{2}x^2$.

This parabola is shown in **FIGURE 9**. The coefficient $-\frac{1}{2}$ affects the shape of the graph—the $\frac{1}{2}$ makes the parabola wider $\left(\text{since the values of } \frac{1}{2}x^2 \text{ increase more slowly than those of } x^2\right)$, and the negative sign makes the parabola open down. The graph is not shifted in any direction. Unlike the parabolas graphed in **Examples 1–3**, the vertex here has the *greatest* function value of any point on the graph.

x	f(x)
-2	-2
-1	$-\frac{1}{2}$
0	0
1	$-\frac{1}{2}$
2	-2

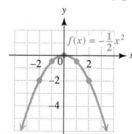

$f(x) = -\frac{1}{2}x^2$
Vertex: $(0, 0)$
Axis: $x = 0$
Domain: $(-\infty, \infty)$
Range: $(-\infty, 0]$

FIGURE 9

NOW TRY

NOW TRY ANSWERS

3.

vertex: $(-1, -2)$; axis: $x = -1$;
domain: $(-\infty, \infty)$; range: $[-2, \infty)$

4.

$f(x) = -3x^2$

vertex: $(0, 0)$; axis: $x = 0$;
domain: $(-\infty, \infty)$; range: $(-\infty, 0]$

General Characteristics of $F(x) = a(x - h)^2 + k$ $(a \neq 0)$

1. The graph of the quadratic function defined by
$$F(x) = a(x - h)^2 + k, \quad \text{with } a \neq 0,$$
is a parabola with vertex (h, k) and the vertical line $x = h$ as axis.

2. The graph opens up if a is positive and down if a is negative.

3. The graph is wider than that of $f(x) = x^2$ if $0 < |a| < 1$.
The graph is narrower than that of $f(x) = x^2$ if $|a| > 1$.

NOW TRY
EXERCISE 5

Graph $f(x) = 2(x - 1)^2 + 2$.

EXAMPLE 5 Using the General Characteristics to Graph a Parabola

Graph $F(x) = -2(x + 3)^2 + 4$.

The parabola opens down (because $a < 0$) and is narrower than the graph of $f(x) = x^2$, since $|-2| = 2$ and $2 > 1$. This causes values of $F(x)$ to decrease more quickly than those of $f(x) = -x^2$. This parabola has vertex $(-3, 4)$, as shown in **FIGURE 10**. To complete the graph, we plotted the ordered pairs $(-4, 2)$ and, by symmetry, $(-2, 2)$. Symmetry can be used to find additional ordered pairs that satisfy the equation.

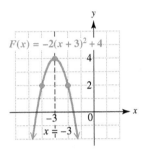

$F(x) = -2(x + 3)^2 + 4$
Vertex: $(-3, 4)$
Axis: $x = -3$
Domain: $(-\infty, \infty)$
Range: $(-\infty, 4]$

FIGURE 10

NOW TRY

OBJECTIVE 4 Find a quadratic function to model data.

EXAMPLE 6 Modeling the Number of Multiple Births

The number of higher-order multiple births (triplets or more) in the United States has declined in recent years, as shown by the data in the table. Here, x represents the number of years since 1995 and y represents the number of higher-order multiple births.

Year	x	y
1995	0	4973
1996	1	5939
1997	2	6737
1999	4	7321
2001	6	7471
2003	8	7663
2004	9	7275
2005	10	6694

Source: National Center for Health Statistics.

NOW TRY ANSWER
5.

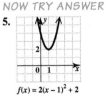

$f(x) = 2(x - 1)^2 + 2$

Find a quadratic function that models the data.

A scatter diagram of the ordered pairs (x, y) is shown in **FIGURE 11** on the next page. The general shape suggested by the scatter diagram indicates that a parabola should approximate these points, as shown by the dashed curve in **FIGURE 12**. The equation for such a parabola would have a negative coefficient for x^2 since the graph opens down.

NOW TRY
EXERCISE 6
Using the points $(0, 4973)$, $(4, 7321)$, and $(8, 7663)$, find another quadratic model for the data on higher-order multiple births in **Example 6.**

U.S. HIGHER-ORDER MULTIPLE BIRTHS

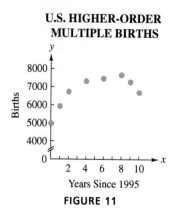

Years Since 1995

FIGURE 11

U.S. HIGHER-ORDER MULTIPLE BIRTHS

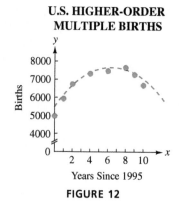

Years Since 1995

FIGURE 12

To find a quadratic function of the form

$$y = ax^2 + bx + c$$

that models, or *fits*, these data, we choose three representative ordered pairs and use them to write a system of three equations. Using

$$(0, 4973), \quad (4, 7321), \quad \text{and} \quad (10, 6694),$$

we substitute the *x*- and *y*-values from the ordered pairs into the quadratic form $y = ax^2 + bx + c$ to get three equations.

$$a(0)^2 + b(0) + c = 4973 \qquad \text{or} \qquad c = 4973 \qquad (1)$$
$$a(4)^2 + b(4) + c = 7321 \qquad \text{or} \qquad 16a + 4b + c = 7321 \qquad (2)$$
$$a(10)^2 + b(10) + c = 6694 \qquad \text{or} \qquad 100a + 10b + c = 6694 \qquad (3)$$

We can find the values of *a*, *b*, and *c* by solving this system of three equations in three variables using the methods of **Section 8.4.** From equation (1), $c = 4973$. Substitute 4973 for *c* in equations (2) and (3) to obtain two equations.

$$16a + 4b + 4973 = 7321, \qquad \text{or} \qquad 16a + 4b = 2348 \qquad (4)$$
$$100a + 10b + 4973 = 6694, \qquad \text{or} \qquad 100a + 10b = 1721 \qquad (5)$$

We can eliminate *b* from this system of equations in two variables by multiplying equation (4) by -5 and equation (5) by 2, and adding the results.

$$120a = -8298$$

$$a = -69.15 \qquad \text{Divide by 120. Use a calculator.}$$

We substitute -69.15 for *a* in equation (4) or (5) to find that $b = 863.6$. Using the values we have found for *a*, *b*, and *c*, our model is defined by

$$y = -69.15x^2 + 863.6x + 4973. \qquad \text{NOW TRY}$$

NOTE In **Example 6,** if we had chosen three different ordered pairs of data, a slightly different model would result. The *quadratic regression* feature on a graphing calculator can also be used to generate the quadratic model that best fits given data. See your owner's manual for details.

NOW TRY ANSWER
6. $y = -62.69x^2 + 837.75x + 4973$

11.6 EXERCISES

MyMathLab

Math XL
PRACTICE · WATCH · DOWNLOAD · READ · REVIEW

🌐 *Complete solution available on the Video Resources on DVD*

1. *Concept Check* Match each quadratic function with its graph from choices A–D.

(a) $f(x) = (x + 2)^2 - 1$

(b) $f(x) = (x + 2)^2 + 1$

(c) $f(x) = (x - 2)^2 - 1$

(d) $f(x) = (x - 2)^2 + 1$

A.

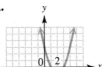

B.

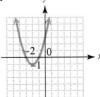

C.

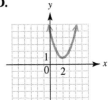

D.

2. *Concept Check* Match each quadratic function with its graph from choices A–D.

(a) $f(x) = -x^2 + 2$

(b) $f(x) = -x^2 - 2$

(c) $f(x) = -(x + 2)^2$

(d) $f(x) = -(x - 2)^2$

A.

B.

 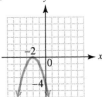

C.

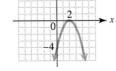 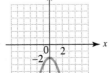 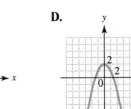

D.

Identify the vertex of each parabola. ***See Examples 1–4.***

3. $f(x) = -3x^2$ **4.** $f(x) = \dfrac{1}{2}x^2$ **5.** $f(x) = x^2 + 4$ **6.** $f(x) = x^2 - 4$

7. $f(x) = (x - 1)^2$ **8.** $f(x) = (x + 3)^2$ **9.** $f(x) = (x + 3)^2 - 4$

10. $f(x) = (x + 5)^2 - 8$ **11.** $f(x) = -(x - 5)^2 + 6$ **12.** $f(x) = -(x - 2)^2 + 1$

For each quadratic function, tell whether the graph opens up or down and whether the graph is wider, narrower, or the same shape as the graph of $f(x) = x^2$. ***See Examples 4 and 5.***

13. $f(x) = -\dfrac{2}{5}x^2$ **14.** $f(x) = -2x^2$

15. $f(x) = 3x^2 + 1$ **16.** $f(x) = \dfrac{2}{3}x^2 - 4$

17. $f(x) = -4(x + 2)^2 + 5$ **18.** $f(x) = -\dfrac{1}{3}(x + 6)^2 + 3$

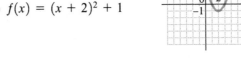 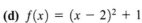 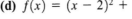 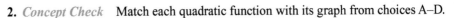

19. *Concept Check* Match each quadratic function with the description of the parabola that is its graph.

(a) $f(x) = (x - 4)^2 - 2$

(b) $f(x) = (x - 2)^2 - 4$

(c) $f(x) = -(x - 4)^2 - 2$

(d) $f(x) = -(x - 2)^2 - 4$

A. Vertex $(2, -4)$, opens down

B. Vertex $(2, -4)$, opens up

C. Vertex $(4, -2)$, opens down

D. Vertex $(4, -2)$, opens up

20. *Concept Check* For $f(x) = a(x - h)^2 + k$, in what quadrant is the vertex if

(a) $h > 0, k > 0$ (b) $h > 0, k < 0$ (c) $h < 0, k > 0$ (d) $h < 0, k < 0$?

Graph each parabola. Plot at least two points as well as the vertex. Give the vertex, axis, domain, and range in Exercises 27–36. ***See Examples 1–5.***

21. $f(x) = -2x^2$

22. $f(x) = -\frac{1}{3}x^2$

23. $f(x) = x^2 - 1$

24. $f(x) = x^2 + 3$

25. $f(x) = -x^2 + 2$

26. $f(x) = -x^2 - 2$

27. $f(x) = (x - 4)^2$

28. $f(x) = (x + 1)^2$

29. $f(x) = (x + 2)^2 - 1$

30. $f(x) = (x - 1)^2 + 2$

31. $f(x) = 2(x - 2)^2 - 4$

32. $f(x) = 3(x - 2)^2 + 1$

33. $f(x) = -\frac{1}{2}(x + 1)^2 + 2$

34. $f(x) = -\frac{2}{3}(x + 2)^2 + 1$

35. $f(x) = 2(x - 2)^2 - 3$

36. $f(x) = \frac{4}{3}(x - 3)^2 - 2$

Concept Check In Exercises 37–42, tell whether a linear or quadratic function would be a more appropriate model for each set of graphed data. If linear, tell whether the slope should be positive or negative. If quadratic, tell whether the coefficient a of x^2 should be positive or negative. ***See Example 6.***

37. TIME SPENT PLAYING VIDEO GAMES

Source: Veronis Suhler Stevenson.

38. AVERAGE DAILY VOLUME OF FIRST-CLASS MAIL

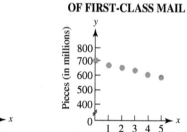

Source: General Accounting Office.

39. FOOD ASSISTANCE SPENDING IN IOWA

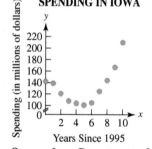

Source: Iowa Department of Human Services.

40. PLASMA TV SALES IN U.S.

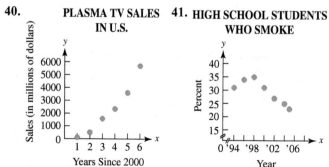

Source: Consumer Electronics Association.

41. HIGH SCHOOL STUDENTS WHO SMOKE

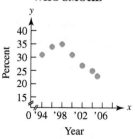

Source: www.cdc.gov

42. SOCIAL SECURITY ASSETS*

*Projected

Source: Social Security Administration.

Solve each problem. ***See Example 6.***

43. Sales of digital cameras in the United States (in millions of dollars) between 2000 and 2006 are shown in the table. In the year column, 0 represents 2000, 1 represents 2001, and so on.

Year	Sales
0	1825
1	1972
2	2794
3	3921
4	4739
5	5611
6	7805

Source: Consumer Electronics Association.

(a) Use the ordered pairs (year, sales) to make a scatter diagram of the data.

(b) Use the scatter diagram to decide whether a linear or quadratic function would better model the data. If quadratic, should the coefficient a of x^2 be positive or negative?

(c) Use the ordered pairs $(0, 1825)$, $(3, 3921)$, and $(6, 7805)$ to find a quadratic function that models the data. Round the values of a, b, and c in your model to the nearest tenth, as necessary.

(d) Use your model from part (c) to approximate the sales of digital cameras in the United States in 2007. Round your answer to the nearest whole number (of millions).

(e) Sales of digital cameras were $6517 million in 2007. Based on this, is the model valid for 2007? Explain.

44. The number (in thousands) of new, privately owned housing units started in the United States is shown in the table for the years 2002–2008. In the year column, 2 represents 2002, 3 represents 2003, and so on.

Year	Housing Starts (thousands)
2	1700
3	1850
4	1960
5	2070
6	1800
7	1360
8	910

Source: U.S. Census Bureau.

(a) Use the ordered pairs (year, housing starts) to make a scatter diagram of the data.

(b) Would a linear or quadratic function better model the data?

(c) Should the coefficient a of x^2 in a quadratic model be positive or negative?

(d) Use the ordered pairs $(2, 1700)$, $(4, 1960)$, and $(7, 1360)$ to find a quadratic function that models the data. Round the values of a, b, and c in your model to the nearest whole number, as necessary.

(e) Use your model from part (d) to approximate the number of housing starts during 2003 and 2008 to the nearest thousand. How well does the model approximate the actual data from the table?

45. In **Example 6,** we determined that the quadratic function defined by

$$y = -69.15x^2 + 863.6x + 4973$$

modeled the number of higher-order multiple births, where x represents the number of years since 1995.

(a) Use this model to approximate the number of higher-order births in 2006 to the nearest whole number.

(b) The actual number of higher-order births in 2006 was 6540. (*Source:* National Center for Health Statistics.) How does the approximation using the model compare to the actual number for 2006?

46. Should the model from **Exercise 45** be used to approximate the rate of higher-order multiple births in years after 2006? Explain.

TECHNOLOGY INSIGHTS   EXERCISES 47–48

*Recall from **Sections 3.2 and 7.1** that the x-value of the x-intercept of the graph of the line $y = mx + b$ is the solution of the linear equation $mx + b = 0$. In the same way, the x-values of the x-intercepts of the graph of the parabola $y = ax^2 + bx + c$ are the real solutions of the quadratic equation $ax^2 + bx + c = 0$.*

In Exercises 47–48, the calculator graphs show the x-values of the x-intercepts of the graph of the polynomial in the equation. Use the graphs to solve each equation.

47. $x^2 - x - 20 = 0$

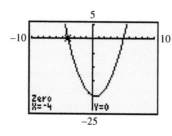 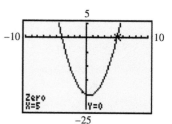

48. $x^2 + 9x + 14 = 0$

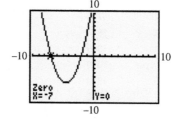 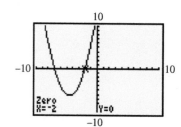

PREVIEW EXERCISES

*Complete each factoring. **See Section 5.1.***

49. $-2x^2 + 6x = $ _____ $(x^2 - 3x)$

50. $-3x^2 - 15x = $ _____ $(x^2 + 5x)$

*Solve each quadratic equation by factoring or by completing the square. **See Sections 11.1 and 11.2.***

51. $x^2 + 3x - 4 = 0$

52. $x^2 - x - 6 = 0$

53. $x^2 + 6x - 3 = 0$

54. $x^2 + 8x - 4 = 0$

OBJECTIVE 4 Use quadratic functions to solve problems involving maximum or minimum value. The vertex of the graph of a quadratic function is either the highest or the lowest point on the parabola. It provides the following information.

1. The y-value of the vertex gives the maximum or minimum value of y.

2. The x-value tells where the maximum or minimum occurs.

PROBLEM-SOLVING HINT

In many applied problems we must find the greatest or least value of some quantity. When we can express that quantity in terms of a quadratic function, the value of k in the vertex (h, k) gives that optimum value.

⌒ NOW TRY
↳ EXERCISE 6

Solve the problem in **Example 6** if the farmer has only 80 ft of fencing.

EXAMPLE 6 Finding the Maximum Area of a Rectangular Region

A farmer has 120 ft of fencing to enclose a rectangular area next to a building. (See **FIGURE 15**.) Find the maximum area he can enclose and the dimensions of the field when the area is maximized.

FIGURE 15

Let x = the width of the field.

$$x + x + \text{length} = 120 \qquad \text{Sum of the sides is 120 ft.}$$
$$2x + \text{length} = 120 \qquad \text{Combine like terms.}$$
$$\text{length} = 120 - 2x \qquad \text{Subtract } 2x.$$

The area $\mathcal{A}(x)$ is given by the product of the length and width.

$$\mathcal{A}(x) = (120 - 2x)x \qquad \text{Area = length} \cdot \text{width}$$
$$\mathcal{A}(x) = 120x - 2x^2 \qquad \text{Distributive property}$$

To determine the maximum area, use the vertex formula to find the vertex of the parabola given by $\mathcal{A}(x) = 120x - 2x^2$. Write the equation in standard form.

$$\mathcal{A}(x) = -2x^2 + 120x \qquad a = -2, b = 120, c = 0$$

Then $\qquad x = \dfrac{-b}{2a} = \dfrac{-120}{2(-2)} = \dfrac{-120}{-4} = 30,$

and $\qquad \mathcal{A}(30) = -2(30)^2 + 120(30) = -2(900) + 3600 = 1800.$

The graph is a parabola that opens down, and its vertex is $(30, 1800)$. Thus, the maximum area will be 1800 ft². This area will occur if x, the width of the field, is 30 ft and the length is

$$120 - 2(30) = 60 \text{ ft.} \qquad \qquad \text{NOW TRY} ⤸$$

NOW TRY ANSWER

6. The field should be 20 ft by 40 ft with maximum area 800 ft².

> ⚠ **CAUTION** *Be careful when interpreting the meanings of the coordinates of the vertex.* The first coordinate, *x*, gives the value for which the *function value, y* or *f(x)*, is a maximum or a minimum. Be sure to read the problem carefully to determine whether you are asked to find the value of the independent variable, the function value, or both.

 NOW TRY
EXERCISE 7

A stomp rocket is launched from the ground with an initial velocity of 48 ft per sec so that its distance in feet above the ground after *t* seconds is

$$s(t) = -16t^2 + 48t.$$

Find the maximum height attained by the rocket and the number of seconds it takes to reach that height.

EXAMPLE 7 Finding the Maximum Height Attained by a Projectile

If air resistance is neglected, a projectile on Earth shot straight upward with an initial velocity of 40 m per sec will be at a height *s* in meters given by

$$s(t) = -4.9t^2 + 40t,$$

where *t* is the number of seconds elapsed after projection. After how many seconds will it reach its maximum height, and what is this maximum height?

For this function, $a = -4.9$, $b = 40$, and $c = 0$. Use the vertex formula.

$$t = \frac{-b}{2a} = \frac{-40}{2(-4.9)} \approx 4.1 \qquad \text{Use a calculator.}$$

This indicates that the maximum height is attained at 4.1 sec. To find this maximum height, calculate $s(4.1)$.

$$s(t) = -4.9t^2 + 40t$$
$$s(4.1) = -4.9(4.1)^2 + 40(4.1) \qquad \text{Let } t = 4.1.$$
$$s(4.1) \approx 81.6 \qquad \text{Use a calculator.}$$

The projectile will attain a maximum height of approximately 81.6 m at 4.1 sec.

NOW TRY

OBJECTIVE 5 Graph parabolas with horizontal axes. If *x* and *y* are interchanged in the equation

$$y = ax^2 + bx + c,$$

the equation becomes

$$x = ay^2 + by + c.$$

Because of the interchange of the roles of *x* and *y*, these parabolas are horizontal (with horizontal lines as axes).

Graph of a Horizontal Parabola

The graph of $x = ay^2 + by + c$ or $x = a(y - k)^2 + h$ is a parabola.

- The vertex of the parabola is (h, k).
- The axis is the horizontal line $y = k$.
- The graph opens to the right if $a > 0$ and to the left if $a < 0$.

NOW TRY ANSWER
7. 36 ft; 1.5 sec

NOW TRY
EXERCISE 8

Graph $x = (y + 2)^2 - 1$.
Give the vertex, axis, domain,
and range.

EXAMPLE 8 Graphing a Horizontal Parabola ($a = 1$)

Graph $x = (y - 2)^2 - 3$. Give the vertex, axis, domain, and range.

This graph has its vertex at $(-3, 2)$, since the roles of x and y are interchanged. It opens to the right (the positive x-direction) because $a = 1$ and $1 > 0$, and has the same shape as $y = x^2$. Plotting a few additional points gives the graph shown in **FIGURE 16**.

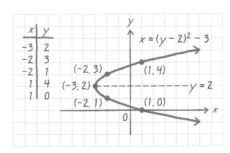

$x = (y - 2)^2 - 3$
Vertex: $(-3, 2)$
Axis: $y = 2$
Domain: $[-3, \infty)$
Range: $(-\infty, \infty)$

FIGURE 16

NOW TRY

NOW TRY
EXERCISE 9

Graph $x = -3y^2 - 6y - 5$.
Give the vertex, axis, domain,
and range.

EXAMPLE 9 Completing the Square to Graph a Horizontal Parabola ($a \neq 1$)

Graph $x = -2y^2 + 4y - 3$. Give the vertex, axis, domain, and range of the relation.

$$x = -2y^2 + 4y - 3$$

$$= -2(y^2 - 2y) - 3 \qquad \text{Factor out } -2.$$

$$= -2(y^2 - 2y + 1 - 1) - 3 \qquad \begin{array}{l}\text{Complete the square within the}\\ \text{parentheses. Add and subtract 1.}\end{array}$$

$$= -2(y^2 - 2y + 1) + (-2)(-1) - 3 \qquad \text{Distributive property}$$

Be careful here.

$$x = -2(y - 1)^2 - 1 \qquad \text{Factor. Simplify.}$$

Because of the negative coefficient -2 in $x = -2(y - 1)^2 - 1$, the graph opens to the left (the negative x-direction). The graph is narrower than the graph of $y = x^2$ because $|-2| > 1$. See **FIGURE 17**.

NOW TRY ANSWERS
8.

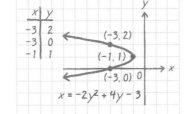

vertex: $(-1, -2)$; axis: $y = -2$;
domain: $[-1, \infty)$; range: $(-\infty, \infty)$

9.

$x = -2y^2 + 4y - 3$
Vertex: $(-1, 1)$
Axis: $y = 1$
Domain: $(-\infty, -1]$
Range: $(-\infty, \infty)$

FIGURE 17

NOW TRY

vertex: $(-2, -1)$; axis: $y = -1$;
domain: $(-\infty, -2]$; range: $(-\infty, \infty)$

⚠ **CAUTION** *Only quadratic equations solved for y (whose graphs are vertical parabolas) are examples of functions.* The horizontal parabolas in **Examples 8 and 9** are *not* graphs of functions, because they do not satisfy the conditions of the vertical line test.

In summary, the graphs of parabolas fall into the following categories.

Graphs of Parabolas

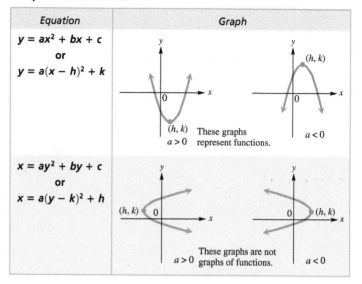

Equation	Graph
$y = ax^2 + bx + c$ or $y = a(x - h)^2 + k$	These graphs represent functions.
$x = ay^2 + by + c$ or $x = a(y - k)^2 + h$	These graphs are not graphs of functions.

11.7 EXERCISES

MyMathLab | Math XL PRACTICE | WATCH | DOWNLOAD | READ | REVIEW

 Complete solution available on the Video Resources on DVD

Concept Check   In Exercises 1–4, answer each question.

1. How can you determine just by looking at the equation of a parabola whether it has a vertical or a horizontal axis?

2. Why can't the graph of a quadratic function be a parabola with a horizontal axis?

3. How can you determine the number of x-intercepts of the graph of a quadratic function without graphing the function?

4. If the vertex of the graph of a quadratic function is $(1, -3)$, and the graph opens down, how many x-intercepts does the graph have?

*Find the vertex of each parabola. **See Examples 1–3.***

5. $f(x) = x^2 + 8x + 10$

6. $f(x) = x^2 + 10x + 23$

7. $f(x) = -2x^2 + 4x - 5$

8. $f(x) = -3x^2 + 12x - 8$

9. $f(x) = x^2 + x - 7$

10. $f(x) = x^2 - x + 5$

*Find the vertex of each parabola. For each equation, decide whether the graph opens up, down, to the left, or to the right, and whether it is wider, narrower, or the same shape as the graph of $y = x^2$. If it is a parabola with vertical axis, find the discriminant and use it to determine the number of x-intercepts. **See Examples 1–3, 5, 8, and 9.***

11. $f(x) = 2x^2 + 4x + 5$

12. $f(x) = 3x^2 - 6x + 4$

13. $f(x) = -x^2 + 5x + 3$

14. $f(x) = -x^2 + 7x + 2$

15. $x = \frac{1}{3}y^2 + 6y + 24$

16. $x = \frac{1}{2}y^2 + 10y - 5$

Concept Check   *Match each equation in Exercises 17–22 with its graph in choices A–F.*

17. $y = 2x^2 + 4x - 3$

18. $y = -x^2 + 3x + 5$

19. $y = -\dfrac{1}{2}x^2 - x + 1$

20. $x = y^2 + 6y + 3$

21. $x = -y^2 - 2y + 4$

22. $x = 3y^2 + 6y + 5$

A.
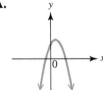

B.
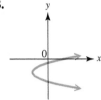

C.

D.
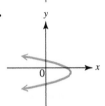

E.
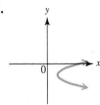

F.
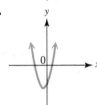

*Graph each parabola. (Use the results of **Exercises 5–8** to help graph the parabolas in Exercises 23–26.) Give the vertex, axis, domain, and range. **See Examples 4, 8, and 9.***

23. $f(x) = x^2 + 8x + 10$

24. $f(x) = x^2 + 10x + 23$

25. $f(x) = -2x^2 + 4x - 5$

26. $f(x) = -3x^2 + 12x - 8$

27. $x = (y + 2)^2 + 1$

28. $x = (y + 3)^2 - 2$

29. $x = -\dfrac{1}{5}y^2 + 2y - 4$

30. $x = -\dfrac{1}{2}y^2 - 4y - 6$

31. $x = 3y^2 + 12y + 5$

32. $x = 4y^2 + 16y + 11$

*Solve each problem. **See Examples 6 and 7.***

33. Find the pair of numbers whose sum is 40 and whose product is a maximum. (*Hint:* Let x and $40 - x$ represent the two numbers.)

34. Find the pair of numbers whose sum is 60 and whose product is a maximum.

35. Polk Community College wants to construct a rectangular parking lot on land bordered on one side by a highway. It has 280 ft of fencing that is to be used to fence off the other three sides. What should be the dimensions of the lot if the enclosed area is to be a maximum? What is the maximum area?

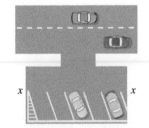

36. Bonnie Wolansky has 100 ft of fencing material to enclose a rectangular exercise run for her dog. One side of the run will border her house, so she will only need to fence three sides. What dimensions will give the enclosure the maximum area? What is the maximum area?

37. If an object on Earth is projected upward with an initial velocity of 32 ft per sec, then its height after t seconds is given by

$$s(t) = -16t^2 + 32t.$$

Find the maximum height attained by the object and the number of seconds it takes to hit the ground.

38. A projectile on Earth is fired straight upward so that its distance (in feet) above the ground t seconds after firing is given by

$$s(t) = -16t^2 + 400t.$$

Find the maximum height it reaches and the number of seconds it takes to reach that height.

39. After experimentation, two physics students from American River College find that when a bottle of California wine is shaken several times, held upright, and uncorked, its cork travels according to the function defined by

$$s(t) = -16t^2 + 64t + 1,$$

where s is its height in feet above the ground t seconds after being released. After how many seconds will it reach its maximum height? What is the maximum height?

40. Professor Barbu has found that the number of students attending his intermediate algebra class is approximated by

$$S(x) = -x^2 + 20x + 80,$$

where x is the number of hours that the Campus Center is open daily. Find the number of hours that the center should be open so that the number of students attending class is a maximum. What is this maximum number of students?

41. Klaus Loewy has a taco stand. He has found that his daily costs are approximated by

$$C(x) = x^2 - 40x + 610,$$

where $C(x)$ is the cost, in dollars, to sell x units of tacos. Find the number of units of tacos he should sell to minimize his costs. What is the minimum cost?

42. Mohammad Asghar has a frozen yogurt cart. His daily costs are approximated by

$$C(x) = x^2 - 70x + 1500,$$

where $C(x)$ is the cost, in dollars, to sell x units of frozen yogurt. Find the number of units of frozen yogurt he must sell to minimize his costs. What is the minimum cost?

43. The total receipts from individual income taxes by the U.S. Treasury in the years 2000–2007 can be modeled by the quadratic function defined by

$$f(x) = 22.88x^2 - 141.3x + 1044,$$

where $x = 0$ represents 2000, $x = 1$ represents 2001, and so on, and $f(x)$ is in billions of dollars. (*Source: World Almanac and Book of Facts.*)

(a) Since the coefficient of x^2 given in the model is positive, the graph of this quadratic function is a parabola that opens up. Will the y-value of the vertex of this graph be a maximum or minimum?

(b) In what year during this period were total receipts from individual taxes a minimum? (Round down for the year.) Use the actual x-value of the vertex, to the nearest tenth, to find this amount.

44. The percent of births in the United States to teenage mothers in the years 1990–2005 can be modeled by the quadratic function defined by

$$f(x) = -0.0198x^2 + 0.1054x + 12.87,$$

where $x = 0$ represents 1990, $x = 1$ represents 1991, and so on. (*Source:* U.S. National Center for Health Statistics.)

(a) Since the coefficient of x^2 in the model is negative, the graph of this quadratic function is a parabola that opens down. Will the y-value of the vertex of this graph be a maximum or a minimum?

(b) In what year during this period was the percent of births in the U.S. to teenage mothers a maximum? (Round down for the year.) Use the actual x-value of the vertex, to the nearest tenth, to find this percent.

45. The graph on the next page shows how Social Security trust fund assets are expected to change, and suggests that a quadratic function would be a good fit to the data. The data are approximated by the function defined by

$$f(x) = -20.57x^2 + 758.9x - 3140.$$

In the model, $x = 10$ represents 2010, $x = 15$ represents 2015, and so on, and $f(x)$ is in billions of dollars.

(a) *Concept Check* How could you have predicted this quadratic model would have a negative coefficient for x^2, based only on the graph shown?

(b) Algebraically determine the vertex of the graph, with coordinates to four significant digits.

(c) Interpret the answer to part (b) as it applies to this application.

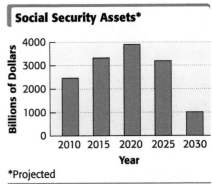

*Projected

Source: Social Security Administration.

46. The graph shows the performance of investment portfolios with different mixtures of U.S. and foreign investments over a 25-yr period.

(a) Is this the graph of a function? Explain.

(b) What investment mixture shown on the graph appears to represent the vertex? What relative amount of risk does this point represent? What return on investment does it provide?

(c) Which point on the graph represents the riskiest investment mixture? What return on investment does it provide?

LOOKING FOR THE RIGHT MIX

A portfolio that includes international investments potentially can produce higher returns with lower risk than a 100% U.S. stock portfolio.

Source: Financial Ink Newsletter, Investment Management and Research, Inc. Thanks to David Van Geffen for this information.

47. A charter flight charges a fare of $200 per person, plus $4 per person for each unsold seat on the plane. If the plane holds 100 passengers and if x represents the number of unsold seats, find the following.

(a) A function defined by $R(x)$ that describes the total revenue received for the flight (*Hint:* Multiply the number of people flying, $100 - x$, by the price per ticket, $200 + 4x$.)

(b) The graph of the function from part (a)

(c) The number of unsold seats that will produce the maximum revenue

(d) The maximum revenue

48. For a trip to a resort, a charter bus company charges a fare of $48 per person, plus $2 per person for each unsold seat on the bus. If the bus has 42 seats and x represents the number of unsold seats, find the following.

(a) A function defined by $R(x)$ that describes the total revenue from the trip (*Hint:* Multiply the total number riding, $42 - x$, by the price per ticket, $48 + 2x$.)

(b) The graph of the function from part (a)

(c) The number of unsold seats that produces the maximum revenue

(d) The maximum revenue

PREVIEW EXERCISES

Graph each interval on a number line. ***See Section 2.8.***

49. $[1, 5]$

50. $(-6, 1]$

51. $(-\infty, 1] \cup [5, \infty)$

Solve each inequality. ***See Section 2.8.***

52. $3 - x \le 5$

53. $-2x + 1 < 4$

54. $-\dfrac{1}{2}x - 3 > 5$

11.8 Polynomial and Rational Inequalities

OBJECTIVE 1 Solve quadratic inequalities. Now we combine the methods of solving linear inequalities with the methods of solving quadratic equations to solve *quadratic inequalities.*

Quadratic Inequality

A **quadratic inequality** can be written in the form

$$ax^2 + bx + c < 0, \qquad ax^2 + bx + c > 0,$$
$$ax^2 + bx + c \le 0, \qquad \text{or} \qquad ax^2 + bx + c \ge 0,$$

where a, b, and c are real numbers, with $a \ne 0$.

One way to solve a quadratic inequality is by graphing the related quadratic function.

EXAMPLE 1 Solving Quadratic Inequalities by Graphing

Solve each inequality.

(a) $x^2 - x - 12 > 0$

To solve the inequality, we graph the related quadratic function defined by $f(x) = x^2 - x - 12$. We are particularly interested in the x-intercepts, which are found as in **Section 11.7** by letting $f(x) = 0$ and solving the following quadratic equation.

$$x^2 - x - 12 = 0$$
$$(x - 4)(x + 3) = 0 \qquad \text{Factor.}$$
$$x - 4 = 0 \quad \text{or} \quad x + 3 = 0 \qquad \text{Zero-factor property}$$
$$x = 4 \quad \text{or} \qquad x = -3 \leftarrow \text{The } x\text{-intercepts are } (4,0) \text{ and } (-3,0).$$

The graph, which opens up since the coefficient of x^2 is positive, is shown in **FIGURE 18(a)**. Notice from this graph that x-values less than -3 or greater than 4 result in y-values *greater than* 0. Thus, the solution set of $x^2 - x - 12 > 0$, written in interval notation, is $(-\infty, -3) \cup (4, \infty)$.

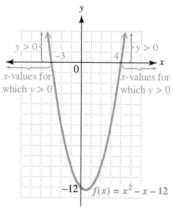

The graph is *above* the x-axis for $(-\infty, -3) \cup (4, \infty)$.

(a)

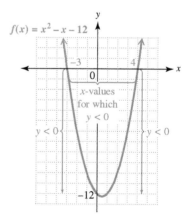

The graph is *below* the x-axis for $(-3, 4)$.

(b)

FIGURE 18

NOW TRY
EXERCISE 1

Use the graph to solve each quadratic inequality.

$f(x) = x^2 - 3x - 4$

(a) $x^2 - 3x - 4 > 0$

(b) $x^2 - 3x - 4 < 0$

(b) $x^2 - x - 12 < 0$

We want values of y that are *less than* 0. Referring to **FIGURE 18(b)**, we notice from the graph that x-values between -3 and 4 result in y-values less than 0. Thus, the solution set of $x^2 - x - 12 < 0$, written in interval notation, is $(-3, 4)$.   NOW TRY

NOTE If the inequalities in **Example 1** had used $\geq$ and $\leq$, the solution sets would have included the x-values of the intercepts, which make the quadratic expression equal to 0. They would have been written in interval notation as

$$(-\infty, -3] \cup [4, \infty) \quad \text{and} \quad [-3, 4].$$

Square brackets would indicate that the endpoints -3 and 4 are *included* in the solution sets.

Another method for solving a quadratic inequality uses the basic ideas of **Example 1** without actually graphing the related quadratic function.

EXAMPLE 2   Solving a Quadratic Inequality Using Test Numbers

Solve and graph the solution set of $x^2 - x - 12 > 0$.

Solve the quadratic equation $x^2 - x - 12 = 0$ by factoring, as in **Example 1(a)**.

$$(x - 4)(x + 3) = 0$$

$$x - 4 = 0 \quad \text{or} \quad x + 3 = 0$$

$$x = 4 \quad \text{or} \quad x = -3$$

The numbers 4 and -3 divide a number line into Intervals A, B, and C, as shown in **FIGURE 19**. *Be careful to put the lesser number on the left.*

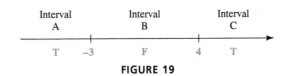

FIGURE 19

Notice the similarity between **FIGURE 19** and the x-axis with intercepts $(-3, 0)$ and $(4, 0)$ in **FIGURE 18(a)**.

The numbers 4 and -3 are the only numbers that make the quadratic expression $x^2 - x - 12$ equal to 0. All other numbers make the expression either positive or negative. The sign of the expression can change from positive to negative or from negative to positive only at a number that makes it 0. Therefore, if one number in an interval satisfies the inequality, then all the numbers in that interval will satisfy the inequality.

To see if the numbers in Interval A satisfy the inequality, choose any number from Interval A in **FIGURE 19** (that is, any number less than -3). We choose -5. Substitute this test number for x in the original inequality $x^2 - x - 12 > 0$.

$$x^2 - x - 12 > 0 \quad \text{Original inequality}$$

$$(-5)^2 - (-5) - 12 \overset{?}{>} 0 \quad \text{Let } x = -5.$$

Use parentheses to avoid sign errors.

$$25 + 5 - 12 \overset{?}{>} 0 \quad \text{Simplify.}$$

$$18 > 0 \checkmark \quad \text{True}$$

Because -5 satisfies the inequality, *all* numbers from Interval A are solutions.

NOW TRY ANSWERS
1. **(a)** $(-\infty, -1) \cup (4, \infty)$
   (b) $(-1, 4)$

Solve and graph the solution set.

$$x^2 + 2x - 8 > 0$$

Now try 0 from Interval B.

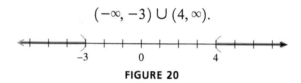

$$x^2 - x - 12 > 0 \qquad \text{Original inequality}$$
$$0^2 - 0 - 12 \overset{?}{>} 0 \qquad \text{Let } x = 0.$$
$$-12 > 0 \qquad \text{False}$$

The numbers in Interval B are *not* solutions. Verify that the test number 5 from Interval C satisfies the inequality, so all numbers there are also solutions.

Based on these results (shown by the colored letters in **FIGURE 19**), the solution set includes the numbers in Intervals A and C, as shown on the graph in **FIGURE 20**. The solution set is written in interval notation as

$$(-\infty, -3) \cup (4, \infty).$$

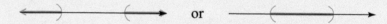

FIGURE 20

This agrees with the solution set found in **Example 1(a).**   NOW TRY

In summary, follow these steps to solve a quadratic inequality.

Solving a Quadratic Inequality

Step 1   **Write the inequality as an equation and solve it.**

Step 2   **Use the solutions from Step 1 to determine intervals.** Graph the numbers found in Step 1 on a number line. These numbers divide the number line into intervals.

Step 3   **Find the intervals that satisfy the inequality.** Substitute a test number from each interval into the original inequality to determine the intervals that satisfy the inequality. All numbers in those intervals are in the solution set. A graph of the solution set will usually look like one of these. (Square brackets might be used instead of parentheses.)

or

Step 4   **Consider the endpoints separately.** The numbers from Step 1 are included in the solution set if the inequality symbol is $\leq$ or $\geq$. They are not included if it is $<$ or $>$.

Solve each inequality.

(a) $(4x - 1)^2 > -3$

(b) $(4x - 1)^2 < -3$

NOW TRY ANSWERS

2. $(-\infty, -4) \cup (2, \infty)$

3. (a) $(-\infty, \infty)$ **(b)** $\emptyset$

EXAMPLE 3   Solving Special Cases

Solve each inequality.

(a) $(2x - 3)^2 > -1$

Because $(2x - 3)^2$ is never negative, it is always greater than -1. Thus, the solution set for $(2x - 3)^2 > -1$ is the set of all real numbers, $(-\infty, \infty)$.

(b) $(2x - 3)^2 < -1$

Using the same reasoning as in part (a), there is no solution for this inequality. The solution set is $\emptyset$.   NOW TRY

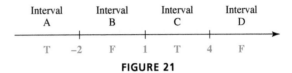

OBJECTIVE 2 Solve polynomial inequalities of degree 3 or greater.

EXAMPLE 4 Solving a Third-Degree Polynomial Inequality

Solve and graph the solution set of $(x - 1)(x + 2)(x - 4) \leq 0$.

This is a *cubic* (third-degree) inequality rather than a quadratic inequality, but it can be solved using the preceding method by extending the zero-factor property to more than two factors. (Step 1)

$$(x - 1)(x + 2)(x - 4) = 0 \qquad \text{Set the factored polynomial } equal \text{ to 0.}$$

$$x - 1 = 0 \quad \text{or} \quad x + 2 = 0 \quad \text{or} \quad x - 4 = 0 \qquad \text{Zero-factor property}$$

$$x = 1 \quad \text{or} \quad x = -2 \quad \text{or} \quad x = 4 \qquad \text{Solve each equation.}$$

Locate the numbers -2, 1, and 4 on a number line, as in **FIGURE 21**, to determine the Intervals A, B, C, and D. (Step 2)

Interval A		Interval B		Interval C		Interval D

$$\begin{array}{ccccccc} \text{T} & -2 & \text{F} & 1 & \text{T} & 4 & \text{F} \end{array}$$

FIGURE 21

Substitute a test number from each interval in the *original* inequality to determine which intervals satisfy the inequality. (Step 3)

Interval	Test Number	Test of Inequality	True or False?
A	-3	$-28 \leq 0$	T
B	0	$8 \leq 0$	F
C	2	$-8 \leq 0$	T
D	5	$28 \leq 0$	F

We use a table to organize this information. (Verify it.)

The numbers in Intervals A and C are in the solution set, which is written in interval notation as $(-\infty, -2] \cup [1, 4]$, and graphed in **FIGURE 22**. The three endpoints are included since the inequality symbol, $\leq$, includes equality. (Step 4)

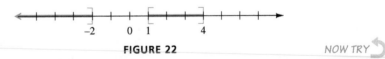

FIGURE 22

NOW TRY

OBJECTIVE 3 Solve rational inequalities. Inequalities that involve rational expressions, called **rational inequalities,** are solved similarly using the following steps.

Solving a Rational Inequality

Step 1 **Write the inequality so that 0 is on one side** and there is a single fraction on the other side.

Step 2 **Determine the numbers that make the numerator or denominator equal to 0.**

Step 3 **Divide a number line into intervals.** Use the numbers from Step 2.

Step 4 **Find the intervals that satisfy the inequality.** Test a number from each interval by substituting it into the *original* inequality.

Step 5 **Consider the endpoints separately.** Exclude any values that make the denominator 0.

NOW TRY EXERCISE 4

Solve and graph the solution set.

$(x + 4)(x - 3)(2x + 1) \leq 0$

NOW TRY ANSWER

4. $(-\infty, -4] \cup \left[-\frac{1}{2}, 3\right]$

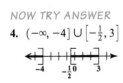

⚠ CAUTION *When solving a rational inequality, any number that makes the denominator 0 must be excluded from the solution set.*

◝ NOW TRY
◝ EXERCISE 5

Solve and graph the solution set.

$$\frac{3}{x + 1} > 4$$

EXAMPLE 5 Solving a Rational Inequality

Solve and graph the solution set of $\dfrac{-1}{x - 3} > 1$.

Write the inequality so that 0 is on one side. (Step 1)

$$\frac{-1}{x - 3} - 1 > 0 \qquad \text{Subtract 1.}$$

$$\frac{-1}{x - 3} - \frac{x - 3}{x - 3} > 0 \qquad \text{Use } x - 3 \text{ as the common denominator.}$$

Be careful with signs. $\dfrac{-1 - x + 3}{x - 3} > 0 \qquad$ Write the left side as a single fraction.

$$\frac{-x + 2}{x - 3} > 0 \qquad \text{Combine like terms in the numerator.}$$

The sign of $\frac{-x + 2}{x - 3}$ will change from positive to negative or negative to positive only at those numbers that make the numerator or denominator 0. The number 2 makes the numerator 0, and 3 makes the denominator 0. (Step 2) These two numbers, 2 and 3, divide a number line into three intervals. See **FIGURE 23**. (Step 3)

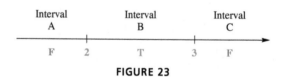

FIGURE 23

Testing a number from each interval in the *original* inequality, $\frac{-1}{x - 3} > 1$, gives the results shown in the table. (Step 4)

Interval	Test Number	Test of Inequality	True or False?
A	0	$\frac{1}{3} > 1$	F
B	2.5	$2 > 1$	T
C	4	$-1 > 1$	F

The solution set is the interval $(2, 3)$. This interval does not include 3 since it would make the denominator of the original equality 0. The number 2 is not included either since the inequality symbol, $>$, does not include equality. (Step 5) See **FIGURE 24**.

NOW TRY ANSWER
5. $\left(-1, -\frac{1}{4}\right)$

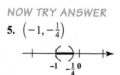

FIGURE 24

NOW TRY ↻

NOW TRY
EXERCISE 6

Solve and graph the solution set.

$$\frac{x-3}{x+3} \leq 2$$

EXAMPLE 6 **Solving a Rational Inequality**

Solve and graph the solution set of $\dfrac{x-2}{x+2} \leq 2$.

Write the inequality so that 0 is on one side. (Step 1)

$$\frac{x-2}{x+2} - 2 \leq 0 \qquad \text{Subtract 2.}$$

$$\frac{x-2}{x+2} - \frac{2(x+2)}{x+2} \leq 0 \qquad \text{Use } x+2 \text{ as the common denominator.}$$

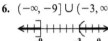 Be careful with signs.
$$\frac{x-2-2x-4}{x+2} \leq 0 \qquad \text{Write as a single fraction.}$$

$$\frac{-x-6}{x+2} \leq 0 \qquad \text{Combine like terms in the numerator.}$$

The number -6 makes the numerator 0, and -2 makes the denominator 0. (Step 2) These two numbers determine three intervals. (Step 3) Test one number from each interval (Step 4) to see that the solution set is

$$(-\infty, -6] \cup (-2, \infty).$$

The number -6 satisfies the original inequality, but -2 does not since it makes the denominator 0. (Step 5) **FIGURE 25** shows a graph of the solution set.

NOW TRY ANSWER
6. $(-\infty, -9] \cup (-3, \infty)$

FIGURE 25

NOW TRY

11.8 EXERCISES

In Exercises 1–3, the graph of a quadratic function f is given. Use the graph to find the solution set of each equation or inequality. **See Example 1.**

1. (a) $x^2 - 4x + 3 = 0$ **2.** (a) $3x^2 + 10x - 8 = 0$ **3.** (a) $-x^2 + 3x + 10 = 0$

   (b) $x^2 - 4x + 3 > 0$ (b) $3x^2 + 10x - 8 \geq 0$ (b) $-x^2 + 3x + 10 \geq 0$

   (c) $x^2 - 4x + 3 < 0$ (c) $3x^2 + 10x - 8 < 0$ (c) $-x^2 + 3x + 10 \leq 0$

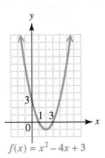

$f(x) = x^2 - 4x + 3$

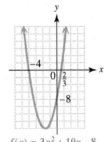

$f(x) = 3x^2 + 10x - 8$

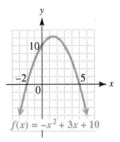

$f(x) = -x^2 + 3x + 10$

4. *Concept Check* The solution set of the inequality $x^2 + x - 12 < 0$ is the interval $(-4, 3)$. Without actually performing any work, give the solution set of the inequality $x^2 + x - 12 \geq 0$.

Solve each inequality, and graph the solution set. ***See Example 2.*** *(Hint: In Exercises 21 and 22, use the quadratic formula.)*

5. $(x + 1)(x - 5) > 0$ **6.** $(x + 6)(x - 2) > 0$

7. $(x + 4)(x - 6) < 0$ **8.** $(x + 4)(x - 8) < 0$

9. $x^2 - 4x + 3 \geq 0$ **10.** $x^2 - 3x - 10 \geq 0$

11. $10x^2 + 9x \geq 9$ **12.** $3x^2 + 10x \geq 8$

13. $4x^2 - 9 \leq 0$ **14.** $9x^2 - 25 \leq 0$

15. $6x^2 + x \geq 1$ **16.** $4x^2 + 7x \geq -3$

17. $z^2 - 4z \geq 0$ **18.** $x^2 + 2x < 0$

19. $3x^2 - 5x \leq 0$ **20.** $2z^2 + 3z > 0$

21. $x^2 - 6x + 6 \geq 0$ **22.** $3x^2 - 6x + 2 \leq 0$

Solve each inequality. ***See Example 3.***

23. $(4 - 3x)^2 \geq -2$ **24.** $(7 - 6x)^2 \geq -1$

25. $(3x + 5)^2 \leq -4$ **26.** $(8x + 5)^2 \leq -5$

Solve each inequality, and graph the solution set. ***See Example 4.***

27. $(x - 1)(x - 2)(x - 4) < 0$ **28.** $(2x + 1)(3x - 2)(4x + 7) < 0$

29. $(x - 4)(2x + 3)(3x - 1) \geq 0$ **30.** $(x + 2)(4x - 3)(2x + 7) \geq 0$

Solve each inequality, and graph the solution set. ***See Examples 5 and 6.***

31. $\dfrac{x - 1}{x - 4} > 0$ **32.** $\dfrac{x + 1}{x - 5} > 0$ **33.** $\dfrac{2x + 3}{x - 5} \leq 0$

34. $\dfrac{3x + 7}{x - 3} \leq 0$ **35.** $\dfrac{8}{x - 2} \geq 2$ **36.** $\dfrac{20}{x - 1} \geq 1$

37. $\dfrac{3}{2x - 1} < 2$ **38.** $\dfrac{6}{x - 1} < 1$ **39.** $\dfrac{x - 3}{x + 2} \geq 2$

40. $\dfrac{m + 4}{m + 5} \geq 2$ **41.** $\dfrac{x - 8}{x - 4} < 3$ **42.** $\dfrac{2t - 3}{t + 1} > 4$

43. $\dfrac{4k}{2k - 1} < k$ **44.** $\dfrac{r}{r + 2} < 2r$ **45.** $\dfrac{2x - 3}{x^2 + 1} \geq 0$

46. $\dfrac{9x - 8}{4x^2 + 25} < 0$ **47.** $\dfrac{(3x - 5)^2}{x + 2} > 0$ **48.** $\dfrac{(5x - 3)^2}{2x + 1} \leq 0$

PREVIEW EXERCISES

Give the domain and the range of each function. ***See Section 7.3.***

49. $\{(0, 1), (1, 2), (2, 4), (3, 8)\}$ **50.** $f(x) = x^2$

Decide whether each graph is that of a function. ***See Section 7.3.***

51.

52.

CHAPTER (11) SUMMARY

11.1
quadratic equation

11.4
quadratic in form

axis
quadratic function

11.8
quadratic inequality
rational inequality

11.3
quadratic formula
discriminant

11.6
parabola
vertex

TEST YOUR WORD POWER

See how well you have learned the vocabulary in this chapter.

1. The **quadratic formula** is
   A. a formula to find the number of solutions of a quadratic equation
   B. a formula to find the type of solutions of a quadratic equation
   C. the standard form of a quadratic equation
   D. a general formula for solving any quadratic equation.

2. A **quadratic function** is a function that can be written in the form
   A. $f(x) = mx + b$ for real numbers m and b
   B. $f(x) = \dfrac{P(x)}{Q(x)}$, where $Q(x) \neq 0$
   C. $f(x) = ax^2 + bx + c$ for real numbers a, b, and c $(a \neq 0)$
   D. $f(x) = \sqrt{x}$ for $x \geq 0$.

3. A **parabola** is the graph of
   A. any equation in two variables
   B. a linear equation
   C. an equation of degree 3
   D. a quadratic equation in two variables, where one is first-degree.

4. The **vertex** of a parabola is
   A. the point where the graph intersects the y-axis
   B. the point where the graph intersects the x-axis
   C. the lowest point on a parabola that opens up or the highest point on a parabola that opens down
   D. the origin.

5. The **axis** of a parabola is
   A. either the x-axis or the y-axis
   B. the vertical line (of a vertical parabola) or the horizontal line (of a horizontal parabola) through the vertex
   C. the lowest or highest point on the graph of a parabola
   D. a line through the origin.

6. A parabola is **symmetric about its axis** since
   A. its graph is near the axis
   B. its graph is identical on each side of the axis
   C. its graph looks different on each side of the axis
   D. its graph intersects the axis.

ANSWERS

1. D; *Example:* The solutions of $ax^2 + bx + c = 0$ $(a \neq 0)$ are given by $x = \dfrac{-b \pm \sqrt{b^2 - 4ac}}{2a}$. **2.** C; *Examples:* $f(x) = x^2 - 2$, $f(x) = (x + 4)^2 + 1$, $f(x) = x^2 - 4x + 5$ **3.** D; *Examples:* See the figures in the Quick Review for **Sections 11.6 and 11.7.** **4.** C; *Example:* The graph of $y = (x + 3)^2$ has vertex $(-3, 0)$, which is the lowest point on the graph. **5.** B; *Example:* The axis of $y = (x + 3)^2$ is the vertical line $x = -3$. **6.** B; *Example:* Since the graph of $y = (x + 3)^2$ is symmetric about its axis $x = -3$, the points $(-2, 1)$ and $(-4, 1)$ are on the graph.

QUICK REVIEW

CONCEPTS	EXAMPLES
11.1 Solving Quadratic Equations by the Square Root Property	

Square Root Property

If x and k are complex numbers and $x^2 = k$, then

$$x = \sqrt{k} \quad \text{or} \quad x = -\sqrt{k}.$$

Solve $(x - 1)^2 = 8$.

$$x - 1 = \sqrt{8} \quad \text{or} \quad x - 1 = -\sqrt{8}$$
$$x = 1 + 2\sqrt{2} \quad \text{or} \quad x = 1 - 2\sqrt{2}$$

The solution set is $\left\{1 + 2\sqrt{2},\, 1 - 2\sqrt{2}\right\}$, or $\left\{1 \pm 2\sqrt{2}\right\}$.

(continued)

CONCEPTS	EXAMPLES

11.2 Solving Quadratic Equations by Completing the Square

Completing the Square

To solve $ax^2 + bx + c = 0$ (with $a \neq 0$):

Step 1 If $a \neq 1$, divide each side by a.

Step 2 Write the equation with the variable terms on one side and the constant on the other.

Step 3 Take half the coefficient of x and square it.

Step 4 Add the square to each side.

Step 5 Factor the perfect square trinomial, and write it as the square of a binomial. Simplify the other side.

Step 6 Use the square root property to complete the solution.

Solve $2x^2 - 4x - 18 = 0$.

$$x^2 - 2x - 9 = 0 \qquad \text{Divide by 2.}$$
$$x^2 - 2x = 9 \qquad \text{Add 9.}$$
$$\left[\tfrac{1}{2}(-2)\right]^2 = (-1)^2 = 1$$
$$x^2 - 2x + 1 = 9 + 1 \qquad \text{Add 1.}$$
$$(x - 1)^2 = 10 \qquad \text{Factor. Add.}$$

$x - 1 = \sqrt{10}$ or $x - 1 = -\sqrt{10}$ Square root property

$x = 1 + \sqrt{10}$ or $x = 1 - \sqrt{10}$

The solution set is $\left\{1 + \sqrt{10}, 1 - \sqrt{10}\right\}$, or $\left\{1 \pm \sqrt{10}\right\}$

11.3 Solving Quadratic Equations by the Quadratic Formula

Quadratic Formula

The solutions of $ax^2 + bx + c = 0$ (with $a \neq 0$) are given by

$$x = \frac{-b \pm \sqrt{b^2 - 4ac}}{2a}.$$

The Discriminant

If a, b, and c are integers, then the discriminant, $b^2 - 4ac$, of $ax^2 + bx + c = 0$ determines the number and type of solutions as follows.

Discriminant	Number and Type of Solutions
Positive, the square of an integer	Two rational solutions
Positive, not the square of an integer	Two irrational solutions
Zero	One rational solution
Negative	Two nonreal complex solutions

Solve $3x^2 + 5x + 2 = 0$.

$$x = \frac{-5 \pm \sqrt{5^2 - 4(3)(2)}}{2(3)} = \frac{-5 \pm 1}{6}$$

$$x = \frac{-5 + 1}{6} = -\frac{2}{3} \quad \text{or} \quad x = \frac{-5 - 1}{6} = -1$$

The solution set is $\left\{-1, -\frac{2}{3}\right\}$.

For $x^2 + 3x - 10 = 0$, the discriminant is

$$3^2 - 4(1)(-10) = 49. \qquad \text{Two rational solutions}$$

For $4x^2 + x + 1 = 0$, the discriminant is

$$1^2 - 4(4)(1) = -15. \qquad \text{Two nonreal complex solutions}$$

11.4 Equations Quadratic in Form

A nonquadratic equation that can be written in the form

$$au^2 + bu + c = 0,$$

for $a \neq 0$ and an algebraic expression u, is called quadratic in form. Substitute u for the expression, solve for u, and then solve for the variable in the expression.

Solve $3(x + 5)^2 + 7(x + 5) + 2 = 0$.

$$3u^2 + 7u + 2 = 0 \qquad \text{Let } u = x + 5.$$
$$(3u + 1)(u + 2) = 0 \qquad \text{Factor.}$$

$u = -\dfrac{1}{3}$ or $u = -2$

$x + 5 = -\dfrac{1}{3}$ or $x + 5 = -2$ $x + 5 = u$

$x = -\dfrac{16}{3}$ or $x = -7$ Subtract 5.

The solution set is $\left\{-7, -\frac{16}{3}\right\}$.

(continued)

CONCEPTS	EXAMPLES

11.5 Formulas and Further Applications

To solve a formula for a squared variable, proceed as follows.

(a) If the variable appears only to the second power: Isolate the squared variable on one side of the equation, and then use the square root property.

(b) If the variable appears to the first and second powers: Write the equation in standard form, and then use the quadratic formula.

Solve $A = \dfrac{2mp}{r^2}$ for r.

$r^2 A = 2mp$ Multiply by r^2.

$r^2 = \dfrac{2mp}{A}$ Divide by A.

$r = \pm\sqrt{\dfrac{2mp}{A}}$ Square root property

$r = \dfrac{\pm\sqrt{2mpA}}{A}$ Rationalize denominator.

Solve $x^2 + rx = t$ for x.

$x^2 + rx - t = 0$ Standard form

$x = \dfrac{-r \pm \sqrt{r^2 - 4(1)(-t)}}{2(1)}$

$a = 1, b = r, c = -t$

$x = \dfrac{-r \pm \sqrt{r^2 + 4t}}{2}$

11.6 Graphs of Quadratic Functions

1. The graph of the quadratic function defined by $F(x) = a(x - h)^2 + k$, $a \neq 0$, is a parabola with vertex at (h, k) and the vertical line $x = h$ as axis.

2. The graph opens up if a is positive and down if a is negative.

3. The graph is wider than the graph of $f(x) = x^2$ if $0 < |a| < 1$ and narrower if $|a| > 1$.

Graph $f(x) = -(x + 3)^2 + 1$.

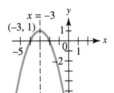

The graph opens down since $a < 0$.

Vertex: $(-3, 1)$

Axis: $x = -3$

Domain: $(-\infty, \infty)$

Range: $(-\infty, 1]$

11.7 More about Parabolas and Their Applications

The vertex of the graph of $f(x) = ax^2 + bx + c$, $a \neq 0$, may be found by completing the square.

The vertex has coordinates $\left(\dfrac{-b}{2a}, f\left(\dfrac{-b}{2a}\right)\right)$.

Graphing a Quadratic Function

Step 1   Determine whether the graph opens up or down.

Step 2   Find the vertex.

Step 3   Find the x-intercepts (if any). Find the y-intercept.

Step 4   Find and plot additional points as needed.

Graph $f(x) = x^2 + 4x + 3$.

The graph opens up since $a > 0$.

Vertex: $(-2, -1)$

The solutions of $x^2 + 4x + 3 = 0$ are -1 and -3, so the x-intercepts are $(-1, 0)$ and $(-3, 0)$.

$f(0) = 3$, so the y-intercept is $(0, 3)$.

Domain: $(-\infty, \infty)$

Range: $[-1, \infty)$

Horizontal Parabolas

The graph of

$$x = ay^2 + by + c \quad \text{or} \quad x = a(y - k)^2 + h$$

is a horizontal parabola with vertex (h, k) and the horizontal line $y = k$ as axis. The graph opens to the right if $a > 0$ and to the left if $a < 0$.

Horizontal parabolas do not represent functions.

Graph $x = 2y^2 + 6y + 5$.

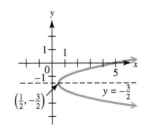

The graph opens to the right since $a > 0$.

Vertex: $\left(\dfrac{1}{2}, -\dfrac{3}{2}\right)$

Axis: $y = -\dfrac{3}{2}$

Domain: $\left[\dfrac{1}{2}, \infty\right)$

Range: $(-\infty, \infty)$

(continued)

CONCEPTS	EXAMPLES

11.8 Polynomial and Rational Inequalities

Solving a Quadratic (or Higher-Degree Polynomial) Inequality

Step 1 Write the inequality as an equation and solve.

Solve $2x^2 + 5x + 2 < 0$.

$$2x^2 + 5x + 2 = 0$$
$$(2x + 1)(x + 2) = 0$$
$$x = -\frac{1}{2} \quad \text{or} \quad x = -2$$

Step 2 Use the numbers found in Step 1 to divide a number line into intervals.

Intervals: $(-\infty, -2)$, $\left(-2, -\frac{1}{2}\right)$, $\left(-\frac{1}{2}, \infty\right)$

Step 3 Substitute a test number from each interval into the original inequality to determine the intervals that belong to the solution set.

Step 4 Consider the endpoints separately.

Test values: $-3, -1, 0$
$x = -3$ makes the original inequality false, $x = -1$ makes it true, and $x = 0$ makes it false. Choose the interval(s) which yield(s) a true statement. The solution set is the interval $\left(-2, -\frac{1}{2}\right)$.

Solving a Rational Inequality

Step 1 Write the inequality so that 0 is on one side and there is a single fraction on the other side.

Solve $\dfrac{x}{x + 2} \geq 4$.

$$\frac{x}{x + 2} - 4 \geq 0 \qquad \text{Subtract 4.}$$

$$\frac{x}{x + 2} - \frac{4(x + 2)}{x + 2} \geq 0 \qquad \text{Write with a common denominator.}$$

$$\frac{-3x - 8}{x + 2} \geq 0 \qquad \text{Subtract fractions.}$$

Step 2 Determine the numbers that make the numerator or denominator 0.

$-\frac{8}{3}$ makes the numerator 0, and -2 makes the denominator 0.

Step 3 Use the numbers from Step 2 to divide a number line into intervals.

Step 4 Substitute a test number from each interval into the original inequality to determine the intervals that belong to the solution set.

-4 from A makes the original inequality false, $-\frac{7}{3}$ from B makes it true, and 0 from C makes it false.

Step 5 Consider the endpoints separately.

The solution set is the interval $\left[-\frac{8}{3}, -2\right)$. The endpoint -2 is not included since it makes the denominator 0.

CHAPTER 11

REVIEW EXERCISES

11.1 *Solve each equation by using the square root property.*

1. $t^2 = 121$

2. $p^2 = 3$

3. $(2x + 5)^2 = 100$

*4. $(3x - 2)^2 = -25$

---

*This exercise requires knowledge of complex numbers.

5. *Concept Check* A student gave the following "solution." *WHAT WENT WRONG?*

$$x^2 = 12$$

$$x = \sqrt{12} \qquad \text{Square root property}$$

$$x = 2\sqrt{3} \qquad \text{Simplify.}$$

Solution set: $\{2\sqrt{3}\}$

6. The Singapore Flyer, the world's largest Ferris wheel as of 2008, has a height of 165 m. To find how long it would take a wallet dropped from the top of the Singapore Flyer to reach the ground, use the metric version of Galileo's formula,

$$d = 4.9t^2 \quad \text{(where } d \text{ is in meters).}$$

Round your answer to the nearest tenth of a second. (*Source:* www.singaporeflyer.com)

11.2 *Solve each equation by completing the square.*

7. $x^2 + 4x = 15$ **8.** $2x^2 - 3x = -1$

9. $2z^2 + 8z - 3 = 0$ ***10.** $4x^2 - 3x + 6 = 0$

11.3 *Solve each equation by using the quadratic formula.*

11. $2x^2 + x - 21 = 0$ **12.** $x^2 + 5x = 7$ **13.** $(t + 3)(t - 4) = -2$

*14. $2x^2 + 3x + 4 = 0$ ***15.** $3p^2 = 2(2p - 1)$ **16.** $x(2x - 7) = 3x^2 + 3$

Use the discriminant to predict whether the solutions to each equation are

A. *two rational numbers*   **B.** *one rational number*

C. *two irrational numbers*   **D.** *two nonreal complex numbers.*

17. (a) $x^2 + 5x + 2 = 0$ **(b)** $4t^2 = 3 - 4t$

18. (a) $4x^2 = 6x - 8$ **(b)** $9z^2 + 30z + 25 = 0$

11.4 *Solve each equation. Check your solutions.*

19. $\dfrac{15}{x} = 2x - 1$ **20.** $\dfrac{1}{n} + \dfrac{2}{n + 1} = 2$

21. $-2r = \sqrt{\dfrac{48 - 20r}{2}}$ **22.** $8(3x + 5)^2 + 2(3x + 5) - 1 = 0$

23. $2x^{2/3} - x^{1/3} - 28 = 0$ **24.** $p^4 - 10p^2 + 9 = 0$

Solve each problem. Round answers to the nearest tenth, as necessary.

25. Bahaa Mourad paddled a canoe 20 mi upstream, then paddled back. If the rate of the current was 3 mph and the total trip took 7 hr, what was Bahaa's rate?

26. Carol-Ann Vassell drove 8 mi to pick up a friend, and then drove 11 mi to a mall at a rate 15 mph faster. If Carol-Ann's total travel time was 24 min, what was her rate on the trip to pick up her friend?

27. An old machine processes a batch of checks in 1 hr more time than a new one. How long would it take the old machine to process a batch of checks that the two machines together process in 2 hr?

28. Zoran Pantic can process a stack of invoices 1 hr faster than Claude Sassine can. Working together, they take 1.5 hr. How long would it take each person working alone?

11.5 *Solve each formula for the indicated variable. (Give answers with $\pm$.)*

29. $k = \dfrac{rF}{wv^2}$ for v **30.** $p = \sqrt{\dfrac{yz}{6}}$ for y **31.** $mt^2 = 3mt + 6$ for t

---

*This exercise requires knowledge of complex numbers.

Solve each problem. Round answers to the nearest tenth, as necessary.

32. A large machine requires a part in the shape of a right triangle with a hypotenuse 9 ft less than twice the length of the longer leg. The shorter leg must be $\frac{3}{4}$ the length of the longer leg. Find the lengths of the three sides of the part.

33. A square has an area of 256 cm². If the same amount is removed from one dimension and added to the other, the resulting rectangle has an area 16 cm² less. Find the dimensions of the rectangle.

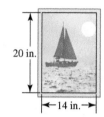

34. Allen Moser wants to buy a mat for a photograph that measures 14 in. by 20 in. He wants to have an even border around the picture when it is mounted on the mat. If the area of the mat he chooses is 352 in.², how wide will the border be?

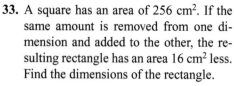

35. If a square piece of cardboard has 3-in. squares cut from its corners and then has the flaps folded up to form an open-top box, the volume of the box is given by the formula $V = 3(x - 6)^2$, where x is the length of each side of the original piece of cardboard in inches. What original length would yield a box with volume 432 in.³?

36. Wachovia Center Tower in Raleigh, North Carolina, is 400 ft high. Suppose that a ball is projected upward from the top of the tower, and its position in feet above the ground is given by the quadratic function defined by

$$f(t) = -16t^2 + 45t + 400,$$

where t is the number of seconds elapsed. How long will it take for the ball to reach a height of 200 ft above the ground? (*Source: World Almanac and Book of Facts.*)

37. A searchlight moves horizontally back and forth along a wall with the distance of the light from a starting point at t minutes given by the quadratic function defined by

$$f(t) = 100t^2 - 300t.$$

How long will it take before the light returns to the starting point?

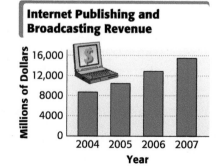

38. Internet publishing and broadcasting revenue in the United States (in millions of dollars) for the years 2004–2007 is shown in the graph and can be modeled by the quadratic function defined by

$$f(x) = 230.5x^2 - 252.9x + 5987.$$

In the model, $x = 4$ represents 2004, $x = 5$ represents 2005, and so on.

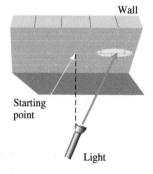

Internet Publishing and Broadcasting Revenue

Source: U.S. Census Bureau.

(a) Use the model to approximate revenue from Internet publishing and broadcasting in 2007 to the nearest million dollars. How does this result compare to the number suggested by the graph?

(b) Based on the model, in what year did the revenue from Internet publishing and broadcasting reach $14,000 million ($14 billion)? (Round down for the year.) How does this result compare to the number shown in the graph?

11.6 – 11.7   *Identify the vertex of each parabola.*

39. $f(x) = -(x - 1)^2$

40. $f(x) = (x - 3)^2 + 7$

41. $x = (y - 3)^2 - 4$

42. $y = -3x^2 + 4x - 2$

Graph each parabola. Give the vertex, axis, domain, and range.

43. $y = 2(x - 2)^2 - 3$

44. $f(x) = -2x^2 + 8x - 5$

45. $x = 2(y + 3)^2 - 4$

46. $x = -\dfrac{1}{2}y^2 + 6y - 14$

Solve each problem.

47. Total consumer spending on computers, peripherals, and software in the United States for selected years is given in the table. Let $x = 0$ represent 1985, $x = 5$ represent 1990, and so on.

(a) Use the data for 1985, 1995, and 2005 in the quadratic form $ax^2 + bx + c = y$ to write a system of three equations.

(b) Solve the system from part (a) to get a quadratic function f that models the data.

(c) Use the model found in part (b) to approximate consumer spending for computers, peripherals, and software games in 2006 to the nearest tenth. How does your answer compare to the actual data from the table?

CONSUMER SPENDING ON COMPUTERS, PERIPHERALS, AND SOFTWARE

Year	Spending (billions of dollars)
1985	2.9
1990	8.9
1995	24.3
2000	43.8
2004	51.6
2005	56.5
2006	61.4

Source: Bureau of Economic Analysis.

48. The height (in feet) of a projectile t seconds after being fired from Earth into the air is given by

$$f(t) = -16t^2 + 160t.$$

Find the number of seconds required for the projectile to reach maximum height. What is the maximum height?

49. Find the length and width of a rectangle having a perimeter of 200 m if the area is to be a maximum. What is the maximum area?

11.8   *Solve each inequality, and graph the solution set.*

50. $(x - 4)(2x + 3) > 0$

51. $x^2 + x \leq 12$

52. $(x + 2)(x - 3)(x + 5) \leq 0$

53. $(4x + 3)^2 \leq -4$

54. $\dfrac{6}{2z - 1} < 2$

55. $\dfrac{3t + 4}{t - 2} \leq 1$

MIXED REVIEW EXERCISES

Solve.

56. $V = r^2 + R^2 h$ for R

*57. $3t^2 - 6t = -4$

58. $(3x + 11)^2 = 7$

59. $S = \dfrac{Id^2}{k}$ for d

60. $(8x - 7)^2 \geq -1$

61. $2x - \sqrt{x} = 6$

*This exercise requires knowledge of complex numbers.

(continued)

62. $x^4 - 8x^2 = -1$ **63.** $\dfrac{-2}{x + 5} \le -5$ **64.** $6 + \dfrac{15}{s^2} = -\dfrac{19}{s}$

65. $(x^2 - 2x)^2 = 11(x^2 - 2x) - 24$ **66.** $(r - 1)(2r + 3)(r + 6) < 0$

67. *Concept Check* Match each equation in parts (a)–(f) with the figure that most closely resembles its graph in choices A–F.

(a) $g(x) = x^2 - 5$ **(b)** $h(x) = -x^2 + 4$ **(c)** $F(x) = (x - 1)^2$

(d) $G(x) = (x + 1)^2$ **(e)** $H(x) = (x - 1)^2 + 1$ **(f)** $K(x) = (x + 1)^2 + 1$

A.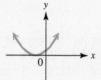

B.

C.

D.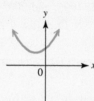

E.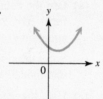

F.

68. Graph $f(x) = 4x^2 + 4x - 2$. Give the vertex, axis, domain, and range.

69. In 4 hr, Rajeed Carriman can go 15 mi upriver and come back. The rate of the current is 5 mph. Find the rate of the boat in still water.

70. Two pieces of a large wooden puzzle fit together to form a rectangle with length 1 cm less than twice the width. The diagonal, where the two pieces meet, is 2.5 cm in length. Find the length and width of the rectangle.

CHAPTER 11

TEST  **CHAPTER Test Prep VIDEOS**

Step-by-step test solutions are found on the Chapter Test Prep Videos available via the Video Resources on DVD, in *MyMathLab*, or on *YouTube* (search "LialCombinedAlgebra").

View the complete solutions to all Chapter Test exercises on the Video Resources on DVD.

Solve each equation by using the square root property.

1. $t^2 = 54$ **2.** $(7x + 3)^2 = 25$

3. Solve $x^2 + 2x = 4$ by completing the square.

Solve each equation by using the quadratic formula.

4. $2x^2 - 3x - 1 = 0$ ***5.** $3t^2 - 4t = -5$

***6.** *Concept Check* If k is a negative number, then which one of the following equations will have two nonreal complex solutions?

   A. $x^2 = 4k$ **B.** $x^2 = -4k$ **C.** $(x + 2)^2 = -k$ **D.** $x^2 + k = 0$

7. What is the discriminant for $2x^2 - 8x - 3 = 0$? How many and what type of solutions does this equation have? (Do not actually solve.)

---

*This exercise requires knowledge of complex numbers.

Solve by any method.

8. $3x = \sqrt{\dfrac{9x + 2}{2}}$

9. $3 - \dfrac{16}{x} - \dfrac{12}{x^2} = 0$

10. $4x^2 + 7x - 3 = 0$

11. $9x^4 + 4 = 37x^2$

12. $12 = (2n + 1)^2 + (2n + 1)$

13. Solve $S = 4\pi r^2$ for r. (Leave $\pm$ in your answer.)

Solve each problem.

14. Terry and Callie do word processing. For a certain prospectus, Callie can prepare it 2 hr faster than Terry can. If they work together, they can do the entire prospectus in 5 hr. How long will it take each of them working alone to prepare the prospectus? Round your answers to the nearest tenth of an hour.

15. Qihong Shen paddled a canoe 10 mi upstream and then paddled back to the starting point. If the rate of the current was 3 mph and the entire trip took $3\frac{1}{2}$ hr, what was Qihong's rate?

16. Endre Borsos has a pool 24 ft long and 10 ft wide. He wants to construct a concrete walk around the pool. If he plans for the walk to be of uniform width and cover 152 ft², what will the width of the walk be?

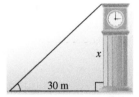

17. At a point 30 m from the base of a tower, the distance to the top of the tower is 2 m more than twice the height of the tower. Find the height of the tower.

18. *Concept Check*   Which one of the following figures most closely resembles the graph of $f(x) = a(x - h)^2 + k$ if $a < 0, h > 0$, and $k < 0$?

A. 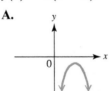 **B.** 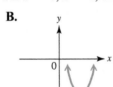 **C.** 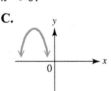 **D.**

Graph each parabola. Identify the vertex, axis, domain, and range.

19. $f(x) = \dfrac{1}{2}x^2 - 2$

20. $f(x) = -x^2 + 4x - 1$

21. $x = -(y - 2)^2 + 2$

Solve each problem.

22. The total number (in millions) of civilians employed in the United States during the years 2004–2008 can be modeled by the quadratic function defined by

$$f(x) = -0.529x^2 + 8.00x + 115$$

where $x = 4$ represents 2004, $x = 5$ represents 2005, and so on. (*Source:* U.S. Bureau of Labor Statistics.)

(a) Based on this model, how many civilians, to the nearest million, were employed in the United States in 2004?

(b) In what year during this period was the maximum civilian employment? (Round down for the year.) To the nearest million, what was the total civilian employment in that year? Use the actual x-value, to the nearest tenth, to find this number.

23. Houston Community College is planning to construct a rectangular parking lot on land bordered on one side by a highway. The plan is to use 640 ft of fencing to fence off the other three sides. What should the dimensions of the lot be if the enclosed area is to be a maximum?

Solve each inequality, and graph the solution set.

24. $2x^2 + 7x > 15$

25. $\dfrac{5}{t - 4} \leq 1$

CHAPTERS $\left(1\text{–}11\right)$ CUMULATIVE REVIEW EXERCISES

1. Let $S = \left\{-\frac{7}{3}, -2, -\sqrt{3}, 0, 0.7, \sqrt{12}, \sqrt{-8}, 7, \frac{32}{3}\right\}$. List the elements of S that are elements of each set.

   (a) Integers   (b) Rational numbers   (c) Real numbers   (d) Complex numbers

Solve each equation or inequality.

2. $7 - (4 + 3t) + 2t = -6(t - 2) - 5$

3. $|6x - 9| = |-4x + 2|$

4. $2x = \sqrt{\dfrac{5x + 2}{3}}$

5. $\dfrac{3}{x - 3} - \dfrac{2}{x - 2} = \dfrac{3}{x^2 - 5x + 6}$

6. $(r - 5)(2r + 3) = 1$

7. $x^4 - 5x^2 + 4 = 0$

8. $-2x + 4 \leq -x + 3$

9. $|3x - 7| \leq 1$

10. $x^2 - 4x + 3 < 0$

11. $\dfrac{3}{p + 2} > 1$

Graph each relation. Tell whether or not y can be expressed as a function f of x, and if so, give its domain and range, and write using function notation.

12. $4x - 5y = 15$

13. $4x - 5y < 15$

14. $y = -2(x - 1)^2 + 3$

15. Find the slope and intercepts of the line with equation
$$-2x + 7y = 16.$$

16. Write an equation for the specified line. Express each equation in slope-intercept form.

   (a) Through $(2, -3)$ and parallel to the line with equation $5x + 2y = 6$

   (b) Through $(-4, 1)$ and perpendicular to the line with equation $5x + 2y = 6$

Write with positive exponents only. Assume that variables represent positive real numbers.

17. $\left(\dfrac{x^{-3}y^2}{x^5y^{-2}}\right)^{-1}$

18. $\dfrac{(4x^{-2})^2(2y^3)}{8x^{-3}y^5}$

Perform the indicated operations.

19. $\left(\dfrac{2}{3}t + 9\right)^2$

20. Divide $4x^3 + 2x^2 - x + 26$ by $x + 2$.

Factor completely.

21. $24m^2 + 2m - 15$

22. $8x^3 + 27y^3$

23. $9x^2 - 30xy + 25y^2$

Perform the indicated operations or simplify the complex fraction, and express each answer in lowest terms. Assume denominators are nonzero.

24. $\dfrac{5x + 2}{-6} \div \dfrac{15x + 6}{5}$

25. $\dfrac{3}{2 - x} - \dfrac{5}{x} + \dfrac{6}{x^2 - 2x}$

26. $\dfrac{\dfrac{r}{s} - \dfrac{s}{r}}{\dfrac{r}{s} + 1}$

Solve each system of equations.

27. $2x - 4y = 10$
$9x + 3y = 3$

28. $x + y + 2z = 3$
$-x + y + z = -5$
$2x + 3y - z = -8$

29. In 2009, the two American computer software companies with the greatest revenues were Microsoft and Oracle. The two companies had combined revenues of $82.8 billion. Revenues for Microsoft were $6.8 billion less than three times those of Oracle. What were the 2009 revenues for each company? (*Source: Fortune.*)

Simplify each radical expression.

30. $\sqrt[3]{\dfrac{27}{16}}$

31. $\dfrac{2}{\sqrt{7} - \sqrt{5}}$

32. Two cars left an intersection at the same time, one heading due south and the other due east. Later they were exactly 95 mi apart. The car heading east had gone 38 mi less than twice as far as the car heading south. How far had each car traveled?

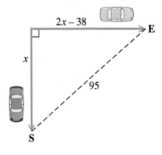

Sets

OBJECTIVES

1. Learn the vocabulary and symbols used to discuss sets.
2. Decide whether a set is finite or infinite.
3. Decide whether a given set is a subset of another set.
4. Find the complement of a set.
5. Find the union and the intersection of two sets.

NOW TRY
EXERCISE 1

List the elements of the set of odd natural numbers less than 13.

OBJECTIVE 1 **Learn the vocabulary and symbols used to discuss sets.** A **set** is a collection of objects. These objects are called the **elements** of the set. A set is represented by listing its elements between **braces,** { }.* The order in which the elements of a set are listed is unimportant.

Capital letters are used to name sets. To state that 5 is an element of

$$S = \{1, 2, 3, 4, 5\},$$

write $5 \in S$. The statement $6 \notin S$ means that 6 is not an element of S.

The set with no elements is called the **empty set,** or the **null set.** The symbol $\emptyset$ or { } is used for the empty set. If we let A be the set of all negative natural numbers, then A is the empty set.

$$A = \emptyset \quad \text{or} \quad A = \{ \ \}$$

⚠ **CAUTION** Do not make the common error of writing the empty set as $\{\emptyset\}$.

EXAMPLE 1 **Listing the Elements of Sets**

Represent each set by listing its elements.

(a) The set of states in the United States that border the Pacific Ocean is

{California, Oregon, Washington, Hawaii, Alaska}.

(b) The set of all counting numbers less than $6 = \{1, 2, 3, 4, 5\}$.

(c) The set of all counting numbers less than $0 = \emptyset$ NOW TRY

In any discussion of sets, there is some set that includes all the elements under consideration. This set is called the **universal set** for that situation. For example, if the discussion is about presidents of the United States, then the set of all presidents of the United States is the universal set. The universal set is denoted U.

OBJECTIVE 2 **Decide whether a set is finite or infinite.** In **Example 1,** there are five elements in the set in part (a) and five in part (b). If the number of elements in a set is either 0 or a counting number, then the set is **finite.** By contrast, the set of natural numbers is an **infinite** set, because there is no final natural number. We can list the elements of the set of natural numbers as

$$N = \{1, 2, 3, 4, \ldots\},$$

where the three dots indicate that the set continues indefinitely. Not all infinite sets can be listed in this way. For example, there is no way to list the elements in the set of all real numbers between 1 and 2.

NOW TRY ANSWER
1. $\{1, 3, 5, 7, 9, 11\}$

---

*Some people refer to this convention as *roster notation.*

NOW TRY
EXERCISE 2

List the elements of each set if possible. Decide whether each set is finite or infinite.

(a) The set of negative integers

(b) The set of even natural numbers between 11 and 19

EXAMPLE 2   **Distinguishing between Finite and Infinite Sets**

List the elements of each set if possible. Decide whether each set is finite or infinite.

(a) The set of all integers
One way to list the elements is $\{\ldots, -2, -1, 0, 1, 2, \ldots\}$. The set is infinite.

(b) The set of all natural numbers between 0 and 5
$\{1, 2, 3, 4\}$ The set is finite.

(c) The set of all irrational numbers
This is an infinite set whose elements cannot be listed.   **NOW TRY**

Two sets are equal if they have exactly the same elements. Thus, the set of natural numbers and the set of positive integers are equal sets. Also, the sets

$$\{1, 2, 4, 7\} \quad \text{and} \quad \{4, 2, 7, 1\} \quad \text{are equal.}$$

The order of the elements does not make a difference.

OBJECTIVE 3   **Decide whether a given set is a subset of another set.** If all elements of a set A are also elements of another set B, then we say that A is a **subset** of B, written $A \subseteq B$. We use the symbol $A \nsubseteq B$ to mean that A is not a subset of B.

NOW TRY
EXERCISE 3

Let
$$A = \{1, 3, 5, 7, 9, 11\},$$
$$B = \{1, 5, 7, 9\}, \text{ and}$$
$$C = \{1, 9, 11\}.$$

Tell whether each statement is *true* or *false*.

(a) $B \subseteq A$ **(b)** $C \subseteq B$

(c) $C \nsubseteq A$

EXAMPLE 3   **Using Subset Notation**

Let $A = \{1, 2, 3, 4\}$, $B = \{1, 4\}$, and $C = \{1\}$. Then

$$B \subseteq A, \qquad C \subseteq A, \qquad \text{and} \qquad C \subseteq B,$$

but
$$A \nsubseteq B, \qquad A \nsubseteq C, \qquad \text{and} \qquad B \nsubseteq C. \qquad \text{ \textbf{NOW TRY}}$$

The empty set is defined to be a subset of any set. Thus, the set $M = \{a, b\}$ has four subsets:

$$\{a, b\}, \quad \{a\}, \quad \{b\}, \quad \text{and} \quad \emptyset.$$

How many subsets does $N = \{a, b, c\}$ have? There is one subset with three elements: $\{a, b, c\}$. There are three subsets with two elements:

$$\{a, b\}, \quad \{a, c\}, \quad \text{and} \quad \{b, c\}.$$

There are three subsets with one element:

$$\{a\}, \quad \{b\}, \quad \text{and} \quad \{c\}.$$

There is one subset with no elements: $\emptyset$. Thus, set N has eight subsets.
The following generalization can be made and proved in more advanced courses.

Number of Subsets of a Set

A set with n elements has 2^n subsets.

NOW TRY ANSWERS
2. (a) $\{-1, -2, -3, -4, \ldots\}$;
   infinite
   (b) $\{12, 14, 16, 18\}$; finite
3. (a) true   **(b)** false   **(c)** false

To illustrate the relationships between sets, **Venn diagrams** are often used. A rectangle represents the universal set, U. The sets under discussion are represented by regions within the rectangle. The Venn diagram in **FIGURE 1** on the next page shows that $B \subseteq A$.

$B \subseteq A$

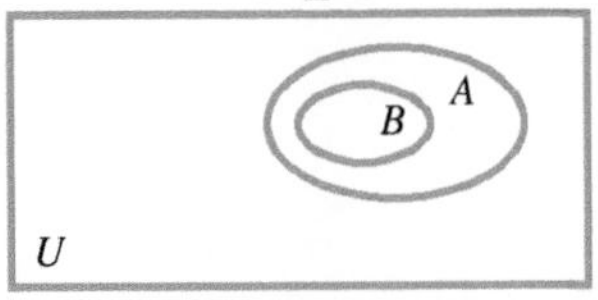

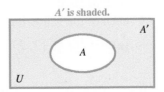

FIGURE 1

OBJECTIVE 4 **Find the complement of a set.** For every set A, there is a set A', the **complement** of A, that contains all the elements of U that are not in A. The shaded region in the Venn diagram in **FIGURE 2** represents A'.

A' is shaded.

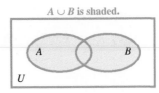

FIGURE 2

NOW TRY
EXERCISE 4

Let

$$U = \{2, 4, 6, 8, 10, 12, 14\}$$
and $M = \{2, 10, 12, 14\}$.
List the elements in M'.

EXAMPLE 4   Determining Complements of a Set

Given $U = \{a, b, c, d, e, f, g\}$, $A = \{a, b, c\}$, $B = \{a, d, f, g\}$, and $C = \{d, e\}$, list the elements of A', B', and C'.

$$A' = \{d, e, f, g\}, \quad B' = \{b, c, e\}, \quad \text{and} \quad C' = \{a, b, c, f, g\}. \qquad \text{NOW TRY}$$

OBJECTIVE 5 **Find the union and the intersection of two sets.** The **union** of two sets A and B, written $A \cup B$, is the set of all elements of A together with all elements of B. Thus, for the sets in **Example 4,**

$$A \cup B = \{a, b, c, d, f, g\} \quad \text{and} \quad A \cup C = \{a, b, c, d, e\}.$$

In **FIGURE 3**, the shaded region is the union of sets A and B.

$A \cup B$ is shaded.

FIGURE 3

NOW TRY
EXERCISE 5

If $M = \{1, 3, 5, 7, 9\}$ and $N = \{0, 3, 6, 9\}$, find $M \cup N$.

EXAMPLE 5   Finding the Union of Two Sets

If $M = \{2, 5, 7\}$ and $N = \{1, 2, 3, 4, 5\}$, find $M \cup N$.

$$M \cup N = \{1, 2, 3, 4, 5, 7\} \qquad \text{NOW TRY}$$

The **intersection** of two sets A and B, written $A \cap B$, is the set of all elements that belong to both A and B. For example, if

$$A = \{\text{José, Ellen, Marge, Kevin}\}$$

and

$$B = \{\text{José, Patrick, Ellen, Sue}\},$$

then

$$A \cap B = \{\text{José, Ellen}\}.$$

NOW TRY ANSWERS
4. $\{4, 6, 8\}$
5. $\{0, 1, 3, 5, 6, 7, 9\}$

The shaded region in **FIGURE 4** represents the intersection of the two sets A and B.

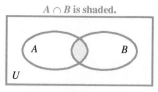

$A \cap B$ is shaded.

FIGURE 4

NOW TRY
EXERCISE 6
If $M = \{1, 3, 5, 7, 9\}$ and
$N = \{0, 3, 6, 9\}$, find $M \cap N$.

EXAMPLE 6 Finding the Intersection of Two Sets

Suppose that $P = \{3, 9, 27\}$, $Q = \{2, 3, 10, 18, 27, 28\}$, and $R = \{2, 10, 28\}$. Find each of the following.

(a) $P \cap Q = \{3, 27\}$ **(b)** $Q \cap R = \{2, 10, 28\} = R$ **(c)** $P \cap R = \emptyset$

NOW TRY

Sets like P and R in **Example 6** that have no elements in common are called **disjoint sets.** The Venn diagram in **FIGURE 5** shows a pair of disjoint sets.

NOW TRY
EXERCISE 7
Let

$U = \{1, 2, 4, 5, 7, 8, 9, 10\}$,
$A = \{1, 4, 7, 9, 10\}$,
$B = \{2, 5, 8\}$, and
$C = \{5\}$.

Find each of the following.
(a) $B \cup C$ **(b)** $A \cap B$ **(c)** C'

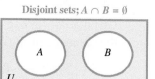

Disjoint sets; $A \cap B = \emptyset$

FIGURE 5

EXAMPLE 7 Using Set Operations

Let $U = \{2, 5, 7, 10, 14, 20\}$, $A = \{2, 10, 14, 20\}$, $B = \{5, 7\}$, and $C = \{2, 5, 7\}$. Find each of the following.

(a) $A \cup B = \{2, 5, 7, 10, 14, 20\} = U$ **(b)** $A \cap B = \emptyset$

(c) $B \cup C = \{2, 5, 7\} = C$ **(d)** $B \cap C = \{5, 7\} = B$

(e) $A' = \{5, 7\} = B$

NOW TRY

NOW TRY ANSWERS
6. $\{3, 9\}$
7. (a) $\{2, 5, 8\} = B$ **(b)** $\emptyset$
    (c) $\{1, 2, 4, 7, 8, 9, 10\}$

EXERCISES   **MyMathLab**   Math XL PRACTICE   WATCH   DOWNLOAD   READ   REVIEW

List the elements of each set. ***See Examples 1 and 2.***

1. The set of all natural numbers less than 8

2. The set of all integers between 4 and 10

3. The set of seasons

4. The set of months of the year

5. The set of women presidents of the United States before 2008

6. The set of all living humans who are more than 200 years old

7. The set of letters of the alphabet between K and M

8. The set of letters of the alphabet between D and H

9. The set of positive even integers

10. The set of all multiples of 5

11. Which of the sets described in **Exercises 1–10** are infinite sets?

12. Which of the sets described in **Exercises 1–10** are finite sets?

Concept Check   *Tell whether each statement is* true *or* false.

13. $5 \in \{1, 2, 5, 8\}$

14. $6 \in \{1, 2, 3, 4, 5\}$

15. $2 \in \{1, 3, 5, 7, 9\}$

16. $1 \in \{6, 2, 5, 1\}$

17. $7 \notin \{2, 4, 6, 8\}$

18. $7 \notin \{1, 3, 5, 7\}$

19. $\{2, 4, 9, 12, 13\} = \{13, 12, 9, 4, 2\}$

20. $\{7, 11, 4\} = \{7, 11, 4, 0\}$

Let

$$A = \{1, 3, 4, 5, 7, 8\}, \quad B = \{2, 4, 6, 8\}, \quad C = \{1, 3, 5, 7\}, \quad D = \{1, 2, 3\},$$
$$E = \{3, 7\}, \quad \text{and} \quad U = \{1, 2, 3, 4, 5, 6, 7, 8, 9, 10\}.$$

Tell whether each statement is true *or* false. ***See Examples 3, 5, 6, and 7.***

21. $A \subseteq U$

22. $D \subseteq A$

23. $\emptyset \subseteq A$

24. $\{1, 2\} \subseteq D$

25. $C \subseteq A$

26. $A \subseteq C$

27. $D \subseteq B$

28. $E \subseteq C$

29. $D \nsubseteq E$

30. $E \nsubseteq A$

31. There are exactly 4 subsets of E.

32. There are exactly 8 subsets of D.

33. There are exactly 12 subsets of C.

34. There are exactly 16 subsets of B.

35. $\{4, 6, 8, 12\} \cap \{6, 8, 14, 17\} = \{6, 8\}$

36. $\{2, 5, 9\} \cap \{1, 2, 3, 4, 5\} = \{2, 5\}$

37. $\{3, 1, 0\} \cap \{0, 2, 4\} = \{0\}$

38. $\{4, 2, 1\} \cap \{1, 2, 3, 4\} = \{1, 2, 3\}$

39. $\{3, 9, 12\} \cap \emptyset = \{3, 9, 12\}$

40. $\{3, 9, 12\} \cup \emptyset = \emptyset$

41. $\{3, 5, 7, 9\} \cup \{4, 6, 8\} = \emptyset$

42. $\{1, 2, 3\} \cup \{1, 2, 3\} = \{1, 2, 3\}$

43. $\{4, 9, 11, 7, 3\} \cup \{1, 2, 3, 4, 5\} = \{1, 2, 3, 4, 5, 7, 9, 11\}$

44. $\{5, 10, 15, 20\} \cup \{5, 15, 30\} = \{5, 15\}$

Let

$$U = \{a, b, c, d, e, f, g, h\}, \quad A = \{a, b, c, d, e, f\},$$
$$B = \{a, c, e\}, \quad C = \{a, f\}, \quad \text{and} \quad D = \{d\}.$$

List the elements in each set. ***See Examples 4–7.***

45. A'

46. B'

47. C'

48. D'

49. $A \cap B$

50. $B \cap A$

51. $A \cap D$

52. $B \cap D$

53. $B \cap C$

54. $A \cup B$

55. $B \cup D$

56. $B \cup C$

57. $C \cup B$

58. $C \cup D$

59. $A \cap \emptyset$

60. $B \cup \emptyset$

61. Name every pair of disjoint sets among sets A–D in the directions for **Exercises 45–60**.

62. Show that for sets B and D in the directions for **Exercises 45–60**,

$$(B \cup D)' = B' \cap D'.$$

Review of Exponents, Polynomials, and Factoring

(Transition from Beginning to Intermediate Algebra)

OBJECTIVE 1 Review the basic rules for exponents. In **Sections 4.1 and 4.2,** we introduced the following definitions and rules for working with exponents.

Definitions and Rules for Exponents

If no denominators are 0, the following are true for any integers m and n.

		Examples
Product rule	$a^m \cdot a^n = a^{m+n}$	$7^4 \cdot 7^5 = 7^9$
Zero exponent	$a^0 = 1$	$(-3)^0 = 1$
Negative exponent	$a^{-n} = \dfrac{1}{a^n}$	$5^{-3} = \dfrac{1}{5^3}$
Quotient rule	$\dfrac{a^m}{a^n} = a^{m-n}$	$\dfrac{2^2}{2^5} = 2^{-3} = \dfrac{1}{2^3}$
Power rules (a)	$(a^m)^n = a^{mn}$	$(4^2)^3 = 4^6$
(b)	$(ab)^m = a^m b^m$	$(3k)^4 = 3^4 k^4$
(c)	$\left(\dfrac{a}{b}\right)^m = \dfrac{a^m}{b^m}$	$\left(\dfrac{2}{3}\right)^2 = \dfrac{2^2}{3^2}$
Negative-to-positive rules	$\dfrac{a^{-m}}{b^{-n}} = \dfrac{b^n}{a^m}$	$\dfrac{2^{-4}}{5^{-3}} = \dfrac{5^3}{2^4}$
	$\left(\dfrac{a}{b}\right)^{-m} = \left(\dfrac{b}{a}\right)^m$	$\left(\dfrac{4}{7}\right)^{-2} = \left(\dfrac{7}{4}\right)^2$

EXAMPLE 1 Applying Definitions and Rules for Exponents

Simplify. Write answers using only positive exponents. Assume that all variables represent nonzero real numbers.

(a) $(x^2 y^{-3})(x^{-5} y^7)$

$= (x^{2+(-5)})(y^{-3+7})$ Product rule

$= x^{-3} y^4$ Add exponents.

$= \dfrac{1}{x^3} y^4,$ or $\dfrac{y^4}{x^3}$ Definition of negative exponent; $\frac{1}{x^3} y^4 = \frac{1}{x^3} \cdot \frac{y^4}{1} = \frac{y^4}{x^3}$

899

NOW TRY
EXERCISE 1

Simplify. Write answers using only positive exponents. Assume that all variables represent nonzero real numbers.

(a) $(m^{-8}n^4)(m^4n^{-3})$

(b) $-8^0 + 8^0$

(c) $\dfrac{(p^{-3}q)^4}{(p^2q^5)^2}$

(d) $\left(\dfrac{2x^{-2}y}{x^2y^{-4}}\right)^{-4}$

(b) $(-5)^0 + (-5^0)$

$= 1 + (-1)$ $(-5^0) = -1 \cdot 5^0 = -1 \cdot 1 = -1$

$= 0$ Add.

(c) $\dfrac{(t^5s^{-4})^2}{(t^{-3}s^5)^3}$

$= \dfrac{t^{10}s^{-8}}{t^{-9}s^{15}}$ Power rule (b)

$= \dfrac{t^{10}t^9}{s^{15}s^8}$ Negative-to-positive rule

$= \dfrac{t^{10+9}}{s^{15+8}},$ or $\dfrac{t^{19}}{s^{23}}$ Product rule

(d) $\left(\dfrac{-3x^{-4}y}{x^5y^{-4}}\right)^{-2}$

$= \left(\dfrac{x^5y^{-4}}{-3x^{-4}y}\right)^2$ Negative-to-positive rule

$= \dfrac{x^{10}y^{-8}}{9x^{-8}y^2}$ Power rules (b) and (c)

$= \dfrac{x^{18}}{9y^{10}}$ Quotient rule

(e) $(2x^2y^3z)^2(x^4y^2)^3$

$= (4x^4y^6z^2)(x^{12}y^6)$ Power rule (b)

$= 4x^{16}y^{12}z^2$ Product rule

NOW TRY

OBJECTIVE 2 Review addition, subtraction, and multiplication of polynomials. These arithmetic operations with polynomials were covered in **Sections 4.4–4.6.**

Adding and Subtracting Polynomials

To add polynomials, add like terms.

To subtract polynomials, change all signs in the second polynomial and add the result to the first polynomial.

NOW TRY
EXERCISE 2

Add or subtract as indicated.

(a) $(3x^3 + x^2 - 5x - 6) +$
$(-6x^3 + 2x^2 + 4x - 1)$

(b) Subtract.

$\quad 4x^2 + 7x - 5$
$\underline{-5x^2 - 2x + 3}$

EXAMPLE 2 Adding and Subtracting Polynomials

Add or subtract as indicated.

(a) $(-4x^3 + 3x^2 - 8x + 2) + (5x^3 - 8x^2 + 12x - 3)$

$= (-4x^3 + 5x^3) + (3x^2 - 8x^2) + (-8x + 12x) + (2 - 3)$
   Commutative and associative properties

$= (-4 + 5)x^3 + (3 - 8)x^2 + (-8 + 12)x + (2 - 3)$
   Distributive property

$= x^3 - 5x^2 + 4x - 1$ Simplify.

(b) $-4(x^2 + 3x - 6) - (2x^2 - 3x + 7)$

$= -4x^2 - 12x + 24 - 2x^2 + 3x - 7$ Distributive property; definition of subtraction

$= -6x^2 - 9x + 17$ Combine like terms.

(c) Subtract.

$\quad 2t^2 - 3t - 4$ Change the sign of each term in $-8t^2 + 4t - 1$, and add.
$\underline{-8t^2 + 4t - 1}$

$\quad 2t^2 - 3t - 4$
$\underline{\quad 8t^2 - 4t + 1}$ Change signs.
$\quad 10t^2 - 7t - 3$ Add.

NOW TRY

NOW TRY ANSWERS

1. (a) $\dfrac{n}{m^4}$ (b) 0

   (c) $\dfrac{1}{p^{16}q^6}$ (d) $\dfrac{x^{16}}{16y^{20}}$

2. (a) $-3x^3 + 3x^2 - x - 7$
   (b) $9x^2 + 9x - 8$

Multiplying Polynomials

To multiply two polynomials, multiply each term of the second polynomial by each term of the first polynomial and add the products. In particular, when multiplying two binomials, use the FOIL method. (See **Section 4.5.**)

The special product rules are useful when multiplying binomials.

Special Product Rules

For x and y, the following are true.

$$\left.\begin{array}{l} (x + y)^2 = x^2 + 2xy + y^2 \\ (x - y)^2 = x^2 - 2xy + y^2 \end{array}\right\} \quad \text{Square of a binomial}$$

$$(x + y)(x - y) = x^2 - y^2 \quad \begin{array}{l}\text{Product of the sum and} \\ \text{difference of two terms}\end{array}$$

NOW TRY
EXERCISE 3

Find each product.

(a) $(6x - 5)(2x - 3)$

(b) $(4m - 3n)(4m + 3n)$

(c) $(7z + 1)^2$

(d) $(r + 3)(r^2 - 3r + 9)$

EXAMPLE 3   Multiplying Polynomials

Find each product.

(a) $(4y - 1)(3y + 2)$

$$\underbrace{\text{First}}_{\text{terms}} \quad \underbrace{\text{Outer}}_{\text{terms}} \quad \underbrace{\text{Inner}}_{\text{terms}} \quad \underbrace{\text{Last}}_{\text{terms}}$$

$$= 4y(3y) + 4y(2) - 1(3y) - 1(2) \qquad \text{FOIL method}$$

$$= 12y^2 + 8y - 3y - 2 \qquad \text{Multiply.}$$

$$= 12y^2 + 5y - 2 \qquad \text{Combine like terms.}$$

(b) $(3x + 5y)(3x - 5y) \quad \boxed{(ab)^2 = a^2b^2, \textbf{not } ab^2.}$

$$= (3x)^2 - (5y)^2 \qquad (x + y)(x - y) = x^2 - y^2$$

$$= 9x^2 - 25y^2 \qquad \text{Power rule (b)}$$

(c) $(2t + 3)^2$

$$= (2t)^2 + 2(2t)(3) + 3^2 \qquad (x + y)^2 = x^2 + 2xy + y^2$$

$$= 4t^2 + 12t + 9 \qquad \boxed{\begin{array}{l}\text{Remember the} \\ \text{middle term.}\end{array}}$$

(d) $(5x - 1)^2$

$$= (5x)^2 - 2(5x)(1) + 1^2 \qquad (x - y)^2 = x^2 - 2xy + y^2$$

$$= 25x^2 - 10x + 1 \qquad (5x)^2 = 5^2 x^2 = 25x^2$$

(e) $(3x + 2)(9x^2 - 6x + 4)$

$$\begin{array}{r} 9x^2 - 6x + 4 \\ \underline{3x + 2} \\ 18x^2 - 12x + 8 \\ 27x^3 - 18x^2 + 12x \\ \hline 27x^3 \qquad\qquad\qquad + 8 \end{array}$$

Multiply vertically.

$\leftarrow 2(9x^2 - 6x + 4)$

$\leftarrow 3x(9x^2 - 6x + 4)$

Add.

$\boxed{\begin{array}{l}\text{Be sure to write like} \\ \text{terms in columns.}\end{array}}$

The product is the sum of cubes, $27x^3 + 8$.

NOW TRY

NOW TRY ANSWERS

3. **(a)** $12x^2 - 28x + 15$

(b) $16m^2 - 9n^2$

(c) $49z^2 + 14z + 1$

(d) $r^3 + 27$

OBJECTIVE 3 **Review factoring techniques.** Factoring, which involves writing a polynomial as a product, was covered in **Chapter 5.** Here are some general guidelines to use when factoring.

Factoring a Polynomial

1. **Is there a common factor?** If so, factor it out.

2. **How many terms are in the polynomial?**

   Two terms: Check to see whether it is a difference of squares or the sum or difference of cubes. If so, factor as in **Section 5.4.**

   $$x^2 - y^2 = (x + y)(x - y) \qquad \text{Difference of squares}$$
   $$x^3 - y^3 = (x - y)(x^2 + xy + y^2) \qquad \text{Difference of cubes}$$
   $$x^3 + y^3 = (x + y)(x^2 - xy + y^2) \qquad \text{Sum of cubes}$$

   Three terms: Is it a perfect square trinomial?

   $$x^2 + 2xy + y^2 = (x + y)^2$$
   $$x^2 - 2xy + y^2 = (x - y)^2 \qquad \text{Perfect square trinomials}$$

   If the trinomial is not a perfect square, check to see whether the coefficient of the second-degree term is 1. If so, use the method of **Section 5.2.** If the coefficient of the second-degree term of the trinomial is not 1, use the general factoring methods of **Section 5.3.**

   Four terms: Try to factor the polynomial by grouping, as in **Section 5.1.**

3. **Can any factors be factored further?** If so, factor them.

EXAMPLE 4 **Factoring Polynomials**

Factor each polynomial completely.

(a) $6x^2y^3 - 12x^3y^2$

$$= 6x^2y^2 \cdot y - 6x^2y^2 \cdot 2x \qquad 6x^2y^2 \text{ is the greatest common factor.}$$
$$= 6x^2y^2(y - 2x) \qquad \text{Distributive property}$$

(b) $3x^2 - x - 2$

To find the factors, find two terms that multiply to give $3x^2$ (here $3x$ and x) and two terms that multiply to give -2 (here $+2$ and -1). Make sure that the sum of the outer and inner products in the factored form is $-x$.

$$3x^2 - x - 2 \quad \text{factors as} \quad (3x + 2)(x - 1).$$

CHECK   To check, multiply the factors using the FOIL method.

(c) $3x^2 - 27x + 42$

$$= 3(x^2 - 9x + 14) \qquad \text{Factor out the common factor.}$$
$$= 3(x - 7)(x - 2) \qquad \text{Factor the trinomial.}$$

(d) $100t^2 - 81$

$$= (10t)^2 - 9^2 \qquad \text{Difference of squares}$$
$$= (10t + 9)(10t - 9) \qquad x^2 - y^2 = (x + y)(x - y)$$

OBJECTIVE 2 Use the remainder theorem to evaluate a polynomial. We can use synthetic division to evaluate polynomials. For example, in the synthetic division of **Example 2,** where the polynomial was divided by $x - 2$, the remainder was -6.

Replacing x in the polynomial with 2 gives

$$-4x^5 + x^4 + 6x^3 + 2x^2 + 50$$

$$= -4 \cdot 2^5 + 2^4 + 6 \cdot 2^3 + 2 \cdot 2^2 + 50 \qquad \text{Replace } x \text{ with 2.}$$

$$= -4 \cdot 32 + 16 + 6 \cdot 8 + 2 \cdot 4 + 50 \qquad \text{Evaluate the powers.}$$

$$= -128 + 16 + 48 + 8 + 50 \qquad \text{Multiply.}$$

$$= -6, \qquad \text{Add.}$$

the same number as the remainder. Dividing by $x - 2$ produced a remainder equal to the result when x is replaced with 2. This always happens, as the following **remainder theorem** states. This result is proved in more advanced courses.

Remainder Theorem

If the polynomial $P(x)$ is divided by $x - k$, then the remainder is equal to $P(k)$.

NOW TRY
EXERCISE 3
Let $P(x) = 3x^3 - 2x^2 + 5x + 30$. Use synthetic division to evaluate $P(-2)$.

EXAMPLE 3 Using the Remainder Theorem

Let $P(x) = 2x^3 - 5x^2 - 3x + 11$. Use synthetic division to evaluate $P(-2)$.

Use the remainder theorem, and divide $P(x)$ by $x - (-2)$.

$$
\text{Value of } k \rightarrow -2) \overline{\begin{array}{rrrr} 2 & -5 & -3 & 11 \\ & -4 & 18 & -30 \\ \hline 2 & -9 & 15 & -19 \end{array}} \leftarrow \text{Remainder}
$$

Thus, $P(-2) = -19$.

NOW TRY

OBJECTIVE 3 Decide whether a given number is a solution of an equation. We can also use the remainder theorem to do this.

NOW TRY
EXERCISE 4
Use synthetic division to decide whether -4 is a solution of the equation.

$$5x^3 + 19x^2 - 2x + 8 = 0$$

EXAMPLE 4 Using the Remainder Theorem

Use synthetic division to decide whether -5 is a solution of the equation.

$$2x^4 + 12x^3 + 6x^2 - 5x + 75 = 0$$

If synthetic division gives a remainder of 0, then -5 is a solution. Otherwise, it is not.

$$
\text{Proposed solution} \rightarrow -5) \overline{\begin{array}{rrrrr} 2 & 12 & 6 & -5 & 75 \\ & -10 & -10 & 20 & -75 \\ \hline 2 & 2 & -4 & 15 & 0 \end{array}} \leftarrow \text{Remainder}
$$

Since the remainder is 0, the polynomial has value 0 when $k = -5$. So -5 is a solution of the given equation.

NOW TRY

The synthetic division in **Example 4** shows that $x - (-5)$ divides the polynomial with 0 remainder. Thus $x - (-5) = x + 5$ is a *factor* of the polynomial and

$$2x^4 + 12x^3 + 6x^2 - 5x + 75 \quad \text{factors as} \quad (x + 5)(2x^3 + 2x^2 - 4x + 15).$$

NOW TRY ANSWERS
3. -12 **4.** yes

The second factor is the quotient polynomial found in the last row of the synthetic division.

EXERCISES

MyMathLab PRACTICE WATCH DOWNLOAD READ REVIEW

Use synthetic division to find each quotient. See Examples 1 and 2.

1. $\dfrac{x^2 - 6x + 5}{x - 1}$

2. $\dfrac{x^2 - 4x - 21}{x + 3}$

3. $\dfrac{4m^2 + 19m - 5}{m + 5}$

4. $\dfrac{3x^2 - 5x - 12}{x - 3}$

5. $\dfrac{2a^2 + 8a + 13}{a + 2}$

6. $\dfrac{4y^2 - 5y - 20}{y - 4}$

7. $(p^2 - 3p + 5) \div (p + 1)$

8. $(z^2 + 4z - 6) \div (z - 5)$

9. $\dfrac{4a^3 - 3a^2 + 2a - 3}{a - 1}$

10. $\dfrac{5p^3 - 6p^2 + 3p + 14}{p + 1}$

11. $(x^5 - 2x^3 + 3x^2 - 4x - 2) \div (x - 2)$

12. $(2y^5 - 5y^4 - 3y^2 - 6y - 23) \div (y - 3)$

13. $(-4r^6 - 3r^5 - 3r^4 + 5r^3 - 6r^2 + 3r + 3) \div (r - 1)$

14. $(2t^6 - 3t^5 + 2t^4 - 5t^3 + 6t^2 - 3t - 2) \div (t - 2)$

15. $(-3y^5 + 2y^4 - 5y^3 - 6y^2 - 1) \div (y + 2)$

16. $(m^6 + 2m^4 - 5m + 11) \div (m - 2)$

Use the remainder theorem to find $P(k)$. See Example 3.

17. $P(x) = 2x^3 - 4x^2 + 5x - 3; k = 2$

18. $P(x) = x^3 + 3x^2 - x + 5; k = -1$

19. $P(x) = -x^3 - 5x^2 - 4x - 2; k = -4$

20. $P(x) = -x^3 + 5x^2 - 3x + 4; k = 3$

21. $P(x) = 2x^3 - 4x^2 + 5x - 33; k = 3$

22. $P(x) = x^3 - 3x^2 + 4x - 4; k = 2$

23. Explain why a 0 remainder in synthetic division of $P(x)$ by $x - k$ indicates that k is a solution of the equation $P(x) = 0$.

24. Explain why it is important to insert 0s as placeholders for missing terms before performing synthetic division.

Use synthetic division to decide whether the given number is a solution of the equation. See Example 4.

25. $x^3 - 2x^2 - 3x + 10 = 0; x = -2$

26. $x^3 - 3x^2 - x + 10 = 0; x = -2$

27. $3x^3 + 2x^2 - 2x + 11 = 0; x = -2$

28. $3x^3 + 10x^2 + 3x - 9 = 0; x = -2$

29. $2x^3 - x^2 - 13x + 24 = 0; x = -3$

30. $5x^3 + 22x^2 + x - 28 = 0; x = -4$

31. $x^4 + 2x^3 - 3x^2 + 8x - 8 = 0; x = -2$

32. $x^4 - x^3 - 6x^2 + 5x + 10 = 0; x = -2$

RELATING CONCEPTS EXERCISES 33–38

FOR INDIVIDUAL OR GROUP WORK

We can show a connection between dividing one polynomial by another and factoring the first polynomial. Let $P(x) = 2x^2 + 5x - 12$. **Work Exercises 33–38 in order.**

33. Factor $P(x)$.

34. Solve $P(x) = 0$.

35. Evaluate $P(-4)$.

36. Evaluate $P\left(\frac{3}{2}\right)$.

37. Complete the following sentence: If $P(a) = 0$, then $x -$ _____ is a factor of $P(x)$.

38. Use the conclusion reached in **Exercise 37** to decide whether $x - 3$ is a factor of $Q(x) = 3x^3 - 4x^2 - 17x + 6$. Factor $Q(x)$ completely.

An Introduction to Calculators

There is little doubt that the appearance of handheld calculators more than three decades ago and the later development of scientific and graphing calculators have changed the methods of learning and studying mathematics forever. For example, computations with tables of logarithms and slide rules made up an important part of mathematics courses prior to 1970. Today, with the widespread availability of calculators, these topics are studied only for their historical significance.

Calculators come in a large array of different types, sizes, and prices. ***For the course for which this textbook is intended, the most appropriate type is the scientific calculator,*** which costs $10–$20.

In this introduction, we explain some of the features of scientific and graphing calculators. However, remember that calculators vary among manufacturers and models and that, while the methods explained here apply to many of them, they may not apply to your specific calculator. ***This introduction is only a guide and is not intended to take the place of your owner's manual.*** Always refer to the manual whenever you need an explanation of how to perform a particular operation.

Scientific Calculators

Scientific calculators are capable of much more than the typical four-function calculator that you might use for balancing your checkbook. Most scientific calculators use *algebraic logic.* (Models sold by Texas Instruments, Sharp, Casio, and Radio Shack, for example, use algebraic logic.) A notable exception is Hewlett-Packard, a company whose calculators use *Reverse Polish Notation* (RPN). In this introduction, we explain the use of calculators with algebraic logic.

Arithmetic Operations   To perform an operation of arithmetic, simply enter the first number, press the operation key $(+)$, $(-)$, $(\times)$, or $(\div)$, enter the second number, and then press the $(=)$ key. For example, to add 4 and 3, use the following keystrokes.

(4) $(+)$ (3) $(=)$ $\boxed{7}$

Change Sign Key   The key marked $(+/-)$ allows you to change the sign of a display. This is particularly useful when you wish to enter a negative number. For example, to enter -3, use the following keystrokes.

(3) $(+/-)$ $\boxed{-3}$

Memory Key   Scientific calculators can hold a number in memory for later use. The label of the memory key varies among models; two of these are Ⓜ and (STO). The (M+) and (M−) keys allow you to add to or subtract from the value currently in memory. The memory recall key, labeled (MR), (RM), or (RCL), allows you to retrieve the value stored in memory.

Suppose that you wish to store the number 5 in memory. Enter 5, and then press the key for memory. You can then perform other calculations. When you need to retrieve the 5, press the key for memory recall.

If a calculator has a constant memory feature, the value in memory will be retained even after the power is turned off. Some advanced calculators have more than one memory. Read the owner's manual for your model to see exactly how memory is activated.

Clearing/Clear Entry Keys   The key Ⓒ or (CE) allows you to clear the display or clear the last entry entered into the display. In some models, pressing the Ⓒ key once will clear the last entry, while pressing it twice will clear the entire operation in progress.

Second Function Key   This key, usually marked (2nd), is used in conjunction with another key to activate a function that is printed *above* an operation key (and not on the key itself). For example, suppose you wish to find the square of a number, and the squaring function (explained in more detail later) is printed above another key. You would need to press (2nd) before the desired squaring function can be activated.

Square Root Key   Pressing (√) or (√x) will give the square root (or an approximation of the square root) of the number in the display. On some scientific calculators, the square root key is pressed *before* entering the number, while other calculators use the opposite order. Experiment with your calculator to see which method it uses. For example, to find the square root of 36, use the following keystrokes.

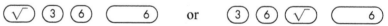

The square root of 2 is an example of an irrational number (**Chapter 10**). The calculator will give an approximation of its value, since the decimal for $\sqrt{2}$ never terminates and never repeats. The number of digits shown will vary among models. To find an approximation for $\sqrt{2}$, use the following keystrokes.

An approximation for $\sqrt{2}$

Squaring Key   The (x^2) key allows you to square the entry in the display. For example, to square 35.7, use the following keystrokes.

③ ⑤ ⊙ ⑦ (x^2) (1274.49)

The squaring key and the square root key are often found together, with one of them being a second function (that is, activated by the second function key previously described).

Reciprocal Key   The key marked (1/x) is the reciprocal key. (When two numbers have a product of 1, they are called *reciprocals*. See **Chapter 1.**) Suppose that you wish to find the reciprocal of 5. Use the following keystrokes.

⑤ (1/x) (0.2)

Inverse Key   Some calculators have an inverse key, marked (INV). Inverse operations are operations that "undo" each other. For example, the operations of squaring and taking the square root are inverse operations. The use of the (INV) key varies among different models of calculators, so read your owner's manual carefully.

Exponential Key   The key marked (x^y) or (y^x) allows you to raise a number to a power. For example, if you wish to raise 4 to the fifth power (that is, find 4^5, as explained in **Chapter 1**), use the following keystrokes.

$$\boxed{4}\ \boxed{x^y}\ \boxed{5}\ \boxed{=}\ \boxed{1024}$$

Root Key   Some calculators have a key specifically marked $(\sqrt[x]{x})$ or $(\sqrt[x]{y})$; with others, the operation of taking roots is accomplished by using the inverse key in conjunction with the exponential key. Suppose, for example, your calculator is of the latter type and you wish to find the fifth root of 1024. Use the following keystrokes.

$$\boxed{1}\ \boxed{0}\ \boxed{2}\ \boxed{4}\ \boxed{INV}\ \boxed{x^y}\ \boxed{5}\ \boxed{=}\ \boxed{4}$$

Notice how this "undoes" the operation explained in the discussion of the exponential key.

Pi Key   The number π is an important number in mathematics. It occurs, for example, in the area and circumference formulas for a circle. One popular model gives the following display when the (π) key is pressed. (Because π is irrational, the display shows only an approximation.)

$$\boxed{3.1415927}\qquad \text{An approximation for } \pi$$

Methods of Display   When decimal approximations are shown on scientific calculators, they are either *truncated* or *rounded*. To see how a particular model is programmed, evaluate 1/18 as an example. If the display shows 0.0555555 (last digit 5), the calculator truncates the display. If the display shows 0.0555556 (last digit 6), the calculator rounds the display.

When very large or very small numbers are obtained as answers, scientific calculators often express these numbers in scientific notation (**Chapter 4**). For example, if you multiply 6,265,804 by 8,980,591, the display might look like this:

$$\boxed{5.6270623\ 13}$$

The 13 at the far right means that the number on the left is multiplied by 10^{13}. This means that the decimal point must be moved 13 places to the right if the answer is to be expressed in its usual form. Even then, the value obtained will only be an approximation: 56,270,623,000,000.

Graphing Calculators

While you are not expected to have a graphing calculator to study from this book, we include the following as background information and reference should your course or future courses require the use of graphing calculators.

Basic Features   In addition to possessing the typical keys found on scientific calculators, graphing calculators have keys that can be used to create graphs, make tables, analyze data, and change settings. One of the major differences between graphing and scientific calculators is that a graphing calculator has a larger viewing screen with graphing capabilities. The following screens illustrate the graphs of $Y = X$ and $Y = X^2$. (We use screens from a Texas Instruments calculator in our illustrations.)

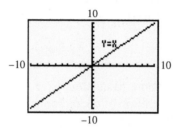 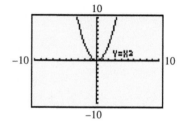

If you look closely at the screens, you will see that the graphs appear to be jagged rather than smooth. The reason for this is that graphing calculators have much lower resolution than computer screens. Because of this, graphs generated by graphing calculators must be interpreted carefully.

Editing Input   The screen of a graphing calculator can display several lines of text at a time. This feature allows you to view both previous and current expressions. If an incorrect expression is entered, an error message is displayed. The erroneous expression can be viewed and corrected by using various editing keys, much like a word-processing program. You do not need to enter the entire expression again. Many graphing calculators can also recall past expressions for editing or updating. The screen on the left shows how two expressions are evaluated. The final line is entered incorrectly, and the resulting error message is shown in the screen on the right.

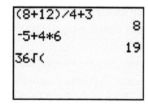 

Order of Operations   Arithmetic operations on graphing calculators are usually entered as they are written in mathematical expressions. For example, to evaluate $\sqrt{36}$ you would first press the square root key and then enter 36. See the left screen below. The order of operations on a graphing calculator is also important, and current models assist the user by inserting parentheses when typical errors might occur. The open parenthesis that follows the square root symbol is automatically entered by the calculator so that an expression such as $\sqrt{2 \times 8}$ will not be calculated incorrectly as $\sqrt{2} \times 8$. Compare the two entries and their results in the screen on the right.

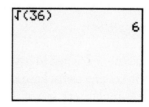 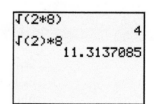

Viewing Windows   The viewing window for a graphing calculator is similar to the viewfinder in a camera. A camera usually cannot take a photograph of an entire view of a scene. The camera must be centered on some object and can capture only a portion of the available scenery. A camera with a zoom lens can photograph different views of the same scene by zooming in and out. Graphing calculators have similar capabilities. The *xy*-coordinate plane is infinite. The calculator screen can show only a finite, rectangular region in the plane, and it must be specified before the graph can be drawn. This is done by setting both minimum and maximum values for the *x*- and *y*-axes. The scale (distance between tick marks) is usually specified as well. Determining an appropriate viewing window for a graph is often a challenge, and many times it will take a few attempts before a satisfactory window is found.

The screen on the left shows a standard viewing window, and the graph of Y = 2X + 1 is shown on the right. Using a different window would give a different view of the line.

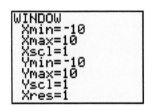
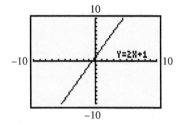

Locating Points on a Graph: Tracing and Tables   Graphing calculators allow you to trace along the graph of an equation and display the coordinates of points on the graph. For example, the screen on the left below indicates that the point $(2, 5)$ lies on the graph of Y = 2X + 1. Tables for equations can also be displayed. The screen on the right shows a partial table for this same equation. Note the middle of the screen, which indicates that when X = 2, Y = 5.

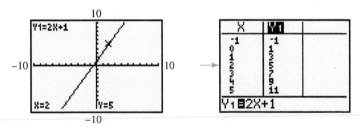

Additional Features   There are many features of graphing calculators that go far beyond the scope of this book. These calculators can be programmed, much like computers. Many of them can solve equations at the stroke of a key, analyze statistical data, and perform symbolic algebraic manipulations. Calculators also provide the opportunity to ask "What if . . . ?" more easily. Values in algebraic expressions can be altered and conjectures tested quickly.

Final Comments   Despite the power of today's calculators, they cannot replace human thought. ***In the entire problem-solving process, your brain is the most important component.*** Calculators are only tools, and like any tool, they must be used appropriately in order to enhance our ability to understand mathematics. Mathematical insight may often be the quickest and easiest way to solve a problem; a calculator may be neither needed nor appropriate. By applying mathematical concepts, you can make the decision whether to use a calculator.

Answers to Selected Exercises

In this section we provide the answers that we think most students will obtain when they work the exercises using the methods explained in the text. If your answer does not look exactly like the one given here, it is not necessarily wrong. In many cases, there are equivalent forms of the answer that are correct. For example, if the answer section shows $\frac{3}{4}$ and your answer is 0.75, you have obtained the right answer, but written it in a different (yet equivalent) form. Unless the directions specify otherwise, 0.75 is just as valid an answer as $\frac{3}{4}$.

In general, if your answer does not agree with the one given in the text, see whether it can be transformed into the other form. If it can, then it is the correct answer. If you still have doubts, talk with your instructor. You might also want to obtain a copy of the *Student's Solutions Manual* that goes with this book. Your college bookstore either has this manual or can order it for you.

1 THE REAL NUMBER SYSTEM

Section 1.1 (pages 10–13)

1. true **3.** false; This is an improper fraction. Its value is 1. **5.** false; The fraction $\frac{13}{39}$ is written in lowest terms as $\frac{1}{3}$. **7.** false; *Product* refers to multiplication, so the product of 10 and 2 is 20. **9.** prime **11.** composite; $2 \cdot 3 \cdot 5$ **13.** composite; $2 \cdot 2 \cdot 2 \cdot 2 \cdot 2 \cdot 2$ **15.** neither **17.** composite; $3 \cdot 19$ **19.** prime **21.** composite; $2 \cdot 2 \cdot 31$ **23.** composite; $2 \cdot 2 \cdot 5 \cdot 5 \cdot 5$ **25.** composite; $2 \cdot 7 \cdot 13 \cdot 19$ **27.** $\frac{1}{2}$ **29.** $\frac{5}{6}$ **31.** $\frac{16}{25}$ **33.** $\frac{1}{5}$ **35.** $\frac{6}{5}$ **37.** C **39.** $\frac{24}{35}$ **41.** $\frac{5}{8}$ **43.** $\frac{6}{25}$ **45.** $\frac{6}{5}$, or $1\frac{1}{5}$ **47.** 9 **49.** $\frac{65}{12}$, or $5\frac{5}{12}$ **51.** $\frac{38}{5}$, or $7\frac{3}{5}$ **53.** $\frac{10}{3}$, or $3\frac{1}{3}$ **55.** 12 **57.** $\frac{1}{16}$ **59.** 10 **61.** 18 **63.** $\frac{35}{24}$, or $1\frac{11}{24}$ **65.** $\frac{84}{47}$, or $1\frac{37}{47}$ **67.** A **69.** $\frac{11}{15}$ **71.** $\frac{2}{3}$ **73.** $\frac{8}{9}$ **75.** $\frac{29}{24}$, or $1\frac{5}{24}$ **77.** $\frac{43}{8}$, or $5\frac{3}{8}$ **79.** $\frac{101}{20}$, or $5\frac{1}{20}$ **81.** $\frac{5}{9}$ **83.** $\frac{2}{3}$ **85.** $\frac{1}{4}$ **87.** $\frac{17}{36}$ **89.** $\frac{67}{20}$, or $3\frac{7}{20}$ **91.** $\frac{11}{12}$ **93.** 6 cups **95.** $1\frac{1}{8}$ in. **97.** $\frac{9}{16}$ in. **99.** $618\frac{3}{4}$ ft **101.** $5\frac{5}{24}$ in. **103.** 8 cakes (There will be some sugar left over.) **105.** $16\frac{5}{8}$ yd **107.** $3\frac{3}{8}$ in. **109.** $\frac{1}{20}$ **111.** about $5\frac{8}{25}$ million, or 5,320,000 **113. (a)** $\frac{1}{2}$ **(b)** $\frac{1}{4}$ **(c)** $\frac{1}{3}$ **(d)** $\frac{1}{6}$

Section 1.2 (pages 19–21)

1. false; 6^2 means that 6 is used as a factor 2 times; so $6^2 = 6 \cdot 6 = 36$. **3.** false; 1 raised to *any* power is 1. Here, $1^3 = 1 \cdot 1 \cdot 1 = 1$. **5.** false; $4 + 3(8 - 2)$ means $4 + 3 \cdot 6$, which simplifies to $4 + 18$, or 22. The common error leading to 42 is adding 4 to 3 and then multiplying by 6. One must follow the order of operations. **7.** 9 **9.** 49 **11.** 144 **13.** 64 **15.** 1000 **17.** 81 **19.** 1024 **21.** $\frac{1}{36}$ **23.** $\frac{16}{81}$ **25.** 0.064 **27.** 32 **29.** 58 **31.** 22.2 **33.** $\frac{49}{30}$, or $1\frac{19}{30}$ **35.** 12 **37.** 13 **39.** 26 **41.** 4 **43.** 42 **45.** 5 **47.** 41 **49.** 95 **51.** 90 **53.** 14 **55.** 9 **57.** $16 \leq 16$; true **59.** $61 \leq 60$; false **61.** $0 \geq 0$; true **63.** $45 \geq 46$; false **65.** $66 > 72$; false **67.** $2 \geq 3$; false

69. $3 \geq 3$; true **71.** $3 \cdot (6 + 4) \cdot 2 = 60$ **73.** $10 - (7 - 3) = 6$ **75.** $(8 + 2)^2 = 100$ **77.** Five is less than seventeen; true **79.** Five is not equal to eight; true **81.** Seven is greater than or equal to fourteen; false **83.** Fifteen is less than or equal to 15; true **85.** $15 = 5 + 10$ **87.** $9 > 5 - 4$ **89.** $16 \neq 19$ **91.** $\frac{1}{2} \leq \frac{2}{4}$ **93.** $20 > 5$ **95.** $1.3 \leq 2.5$ **97. (a)** $14.7 - 40 \cdot 0.13$ **(b)** 9.5 **(c)** 8.075; walking (5 mph) **99.** Answers will vary.

Section 1.3 (pages 26–27)

1. B **3.** A **5.** $2x^3 = 2 \cdot x \cdot x \cdot x$, while $2x \cdot 2x \cdot 2x = (2x)^3$. **7.** The exponent 2 applies only to its base, which is x. **9. (a)** 11 **(b)** 13 **11. (a)** 16 **(b)** 24 **13. (a)** 64 **(b)** 144 **15. (a)** $\frac{5}{3}$ **(b)** $\frac{7}{3}$ **17. (a)** $\frac{7}{8}$ **(b)** $\frac{13}{12}$ **19. (a)** 52 **(b)** 114 **21. (a)** 25.836 **(b)** 38.754 **23. (a)** 24 **(b)** 28 **25. (a)** 12 **(b)** 33 **27. (a)** 6 **(b)** $\frac{9}{5}$ **29. (a)** $\frac{4}{3}$ **(b)** $\frac{13}{6}$ **31. (a)** $\frac{2}{7}$ **(b)** $\frac{16}{27}$ **33. (a)** 12 **(b)** 55 **35. (a)** 1 **(b)** $\frac{28}{17}$ **37. (a)** 3.684 **(b)** 8.841 **39.** $12x$ **41.** $x + 9$ **43.** $x - 4$ **45.** $7 - x$ **47.** $x - 8$ **49.** $\frac{18}{x}$ **51.** $6(x - 4)$ **53.** An expression cannot be solved—it indicates a series of operations to perform. An expression is simplified. An equation is solved. **55.** yes **57.** no **59.** yes **61.** yes **63.** yes **65.** no **67.** $x + 8 = 18$; 10 **69.** $16 - \frac{3}{4}x = 13$; 4 **71.** $2x + 1 = 5$; 2 **73.** $3x = 2x + 8$; 8 **75.** expression **77.** equation **79.** equation **81.** 64.9 yr **83.** 73.8 yr **85.** Life expectancy has increased over 13 yr during this time.

Section 1.4 (pages 34–36)

1. 2,866,000 **3.** −52,000 **5.** −11.2; 8.6 **7.** 82.60 **9.** 4 **11.** 0 **13.** One example is $\sqrt{13}$. There are others. **15.** true **17.** true **19.** false

In Exercises 21–25, answers will vary.

21. $\frac{1}{2}, \frac{5}{8}, 1\frac{3}{4}$ **23.** $-3\frac{1}{2}, -\frac{2}{3}, \frac{3}{7}$ **25.** $\sqrt{5}, \pi, -\sqrt{3}$ **27. (a)** 3, 7 **(b)** 0, 3, 7 **(c)** −9, 0, 3, 7 **(d)** $-9, -1\frac{1}{4}, -\frac{3}{5}, 0, 0.\overline{1}, 3, 5.9, 7$ **(e)** $-\sqrt{7}, \sqrt{5}$ **(f)** All are real numbers. **29.** [number line: $-6 \; -4 \; -2 \; 0 \; 2$]

31. [number line: $-6 \; -4 \; -2 \; 0 \; 2 \; 4$] **33.** [number line labeled $-3\frac{4}{5}, -1\frac{5}{8}, \frac{1}{4}, 2\frac{1}{2}$; $-4 \; -2 \; 0 \; 2 \; 4$] **35. (a)** A **(b)** A **(c)** B **(d)** B **37. (a)** 7 **(b)** 7 **39. (a)** −8 **(b)** 8 **41. (a)** $\frac{3}{4}$ **(b)** $\frac{3}{4}$ **43.** 6 **45.** −12 **47.** $-\frac{2}{3}$ **49.** 3 **51.** This is not true. The absolute value of 0 is 0, and 0 is not positive. A more accurate way of describing absolute value is to say that *absolute value is never negative*, or *absolute value is always nonnegative*. **53.** −11 **55.** −7 **57.** 4 **59.** $|-3.5|$, or 3.5 **61.** $-|-6|$, or −6 **63.** $|5 - 3|$, or 2 **65.** true **67.** true **69.** true **71.** false **73.** true **75.** false **77.** fuel and other utilities, 2004 to 2005 **79.** apparel and upkeep, 2006 to 2007

Section 1.5 (pages 44–48)

1. negative   **3.** negative

5. -8; -6; 2   **7.** positive   **9.** negative   **11.** -8 **13.** -12 **15.** 2
17. -2 **19.** 8.9   **21.** 12   **23.** 5   **25.** 2   **27.** -9 **29.** 0   **31.** $\frac{1}{2}$
33. $-\frac{19}{24}$ **35.** $-\frac{3}{4}$ **37.** -7.7 **39.** -8 **41.** 0   **43.** -20 **45.** -3
47. -4 **49.** -8 **51.** -14 **53.** 9   **55.** -4 **57.** 4   **59.** $\frac{3}{4}$
61. $-\frac{11}{8}$, or $-1\frac{3}{8}$ **63.** $\frac{15}{8}$, or $1\frac{7}{8}$ **65.** 11.6   **67.** -9.9 **69.** 10
71. -5 **73.** 11   **75.** -10 **77.** 22   **79.** -2 **81.** $-\frac{17}{8}$, or $-2\frac{1}{8}$
83. $-\frac{1}{4}$, or -0.25 **85.** -6 **87.** -12 **89.** -5.90617
91. $-5 + 12 + 6$; 13   **93.** $[-19 + (-4)] + 14$; -9
95. $[-4 + (-10)] + 12$; -2 **97.** $\left[\frac{5}{7} + \left(-\frac{9}{7}\right)\right] + \frac{2}{7}$; $-\frac{2}{7}$
99. $4 - (-8)$; 12   **101.** $-2 - 8$; -10 **103.** $[9 + (-4)] - 7$; -2
105. $[8 - (-5)] - 12$; 1   **107.** -12 **109.** $-56°F$ **111.** $-69°F$
113. -184 m   **115. (a)** 7.4%   **(b)** Americans spent more money than
they earned, which means they had to dip into savings or increase borrowing.
117. $3173   **119.** 17   **121.** $1045.55   **123.** $323.83
125. 30.4 billion dollars   **127.** 3.1 billion dollars   **129.** 50,395 ft
131. 1345 ft   **133.** 136 ft

Section 1.6 (pages 56–59)

1. greater than 0   **3.** less than 0   **5.** greater than 0   **7.** equal to 0
9. undefined; 0; Examples include $\frac{1}{0}$, which is undefined, and $\frac{0}{1}$, which
equals 0.   **11.** -30 **13.** 30   **15.** 120   **17.** -33 **19.** 0   **21.** -2.38
23. $\frac{5}{12}$ **25.** $-\frac{1}{6}$ **27.** 6   **29.** $-32, -16, -8, -4, -2, -1, 1, 2, 4, 8,$
$16, 32$ **31.** $-40, -20, -10, -8, -5, -4, -2, -1, 1, 2, 4, 5, 8, 10,$
$20, 40$ **33.** $-31, -1, 1, 31$ **35.** 3   **37.** -7 **39.** 8   **41.** -6
43. $\frac{32}{3}$, or $10\frac{2}{3}$ **45.** -4 **47.** 0   **49.** undefined   **51.** -11 **53.** -2
55. 35   **57.** 13   **59.** -22 **61.** 6   **63.** -18 **65.** 67   **67.** -8
69. 3   **71.** 7   **73.** 4   **75.** -1 **77.** 4   **79.** -3 **81.** 47   **83.** 72
85. $-\frac{78}{25}$ **87.** 0   **89.** -23 **91.** 2   **93.** $9 + (-9)(2)$; -9
95. $-4 - 2(-1)(6)$; 8   **97.** $(1.5)(-3.2) - 9$; -13.8
99. $12[9 - (-8)]$; 204   **101.** $\frac{-12}{-5 + (-1)}$; 2   **103.** $\frac{15 + (-3)}{4(-3)}$; -1
105. $\frac{2}{3}[8 - (-1)]$; 6   **107.** $0.20(-5 \cdot 6)$; -6
109. $\left(\frac{1}{2} + \frac{5}{8}\right)\left(\frac{3}{5} - \frac{1}{3}\right)$; $\frac{3}{10}$ **111.** $\frac{-\frac{1}{2}\left(\frac{3}{4}\right)}{-\frac{2}{3}}$; $\frac{9}{16}$ **113.** $\frac{x}{3} = -3$; -9
115. $x - 6 = 4$; 10   **117.** $x + 5 = -5$; -10 **119.** $8\frac{2}{5}$ **121.** 4
123. 2   **125. (a)** 6 is divisible by 2.   **(b)** 9 is not divisible by 2.
127. (a) 64 is divisible by 4.   **(b)** 35 is not divisible by 4.
129. (a) 2 is divisible by 2 and $1 + 5 + 2 + 4 + 8 + 2 + 2 = 24$
is divisible by 3.   **(b)** Although 0 is divisible by 2,
$2 + 8 + 7 + 3 + 5 + 9 + 0 = 34$ is not divisible by 3.
131. (a) $4 + 1 + 1 + 4 + 1 + 0 + 7 = 18$ is divisible by 9.
(b) $2 + 2 + 8 + 7 + 3 + 2 + 1 = 25$ is not divisible by 9.

Summary Exercises on Operations with Real Numbers (pages 59–60)

1. -16 **2.** 4   **3.** 0   **4.** -24 **5.** -17 **6.** 76   **7.** -18 **8.** 90
9. 38   **10.** 4   **11.** -5 **12.** 5   **13.** $-\frac{7}{2}$, or $-3\frac{1}{2}$ **14.** 4   **15.** 13

16. $\frac{5}{4}$, or $1\frac{1}{4}$ **17.** 9   **18.** $\frac{37}{10}$, or $3\frac{7}{10}$ **19.** 0   **20.** 25   **21.** 14
22. undefined   **23.** -4 **24.** $\frac{6}{5}$, or $1\frac{1}{5}$ **25.** -1 **26.** $\frac{52}{37}$, or $1\frac{15}{37}$
27. $\frac{17}{16}$, or $1\frac{1}{16}$ **28.** $-\frac{2}{3}$ **29.** 3.33   **30.** 1.02   **31.** -13 **32.** 0
33. 24   **34.** -7 **35.** 37   **36.** -3 **37.** -1 **38.** $\frac{1}{2}$ **39.** $-\frac{5}{13}$
40. 5   **41.** $-\frac{8}{27}$ **42.** 4

Section 1.7 (pages 67–69)

1. (a) B   **(b)** F   **(c)** C   **(d)** I   **(e)** B   **(f)** D, F   **(g)** B   **(h)** A
(i) G   **(j)** H   **3.** yes   **5.** no   **7.** no   **9.** (foreign sales) clerk; foreign
(sales clerk)   **11.** -15; commutative property   **13.** 3; commutative
property   **15.** 6; associative property   **17.** 7; associative property
19. Subtraction is not associative.   **21.** row 1: $-5, \frac{1}{5}$; row 2: $10, -\frac{1}{10}$;
row 3: $\frac{1}{2}, -2$; row 4: $-\frac{3}{8}, \frac{8}{3}$; row 5: $-x, \frac{1}{x}$; row 6: $y, -\frac{1}{y}$; opposite;
the same   **23.** commutative property   **25.** associative property
27. associative property   **29.** inverse property   **31.** inverse property
33. identity property   **35.** commutative property   **37.** distributive
property   **39.** identity property   **41.** distributive property
43. 150   **45.** 2010   **47.** 400   **49.** 1400   **51.** 470
53. -9300 **55.** 11   **57.** 0   **59.** -0.38 **61.** 1   **63.** The expression
following the first equals symbol should be $-3(4) - 3(-6)$.
$-3(4 - 6)$ means $-3(4) - 3(-6)$, which simplifies to $-12 + 18$, or 6.
65. 85   **67.** $4t + 12$ **69.** $7z - 56$ **71.** $-8r - 24$ **73.** $-2x - \frac{3}{4}$
75. $-5y + 20$ **77.** $-16y - 20z$ **79.** $8(z + w)$ **81.** $7(2v + 5r)$
83. $24r + 32s - 40y$ **85.** $-24x - 9y - 12z$ **87.** $5(x + 3)$
89. $-4t - 3m$ **91.** $5c + 4d$ **93.** $q - 5r + 8s$

Section 1.8 (pages 72–74)

1. B   **3.** C   **5.** $4r + 11$ **7.** $5 + 2x - 6y$ **9.** $-7 + 3p$
11. $2 - 3x$ **13.** -12 **15.** 3   **17.** 1   **19.** -1 **21.** $\frac{1}{2}$ **23.** $\frac{2}{5}$
25. 10   **27.** like   **29.** unlike   **31.** like   **33.** unlike   **35.** The
student made a sign error when applying the distributive property:
$7x - 2(3 - 2x)$ means $7x - 2(3) - 2(-2x)$, which simplifies to
$7x - 6 + 4x$, or $11x - 6$.   **37.** $13y$ **39.** $-9x$ **41.** $13b$
43. $7k + 15$ **45.** $-4y$ **47.** $2x + 6$ **49.** $14 - 7m$ **51.** $-17 + x$
53. $23x$ **55.** $-\frac{1}{3}t - \frac{28}{3}$ **57.** $9y^2$ **59.** $-14p^3 + 5p^2$ **61.** $8x + 15$
63. $5x + 15$ **65.** $-4y + 22$ **67.** $-\frac{3}{2}y + 16$ **69.** $-16y + 63$
71. $4r + 15$ **73.** $12k - 5$ **75.** $-2k - 3$ **77.** $4x - 7$
79. $-23.7y - 12.6$ **81.** $(x + 3) + 5x$; $6x + 3$
83. $(13 + 6x) - (-7x)$; $13 + 13x$ **85.** $2(3x + 4) - (-4 + 6x)$; 12
87. $1000 + 5x$ (dollars)   **88.** $750 + 3y$ (dollars)
89. $1000 + 5x + 750 + 3y$ (dollars)   **90.** $1750 + 5x + 3y$ (dollars)

Chapter 1 Review Exercises (pages 79–83)

1. $\frac{3}{4}$ **2.** $\frac{7}{2}$, or $3\frac{1}{2}$ **3.** $\frac{11}{24}$ **4.** $\frac{59}{16}$, or $3\frac{11}{16}$ **5.** about 1270 thousand
6. about 5079 thousand   **7.** 625   **8.** $\frac{27}{125}$ **9.** 0.0004   **10.** 0.001
11. 27   **12.** 17   **13.** 4   **14.** 399   **15.** 39   **16.** 5   **17.** true   **18.** true
19. false   **20.** $13 < 17$ **21.** $5 + 2 \neq 10$ **22.** $\frac{2}{3} \geq \frac{4}{6}$ **23.** 30
24. 60   **25.** 14   **26.** 13   **27.** $x + 6$ **28.** $8 - x$ **29.** $6x - 9$
30. $12 + \frac{3}{5}x$ **31.** yes   **32.** no   **33.** $2x - 6 = 10$; 8   **34.** $4x = 8$; 2

35.

36.

37. rational numbers, real numbers   **38.** rational numbers, real numbers
39. natural numbers, whole numbers, integers, rational numbers, real
numbers   **40.** irrational numbers, real numbers   **41.** -10 **42.** -9
43. $-\frac{3}{4}$ **44.** $-|23|$ **45.** true   **46.** true   **47.** true   **48.** true
49. (a) 9   **(b)** 9   **50. (a)** 0   **(b)** 0   **51. (a)** -6 **(b)** 6
52. (a) $\frac{5}{7}$ **(b)** $\frac{5}{7}$ **53.** 12   **54.** -3 **55.** -19 **56.** -7 **57.** -6
58. -4 **59.** -17 **60.** $-\frac{29}{36}$ **61.** -21.8 **62.** -14 **63.** -10
64. -19 **65.** -11 **66.** -1 **67.** 7   **68.** $-\frac{43}{35}$, or $-1\frac{8}{35}$ **69.** 10.31
70. -12 **71.** 2   **72.** -3 **73.** $(-31 + 12) + 19; 0$
74. $[-4 + (-8)] + 13; 1$ **75.** $-4 - (-6); 2$
76. $[4 + (-8)] - 5; -9$ **77.** -2 **78.** -1 **79.** \$26.25
80. $-10°$F   **81.** $-\$29$ **82.** $-10°$ **83.** 38   **84.** 9544.2
85. 36   **86.** -105 **87.** $\frac{1}{2}$ **88.** 10.08   **89.** -20 **90.** -10
91. -24 **92.** -35 **93.** 4   **94.** -20 **95.** $-\frac{3}{4}$ **96.** 11.3   **97.** -1
98. 2   **99.** 1   **100.** 0.5   **101.** -18 **102.** -18 **103.** 125
104. -423 **105.** $-4(5) - 9; -29$ **106.** $\frac{5}{6}[12 + (-6)]; 5$
107. $\frac{12}{8 + (-4)}; 3$ **108.** $\frac{-20(12)}{15 - (-15)}; -8$ **109.** $8x = -24; -3$
110. $\frac{x}{3} = -2; -6$ **111.** 32   **112.** -3 **113.** identity property
114. identity property   **115.** inverse property   **116.** inverse property
117. associative property   **118.** associative property   **119.** distributive
property   **120.** commutative property   **121.** $7(y + 2)$
122. $-48 + 12t$ **123.** $3(2s + 5y)$ **124.** $4r - 5s$ **125.** $11m$
126. $16p^2$ **127.** $16p^2 + 2p$ **128.** $-4k + 12$ **129.** $-2m + 29$
130. $-5k - 1$ **131.** $-2(3x) - 7x; -13x$
132. $(5 + 4x) + 8x; 5 + 12x$ **133.** $\frac{8}{3}$, or $2\frac{2}{3}$ **134.** $-\frac{1}{24}$
135. 2   **136.** $-\frac{28}{15}$, or $-1\frac{13}{15}$ **137.** $-\frac{3}{2}$, or $-1\frac{1}{2}$ **138.** $\frac{25}{36}$ **139.** 16
140. 77.6   **141.** 11   **142.** $16t - 36$ **143.** $8x^2 - 21y^2$ **144.** 24
145. Dividing 0 *by* a nonzero number gives a quotient of 0. However, dividing a number *by* 0 is undefined.   **146.** $-47°$F   **147.** -0.84 million
students   **148.** -1.05 million students   **149.** 1.02 million students
150. 1.39 million students

Chapter 1 Test (pages 83–84)

[1.1] **1.** $\frac{7}{11}$ **2.** $\frac{241}{120}$, or $2\frac{1}{120}$ **3.** $\frac{19}{18}$, or $1\frac{1}{18}$ [1.2] **4.** true
[1.4] **5.**

  6. rational numbers, real numbers

7. If -8 and -1 are both graphed on a number line, we see that the point
for -8 is to the *left* of the point for -1. This indicates $-8 < -1$.
[1.6] **8.** $\frac{-6}{2 + (-8)}; 1$ [1.1, 1.4–1.6] **9.** 4   **10.** $-\frac{17}{6}$, or $-2\frac{5}{6}$ **11.** 2
12. 6   **13.** 108   **14.** $\frac{30}{7}$, or $4\frac{2}{7}$ [1.3, 1.5, 1.6] **15.** 6   **16.** 4
[1.6] **17.** -70 **18.** 3   [1.4–1.6] **19.** 7000 m   **20.** 15
21. $-\$1.42$ trillion   [1.7] **22.** B   **23.** D   **24.** E   **25.** A   **26.** C
27. distributive property   **28. (a)** -18 **(b)** -18 **(c)** The distributive
property assures us that the answers must be the same, because
$a(b + c) = ab + ac$ for all a, b, c.   [1.8] **29.** $21x$ **30.** $15x - 3$

2   LINEAR EQUATIONS AND INEQUALITIES IN ONE VARIABLE

Section 2.1 (pages 90–92)

1. (a) expression; $x + 15$ **(b)** expression; $y + 7$ **(c)** equation; $\{-1\}$
(d) equation; $\{-17\}$ **3.** A and B   **5.** $\{12\}$ **7.** $\{31\}$ **9.** $\{-3\}$
11. $\{4\}$ **13.** $\{-9\}$ **15.** $\left\{-\frac{3}{4}\right\}$ **17.** $\{-10\}$ **19.** $\{-13\}$
21. $\{10\}$ **23.** $\left\{\frac{4}{15}\right\}$ **25.** $\{6.3\}$ **27.** $\{-16.9\}$ **29.** $\{7\}$ **31.** $\{-4\}$
33. $\{-3\}$ **35.** $\{0\}$ **37.** $\{2\}$ **39.** $\{-6\}$ **41.** $\{-2\}$ **43.** $\{3\}$
45. $\{0\}$ **47.** $\{0\}$ **49.** $\{-5\}$ **51.** $\{-7\}$ **53.** $\{13\}$ **55.** $\{-4\}$
57. $\{0\}$ **59.** $\left\{\frac{7}{15}\right\}$ **61.** $\{7\}$ **63.** $\{-4\}$ **65.** $\{13\}$ **67.** $\{29\}$
69. $\{18\}$ **71.** $\{12\}$ **73.** Answers will vary. One example is
$x - 6 = -8$.   **75.** $3x = 2x + 17; \{17\}$ **77.** $7x - 6x = -9; \{-9\}$
79. 1   **81.** x **83.** r

Section 2.2 (pages 96–97)

1. (a) multiplication property of equality   **(b)** addition property of
equality   **(c)** multiplication property of equality   **(d)** addition property
of equality   **3.** To find the solution of $-x = 5$, multiply (or divide) each
side by -1, or use the rule "If $-x = a$, then $x = -a$."   **5.** $\frac{5}{4}$ **7.** 10
9. $-\frac{2}{9}$ **11.** -1 **13.** 6   **15.** -4 **17.** 0.12   **19.** -1 **21.** $\{6\}$
23. $\left\{\frac{15}{2}\right\}$ **25.** $\{-5\}$ **27.** $\{-4\}$ **29.** $\left\{-\frac{18}{5}\right\}$, or $\{-3.6\}$
31. $\{12\}$ **33.** $\{0\}$ **35.** $\{-12\}$ **37.** $\left\{\frac{3}{4}\right\}$ **39.** $\{40\}$
41. $\{-12.2\}$ **43.** $\{-48\}$ **45.** $\{72\}$ **47.** $\{-35\}$ **49.** $\{14\}$
51. $\{18\}$ **53.** $\left\{-\frac{27}{35}\right\}$ **55.** $\{-30\}$ **57.** $\{3\}$ **59.** $\{-5\}$ **61.** $\{20\}$
63. $\{7\}$ **65.** $\{0\}$ **67.** $\left\{-\frac{3}{5}\right\}$ **69.** $\{18\}$ **71.** Answers will vary.
One example is $\frac{3}{2}x = -6$.   **73.** $4x = 6; \left\{\frac{3}{2}\right\}$ **75.** $\frac{x}{-5} = 2; \{-10\}$
77. $-3m - 5$ **79.** $-8 + 5p$ **81.** $\{5\}$

Section 2.3 (pages 104–106)

1. Use the addition property of equality to subtract 8 from each side.
3. Clear parentheses by using the distributive property.   **5.** Clear fractions
by multiplying by the LCD, 6.   **7.** D   **9.** $\{4\}$ **11.** $\{-5\}$ **13.** $\left\{\frac{5}{2}\right\}$
15. $\{-1\}$ **17.** $\left\{-\frac{1}{2}\right\}$ **19.** $\{-3\}$ **21.** $\{5\}$ **23.** $\{0\}$ **25.** $\left\{\frac{4}{3}\right\}$
27. $\left\{-\frac{5}{3}\right\}$ **29.** $\{5\}$ **31.** $\{0\}$ **33.** $\emptyset$ **35.** {all real numbers}
37. $\emptyset$ **39.** $\{5\}$ **41.** $\{12\}$ **43.** $\{11\}$ **45.** $\{0\}$ **47.** $\{18\}$
49. $\{120\}$ **51.** $\{6\}$ **53.** $\{15,000\}$ **55.** $\{8\}$ **57.** $\{4\}$ **59.** $\{20\}$
61. {all real numbers}   **63.** $\emptyset$ **65.** $11 - q$ **67.** $\frac{9}{x}$ **69.** $x + 9$
71. $65 - h$ **73.** $x + 15; x - 5$ **75.** $25r$ **77.** $\frac{t}{5}$ **79.** $3x + 2y$
81. $-6 + x$ **83.** $-5 - x$ **85.** $12(x - 9)$

Summary Exercises on Solving Linear Equations (pages 106–107)

1. $\{-5\}$ **2.** $\{4\}$ **3.** $\{-5.1\}$ **4.** $\{12\}$ **5.** $\{-25\}$ **6.** $\{-6\}$
7. $\{0\}$ **8.** $\{-16\}$ **9.** $\{-6\}$ **10.** $\left\{-\frac{96}{5}\right\}$ **11.** {all real numbers}

12. $\left\{\frac{7}{3}\right\}$ **13.** $\{7\}$ **14.** $\{1\}$ **15.** $\{5\}$ **16.** $\{23.7\}$ **17.** $\{6\}$
18. $\{3\}$ **19.** $\emptyset$ **20.** $\emptyset$ **21.** $\{25\}$ **22.** $\{-10.8\}$ **23.** $\{3\}$
24. $\{7\}$ **25.** $\{2\}$ **26.** $\{$all real numbers$\}$ **27.** $\{-2\}$ **28.** $\{70\}$
29. $\left\{\frac{14}{17}\right\}$ **30.** $\{0\}$

Section 2.4 (pages 115–119)

1. D; There cannot be a fractional number of cars.   **3.** A; Distance cannot
be negative.   **5.** 7   **7.** 3   **9.** 6   **11.** -3 **13.** Pennsylvania: 35 screens;
Ohio: 33 screens   **15.** Democrats: 58; Republicans: 40   **17.** Bon Jovi:
$210.7 million; Bruce Springsteen: $204.6 million   **19.** wins: 62;
losses: 20   **21.** orange: 97 mg; pineapple: 25 mg   **23.** 168 DVDs
25. onions: 81.3 kg; grilled steak: 536.3 kg   **27.** 1950 Denver nickel:
$16.00; 1945 Philadelphia nickel: $8.00   **29.** whole wheat: 25.6 oz;
rye: 6.4 oz   **31.** American: 18; United: 11; Southwest: 26   **33.** shortest
piece: 15 in.; middle piece: 20 in.; longest piece: 24 in.   **35.** 36 million mi
37. A and B: 40°; C: 100°   **39.** 68, 69   **41.** 101, 102   **43.** 10, 12
45. 10, 11   **47.** 18   **49.** 15, 17, 19   **51.** 18°   **53.** 20°   **55.** 39°
57. 50°   **59.** 24   **61.** 20

Section 2.5 (pages 125–129)

1. (a) The perimeter of a plane geometric figure is the distance around
the figure.   **(b)** The area of a plane geometric figure is the measure of
the surface covered or enclosed by the figure.   **3.** 180°; the same
5. area   **7.** perimeter   **9.** area   **11.** area   **13.** $P = 26$ **15.** $\mathcal{A} = 64$
17. $b = 4$ **19.** $t = 5.6$ **21.** $I = 1575$ **23.** $B = 14$ **25.** $r = 2.6$
27. $r = 10$ **29.** $\mathcal{A} = 50.24$ **31.** $r = 6$ **33.** $V = 150$ **35.** $V = 52$
37. $V = 7234.56$ **39.** length: 18 in.; width: 9 in.   **41.** length: 14 m;
width: 4 m   **43.** shortest: 5 in.; medium: 7 in.; longest: 8 in.
45. two equal sides: 7 m; third side: 10 m   **47.** about 154,000 ft^2
49. perimeter: 5.4 m; area: 1.8 m^2 **51.** 10 ft   **53.** 194.48 ft^2; 49.42 ft
55. 23,800.10 ft^2 **57.** length: 36 in.; volume: 11,664 in.^{3} **59.** 48°, 132°
61. 55°, 35°   **63.** 51°, 51°   **65.** 105°, 105°   **67.** $t = \dfrac{d}{r}$ **69.** $b = \dfrac{\mathcal{A}}{h}$
71. $d = \dfrac{C}{\pi}$ **73.** $H = \dfrac{V}{LW}$ **75.** $r = \dfrac{I}{pt}$ **77.** $h = \dfrac{2\mathcal{A}}{b}$ **79.** $h = \dfrac{3V}{\pi r^2}$
81. $b = P - a - c$ **83.** $W = \dfrac{P - 2L}{2}$ **85.** $m = \dfrac{y - b}{x}$
87. $y = \dfrac{C - Ax}{B}$ **89.** $r = \dfrac{M - C}{C}$, or $r = \dfrac{M}{C} - 1$ **91.** $a = \dfrac{P - 2b}{2}$,
or $a = \dfrac{P}{2} - b$ **93.** $\{5000\}$ **95.** $\{28\}$ **97.** $\left\{-\frac{1}{12}\right\}$

Section 2.6 (pages 135–139)

1. (a) C   **(b)** D   **(c)** B   **(d)** A   **3.** $\frac{4}{3}$ **5.** $\frac{4}{3}$ **7.** $\frac{15}{2}$ **9.** $\frac{1}{5}$ **11.** $\frac{5}{6}$
13. 10 lb; $0.429   **15.** 32 oz; $0.093   **17.** 128 oz; $0.051   **19.** 36 oz;
$0.049   **21.** 263 oz; $0.076   **23.** true   **25.** false   **27.** true   **29.** $\{35\}$
31. $\{7\}$ **33.** $\left\{\frac{45}{2}\right\}$ **35.** $\{2\}$ **37.** $\{-1\}$ **39.** $\{5\}$ **41.** $\left\{-\frac{31}{5}\right\}$
43. $30.00   **45.** $8.75   **47.** $67.50   **49.** $48.90   **51.** 4 ft
53. 2.7 in.   **55.** 2.0 in.   **57.** $2\frac{5}{8}$ cups   **59.** $428.82   **61.** 50,000 fish
63. $x = 4$ **65.** $x = 2$ **67.** $x = 1$; $y = 4$

69. (a)

(b) 54 ft   **71.** $237   **73.** $272
75. 0.53   **77.** 0.96   **79.** 0.09
81. 1.29   **83.** 80%   **85.** 2%
87. 12.5%   **89.** 220%   **91.** 109.2
93. 700   **95.** 425   **97.** 8%
99. 120%   **101.** $119.25; $675.75
103. 80%   **105.** $3000   **107.** $\{6\}$ **109.** $\{4\}$

Section 2.7 (pages 145–150)

1. 45 L   **3.** $750   **5.** $17.50   **7.** A   **9. (a)** 532,000   **(b)** 798,000
(c) 494,000   **11.** D   **13.** 160 L   **15.** $13\frac{1}{3}$ L   **17.** 4 L   **19.** 20 mL
21. 4 L   **23.** $2100 at 5%; $900 at 4%   **25.** $2500 at 6%; $13,500
at 5%   **27.** 10 nickels   **29.** 44-cent stamps: 25; 17-cent stamps: 20
31. Arabian Mocha: 7 lb; Colombian Decaf: 3.5 lb   **33.** A   **35.** 530 mi
37. 3.483 hr   **39.** 7.97 m per sec   **41.** 8.47 m per sec   **43.** 5 hr
45. $1\frac{3}{4}$ hr   **47.** $7\frac{1}{2}$ hr   **49.** eastbound: 300 mph; westbound: 450 mph
51. 40 mph; 60 mph   **53.** Bob: 7 yr old; Kevin: 21 yr old
55. width: 3 ft; length: 9 ft   **57.** $650   **59.** false   **61.** true   **63.** true

Section 2.8 (pages 160–163)

1. $>$, $<$ (or $<$, $>$); $\geq$, $\leq$ (or $\leq$, $\geq$)   **3.** $(0, \infty)$ **5.** $x > -4$
7. $x \leq 4$ **9.** $(-\infty, 4]$

11. $(-\infty, -3)$

13. $(4, \infty)$

15. $(-\infty, 0]$

17. $\left[-\frac{1}{2}, \infty\right)$

19. $[1, \infty)$

21. $[5, \infty)$

23. $(-\infty, -11)$

25. $(-\infty, 6)$

27. $[-10, \infty)$

29. $(-\infty, -3)$

31. $(-\infty, 0]$

33. $(20, \infty)$

35. $[-3, \infty)$

37. $(-\infty, -3]$

39. $(-1, \infty)$

61. $2p^3 - 6p^2 + 7p - 4 + \dfrac{14}{3p + 1}$ **63.** $x^2 + 3x + 3$ **65.** $2x^2 -$
$2x + 3 + \dfrac{-1}{x + 1}$ **67.** $r^2 - 1 + \dfrac{4}{r^2 - 1}$ **69.** $3x^2 + 3x - 1 + \dfrac{1}{x - 1}$
71. $y^2 - y + 1$ **73.** $a^2 + 1$ **75.** $x^2 - 4x + 2 + \dfrac{9x - 4}{x^2 + 3}$
77. $x^3 + 3x^2 - x + 5$ **79.** $\dfrac{3}{2}a - 10 + \dfrac{77}{2a + 6}$ **81.** $x^2 + \dfrac{8}{3}x -$
$\dfrac{1}{3} + \dfrac{4}{3x - 3}$ **83.** $x^2 + x - 3$ **85.** $48m^2 + 96m + 24$
87. $5x^2 - 11x + 14$ **89.** 1, 2, 3, 6, 9, 18   **91.** 1, 2, 3, 4, 6, 8, 12,
16, 24, 48

Chapter 4 Review Exercises (pages 288–291)

1. 4^{11} **2.** $(-5)^{11}$ **3.** $-72x^7$ **4.** $10x^{14}$ **5.** 19^5x^5 **6.** $(-4)^7y^7$
7. $5p^4t^4$ **8.** $\dfrac{7^6}{5^6}$ **9.** $3^3x^6y^9$ **10.** t^{42} **11.** $6^2x^{16}y^4z^{16}$ **12.** $\dfrac{2^3m^9n^3}{p^6}$
13. The expression is a *sum* of powers of 7, not a *product*.   **14.** 2
15. -1 **16.** -1 **17.** $-\dfrac{1}{49}$ **18.** $\dfrac{64}{25}$ **19.** 5^8 **20.** $\dfrac{1}{81}$ **21.** $\dfrac{3}{4}$ **22.** $\dfrac{1}{36}$
23. x^2 **24.** y^7 **25.** $\dfrac{r^8}{81}$ **26.** $\dfrac{3^5}{p^3}$ **27.** $\dfrac{1}{a^3b^5}$ **28.** $72r^5$ **29.** 4.8×10^7
30. 2.8988×10^{10} **31.** 8.24×10^{-8} **32.** 24,000   **33.** 78,300,000
34. 0.000000897   **35.** 800   **36.** 4,000,000   **37.** 0.025   **38.** 0.000002
39. 0.0000000000016   **40.** 4.2×10^{42} **41.** 9.7×10^4; 5×10^3
42. 1×10^{100} **43.** 1×10^3; 2×10^3; 5×10^4; 1×10^5 **44.** $22m^2$;
degree 2; monomial   **45.** $p^3 - p^2 + 4p + 2$; degree 3; none of these
46. already in descending powers; degree 5; none of these
47. $-8y^5 - 7y^4 + 9y$; degree 5; trinomial   **48.** $7r^4 - 4r^3 + 1$;
degree 4; trinomial   **49.** $13x^3y^2 - 5xy^5 + 21x^2$ **50.** $a^3 + 4a^2$
51. $y^2 - 10y + 9$ **52.** $-13k^4 - 15k^2 + 18k$
53. 1, 4, 5, 4, 1   **54.** 10, 1, -2, 1, 10

55. $a^3 - 2a^2 - 7a + 2$ **56.** $6r^3 + 8r^2 - 17r + 6$
57. $5p^5 - 2p^4 - 3p^3 + 25p^2 + 15p$ **58.** $m^2 - 7m - 18$
59. $6k^2 - 9k - 6$ **60.** $2a^2 + 5ab - 3b^2$ **61.** $12k^2 - 32kq - 35q^2$
62. $s^3 - 3s^2 + 3s - 1$ **63.** $a^2 + 8a + 16$ **64.** $4r^2 + 20rt + 25t^2$
65. $36m^2 - 25$ **66.** $25a^2 - 36b^2$ **67.** $r^3 + 6r^2 + 12r + 8$
68. $25t^3 - 30t^2 + 9t$ **69. (a)** Answers will vary. For example, let $x = 1$
and $y = 2$. $(1 + 2)^2 \neq 1^2 + 2^2$, because $9 \neq 5$.   **(b)** Answers will vary.
For example, let $x = 1$ and $y = 2$. $(1 + 2)^3 \neq 1^3 + 2^3$, because $27 \neq 9$.
70. To find the third power of a binomial, such as $(a + b)^3$, first
square the binomial and then multiply that result by the binomial.
$(a + b)^3 = (a + b)^2(a + b) = (a^2 + 2ab + b^2)(a + b) =$
$a^3 + 3a^2b + 3ab^2 + b^3$ **71.** In both cases, $x = 0$ and $y = 1$ lead to
1 on each side of the inequality. This would not be sufficient to show that,
in general, the inequality is true. It would be necessary to choose other values of x and y.   **72.** $x^6 + 6x^4 + 12x^2 + 8$ **73.** $\dfrac{4}{3}\pi(x + 1)^3$, or
$\dfrac{4}{3}\pi x^3 + 4\pi x^2 + 4\pi x + \dfrac{4}{3}\pi$ **74.** $\dfrac{-5y^2}{3}$ **75.** $y^3 - 2y + 3$

76. $-2m^2n + mn + \dfrac{6n^3}{5}$ **77.** $2mn + 3m^4n^2 - 4n$ **78.** The friend
wrote the second term of the quotient as $-12x$ rather than $-2x$. Here is
the correct method. $\dfrac{6x^2 - 12x}{6} = \dfrac{6x^2}{6} - \dfrac{12x}{6} = x^2 - 2x$ **79.** $2r + 7$
80. $2a^2 + 3a - 1 + \dfrac{6}{5a - 3}$ **81.** $x^2 + 3x - 4$ **82.** $m^2 + 4m - 2$
83. $4x - 5$ **84.** $5y - 10$ **85.** $y^2 + 2y + 4$ **86.** $100x^4 - 10x^2 + 1$
87. $2y^2 - 5y + 4 + \dfrac{-5}{3y^2 + 1}$ **88.** $x^3 - 2x^2 + 4 + \dfrac{-3}{4x^2 - 3}$ **89.** 2
90. $\dfrac{6^3r^6p^3}{5^3}$ **91.** $144a^2 - 1$ **92.** $\dfrac{1}{16}$ **93.** $\dfrac{1}{8^{12}}$ **94.** $p - 3 + \dfrac{5}{2p}$
95. $\dfrac{2}{3m^3}$ **96.** $6k^3 - 21k - 6$ **97.** r^{13} **98.** $4r^2 + 20rs + 25s^2$
99. $-y^2 - 4y + 4$ **100.** $10r^2 + 21r - 10$ **101.** $y^2 + 5y + 1$
102. $\dfrac{5}{2} - \dfrac{4}{5xy} + \dfrac{3x}{2y^2}$ **103.** $10p^2 - 3p - 5$ **104.** $3x^2 + 9x + 25 +$
$\dfrac{80}{x - 3}$ **105.** $49 - 28k + 4k^2$ **106.** $\dfrac{1}{x^4y^{12}}$ **107. (a)** $6x - 2$
(b) $2x^2 + x - 6$ **108. (a)** $20x^4 + 8x^2$ **(b)** $25x^8 + 20x^6 + 4x^4$

Chapter 4 Test (pages 291–292)

[4.1, 4.2] **1.** $\dfrac{1}{625}$ **2.** 2   **3.** $\dfrac{7}{12}$ **4.** $9x^3y^5$ **5.** 8^5 **6.** x^2y^6
7. (a) positive   **(b)** positive   **(c)** negative   **(d)** positive   **(e)** zero
(f) negative   [4.3] **8. (a)** 4.5×10^{10} **(b)** 0.0000036   **(c)** 0.00019
9. (a) 1×10^3; 5.89×10^{12} **(b)** 5.89×10^{15} mi
[4.4] **10.** $-7x^2 + 8x$; 2; binomial   **11.** $4n^4 + 13n^3 - 10n^2$; 4; trinomial
12. 4, -2, -4, -2, 4   **13.** $-2y^2 - 9y + 17$

14. $-21a^3b^2 + 7ab^5 - 5a^2b^2$
15. $-12t^2 + 5t + 8$
[4.5] **16.** $-27x^5 + 18x^4 - 6x^3 + 3x^2$
17. $t^2 - 5t - 24$ **18.** $8x^2 + 2xy - 3y^2$
[4.6] **19.** $25x^2 - 20xy + 4y^2$ **20.** $100v^2 - 9w^2$
[4.5] **21.** $2r^3 + r^2 - 16r + 15$ [4.6] **22.** $12x + 36$; $9x^2 + 54x + 81$
[4.7] **23.** $4y^2 - 3y + 2 + \dfrac{5}{y}$ **24.** $-3xy^2 + 2x^3y^2 + 4y^2$ **25.** $x - 2$
26. $3x^2 + 6x + 11 + \dfrac{26}{x - 2}$

Chapters 1–4 Cumulative Review Exercises (pages 293–294)

[1.1] **1.** $\dfrac{7}{4}$ **2.** 5   **3.** $31\frac{1}{4}$ yd³   [1.6] **4.** \$1836   **5.** 1, 3, 5, 9, 15, 45
6. -8 **7.** $\dfrac{1}{2}$ [1.5] **8.** -4 [1.7] **9.** associative property
10. distributive property   [1.8] **11.** $-10x^2 + 21x - 29$
[2.1–2.3] **12.** $\left\{\dfrac{13}{4}\right\}$ **13.** $\emptyset$ [2.5] **14.** $r = \dfrac{d}{t}$ [2.6] **15.** $\{-5\}$
[2.1–2.3] **16.** $\{-12\}$ **17.** $\{20\}$ **18.** $\{$all real numbers$\}$
[2.4] **19.** exertion: 9443 calories; regulating body temperature:
1757 calories   [2.8] **20.** 11 ft and 22 ft   **21.** $\left(-\infty, -\dfrac{14}{5}\right)$ **22.** $[-4, 2)$
[3.2] **23.**   [3.3, 3.4] **24. (a)** 1   **(b)** $y = x + 6$
[4.1, 4.2] **25.** $\dfrac{5}{4}$ **26.** 1   **27.** $\dfrac{2b}{a^{10}}$
[4.3] **28.** about 10,800,000 km

[4.4] **29.**   **30.** $11x^3 - 14x^2 - x + 14$
[4.5] **31.** $63x^2 + 57x + 12$
[4.7] **32.** $y^2 - 2y + 6$

$y = (x + 4)^2$

5   FACTORING AND APPLICATIONS

Section 5.1 (pages 301–303)

1. 4   **3.** 6   **5.** 1   **7.** 8   **9.** $10x^3$ **11.** xy^2 **13.** $6m^3n^2$ **15.** factored
17. not factored   **19.** $3m^2$ **21.** $2z^4$ **23.** $2mn^4$ **25.** $y + 2$
27. $a - 2$ **29.** $2 + 3xy$ **31.** First, verify that you have factored completely. Then multiply the factors. The product should be the original polynomial.   **33.** $x(x - 4)$ **35.** $3t(2t + 5)$ **37.** $9m(3m^2 - 1)$
39. $8z^2(2z^2 + 3)$ **41.** $6x^2(2x + 1)$ **43.** $5y^6(13y^4 + 7)$
45. in factored form   **47.** $8mn^3(1 + 3m)$ **49.** $13y^2(y^6 + 2y^2 - 3)$
51. $9p^3q(4p^3 + 5p^2q^3 + 9q)$ **53.** $a^3(a^2 + 2b^2 - 3a^2b^2 + 4ab^3)$
55. $(x + 2)(c - d)$ **57.** $(m + 2n)(m + n)$ **59.** $(p - 4)(q^2 + 1)$
61. not in factored form; $(7t + 4)(8 + x)$ **63.** in factored form
65. not in factored form   **67.** The quantities in parentheses are not the same, so there is no common factor of the two terms $18x^2(y + 4)$ and $7(y - 4)$.   **69.** $(p + 4)(p + q)$ **71.** $(a - 2)(a + b)$
73. $(z + 2)(7z - a)$ **75.** $(3r + 2y)(6r - x)$
77. $(a^2 + b^2)(3a + 2b)$ **79.** $(3 - a)(4 - b)$
81. $(4m - p^2)(4m^2 - p)$ **83.** $(y + 3)(y + x)$
85. $(5 - 2p)(m + 3)$ **87.** $(3r + 2y)(6r - t)$
89. $(1 + 2b)(a^5 - 3)$ **91.** commutative property
92. $2x(y - 4) - 3(y - 4)$ **93.** No, because it is not a product. It is the difference between $2x(y - 4)$ and $3(y - 4)$.
94. $(2x - 3)(y - 4)$; yes   **95.** $x^2 - 3x - 54$ **97.** $x^2 + 9x + 14$
99. $2x^4 + 6x^3 + 10x^2$

Section 5.2 (pages 307–309)

1. 1 and 48, -1 and -48, 2 and 24, -2 and -24, 3 and 16, -3 and -16, 4 and 12, -4 and -12, 6 and 8, -6 and -8; The pair with a sum of -19 is -3 and -16.   **3.** 1 and -24, -1 and 24, 2 and -12, -2 and 12, 3 and -8, -3 and 8, 4 and -6, -4 and 6; The pair with a sum of -5 is 3 and -8.   **5.** a and b must have different signs, one positive and one negative.   **7.** A prime polynomial is a polynomial that cannot be factored by using only integers in the factors.   **9.** C   **11.** $a^2 + 13a + 36$
13. $p + 6$ **15.** $x + 11$ **17.** $x - 8$ **19.** $y - 5$ **21.** $x + 11$
23. $y - 9$ **25.** $(y + 8)(y + 1)$ **27.** $(b + 3)(b + 5)$
29. $(m + 5)(m - 4)$ **31.** $(y - 5)(y - 3)$ **33.** prime
35. $(z - 7)(z - 8)$ **37.** $(r - 6)(r + 5)$ **39.** $(a + 4)(a - 12)$
41. prime   **43.** $(x + 16)(x - 2)$ **45.** $(r + 2a)(r + a)$
47. $(t + 2z)(t - 3z)$ **49.** $(x + y)(x + 3y)$ **51.** $(v - 5w)(v - 6w)$
53. $4(x + 5)(x - 2)$ **55.** $2t(t + 1)(t + 3)$ **57.** $2x^4(x - 3)(x + 7)$
59. $5m^2(m^3 + 5m^2 - 8)$ **61.** $mn(m - 6n)(m - 4n)$
63. $a^3(a + 4b)(a - b)$ **65.** $yz(y + 3z)(y - 2z)$
67. $z^8(z - 7y)(z + 3y)$ **69.** $(a + b)(x + 4)(x - 3)$
71. $(2p + q)(r - 9)(r - 3)$ **73.** $2y^2 + y - 28$ **75.** $15z^2 - 4z - 4$

Section 5.3 (pages 314–316)

1. $(2t + 1)(5t + 2)$ **3.** $(3z - 2)(5z - 3)$ **5.** $(2s - t)(4s + 3t)$
7. (a) 2, 12, 24, 11   **(b)** 3, 8 (Order is irrelevant.)   **(c)** $3m, 8m$
(d) $2m^2 + 3m + 8m + 12$ **(e)** $(2m + 3)(m + 4)$
(f) $(2m + 3)(m + 4) = 2m^2 + 11m + 12$ **9.** B   **11.** B   **13.** A
15. $2a + 5b$ **17.** $x^2 + 3x - 4; x + 4, x - 1,$ or $x - 1, x + 4$
19. $2z^2 - 5z - 3; 2z + 1, z - 3,$ or $z - 3, 2z + 1$
21. The binomial $2x - 6$ cannot be a factor because its terms have a common factor of 2, which the polynomial terms do not have.
23. $(3a + 7)(a + 1)$ **25.** $(2y + 3)(y + 2)$
27. $(3m - 1)(5m + 2)$ **29.** $(3s - 1)(4s + 5)$
31. $(5m - 4)(2m - 3)$ **33.** $(4w - 1)(2w - 3)$
35. $(4y + 1)(5y - 11)$ **37.** prime   **39.** $2(5x + 3)(2x + 1)$
41. $3(4x - 1)(2x - 3)$ **43.** $q(5m + 2)(8m - 3)$
45. $3n^2(5n - 3)(n - 2)$ **47.** $y^2(5x - 4)(3x + 1)$
49. $(5a + 3b)(a - 2b)$ **51.** $(4s + 5t)(3s - t)$
53. $m^4n(3m + 2n)(2m + n)$ **55.** $(x - 5)(x - 1)$
57. $(3x + 4)(x + 4)$ **59.** $-5x(2x + 7)(x - 4)$
61. $(12x + 1)(x - 4)$ **63.** $(24y + 7x)(y - 2x)$
65. $(18x^2 - 5y)(2x^2 - 3y)$ **67.** $2(24a + b)(a - 2b)$
69. $x^2y^5(10x - 1)(x + 4)$ **71.** $4ab^2(9a + 1)(a - 3)$
73. $(12x - 5)(2x - 3)$ **75.** $(8x^2 - 3)(3x^2 + 8)$
77. $(4x + 3y)(6x + 5y)$ **79.** $-1(x + 7)(x - 3)$
81. $-1(3x + 4)(x - 1)$ **83.** $-1(a + 2b)(2a + b)$
85. $(m + 1)^3(5q - 2)(5q + 1)$ **87.** $(r + 3)^3(3x + 2y)^2$ **89.** $-4, 4$
91. $-11, -7, 7, 11$ **93.** $49p^2 - 9$ **95.** $x^2 + 12x + 36$

Section 5.4 (pages 323–325)

1. 1; 4; 9; 16; 25; 36; 49; 64; 81; 100; 121; 144; 169; 196; 225; 256; 289; 324; 361; 400   **3.** 1; 8; 27; 64; 125; 216; 343; 512; 729; 1000
5. (a) both of these   **(b)** perfect cube   **(c)** perfect square
(d) perfect square   **7.** $(y + 5)(y - 5)$ **9.** $(x + 12)(x - 12)$
11. prime   **13.** $4(m^2 + 4)$ **15.** $(3r + 2)(3r - 2)$
17. $4(3x + 2)(3x - 2)$ **19.** $(14p + 15)(14p - 15)$
21. $(4r + 5a)(4r - 5a)$ **23.** prime   **25.** $(p^2 + 7)(p^2 - 7)$
27. $(x^2 + 1)(x + 1)(x - 1)$ **29.** $(p^2 + 16)(p + 4)(p - 4)$
31. $k^2 - 9$ can be factored as $(k + 3)(k - 3)$. The completely factored form is $(k^2 + 9)(k + 3)(k - 3)$.   **33.** 10   **35.** 9   **37.** $(w + 1)^2$
39. $(x - 4)^2$ **41.** $2(x + 6)^2$ **43.** $(4x - 5)^2$ **45.** $(7x - 2y)^2$
47. $(8x + 3y)^2$ **49.** $2(5h - 2y)^2$ **51.** $k(4k^2 - 4k + 9)$
53. $z^2(25z^2 + 5z + 1)$ **55.** $(a - 1)(a^2 + a + 1)$
57. $(m + 2)(m^2 - 2m + 4)$ **59.** $(k + 10)(k^2 - 10k + 100)$
61. $(3x - 4)(9x^2 + 12x + 16)$ **63.** $6(p + 1)(p^2 - p + 1)$
65. $5(x + 2)(x^2 - 2x + 4)$ **67.** $(y - 2x)(y^2 + 2yx + 4x^2)$
69. $2(x - 2y)(x^2 + 2xy + 4y^2)$
71. $(2p + 9q)(4p^2 - 18pq + 81q^2)$
73. $(3a + 4b)(9a^2 - 12ab + 16b^2)$
75. $(5t + 2s)(25t^2 - 10ts + 4s^2)$
77. $(2x - 5y^2)(4x^2 + 10xy^2 + 25y^4)$
79. $(3m^2 + 2n)(9m^4 - 6m^2n + 4n^2)$

81. $(x + y)(x^2 - xy + y^2)(x^6 - x^3y^3 + y^6)$ **83.** $\left(p + \frac{1}{3}\right)\left(p - \frac{1}{3}\right)$

85. $\left(6m + \frac{4}{5}\right)\left(6m - \frac{4}{5}\right)$ **87.** $(x + 0.8)(x - 0.8)$ **89.** $\left(t + \frac{1}{2}\right)^2$

91. $(x - 0.5)^2$ **93.** $\left(x + \frac{1}{2}\right)\left(x^2 - \frac{1}{2}x + \frac{1}{4}\right)$ **95.** $4mn$

97. $(m - p + 2)(m + p)$ **99.** $\{4\}$ **101.** $\{-5\}$

Summary Exercises on Factoring (pages 326–327)

1. G   **2.** H   **3.** A   **4.** B   **5.** E   **6.** I   **7.** C   **8.** F   **9.** I   **10.** E

11. $(a - 6)(a + 2)$ **12.** $(a + 8)(a + 9)$ **13.** $6(y - 2)(y + 1)$

14. $7y^4(y + 6)(y - 4)$ **15.** $6(a + 2b + 3c)$

16. $(m - 4n)(m + n)$ **17.** $(p - 11)(p - 6)$ **18.** $(z + 7)(z - 6)$

19. $(5z - 6)(2z + 1)$ **20.** $2(m - 8)(m + 3)$ **21.** $17xy(x^2y + 3)$

22. $5(3y + 1)$ **23.** $8a^3(a - 3)(a + 2)$ **24.** $(4k + 1)(2k - 3)$

25. $(z - 5a)(z + 2a)$ **26.** $50(z^2 - 2)$ **27.** $(x - 5)(x - 4)$

28. $10nr(10nr + 3r^2 - 5n)$ **29.** $(3n - 2)(2n - 5)$

30. $(3y - 1)(3y + 5)$ **31.** $4(4x + 5)$ **32.** $(m + 5)(m - 3)$

33. $(3y - 4)(2y + 1)$ **34.** $(m + 9)(m - 9)$ **35.** $(6z + 1)(z + 5)$

36. $(12x - 1)(x + 4)$ **37.** $(2k - 3)^2$ **38.** $(8p - 1)(p + 3)$

39. $6(3m + 2z)(3m - 2z)$ **40.** $(4m - 3)(2m + 1)$

41. $(3k - 2)(k + 2)$ **42.** $15a^3b^2(3b^3 - 4a + 5a^3b^2)$

43. $7k(2k + 5)(k - 2)$ **44.** $(5 + r)(1 - s)$

45. $(y^2 + 4)(y + 2)(y - 2)$ **46.** $10y^4(2y - 3)$ **47.** $8m(1 - 2m)$

48. $(k + 4)(k - 4)$ **49.** $(z - 2)(z^2 + 2z + 4)$

50. $(y - 8)(y + 7)$ **51.** prime   **52.** $9p^8(3p + 7)(p - 4)$

53. $8m^3(4m^6 + 2m^2 + 3)$ **54.** $(2m + 5)(4m^2 - 10m + 25)$

55. $(4r + 3m)^2$ **56.** $(z - 6)^2$ **57.** $(5h + 7g)(3h - 2g)$

58. $5z(z - 7)(z - 2)$ **59.** $(k - 5)(k - 6)$

60. $4(4p - 5m)(4p + 5m)$ **61.** $3k(k - 5)(k + 1)$

62. $(y - 6k)(y + 2k)$ **63.** $(10p + 3)(100p^2 - 30p + 9)$

64. $(4r - 7)(16r^2 + 28r + 49)$ **65.** $(2 + m)(3 + p)$

66. $(2m - 3n)(m + 5n)$ **67.** $(4z - 1)^2$

68. $5m^2(5m - 3n)(5m - 13n)$ **69.** $3(6m - 1)^2$

70. $(10a + 9y)(10a - 9y)$ **71.** prime   **72.** $(2y + 5)(2y - 5)$

73. $8z(4z - 1)(z + 2)$ **74.** $5(2m - 3)(m + 4)$

75. $(4 + m)(5 + 3n)$ **76.** $(2 - q)(2 - 3p)$

77. $2(3a - 1)(a + 2)$ **78.** $6y^4(3y + 4)(2y - 5)$

79. $(a - b)(a^2 + ab + b^2 + 2)$ **80.** $4(2k - 3)^2$

81. $(8m - 5n)^2$ **82.** $12y^2(6yz^2 + 1 - 2y^2z^2)$

83. $(4k - 3h)(2k + h)$ **84.** $(2a + 5)(a - 6)$

85. $2(x + 4)(x^2 - 4x + 16)$ **86.** $(2a - 3)(4a^2 + 6a + 9)$

87. $(5y - 6z)(2y + z)$ **88.** $(m - 2)^2$ **89.** $(8a - b)(a + 3b)$

90. $(a^2 + 25)(a + 5)(a - 5)$ **91.** $(x^3 - 1)(x^3 + 1)$

92. $(x - 1)(x^2 + x + 1)(x + 1)(x^2 - x + 1)$

93. $(x^2 - 1)(x^4 + x^2 + 1)$ **94.** $(x - 1)(x + 1)(x^4 + x^2 + 1)$

95. The result in **Exercise 92** is factored completely.   **96.** Show that $x^4 + x^2 + 1 = (x^2 + x + 1)(x^2 - x + 1)$.   **97.** difference of squares

98. $(x - 3)(x^2 + 3x + 9)(x + 3)(x^2 - 3x + 9)$

Section 5.5 (pages 334–337)

1. $ax^2 + bx + c$ **3.** factor   **5.** $0; x$ **7.** To solve $2x(3x - 4) = 0$, set each *variable* factor equal to 0 to get $x = 0$ or $3x - 4 = 0$. The *constant*

factor 2 does not introduce solutions into the equation. The solution set is $\left\{0, \frac{4}{3}\right\}$.   **9.** The variable x is another factor to set equal to 0, so the solution set is $\left\{0, \frac{1}{7}\right\}$.   **11.** $\{-5, 2\}$ **13.** $\left\{3, \frac{7}{2}\right\}$ **15.** $\left\{-\frac{1}{2}, \frac{1}{6}\right\}$

17. $\left\{-\frac{5}{6}, 0\right\}$ **19.** $\left\{0, \frac{4}{3}\right\}$ **21.** $\{6\}$ **23.** $\{-2, -1\}$ **25.** $\{1, 2\}$

27. $\{-8, 3\}$ **29.** $\{-1, 3\}$ **31.** $\{-2, -1\}$ **33.** $\{-4\}$ **35.** $\left\{-2, \frac{1}{3}\right\}$

37. $\left\{-\frac{4}{3}, \frac{1}{2}\right\}$ **39.** $\left\{-\frac{2}{3}\right\}$ **41.** $\{-3, 3\}$ **43.** $\left\{-\frac{7}{4}, \frac{7}{4}\right\}$

45. $\{-11, 11\}$ **47.** $\{0, 7\}$ **49.** $\left\{0, \frac{1}{2}\right\}$ **51.** $\{2, 5\}$ **53.** $\left\{-4, \frac{1}{2}\right\}$

55. $\{-17, 4\}$ **57.** $\left\{-\frac{5}{2}, \frac{1}{3}, 5\right\}$ **59.** $\left\{-\frac{7}{2}, -3, 1\right\}$ **61.** $\left\{-\frac{7}{3}, 0, \frac{7}{3}\right\}$

63. $\{-2, 0, 4\}$ **65.** $\{-5, 0, 4\}$ **67.** $\{-3, 0, 5\}$ **69.** $\{-1, 3\}$

71. $\{-1, 3\}$ **73.** $\{3\}$ **75.** $\left\{-\frac{2}{3}, 4\right\}$ **77.** $\left\{-\frac{4}{3}, -1, \frac{1}{2}\right\}$

79. (a) $64; 144; 4; 6$ **(b)** No time has elapsed, so the object hasn't fallen (been released) yet.   **81.** $\{-0.5, 0.1\}$ **83.** 1845 **85.** $9, 10$

Section 5.6 (pages 342–347)

1. Read; variable; equation; Solve; answer; Check, original

3. *Step 3:* $45 = (2x + 1)(x + 1)$; *Step 4:* $x = 4$ or $x = -\frac{11}{2}$;
Step 5: base: 9 units; height: 5 units; *Step 6:* $9 \cdot 5 = 45$

5. *Step 3:* $80 = (x + 8)(x - 8)$; *Step 4:* $x = 12$ or $x = -12$;
Step 5: length: 20 units; width: 4 units; *Step 6:* $20 \cdot 4 = 80$

7. length: 14 cm; width: 12 cm   **9.** base: 12 in.; height: 5 in.

11. height: 13 in.; width: 10 in.   **13.** length: 15 in.; width: 12 in.

15. mirror: 7 ft; painting: 9 ft   **17.** 20, 21   **19.** 0, 1, 2 or 7, 8, 9

21. 7, 9, 11   **23.** $-2, 0, 2$ or 6, 8, 10   **25.** 12 cm   **27.** 12 mi   **29.** 8 ft

31. 112 ft   **33.** 256 ft   **35. (a)** 1 sec   **(b)** $\frac{1}{2}$ sec and $1\frac{1}{2}$ sec   **(c)** 3 sec

(d) The negative solution, -1, does not make sense, since t represents time, which cannot be negative.   **37. (a)** 104.4 million; The result obtained from the model is less than 109 million, the actual number for 2000.

(b) 18   **(c)** 272.7 million; The result is more than 263 million.

(d) 326.6 million   **39.** $\frac{25}{36}$ **41.** $\frac{16}{-9}$, or $-\frac{16}{9}$

Chapter 5 Review Exercises (pages 350–352)

1. $7(t + 2)$ **2.** $30z(2z^2 + 1)$ **3.** $(2y + 3)(x - 4)$

4. $(3y + 2x)(2y + 3)$ **5.** $(x + 3)(x + 2)$ **6.** $(y - 5)(y - 8)$

7. $(q + 9)(q - 3)$ **8.** $(r - 8)(r + 7)$ **9.** $(r + 8s)(r - 12s)$

10. $(p + 12q)(p - 10q)$ **11.** $8p(p + 2)(p - 5)$

12. $3x^2(x + 2)(x + 8)$ **13.** $p^5(p - 2q)(p + q)$

14. $3r^3(r + 3s)(r - 5s)$ **15.** $9x^2y(x + 2)(x - 3)$

16. $2x^5(x - 2y)(x + 3y)$ **17.** r and $6r$, $2r$ and $3r$ **18.** Factor out z.

19. $(2k - 1)(k - 2)$ **20.** $(3r - 1)(r + 4)$ **21.** $(3r + 2)(2r - 3)$

22. $(5z + 1)(2z - 1)$ **23.** $(v + 3)(8v - 7)$

24. $4x^3(3x - 1)(2x - 1)$ **25.** $-3(x + 2)(2x - 5)$

26. $rs(5r + 6s)(2r + s)$ **27.** $4x^2y(3x + y)(4x - y)$ **28.** The student stopped too soon. He needs to factor out the common factor $4x - 1$ to get $(4x - 1)(4x - 5)$ as the correct answer.   **29.** B

30. D   **31.** $(n + 7)(n - 7)$ **32.** $(5b + 11)(5b - 11)$

33. $(7y + 5w)(7y - 5w)$ **34.** $36(2p + q)(2p - q)$ **35.** prime

36. $(r - 6)^2$ **37.** $(3t - 7)^2$ **38.** $(m + 10)(m^2 - 10m + 100)$

39. $(5k + 4x)(25k^2 - 20kx + 16x^2)$

40. $(7x - 4)(49x^2 + 28x + 16)$

41. $(10 - 3x^2)(100 + 30x^2 + 9x^4)$

42. $(x - y)(x + y)(x^2 + xy + y^2)(x^2 - xy + y^2)$

43. $\left\{-\frac{3}{4}, 1\right\}$ **44.** $\{-7, -3, 4\}$ **45.** $\left\{0, \frac{5}{2}\right\}$ **46.** $\{-3, -1\}$

47. $\{1, 4\}$ **48.** $\{3, 5\}$ **49.** $\left\{-\frac{4}{3}, 5\right\}$ **50.** $\left\{-\frac{8}{9}, \frac{8}{9}\right\}$ **51.** $\{0, 8\}$

52. $\{-1, 6\}$ **53.** $\{7\}$ **54.** $\{6\}$ **55.** $\left\{-2, -1, -\frac{2}{5}\right\}$ **56.** $\{-3, 3\}$

57. length: 10 ft; width: 4 ft **58.** 5 ft **59.** 6, 7 or $-5, -4$ **60.** 26 mi

61. (a) 256 ft (b) 1024 ft **62.** (a) 601,000 vehicles; The result is slightly higher than the actual number for 2005. (b) 655,000 vehicles (c) The estimate may be unreliable because the conditions that prevailed in the years 2001–2006 may have changed, causing either a greater increase or a decrease predicted by the model for the number of alternative-fueled vehicles. **63.** D **64.** The factor $(2x + 8)$ has a factor of 2. The completely factored form is $2(x + 4)(3x - 4)$.

65. $(3k + 5)(k + 2)$ **66.** $(z - x)(z - 10x)$

67. $(y^2 + 25)(y + 5)(y - 5)$ **68.** $(3m + 4)(5m - 4p)$

69. $8abc(3b^2c - 7ac^2 + 9ab)$ **70.** $3m(2m + 3)(m - 5)$

71. $6xyz(2xz^2 + 2y - 5x^2yz^3)$ **72.** prime **73.** $(2r + 3q)(6r - 5)$

74. $2a^3(a + 2)(a - 6)$ **75.** $(7t + 4)^2$

76. $(10a + 3)(100a^2 - 30a + 9)$ **77.** $\{0, 7\}$ **78.** $\{-5, 2\}$

79. $\left\{-\frac{2}{5}\right\}$ **80.** $-5, -4, -3$ or $5, 6, 7$ **81.** length: 6 m; width: 4 m

82. 15 m, 36 m, 39 m **83.** 6 m **84.** width: 10 m; length: 17 m

Chapter 5 Test (page 353)

[5.1–5.4] **1.** D **2.** $6x(2x - 5)$ **3.** $m^2n(2mn + 3m - 5n)$

4. $(2x + y)(a - b)$ **5.** $(x + 3)(x - 8)$ **6.** $(2x + 3)(x - 1)$

7. $(5z - 1)(2z - 3)$ **8.** prime **9.** prime **10.** $(2 - a)(6 + b)$

11. $(3y + 8)(3y - 8)$ **12.** $(2x - 7y)^2$ **13.** $-2(x + 1)^2$

14. $3t^2(2t + 9)(t - 4)$ **15.** $(r - 5)(r^2 + 5r + 25)$

16. $8(k + 2)(k^2 - 2k + 4)$ **17.** $(x^2 + 9)(x + 3)(x - 3)$

18. $(3x + 2y)(3x - 2y)(9x^2 + 4y^2)$ **19.** $(3x^3y^2 + 2)^2$

[5.5] **20.** $\left\{\frac{1}{2}, 6\right\}$ **21.** $\left\{-\frac{2}{5}, \frac{2}{5}\right\}$ **22.** $\{0, 9\}$ **23.** $\{10\}$

24. $\left\{-8, -\frac{5}{2}, \frac{1}{3}\right\}$ [5.6] **25.** 6 ft by 9 ft **26.** $-2, -1$ **27.** 17 ft

28. \$8493 billion

Chapters 1–5 Cumulative Review Exercises (pages 354–355)

[2.1–2.3] **1.** $\{0\}$ **2.** $\{0.05\}$ **3.** $\{6\}$ [2.5] **4.** $P = \dfrac{A}{1 + rt}$

5. $110°$ and $70°$ [2.4] **6.** gold: 11; silver: 12; bronze: 6

[2.6] **7.** 230; 205; 38%; 12% [3.1] **8.** (a) negative, positive (b) negative, negative

[3.2, 3.3] **9.** (a) $\left(-\frac{1}{4}, 0\right), (0, 3)$ (b) 12 (c)

[3.3, 3.4] **10.** (a) 16; A slope of (approximately) 16 means that retail sales of prescription drugs increased by about \$16 billion per year.

(b) (2005, 230) [4.1, 4.2] **11.** $\frac{16}{9}$ **12.** 256 **13.** $\dfrac{1}{p^2}$ **14.** $\dfrac{1}{m^6}$

[4.4] **15.** $-4k^2 - 4k + 8$ [4.5] **16.** $45x^2 + 3x - 18$

[4.6] **17.** $9p^2 + 12p + 4$ [4.7] **18.** $4x^3 + 6x^2 - 3x + 10$

[4.3] **19.** $5.5 \times 10^4; 2.0 \times 10^6$ [5.2, 5.3] **20.** $(2a - 1)(a + 4)$

21. $(2m + 3)(5m + 2)$ **22.** $(4t + 3v)(2t + v)$

[5.4] **23.** $(2p - 3)^2$ **24.** $(5r + 9t)(5r - 9t)$

[5.3] **25.** $2pq(3p + 1)(p + 1)$ [5.5] **26.** $\left\{-\frac{2}{3}, \frac{1}{2}\right\}$ **27.** $\{0, 8\}$

[5.6] **28.** 5 m, 12 m, 13 m

6 RATIONAL EXPRESSIONS AND APPLICATIONS

Connections **(page 363)** **1.** $3x^2 + 11x + 8$ cannot be factored, so this quotient cannot be simplified. By long division, the quotient is $3x + 5 + \dfrac{-2}{x + 2}$. **2.** The numerator factors as $(x - 2)(x^2 + 2x + 4)$, so, after simplification, the quotient is $x - 2$. Long division gives the same quotient.

Section 6.1 (pages 364–366)

1. (a) $\frac{7}{10}$ (b) $\frac{8}{15}$ **3.** (a) 0 (b) -1 **5.** (a) $-\frac{64}{15}$ (b) undefined

7. (a) undefined (b) $\frac{8}{25}$ **9.** (a) 0 (b) 0 **11.** (a) 0 (b) undefined

13. A rational expression is a quotient of two polynomials, such as $\dfrac{x^2 + 3x - 6}{x + 4}$. One can think of this as an algebraic fraction. **15.** Division by 0 is undefined. If the denominator of a rational expression equals 0, the expression is undefined. **17.** $y \neq 0$ **19.** $x \neq 6$

21. $x \neq -\frac{5}{3}$ **23.** $m \neq -3, m \neq 2$ **25.** It is never undefined.

27. It is never undefined. **29.** (a) numerator: $x^2, 4x$; denominator: $x, 4$ (b) First factor the numerator, getting $x(x + 4)$. Then divide the numerator and denominator by the common factor $x + 4$ to get $\dfrac{x}{1}$, or x.

31. $3r^2$ **33.** $\frac{2}{5}$ **35.** $\dfrac{x - 1}{x + 1}$ **37.** $\frac{7}{5}$ **39.** $\frac{6}{7}$ **41.** $m - n$ **43.** $\dfrac{2}{t - 3}$

45. $\dfrac{3(2m + 1)}{4}$ **47.** $\dfrac{3m}{5}$ **49.** $\dfrac{3r - 2s}{3}$ **51.** $k - 3$ **53.** $\dfrac{x - 3}{x + 1}$

55. $\dfrac{x + 1}{x - 1}$ **57.** $\dfrac{x + 2}{x - 4}$ **59.** $-\dfrac{3}{7t}$ **61.** $\dfrac{z - 3}{z + 5}$ **63.** $\dfrac{r + s}{r - s}$ **65.** $\dfrac{a + b}{a - b}$

67. $\dfrac{m + n}{2}$ **69.** $\dfrac{x^2 + 1}{x}$ **71.** $1 - p + p^2$ **73.** $x^2 + 3x + 9$

75. $-\dfrac{b^2 + ba + a^2}{a + b}$ **77.** $\dfrac{k^2 - 2k + 4}{k - 2}$ **79.** $\dfrac{z + 3}{z}$ **81.** $\dfrac{1 - 2r}{2}$

83. B, D **85.** -1 **87.** $-(m + 1)$ **89.** -1 **91.** It is already in lowest terms. **93.** B

Answers may vary in Exercises 95, 97, and 99. **95.** $\dfrac{-(x + 4)}{x - 3}, \dfrac{-x - 4}{x - 3}, \dfrac{x + 4}{-(x - 3)}, \dfrac{x + 4}{-x + 3}$ **97.** $\dfrac{-(2x - 3)}{x + 3}, \dfrac{-2x + 3}{x + 3}, \dfrac{2x - 3}{-(x + 3)}, \dfrac{2x - 3}{-x - 3}$

99. $\dfrac{-(3x - 1)}{5x - 6}, \dfrac{-3x + 1}{5x - 6}, \dfrac{3x - 1}{-(5x - 6)}, \dfrac{3x - 1}{-5x + 6}$

101. $x^2 + 3$ **103.** (a) 0 (b) 1.6 (c) 4.1 (d) The waiting time also increases. **105.** $\frac{5}{9}$ **107.** 4

Section 6.2 (pages 371–372)

1. **(a)** B **(b)** D **(c)** C **(d)** A 3. $\dfrac{3a}{2}$ 5. $-\dfrac{4x^4}{3}$ 7. $\dfrac{2}{c+d}$

9. $4(x-y)$ 11. $\dfrac{t^2}{2}$ 13. $\dfrac{x+3}{2x}$ 15. 5 17. $-\dfrac{3}{2t^4}$ 19. $\frac{1}{4}$

21. $-\frac{35}{8}$ 23. $\dfrac{2(x+2)}{x(x-1)}$ 25. $\dfrac{x(x-3)}{6}$ 27. $\frac{10}{9}$ 29. $-\frac{3}{4}$ 31. $-\frac{9}{2}$

33. $\dfrac{p+4}{p+2}$ 35. -1 37. $\dfrac{(2x-1)(x+2)}{x-1}$ 39. $\dfrac{(k-1)^2}{(k+1)(2k-1)}$

41. $\dfrac{4k-1}{3k-2}$ 43. $\dfrac{m+4p}{m+p}$ 45. $\dfrac{m+6}{m+3}$ 47. $\dfrac{y+3}{y+4}$ 49. $\dfrac{m}{m+5}$

51. $\dfrac{r+6s}{r+s}$ 53. $\dfrac{(q-3)^2(q+2)^2}{q+1}$ 55. $\dfrac{x+10}{10}$ 57. $\dfrac{3-a-b}{2a-b}$

59. $-\dfrac{(x+y)^2(x^2-xy+y^2)}{3y(y-x)(x-y)}$, or $\dfrac{(x+y)^2(x^2-xy+y^2)}{3y(x-y)^2}$ 61. $\dfrac{5xy^2}{4q}$

63. $2 \cdot 3^2$ 65. $2^2 \cdot 3^3$ 67. 6 69. $6q^3$

Section 6.3 (pages 376–378)

1. C 3. C 5. 60 7. 1800 9. x^5 11. $30p$ 13. $180y^4$ 15. $84r^5$

17. $15a^5b^3$ 19. $12p(p-2)$ 21. $28m^2(3m-5)$ 23. $30(b-2)$

25. $18(r-2)$ 27. $12p(p+5)^2$ 29. $8(y+2)(y+1)$

31. $c-d$ or $d-c$ 33. $m-3$ or $3-m$ 35. $p-q$ or $q-p$

37. $k(k+5)(k-2)$ 39. $a(a+6)(a-3)$

41. $(p+3)(p+5)(p-6)$ 43. $(k+3)(k-5)(k+7)(k+8)$

45. 7 46. 1 47. identity property of multiplication

48. 7 49. 1 50. identity property of multiplication

51. $\frac{20}{55}$ 53. $\dfrac{-45}{9k}$ 55. $\dfrac{60m^2k^3}{32k^4}$ 57. $\dfrac{57z}{6z-18}$ 59. $\dfrac{-4a}{18a-36}$

61. $\dfrac{6(k+1)}{k(k-4)(k+1)}$ 63. $\dfrac{36r(r+1)}{(r-3)(r+2)(r+1)}$

65. $\dfrac{ab(a+2b)}{2a^3b+a^2b^2-ab^3}$ 67. $\dfrac{(t-r)(4r-t)}{t^3-r^3}$

69. $\dfrac{2y(z-y)(y-z)}{y^4-z^3y}$, or $\dfrac{-2y(y-z)^2}{y^4-z^3y}$ 71. $\frac{11}{8}$ 73. $\frac{13}{20}$

Section 6.4 (pages 383–386)

1. E 3. C 5. B 7. G 9. $\dfrac{11}{m}$ 11. $\dfrac{4}{y+4}$ 13. 1 15. $\dfrac{m-1}{m+1}$

17. b 19. x 21. $y-6$ 23. $\dfrac{1}{x-3}$ 25. $\dfrac{3z+5}{15}$ 27. $\dfrac{10-7r}{14}$

29. $\dfrac{-3x-2}{4x}$ 31. $\dfrac{57}{10x}$ 33. $\dfrac{x+1}{2}$ 35. $\dfrac{5x+9}{6x}$ 37. $\dfrac{7-6p}{3p^2}$

39. $\dfrac{-k-8}{k(k+4)}$ 41. $\dfrac{x+4}{x+2}$ 43. $\dfrac{6m^2+23m-2}{(m+2)(m+1)(m+5)}$

45. $\dfrac{4y^2-y+5}{(y+1)^2(y-1)}$ 47. $\dfrac{3}{t}$ 49. $m-2$ or $2-m$

51. $\dfrac{-2}{x-5}$, or $\dfrac{2}{5-x}$ 53. -4 55. $\dfrac{-5}{x-y^2}$, or $\dfrac{5}{y^2-x}$

57. $\dfrac{x+y}{5x-3y}$, or $\dfrac{-x-y}{3y-5x}$ 59. $\dfrac{-6}{4p-5}$, or $\dfrac{6}{5-4p}$

61. $\dfrac{-m-n}{2(m-n)}$ 63. $\dfrac{-x^2+6x+11}{(x+3)(x-3)(x+1)}$

65. $\dfrac{-5q^2-13q+7}{(3q-2)(q+4)(2q-3)}$ 67. $\dfrac{9r+2}{r(r+2)(r-1)}$

69. $\dfrac{2(x^2+3xy+4y^2)}{(x+y)(x+y)(x+3y)}$, or $\dfrac{2(x^2+3xy+4y^2)}{(x+y)^2(x+3y)}$

71. $\dfrac{15r^2+10ry-y^2}{(3r+2y)(6r-y)(6r+y)}$ 73. **(a)** $\dfrac{9k^2+6k+26}{5(3k+1)}$ **(b)** $\frac{1}{4}$

75. $\dfrac{10x}{49(101-x)}$ 77. $\frac{5}{4}$ 79. $\frac{6}{7}$

Section 6.5 (pages 392–394)

1. **(a)** $6;\frac{1}{6}$ **(b)** $12;-\frac{1}{4}$ **(c)** $\frac{1}{6}\div\left(-\frac{1}{4}\right)$ **(d)** $-\frac{2}{3}$ 3. Choice D is correct, because every sign has been changed in the fraction. This means it was multiplied by $\frac{-1}{-1}=1$. 5. -6 7. $\dfrac{1}{xy}$ 9. $\dfrac{2a^2b}{3}$

11. $\dfrac{m(m+2)}{3(m-4)}$ 13. $\dfrac{2}{x}$ 15. $\dfrac{8}{x}$ 17. $\dfrac{a^2-5}{a^2+1}$ 19. $\frac{31}{50}$ 21. $\dfrac{y^2+x^2}{xy(y-x)}$

23. $\dfrac{40-12p}{85p}$ 25. $\dfrac{5y-2x}{3+4xy}$ 27. $\dfrac{a-2}{2a}$ 29. $\dfrac{z-5}{4}$ 31. $\dfrac{-m}{m+2}$

33. $\dfrac{3m(m-3)}{(m-1)(m-8)}$ 35. $\dfrac{2x-7}{3x+1}$ 37. $\dfrac{y+4}{y-8}$ 39. $\dfrac{x^2y^2}{y^2+x^2}$

41. $\dfrac{y^2+x^2}{xy^2+x^2y}$, or $\dfrac{y^2+x^2}{xy(y+x)}$ 43. $\dfrac{1}{2xy}$ 45. $\dfrac{x-3}{x-5}$ 47. division

49. $\dfrac{\frac{3}{8}+\frac{5}{6}}{2}$ 50. $\frac{29}{48}$ 51. $\frac{29}{48}$ 52. Answers will vary. 53. $\frac{5}{3}$ 55. $\frac{13}{2}$

57. $\dfrac{19r}{15}$ 59. $12x+2$ 61. $-44p^2+27p$ 63. $\left\{\frac{1}{2}\right\}$ 65. $\{-5\}$

Section 6.6 (pages 401–404)

1. expression; $\frac{43}{40}x$ 3. equation; $\left\{\frac{40}{43}\right\}$ 5. expression; $-\frac{1}{10}x$

7. equation; $\{-10\}$ 9. equation; $\{0\}$ 11. $x\neq -2,0$

13. $x\neq -3,4,-\frac{1}{2}$ 15. $x\neq -9,1,-2,2$ 17. $\dfrac{2}{3x}+\dfrac{1}{5x}$ is an expression, not an equation. Only equations and inequalities are "solved."

19. $\left\{\frac{1}{4}\right\}$ 21. $\left\{-\frac{3}{4}\right\}$ 23. $\{-15\}$ 25. $\{7\}$ 27. $\{-15\}$ 29. $\{-5\}$

31. $\{-6\}$ 33. $\varnothing$ 35. $\{5\}$ 37. $\{4\}$ 39. $\{5\}$ 41. $\left\{x\,|\,x\neq \pm\frac{4}{3}\right\}$

43. $\{1\}$ 45. $\{4\}$ 47. $\{5\}$ 49. $\{-4\}$ 51. $\{-2,12\}$ 53. $\varnothing$

55. $\{3\}$ 57. $\{3\}$ 59. $\{-3\}$ 61. $\left\{-\frac{1}{5},3\right\}$ 63. $\left\{-\frac{1}{2},5\right\}$ 65. $\{3\}$

67. $\left\{-\frac{1}{3},3\right\}$ 69. $\{-1\}$ 71. $\{-6\}$ 73. $\left\{-6,\frac{1}{2}\right\}$ 75. $\{6\}$

77. Transform so that the terms with k are on one side and the remaining term is on the other. 79. $F=\dfrac{ma}{k}$ 81. $a=\dfrac{kF}{m}$ 83. $R=\dfrac{E-Ir}{I}$, or $R=\dfrac{E}{I}-r$ 85. $\mathcal{A}=\dfrac{h(B+b)}{2}$ 87. $a=\dfrac{2S-ndL}{nd}$, or $a=\dfrac{2S}{nd}-L$

89. $y=\dfrac{xz}{x+z}$ 91. $t=\dfrac{rs}{rs-2s-3r}$, or $t=\dfrac{-rs}{-rs+2s+3r}$

93. $z=\dfrac{3y}{5-9xy}$, or $z=\dfrac{-3y}{9xy-5}$ 95. $t=\dfrac{2x-1}{x+1}$, or $t=\dfrac{-2x+1}{-x-1}$

97. $\dfrac{288}{t}$ mph 99. $\dfrac{289}{z}$ hr

Summary Exercises on Rational Expressions and Equations (pages 405–406)

1. expression; $\dfrac{10}{p}$ **2.** expression; $\dfrac{y^3}{x^3}$ **3.** expression; $\dfrac{1}{2x^2(x+2)}$

4. equation; $\{9\}$ **5.** expression; $\dfrac{y+2}{y-1}$ **6.** expression;

$\dfrac{5k+8}{k(k-4)(k+4)}$ **7.** equation; $\{39\}$ **8.** expression; $\dfrac{t-5}{3(2t+1)}$

9. expression; $\dfrac{13}{3(p+2)}$ **10.** equation; $\left\{-1,\frac{12}{5}\right\}$ **11.** equation;

$\left\{\frac{1}{7},2\right\}$ **12.** expression; $\dfrac{16}{3k}$ **13.** expression; $\dfrac{7}{12z}$ **14.** equation; $\{13\}$

15. expression; $\dfrac{3m+5}{(m+3)(m+2)(m+1)}$ **16.** expression; $\dfrac{k+3}{5(k-1)}$

17. equation; $\varnothing$ **18.** equation; $\varnothing$ **19.** expression; $\dfrac{t+2}{2(2t+1)}$

20. equation; $\{-7\}$

Section 6.7 (pages 410–414)

1. (a) the amount   **(b)** $5+x$ **(c)** $\dfrac{5+x}{6}=\dfrac{13}{3}$ **3.** $\frac{12}{18}$ **5.** $\frac{12}{3}$ **7.** 12

9. $\frac{1386}{97}$ **11.** 18.809 min   **13.** 314.248 m per min   **15.** 3.275 hr

17. $\dfrac{D}{R}=\dfrac{d}{r}$ **19.** $\dfrac{500}{x-10}=\dfrac{600}{x+10}$ **21.** 8 mph   **23.** 32 mph

25. 165 mph   **27.** 3 mph   **29.** 18.5 mph   **31.** $\frac{1}{10}$ job per hr

33. $\dfrac{1}{8}t+\dfrac{1}{6}t=1$, or $\dfrac{1}{8}+\dfrac{1}{6}=\dfrac{1}{t}$ **35.** $2\frac{2}{5}$ hr   **37.** $5\frac{5}{11}$ hr   **39.** 3 hr

41. $2\frac{7}{10}$ hr   **43.** $9\frac{1}{11}$ min   **45.** 2   **47.** $\frac{5}{2}$ **49.** 0   **51.** $y=-\frac{3}{2}x+4$

Chapter 6 Review Exercises (pages 419–421)

1. (a) $\frac{11}{8}$ **(b)** $\frac{13}{22}$ **2. (a)** undefined   **(b)** 1   **3.** $x\ne 3$ **4.** $y\ne 0$

5. $k\ne -5,-\frac{2}{3}$ **6.** Set the denominator equal to 0 and solve the equation. Any solutions are values for which the rational expression is undefined.   **7.** $\dfrac{b}{3a}$ **8.** -1 **9.** $\dfrac{-(2x+3)}{2}$ **10.** $\dfrac{2p+5q}{5p+q}$

Answers may vary in Exercises 11 and 12.   **11.** $\dfrac{-(4x-9)}{2x+3}$, $\dfrac{-4x+9}{2x+3}$,

$\dfrac{4x-9}{-(2x+3)}$, $\dfrac{4x-9}{-2x-3}$ **12.** $\dfrac{-(8-3x)}{3-6x}$, $\dfrac{-8+3x}{3-6x}$, $\dfrac{8-3x}{-(3-6x)}$,

$\dfrac{8-3x}{-3+6x}$ **13.** $\dfrac{72}{p}$ **14.** 2   **15.** $\frac{5}{8}$ **16.** $\dfrac{r+4}{3}$ **17.** $\dfrac{3a-1}{a+5}$

18. $\dfrac{y-2}{y-3}$ **19.** $\dfrac{p+5}{p+1}$ **20.** $\dfrac{3z+1}{z+3}$ **21.** $108y^4$

22. $(x+3)(x+1)(x+4)$ **23.** $\dfrac{15a}{10a^4}$ **24.** $\dfrac{-54}{18-6x}$ **25.** $\dfrac{15y}{50-10y}$

26. $\dfrac{4b(b+2)}{(b+3)(b-1)(b+2)}$ **27.** $\dfrac{15}{x}$ **28.** $-\dfrac{2}{p}$ **29.** $\dfrac{4k-45}{k(k-5)}$

30. $\dfrac{28+11y}{y(7+y)}$ **31.** $\dfrac{-2-3m}{6}$ **32.** $\dfrac{3(16-x)}{4x^2}$

33. $\dfrac{7a+6b}{(a-2b)(a+2b)}$ **34.** $\dfrac{-k^2-6k+3}{3(k+3)(k-3)}$ **35.** $\dfrac{5z-16}{z(z+6)(z-2)}$

36. $\dfrac{-13p+33}{p(p-2)(p-3)}$ **37.** $\dfrac{4(y-3)}{y+3}$ **38.** $\frac{10}{13}$ **39.** $\dfrac{xw+1}{xw-1}$

40. $\dfrac{(q-p)^2}{pq}$ **41.** $(x-5)(x-3)$, or $x^2-8x+15$ **42.** $\dfrac{y+x}{xy}$

43. $\varnothing$ **44.** $\{-16\}$ **45.** $\{0\}$ **46.** $\{3\}$ **47.** $t=\dfrac{Ry}{m}$

48. $y=\dfrac{4x+5}{3}$ **49.** $m=\dfrac{4+p^2q}{3p^2}$ **50.** $\frac{20}{15}$ **51.** $\frac{3}{18}$ **52.** 10 mph

53. $3\frac{1}{13}$ hr   **54.** 2 hr   **55.** $\dfrac{m+7}{(m-1)(m+1)}$ **56.** $8p^2$ **57.** $\frac{1}{6}$

58. $\dfrac{s^2+t^2}{st(s-t)}$ **59.** 3   **60.** $\dfrac{z+7}{(z+1)(z-1)^2}$ **61.** $\dfrac{-t-1}{(t+2)(t-2)}$, or

$\dfrac{t+1}{(2+t)(2-t)}$ **62.** $\{-2,3\}$ **63.** $v=at+w$ **64.** 150 km per hr

65. $5\frac{1}{11}$ hr   **66. (a)** -3 **(b)** -1 **(c)** $-3,-1$ **67.** $\dfrac{15}{2x}$

68. If $x=0$, the divisor R is equal to 0, and division by 0 is undefined.

69. $(x+3)(x+1)$ **70.** $\dfrac{7}{x+1}$ **71.** $\dfrac{11x+21}{4x}$ **72.** $\varnothing$

73. We know that -3 is not allowed, because P and R are undefined for $x=-3$.   **74.** Rate is equal to distance divided by time. Here, distance is 6 miles and time is $(x+3)$ minutes, so rate $=\dfrac{6}{x+3}$, which is the expression for P.   **75.** $\frac{6}{5},\frac{5}{2}$

Chapter 6 Test (page 422)

[6.1] **1. (a)** $\frac{11}{6}$ **(b)** undefined   **2.** $x\ne -2,4$ **3.** (Answers may vary.) $\dfrac{-(6x-5)}{2x+3}$, $\dfrac{-6x+5}{2x+3}$, $\dfrac{6x-5}{-(2x+3)}$, $\dfrac{6x-5}{-2x-3}$ **4.** $-3x^2y^3$

5. $\dfrac{3a+2}{a-1}$ [6.2] **6.** $\frac{25}{27}$ **7.** $\dfrac{3k-2}{3k+2}$ **8.** $\dfrac{a-1}{a+4}$ **9.** $\dfrac{x-5}{3-x}$

[6.3] **10.** $150p^5$ **11.** $(2r+3)(r+2)(r-5)$ **12.** $\dfrac{240p^2}{64p^3}$

13. $\dfrac{21}{42m-84}$ [6.4] **14.** 2   **15.** $\dfrac{-14}{5(y+2)}$ **16.** $\dfrac{-x^2+x+1}{3-x}$, or

$\dfrac{x^2-x-1}{x-3}$ **17.** $\dfrac{-m^2+7m+2}{(2m+1)(m-5)(m-1)}$ [6.5] **18.** $\dfrac{2k}{3p}$

19. $\dfrac{-2-x}{4+x}$ **20.** $\dfrac{2y^2+x^2}{xy(y-x)}$ [6.6] **21.** $\left\{-\frac{1}{2},1\right\}$ **22.** $\left\{-\frac{1}{2}\right\}$

23. $D=\dfrac{dF-k}{F}$, or $D=d-\dfrac{k}{F}$ [6.7] **24.** 3 mph   **25.** $2\frac{2}{9}$ hr

Chapters 1–6 Cumulative Review Exercises (pages 423–424)

[1.2, 1.5, 1.6] **1.** 2   [2.3] **2.** $\{17\}$ [2.5] **3.** $b=\dfrac{2\mathscr{A}}{h}$ [2.6] **4.** $\left\{-\frac{2}{7}\right\}$

[2.8] **5.** $[-8,\infty)$ [3.1, 3.2] **6. (a)** $(-3,0)$ **(b)** $(0,-4)$

7.   [4.4] **8.**

[4.1, 4.2] **9.** $\dfrac{1}{2^4 x^7}$ **10.** $\dfrac{1}{m^6}$ [4.4] **11.** $k^2 + 2k + 1$

[4.6] **12.** $4a^2 - 4ab + b^2$ [4.5] **13.** $3y^3 + 8y^2 + 12y - 5$

[4.7] **14.** $6p^2 + 7p + 1 + \dfrac{3}{p-1}$ [5.3] **15.** $(4t + 3v)(2t + v)$

16. prime   [5.4]   **17.** $(4x^2 + 1)(2x + 1)(2x - 1)$ [5.5] **18.** $\{-3, 5\}$

19. $\left\{5, -\dfrac{1}{2}, \dfrac{2}{3}\right\}$ [5.6] **20.** -2 or -1 **21.** 6 m   [6.1] **22.** A   **23.** D

[6.4] **24.** $\dfrac{4}{q}$ **25.** $\dfrac{3r + 28}{7r}$ **26.** $\dfrac{7}{15(q-4)}$ **27.** $\dfrac{-k-5}{k(k+1)(k-1)}$

[6.2] **28.** $\dfrac{7(2z+1)}{24}$ [6.5] **29.** $\dfrac{195}{29}$ [6.6] **30.** $\left\{\dfrac{21}{2}\right\}$ **31.** $\{-2, 1\}$

[6.7] **32.** $1\frac{1}{5}$ hr

7   GRAPHS, LINEAR EQUATIONS, AND FUNCTIONS

Connections   **(page 432)**   **1.** x-intercept: $(-2, 0)$; y-intercept: $(0, 3)$
*For Problems 2 and 3, we give each equation solved for y. Graphs are not
included.*   **2.** $y = 4x + 3$ **3.** $y = -0.5x$

Section 7.1 (pages 438–443)

1. (a) I   **(b)** III   **(c)** II   **(d)** IV   **(e)** none   **(f)** none

3.   **5. (a)** $-3; 3; 2; -1$ **7. (a)** $3; 1; -1; 3$

(b)   **(b)**

9. $(6, 0); (0, 4)$ **11.** $(6, 0); (0, -2)$ **13.** $(-2, 0); \left(0, -\dfrac{5}{3}\right)$

   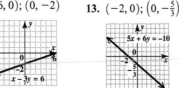

15. none; $(0, 5)$ **17.** $(2, 0)$; none   **19.** $(-4, 0)$; none

21. none; $(0, -2)$ **23.** $(0, 0); (0, 0)$ **25.** $(0, 0); (0, 0)$

27. $(-5, -1)$ **29.** $\left(\dfrac{9}{2}, -\dfrac{3}{2}\right)$ **31.** $\left(0, \dfrac{11}{2}\right)$ **33.** $(2.1, 0.9)$ **35.** $(1, 1)$

37. $\left(-\dfrac{5}{12}, \dfrac{5}{28}\right)$ **39.** B   **41.** A, B, D, G   **43. (a)** C   **(b)** A   **(c)** D
(d) B   **45. (a)** 2   **(b)** 0   **(c)** undefined   **(d)** $-\dfrac{1}{3}$ **(e)** 1   **(f)** -4
47. (a) 8   **(b)** rises   **49. (a)** $\dfrac{5}{6}$ **(b)** rises   **51. (a)** 0   **(b)** horizontal
53. (a) $-\dfrac{1}{2}$ **(b)** falls   **55. (a)** undefined   **(b)** vertical   **57. (a)** -1
(b) falls   **59.** 6   **61.** -3 **63.** $-\dfrac{5}{2}$ **65.** undefined

67. $-\dfrac{1}{2}$ **69.** $\dfrac{5}{2}$

71. 4   **73.** undefined

75. 0   **77.**   **79.**

81.   **83.**   **85.**

87. $-\dfrac{4}{9}; \dfrac{9}{4}$ **89.** parallel   **91.** perpendicular   **93.** neither   **95.** parallel
97. neither   **99.** perpendicular   **101.** $-\$4000$ per yr; The value of the
machine is decreasing $4000 each year during these years.   **103.** 0%
per yr (or no change); The percent of pay raise is not changing—
it is 3% each year during these years.   **105. (a)** 21.2   **(b)** The number
of subscribers increased by an average of 21.2 million each year from
2005 to 2008.   **107. (a)** -5 theaters per yr   **(b)** The negative slope
means that the number of drive-in theaters decreased by an average of
5 each year from 2000 to 2007.   **109.** $1371.67 million per yr; Sales of
plasma TVs increased by an average of $1371.67 million each year from
2003 to 2006.   **111.** $3x - 2y = 19$

Section 7.2 (pages 451–455)

1. A   **3.** A   **5.** $3x + y = 10$ **7.** A   **9.** C   **11.** H   **13.** B
15. $y = 5x + 15$ **17.** $y = -\dfrac{2}{3}x + \dfrac{4}{5}$ **19.** $y = x - 1$
21. $y = \dfrac{2}{5}x + 5$ **23.** $y = \dfrac{2}{3}x + 1$ **25.** $y = -x - 2$
27. (a) $y = x + 4$ **(b)** 1   **(c)** $(0, 4)$ **(d)**

29. (a) $y = -\dfrac{6}{5}x + 6$ **(b)** $-\dfrac{6}{5}$ **(c)** $(0, 6)$ **(d)**

31. (a) $y = \frac{4}{5}x - 4$ **(b)** $\frac{4}{5}$ **(c)** $(0, -4)$ **(d)**

33. (a) $y = -\frac{1}{2}x - 2$ **(b)** $-\frac{1}{2}$ **(c)** $(0, -2)$ **(d)**

35. (a) $2x + y = 18$ **(b)** $y = -2x + 18$ **37. (a)** $3x + 4y = 10$
(b) $y = -\frac{3}{4}x + \frac{5}{2}$ **39. (a)** $x - 2y = -13$ **(b)** $y = \frac{1}{2}x + \frac{13}{2}$
41. (a) $4x - y = 12$ **(b)** $y = 4x - 12$ **43. (a)** $7x - 5y = -20$
(b) $y = 1.4x + 4$ **45.** $y = 5$ **47.** $x = 9$ **49.** $y = -\frac{3}{2}$ **51.** $y = 8$
53. $x = 0.5$ **55. (a)** $2x - y = 2$ **(b)** $y = 2x - 2$
57. (a) $x + 2y = 8$ **(b)** $y = -\frac{1}{2}x + 4$ **59. (a)** $y = 5$ **(b)** $y = 5$
61. (a) $x = 7$ **(b)** not possible **63. (a)** $y = -3$ **(b)** $y = -3$
65. (a) $2x - 13y = -6$ **(b)** $y = \frac{2}{13}x + \frac{6}{13}$ **67. (a)** $y = 3x - 19$
(b) $3x - y = 19$ **69. (a)** $y = \frac{1}{2}x - 1$ **(b)** $x - 2y = 2$
71. (a) $y = -\frac{1}{2}x + 9$ **(b)** $x + 2y = 18$ **73. (a)** $y = 7$ **(b)** $y = 7$
75. $y = 45x$; $(0, 0)$, $(5, 225)$, $(10, 450)$ **77.** $y = 3.10x$; $(0, 0)$,
$(5, 15.50)$, $(10, 31.00)$ **79.** $y = 111x$; $(0, 0)$, $(5, 555)$, $(10, 1110)$
81. (a) $y = 112.50x + 12$ **(b)** $(5, 574.50)$; The cost for 5 tickets
and a parking pass is \$574.50. **(c)** \$237 **83. (a)** $y = 41x + 99$
(b) $(5, 304)$; The cost for a 5-month membership is \$304. **(c)** \$591
85. (a) $y = 60x + 36$ **(b)** $(5, 336)$; The cost of the plan for 5 months
is \$336. **(c)** \$756 **87. (a)** $y = 6x + 30$ **(b)** $(5, 60)$; It costs \$60
to rent the saw for 5 days. **(c)** 18 days **89. (a)** $y = 1294.7x + 3921$;
Sales of digital cameras in the United States increased by
\$1294.7 million per yr from 2003 to 2006. **(b)** \$9099.8 million
91. (a) $y = 5.25x + 22.25$ **(b)** \$48.5 billion; It is greater than the
actual value. **93.** 32; 212 **94.** $(0, 32)$ and $(100, 212)$ **95.** $\frac{9}{5}$
96. $F = \frac{9}{5}C + 32$ **97.** $C = \frac{5}{9}(F - 32)$ **98.** 86° **99.** 10°
100. $-40°$ **101.** $[0, \infty)$ **103.** $[-4, 4]$

Summary Exercises on Slopes and Equations of Lines (page 456)

1. $-\frac{3}{5}$ **2.** $-\frac{4}{7}$ **3.** 2 **4.** $\frac{5}{2}$ **5.** undefined **6.** 0 **7. (a)** $y = -\frac{5}{6}x + \frac{13}{3}$
(b) $5x + 6y = 26$ **8. (a)** $y = 3x + 11$ **(b)** $3x - y = -11$
9. (a) $y = -\frac{5}{2}x$ **(b)** $5x + 2y = 0$ **10. (a)** $y = -8$ **(b)** $y = -8$
11. (a) $y = -\frac{7}{9}$ **(b)** $9y = -7$ **12. (a)** $y = -3x + 10$
(b) $3x + y = 10$ **13. (a)** $y = \frac{2}{3}x + \frac{14}{3}$ **(b)** $2x - 3y = -14$
14. (a) $y = 2x - 10$ **(b)** $2x - y = 10$ **15. (a)** $y = -\frac{5}{2}x + 2$
(b) $5x + 2y = 4$ **16. (a)** $y = \frac{2}{3}x + 8$ **(b)** $2x - 3y = -24$
17. (a) $y = -7x + 3$ **(b)** $7x + y = 3$ **18. (a)** B **(b)** D **(c)** A
(d) C **(e)** E

Section 7.3 (pages 462–464)

1. Answers will vary. A function is a set of ordered pairs in which
each first component corresponds to exactly one second component.
For example, $\{(0, 1), (1, 2), (2, 3), (3, 4)\}$ is a function.

3. independent variable

In Exercises 5 and 7, answers will vary.

5.

7.

x	y
-3	-4
-3	1
2	0

9. function; domain: $\{5, 3, 4, 7\}$; range: $\{1, 2, 9, 6\}$ **11.** not a
function; domain: $\{2, 0\}$; range: $\{4, 2, 5\}$ **13.** function; domain:
$\{-3, 4, -2\}$; range: $\{1, 7\}$ **15.** not a function; domain: $\{1, 0, 2\}$;
range: $\{1, -1, 0, 4, -4\}$ **17.** function; domain: $\{2, 5, 11, 17, 3\}$;
range: $\{1, 7, 20\}$ **19.** not a function; domain: $\{1\}$; range: $\{5, 2, -1, -4\}$
21. function; domain: $\{4, 2, 0, -2\}$; range: $\{-3\}$ **23.** function;
domain: $\{-2, 0, 3\}$; range: $\{2, 3\}$ **25.** function; domain: $(-\infty, \infty)$;
range: $(-\infty, \infty)$ **27.** not a function; domain: $(-\infty, 0]$; range: $(-\infty, \infty)$
29. function; domain: $(-\infty, \infty)$; range: $(-\infty, 4]$ **31.** not a function;
domain: $[-4, 4]$; range: $[-3, 3]$ **33.** function; $(-\infty, \infty)$
35. function; $(-\infty, \infty)$ **37.** function; $(-\infty, \infty)$ **39.** not a function;
$[0, \infty)$ **41.** function; $(-\infty, \infty)$ **43.** function; $(-\infty, 0) \cup (0, \infty)$
45. function; $(-\infty, 4) \cup (4, \infty)$ **47.** function; $\left(-\infty, -\frac{3}{4}\right) \cup \left(-\frac{3}{4}, \infty\right)$
49. not a function; $[1, \infty)$ **51.** function; $(-\infty, 0) \cup (0, \infty)$
53. (a) yes **(b)** domain: $\{2004, 2005, 2006, 2007, 2008\}$; range:
$\{42.3, 42.8, 43.7, 43.8\}$ **(c)** Answers will vary. Two possible answers
are $(2005, 42.3)$ and $(2008, 43.8)$. **55.** -9 **57.** 1 **59.** $y = \frac{1}{2}x - \frac{7}{4}$

Section 7.4 (pages 468–472)

1. B **3.** 4 **5.** -11 **7.** 3 **9.** 2.75 **11.** $-3p + 4$ **13.** $3x + 4$
15. $-3x - 2$ **17.** $-\pi^2 + 4\pi + 1$ **19.** $-3x - 3h + 4$ **21.** -9
23. (a) -1 **(b)** -1 **25. (a)** 2 **(b)** 3 **27. (a)** 15 **(b)** 10
29. (a) 4 **(b)** 1 **31. (a)** 3 **(b)** -3 **33. (a)** -3 **(b)** 2
35. (a) 2 **(b)** 0 **(c)** -1 **37. (a)** $f(x) = -\frac{1}{3}x + 4$ **(b)** 3
39. (a) $f(x) = 3 - 2x^2$ **(b)** -15 **41. (a)** $f(x) = \frac{4}{3}x - \frac{8}{3}$ **(b)** $\frac{4}{3}$
43. line; -2; $-2x + 4$; -2; 3; -2
45. domain: $(-\infty, \infty)$;   **47.** domain: $(-\infty, \infty)$;
range: $(-\infty, \infty)$ range: $(-\infty, \infty)$

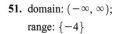

49. domain: $(-\infty, \infty)$;   **51.** domain: $(-\infty, \infty)$;
range: $(-\infty, \infty)$ range: $\{-4\}$

53. domain: $(-\infty, \infty)$; range: $\{0\}$

55. x-axis   **57. (a)** $11.25   **(b)** 3 is the value of the independent variable, which represents a package weight of 3 lb; $f(3)$ is the value of the dependent variable, representing the cost to mail a 3-lb package.   **(c)** $18.75; $f(5) = 18.75$

59. (a) 194.53 cm   **(b)** 177.29 cm   **(c)** 177.41 cm   **(d)** 163.65 cm
61. (a) $f(x) = 12x + 100$ **(b)** 1600; The cost to print 125 t-shirts is $1600.   **(c)** 75; $f(75) = 1000$; The cost to print 75 t-shirts is $1000.
63. (a) 1.1   **(b)** 5   **(c)** -1.2 **(d)** $(0, 3.5)$ **(e)** $f(x) = -1.2x + 3.5$
65. (a) $[0, 100]$; $[0, 3000]$ **(b)** 25 hr; 25 hr   **(c)** 2000 gal
(d) $f(0) = 0$; The pool is empty at time 0.   **(e)** $f(25) = 3000$;
After 25 hr, there are 3000 gal of water in the pool.   **67.** $15x^2 - x - 4$
69. $12x^2 - 11x - 5$ **71.** $3x^2 - 2x$

Section 7.5 (pages 478–480)

1. (a) -10 **(b)** 8   **3. (a)** 8   **(b)** 2   **5. (a)** 8   **(b)** 74
7. (a) -11 **(b)** 4   **9. (a)** $8x - 3$ **(b)** $2x - 17$
11. (a) $-x^2 + 12x - 12$ **(b)** $9x^2 + 4x + 6$ **13.** $x^2 + 2x - 9$
15. 6   **17.** $x^2 - x - 6$ **19.** 6   **21.** -33 **23.** 0   **25.** $-\frac{9}{4}$ **27.** $-\frac{9}{2}$
29. For example, let $f(x) = 2x^3 + 3x^2 + x + 4$ and $g(x) = 2x^4 + 3x^3 - 9x^2 + 2x - 4$. For these functions, $(f - g)(x) = -2x^4 - x^3 + 12x^2 - x + 8$, and $(g - f)(x) = 2x^4 + x^3 - 12x^2 + x - 8$.
Because the two differences are not equal, subtraction of functions is not commutative.   **31.** $10x^2 - 2x$ **33.** $2x^2 - x - 3$ **35.** $8x^3 - 27$
37. $2x^3 - 18x$ **39.** -20 **41.** $2x^2 - 6x$ **43.** 36   **45.** $\frac{35}{4}$ **47.** $\frac{1859}{64}$
49. $5x - 1; 0$ **51.** $2x - 3; -1$ **53.** $4x^2 + 6x + 9; \frac{3}{2}$
55. $\dfrac{x^2 - 9}{2x}$, $x \neq 0$ **57.** $-\frac{5}{4}$ **59.** $\dfrac{x - 3}{2x}$, $x \neq 0$ **61.** 0   **63.** $-\frac{35}{4}$
65. $\frac{7}{2}$ **67.** 6   **69.** 83   **71.** 53   **73.** 13   **75.** $2x^2 + 11$ **77.** $2x - 2$
79. $\frac{97}{4}$ **81.** 8   **83.** $(f \circ g)(x) = 63{,}360x$; It computes the number of inches in x miles.   **85.** $(\mathcal{A} \circ r)(t) = 4\pi t^2$; This is the area of the circular layer as a function of time.   **87.** $\frac{1}{3}$ **89.** 3

Section 7.6 (pages 486–489)

1. direct   **3.** direct   **5.** inverse   **7.** inverse   **9.** inverse   **11.** direct
13. joint   **15.** combined   **17.** increases; decreases   **19.** The perimeter of a square varies directly as the length of its side.   **21.** The surface area of a sphere varies directly as the square of its radius.
23. The area of a triangle varies jointly as the length of its base and height.   **25.** 4; 2; 4π; $\frac{4}{3}\pi$; $\frac{1}{2}$; $\frac{1}{3}\pi$ **27.** 36   **29.** $\frac{16}{9}$ **31.** 0.625   **33.** $\frac{16}{5}$
35. $222\frac{2}{9}$ **37.** $2.919, or $2.91\frac{9}{10}$ **39.** 8 lb   **41.** about 450 cm^3
43. 256 ft   **45.** $106\frac{2}{3}$ mph   **47.** 100 cycles per sec   **49.** $21\frac{1}{3}$ foot-candles   **51.** $420   **53.** about 11.8 lb   **55.** about 448.1 lb
57. about 68,600 calls   **59.** Answers will vary.

61. 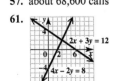   **63.**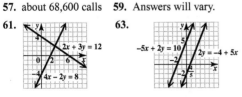

Chapter 7 Review Exercises (pages 493–496)

1.

x	y
0	5
$\frac{10}{3}$	0
2	2
$\frac{14}{3}$	-2

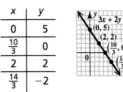

2.

x	y
2	-6
5	-3
3	-5
6	-2

3. $(3, 0); (0, -4)$

4. $\left(\frac{28}{5}, 0\right); (0, 4)$

5. $(10, 0); (0, 4)$

6. $(8, 0); (0, -2)$

7. $(0, 2)$ **8.** $\left(-\frac{9}{2}, \frac{3}{2}\right)$ **9.** $-\frac{7}{5}$ **10.** $-\frac{1}{2}$ **11.** 2   **12.** $\frac{3}{4}$ **13.** undefined
14. $\frac{2}{3}$ **15.** $-\frac{1}{3}$ **16.** undefined   **17.** $-\frac{1}{3}$ **18.** -1 **19.** positive
20. negative   **21.** undefined   **22.** 0   **23.** 12 ft   **24.** $1496 per yr
25. (a) $y = -\frac{1}{3}x - 1$ **(b)** $x + 3y = -3$ **26. (a)** $y = -2$
(b) $y = -2$ **27. (a)** $y = -\frac{4}{3}x + \frac{29}{3}$ **(b)** $4x + 3y = 29$
28. (a) $y = 3x + 7$ **(b)** $3x - y = -7$ **29. (a)** not possible
(b) $x = 2$ **30. (a)** $y = -9x + 13$ **(b)** $9x + y = 13$
31. (a) $y = \frac{7}{5}x + \frac{16}{5}$ **(b)** $7x - 5y = -16$ **32. (a)** $y = -x + 2$
(b) $x + y = 2$ **33. (a)** $y = 4x - 29$ **(b)** $4x - y = 29$
34. (a) $y = -\frac{5}{2}x + 13$ **(b)** $5x + 2y = 26$ **35. (a)** $y = 57x + 159$;
$843   **(b)** $y = 47x + 159$; $723   **36. (a)** $y = 143.75x + 1407.75$;
The revenue from skiing facilities increased by an average of
$143.75 million each year from 2003 to 2007.   **(b)** $2558 million
37. domain: $\{-4, 1\}$; range: $\{2, -2, 5, -5\}$; not a function
38. domain: $\{9, 11, 4, 17, 25\}$; range: $\{32, 47, 69, 14\}$; function
39. domain: $[-4, 4]$; range: $[0, 2]$; function   **40.** domain: $(-\infty, 0]$;
range: $(-\infty, \infty)$; not a function   **41.** function; domain: $(-\infty, \infty)$;
linear function   **42.** not a function; domain: $[0, \infty)$ **43.** function;
domain: $(-\infty, 6) \cup (6, \infty)$ **44.** -6 **45.** -8.52 **46.** -8
47. $-2k^2 + 3k - 6$ **48.** $f(x) = 2x^2$; 18   **49.** C   **50. (a)** yes
(b) domain: $\{1960, 1970, 1980, 1990, 2000, 2009\}$; range: $\{69.7,$
$70.8, 73.7, 75.4, 76.8, 78.1\}$ **(c)** Answers will vary. Two possible
answers are $(1960, 69.7)$ and $(2009, 78.1)$.   **(d)** 73.7; In 1980, life
expectancy at birth was 73.7 yr.   **(e)** 2000   **51. (a)** -11 **(b)** 4
52. (a) $5x^2 - x + 5$ **(b)** $-5x^2 + 5x + 1$ **(c)** 11   **(d)** -9
53. (a) $36x^3 - 9x^2$ **(b)** $4x - 1$, $x \neq 0$ **(c)** -45 **(d)** 7
54. (a) 167   **(b)** 1495   **(c)** 20   **(d)** 42   **(e)** $75x^2 + 220x + 160$
(f) $15x^2 + 10x + 2$ **55.** C   **56.** 430 mm   **57.** 5.59 vibrations
per sec   **58.** 22.5 ft^3

Chapter 7 Test (pages 496–497)

[7.1] **1.** $-\frac{10}{3}$; -2; 0   **2.** $\left(\frac{20}{3}, 0\right)$; $(0, -10)$

3. none; (0, 5) **4.** (2, 0); none

5. $\frac{1}{2}$ **6.** It is a vertical line. **7.** perpendicular **8.** neither

9. -929 farms per yr; The number of farms decreased, on the average, by about 929 each year from 1980 to 2008. [7.2] **10. (a)** $y = -5x + 19$

(b) $5x + y = 19$ **11. (a)** $y = 14$ **(b)** $y = 14$ **12. (a)** $y = -\frac{1}{2}x + 2$

(b) $x + 2y = 4$ **13. (a)** not possible **(b)** $x = 5$

14. (a) $y = -\frac{3}{5}x - \frac{11}{5}$ **(b)** $3x + 5y = -11$ **15. (a)** $y = -\frac{1}{2}x - \frac{3}{2}$

(b) $x + 2y = -3$ **16.** B **17. (a)** $y = 2078x + 51{,}557$

(b) \$61,947; It is more than the actual value. [7.3] **18.** D **19.** D

20. (a) domain: $[0, \infty)$; range: $(-\infty, \infty)$ **(b)** domain: $\{0, -2, 4\}$;

range: $\{1, 3, 8\}$ [7.4] **21. (a)** 0 **(b)** $-a^2 + 2a - 1$

22. domain: $(-\infty, \infty)$; [7.5] **23. (a)** -18 **(b)** $-2x^2 + 12x - 9$

range: $(-\infty, \infty)$ **(c)** $-2x^2 - 2x - 3$ **(d)** -7

24. (a) $x^3 + 4x^2 + 5x + 2$ **(b)** 0

25. (a) $x + 2$, $x \neq -1$ **(b)** 0

26. (a) 23 **(b)** $3x^2 + 11$

(c) $9x^2 + 30x + 27$

[7.6] **27.** 200 amps **28.** 0.8 lb

Chapters 1–7 Cumulative Review Exercises (pages 498–499)

[1.4, 1.5] **1.** always true **2.** never true **3.** sometimes true; For example, $3 + (-3) = 0$, but $3 + (-1) = 2 \neq 0$. **4.** 4 [1.7] **5.** $4m - 3$

[1.6] **6.** $-\frac{19}{2}$ [1.5, 1.6] **7.** -39 **8.** undefined [2.3] **9.** $\left\{\frac{7}{6}\right\}$

10. $\{-1\}$ [2.5] **11.** 6 in. [2.7] **12.** 2 hr

[2.8] **13.** $\left(-3, \frac{7}{2}\right)$

14. $(-\infty, 1]$

[3.2, 7.1] **15.** x-intercept: $(4, 0)$; y-intercept: $\left(0, \frac{12}{5}\right)$

[3.3, 7.1] **16. (a)** $-\frac{6}{5}$ **(b)** $\frac{5}{6}$ [3.4, 7.2] **17. (a)** $y = -\frac{3}{4}x - 1$

(b) $3x + 4y = -4$ **18. (a)** $y = -\frac{4}{3}x + \frac{7}{3}$ **(b)** $4x + 3y = 7$

[4.1, 4.2] **19.** $\frac{y}{18x}$ [4.6] **20.** $49x^2 + 42xy + 9y^2$

[4.4] **21.** $x^3 + 12x^2 - 3x - 7$ [4.7] **22.** $m^2 - 2m + 3$

[5.1–5.4] **23.** $(2w + 7z)(8w - 3z)$ **24.** $(2x - 1 + y)(2x - 1 - y)$

25. $(2p + 3)(4p^2 - 6p + 9)$ [5.5] **26.** $\left\{\frac{1}{3}\right\}$ [5.6] **27.** 4 ft

28. longer sides: 18 in.; distance between: 16 in.

[6.4] **29.** $\dfrac{6x + 22}{(x + 1)(x + 3)}$ [6.2] **30.** $\dfrac{(x + 3)^2}{3x}$ [6.5] **31.** 6

[6.6] **32.** $\{5\}$ [7.3] **33.** domain: $\{14, 91, 75, 23\}$; range: $\{9, 70, 56, 5\}$; not a function; 75 in the domain is paired with two different values, 70 and 56, in the range.

[7.4] **34. (a)** domain: $(-\infty, \infty)$; range: $(-\infty, \infty)$ **(b)** 22 **(c)** 1

[7.2] **35.** -2.02; The per capita consumption of potatoes in the United States decreased by an average of 2.02 lb per yr from 2003 to 2008.

9 INEQUALITIES AND ABSOLUTE VALUE

Section 9.2 (pages 580–582)

1. E; C; D; B; A **3. (a)** one **(b)** two **(c)** none **5.** $\{-12, 12\}$

7. $\{-5, 5\}$ **9.** $\{-6, 12\}$ **11.** $\{-5, 6\}$ **13.** $\left\{-3, \frac{11}{2}\right\}$

15. $\left\{-\frac{19}{2}, \frac{9}{2}\right\}$ **17.** $\{-10, -2\}$ **19.** $\left\{-\frac{32}{3}, 8\right\}$ **21.** $\{-75, 175\}$

23. $(-\infty, -3) \cup (3, \infty)$

25. $(-\infty, -4] \cup [4, \infty)$

27. $(-\infty, -25] \cup [15, \infty)$

29. $(-\infty, -12) \cup (8, \infty)$

31. $(-\infty, -2) \cup (8, \infty)$

33. $\left(-\infty, -\frac{9}{5}\right] \cup [3, \infty)$

35. (a) **(b)**

37. $[-3, 3]$ **39.** $(-4, 4)$

41. $(-25, 15)$

43. $[-12, 8]$

45. $[-2, 8]$ **47.** $\left(-\frac{9}{5}, 3\right)$

49. $(-\infty, -5) \cup (13, \infty)$

51. $(-\infty, -25) \cup (15, \infty)$

53. $\{-6, -1\}$

55. $\left[-\frac{10}{3}, 4\right]$

57. $\left[-\frac{7}{6}, -\frac{5}{6}\right]$

59. $(-\infty, -3] \cup [4, \infty)$ **61.** $\{-5, 1\}$

63. $\{3, 9\}$ **65.** $\{0, 20\}$ **67.** $\{-5, 5\}$ **69.** $\{-5, -3\}$

71. $(-\infty, -3) \cup (2, \infty)$ **73.** $[-10, 0]$ **75.** $\left\{-\frac{5}{3}, \frac{1}{3}\right\}$

77. $(-\infty, 20] \cup [30, \infty)$ **79.** $\{-1, 3\}$ **81.** $\left\{-3, \frac{5}{3}\right\}$ **83.** $\left\{-\frac{1}{3}, -\frac{1}{15}\right\}$

85. $\left\{-\frac{5}{4}\right\}$ **87.** $(-\infty, \infty)$ **89.** $\emptyset$ **91.** $\left\{-\frac{1}{4}\right\}$ **93.** $\emptyset$ **95.** $(-\infty, \infty)$

97. $\left\{-\frac{3}{7}\right\}$ **99.** $\left\{\frac{2}{5}\right\}$ **101.** $(-\infty, \infty)$ **103.** $\emptyset$

105. $|x - 1000| \le 100$; $900 \le x \le 1100$ **107.** 810.5 ft

108. Bank of America Center, Texaco Heritage Plaza **109.** Williams Tower, Bank of America Center, Texaco Heritage Plaza, Enterprise Plaza, Centerpoint Energy Plaza, Continental Center I, Fulbright Tower

110. $|x - 810.5| \ge 95$; $x \ge 905.5$ or $x \le 715.5$

(b) JPMorgan Chase Tower, Wells Fargo Plaza, One Shell Plaza; It makes sense because it includes all buildings *not* listed in the answer to **Exercise 109.**

111.   **113.** no

Summary Exercises on Solving Linear and Absolute Value Equations and Inequalities (page 583)

1. $\{12\}$ **2.** $\{-5, 7\}$ **3.** $\{7\}$ **4.** $\left\{-\frac{2}{5}\right\}$ **5.** $\varnothing$ **6.** $(-\infty, -1]$
7. $\left[-\frac{2}{3}, \infty\right)$ **8.** $\{-1\}$ **9.** $\{-3\}$ **10.** $\left\{1, \frac{11}{3}\right\}$ **11.** $(-\infty, 5]$
12. $(-\infty, \infty)$ **13.** $\{2\}$ **14.** $(-\infty, -8] \cup [8, \infty)$ **15.** $\varnothing$ **16.** $(-\infty,$
17. $(-5.5, 5.5)$ **18.** $\left\{\frac{13}{3}\right\}$ **19.** $\left\{-\frac{96}{5}\right\}$ **20.** $(-\infty, 32]$ $\infty)$
21. $(-\infty, -24)$ **22.** $\left\{\frac{3}{8}\right\}$ **23.** $\left\{\frac{7}{2}\right\}$ **24.** $(-6, 8)$
25. $\{$all real numbers$\}$ **26.** $(-\infty, 5)$ **27.** $(-\infty, -4) \cup (7, \infty)$
28. $\{24\}$ **29.** $\left\{-\frac{1}{5}\right\}$ **30.** $\left(-\infty, -\frac{5}{2}\right]$ **31.** $\left[-\frac{1}{3}, 3\right]$ **32.** $[1, 7]$
33. $\left\{-\frac{1}{6}, 2\right\}$ **34.** $\{-3\}$ **35.** $(-\infty, -1] \cup \left[\frac{5}{3}, \infty\right)$ **36.** $\left[\frac{3}{4}, \frac{15}{8}\right]$
37. $\left\{-\frac{5}{2}\right\}$ **38.** $\{60\}$ **39.** $\left[-\frac{9}{2}, \frac{15}{2}\right]$ **40.** $(1, 9)$ **41.** $(-\infty, \infty)$
42. $\left\{\frac{1}{3}, 9\right\}$ **43.** $\{$all real numbers$\}$ **44.** $\left\{-\frac{10}{9}\right\}$ **45.** $\{-2\}$ **46.** $\varnothing$
47. $(-\infty, -1) \cup (2, \infty)$ **48.** $[-3, -2]$

Connections **(page 589)** We include a calculator graph and supporting explanation only with the answer to Problem 1.

1. (a) $\{-0.6\}$; The graph of $y_1 = 5x + 3$ has x-intercept $(-0.6, 0)$.

(b) $(-0.6, \infty)$; The graph of y_1 lies *above* the x-axis for values of x *greater than* -0.6.

(c) $(-\infty, -0.6)$; The graph of y_1 lies *below* the x-axis for values of x *less than* -0.6.

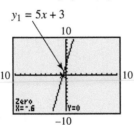

2. (a) $\{-0.5\}$ **(b)** $(-0.5, \infty)$ **(c)** $(-\infty, -0.5)$ **3. (a)** $\{-1.2\}$
(b) $(-\infty, -1.2]$ **(c)** $[-1.2, \infty)$ **4. (a)** $\{-3\}$ **(b)** $(-\infty, -3]$
(c) $[-3, \infty)$

10 **ROOTS, RADICALS, AND ROOT FUNCTIONS**

Section 10.1 (pages 607–611)

1. true **3.** false; Zero has only one square root. **5.** true **7.** $-3, 3$
9. $-8, 8$ **11.** $-13, 13$ **13.** $-\frac{5}{14}, \frac{5}{14}$ **15.** $-30, 30$ **17.** 1 **19.** 7
21. -16 **23.** $-\frac{12}{11}$ **25.** 0.8 **27.** It is not a real number. **29.** It is not a real number. **31.** 19 **33.** 19 **35.** $\frac{2}{3}$ **37.** $3x^2 + 4$ **39.** a must be

positive. **41.** a must be negative. **43.** rational; 5 **45.** irrational; 5.385 **47.** rational; -8 **49.** irrational; -17.321 **51.** It is not a real number. **53.** irrational; 34.641 **55.** 9 and 10 **57.** 7 and 8
59. -7 and -6 **61.** 4 and 5 **63.** 1; 8; 27; 64; 125; 216; 343; 512; 729; 1000 **65. (a)** E **(b)** F **(c)** D **(d)** B **(e)** A **(f)** C
67. -9 **69.** 6 **71.** -4 **73.** -8 **75.** 6 **77.** -2 **79.** It is not a real number. **81.** 2 **83.** It is not a real number. **85.** $\frac{8}{9}$ **87.** $\frac{4}{3}$
89. $-\frac{1}{2}$ **91.** 3 **93.** 0.5 **95.** -0.7 **97.** 0.1

In Exercises 99–105, we give the domain and then the range.

99. $[-3, \infty)$; $[0, \infty)$ **101.** $[0, \infty)$; $[-2, \infty)$

103. $(-\infty, \infty)$; $(-\infty, \infty)$ **105.** $(-\infty, \infty)$; $(-\infty, \infty)$

107. 12 **109.** 10 **111.** 2 **113.** -9 **115.** -5 **117.** $|x|$
119. $|z|$ **121.** x **123.** x^5 **125.** $|x|^5$ (or $|x^5|$) **127.** C **129.** 97.381
131. 16.863 **133.** -9.055 **135.** 7.507 **137.** 3.162 **139.** 1.885
141. A **143.** 1,183,000 cycles per sec **145.** 10 mi **147.** 392,000 mi
149. (a) 1.732 amps **(b)** 2.236 amps **151.** x^1, or x **153.** $\frac{3^3}{2^3}$, or $\frac{27}{8}$

Section 10.2 (pages 617–619)

1. C **3.** A **5.** H **7.** B **9.** D **11.** 13 **13.** 9 **15.** 2 **17.** $\frac{8}{9}$
19. -3 **21.** It is not a real number. **23.** 1000 **25.** 27 **27.** -1024
29. 16 **31.** $\frac{1}{8}$ **33.** $\frac{1}{512}$ **35.** $\frac{9}{25}$ **37.** $\frac{27}{8}$ **39.** $\sqrt{10}$ **41.** $\left(\sqrt[8]{8}\right)^3$
43. $\left(\sqrt[8]{9q}\right)^5 - \left(\sqrt[3]{2x}\right)^2$ **45.** $\frac{1}{\left(\sqrt{2m}\right)^3}$ **47.** $\left(\sqrt[3]{2y + x}\right)^2$
49. $\frac{1}{\left(\sqrt[3]{3m^4 + 2k^2}\right)^2}$ **51.** 64 **53.** 64 **55.** x^{10} **57.** $\sqrt[6]{x^5}$
59. $\sqrt[15]{t^8}$ **61.** 9 **63.** 4 **65.** y **67.** $x^{5/12}$ **69.** $k^{2/3}$
71. $x^3 y^8$ **73.** $\frac{1}{x^{10/3}}$ **75.** $\frac{1}{m^{1/4} n^{3/4}}$ **77.** p^2 **79.** $\frac{c^{11/3}}{b^{11/4}}$ **81.** $\frac{q^{5/3}}{9p^{7/2}}$
83. $p + 2p^2$ **85.** $k^{7/4} - k^{3/4}$ **87.** $6 + 18a$ **89.** $-5x^2 + 5x$
91. $x^{17/20}$ **93.** $\frac{1}{x^{3/2}}$ **95.** $y^{5/6} z^{1/3}$ **97.** $m^{1/12}$ **99.** $x^{1/8}$ **101.** $x^{1/24}$
103. $\sqrt{a^2 + b^2} = \sqrt{3^2 + 4^2} = 5$; $a + b = 3 + 4 = 7$; $5 \ne 7$
105. 4.5 hr **107.** 19.0°; The table gives 19°. **109.** 4.2°; The table gives 4°. **111.** 30; 30; They are the same.

Section 10.3 (pages 626–629)

1. $\sqrt{9}$, or 3 **3.** $\sqrt{36}$, or 6 **5.** $\sqrt{30}$ **7.** $\sqrt{14x}$ **9.** $\sqrt{42pqr}$
11. $\sqrt[3]{10}$ **13.** $\sqrt[3]{14xy}$ **15.** $\sqrt[4]{33}$ **17.** $\sqrt[4]{6x^3}$ **19.** This expression

cannot be simplified by the product rule. **21.** $\frac{8}{11}$ **23.** $\frac{\sqrt{3}}{5}$ **25.** $\frac{\sqrt{x}}{5}$

27. $\frac{p^3}{9}$ **29.** $-\frac{3}{4}$ **31.** $\frac{\sqrt[3]{r^2}}{2}$ **33.** $-\frac{3}{x}$ **35.** $\frac{1}{x^3}$ **37.** $2\sqrt{3}$ **39.** $12\sqrt{2}$

41. $-4\sqrt{2}$ **43.** $-2\sqrt{7}$ **45.** This radical cannot be simplified further.

47. $4\sqrt[3]{2}$ **49.** $-2\sqrt[3]{2}$ **51.** $2\sqrt[3]{5}$ **53.** $-4\sqrt[4]{2}$ **55.** $2\sqrt[5]{2}$

57. $-3\sqrt[5]{2}$ **59.** $2\sqrt[6]{2}$ **61.** His reasoning was incorrect. Here, 8 is a

term, not a factor. **63.** $6k\sqrt{2}$ **65.** $12xy^4\sqrt{xy}$ **67.** $11x^3$ **69.** $-3t^4$

71. $-10m^4z^2$ **73.** $5a^2b^3c^4$ **75.** $\frac{1}{2}r^2t^5$ **77.** $5x\sqrt{2x}$ **79.** $-10r^5\sqrt{5r}$

81. $x^3y^4\sqrt{13x}$ **83.** $2z^2w^3$ **85.** $-2zt^2\sqrt[3]{2z^2t}$ **87.** $3x^3y^4$

89. $-3r^3s^2\sqrt[4]{2r^3s^2}$ **91.** $\frac{y^5\sqrt{y}}{6}$ **93.** $\frac{x^5\sqrt[3]{x}}{3}$ **95.** $4\sqrt{3}$

97. $\sqrt{5}$ **99.** $x^2\sqrt{x}$ **101.** $\sqrt[6]{432}$ **103.** $\sqrt[12]{6912}$ **105.** $\sqrt[6]{x^5}$

107. 5 **109.** $8\sqrt{2}$ **111.** $2\sqrt{14}$ **113.** 13 **115.** $9\sqrt{2}$

117. $\sqrt{17}$ **119.** 5 **121.** $6\sqrt{2}$ **123.** $\sqrt{5y^2-2xy+x^2}$

125. $2\sqrt{106}+4\sqrt{2}$ **127.** 15.3 mi **129.** 27.0 in. **131.** 581

133. $\sqrt{9}+\sqrt{9}=3+3=6$, and $\sqrt{4}=2$; $6\neq2$, so the statement

is false. **135.** MSX-77: 18.4 in.; MSX-83: 17.0 in.; MSX-60: 14.1 in.

137. $22x^4-10x^3$ **139.** $8q^2-3q$

Section 10.4 (pages 632–633)

1. -4 **3.** $7\sqrt{3}$ **5.** $14\sqrt[3]{2}$ **7.** $5\sqrt[4]{2}$ **9.** $24\sqrt{2}$ **11.** The expression

cannot be simplified further. **13.** $20\sqrt{5}$ **15.** $4\sqrt{2x}$

17. $-11m\sqrt{2}$ **19.** $7\sqrt[3]{2}$ **21.** $2\sqrt[3]{x}$ **23.** $-7\sqrt[3]{x^2y}$ **25.** $-x\sqrt[3]{xy^2}$

27. $19\sqrt[4]{2}$ **29.** $x\sqrt[4]{xy}$ **31.** $9\sqrt[4]{2a^3}$ **33.** $(4+3xy)\sqrt[3]{xy^2}$

35. $4t\sqrt[3]{3st}-3s\sqrt{3st}$ **37.** $4x\sqrt[3]{x}+6x\sqrt[4]{x}$ **39.** $2\sqrt{2}-2$

41. $\frac{5\sqrt{5}}{6}$ **43.** $\frac{7\sqrt{2}}{6}$ **45.** $\frac{5\sqrt{2}}{3}$ **47.** $5\sqrt{2}+4$ **49.** $\frac{5+3x}{x^4}$

51. $\frac{m\sqrt[3]{m^2}}{2}$ **53.** $\frac{3x\sqrt[3]{2}-4\sqrt[3]{5}}{x^3}$ **55.** B

57. 15; Each radical expression simplifies to a whole number.

59. A; 42 m **61.** $(12\sqrt{5}+5\sqrt{3})$ in. **63.** $(24\sqrt{2}+12\sqrt{3})$ in.

65. $10x^3y^4-20x^2y$ **67.** a^4-b^2 **69.** $64x^9+144x^6+108x^3+27$

71. $\frac{4x-5}{3x}$

Connections (**page 639**) **1.** $\frac{319}{6(8\sqrt{5}+1)}$ **2.** $\frac{9a-b}{b(3\sqrt{a}-\sqrt{b})}$

3. $\frac{9a-b}{(\sqrt{b}-\sqrt{a})(3\sqrt{a}-\sqrt{b})}$ **4.** $\frac{(3\sqrt{a}+\sqrt{b})(\sqrt{b}+\sqrt{a})}{b-a}$;

Instead of multiplying by the conjugate of the numerator, we use the conjugate of the denominator.

Section 10.5 (pages 640–642)

1. E **3.** A **5.** D **7.** $3\sqrt{6}+2\sqrt{3}$ **9.** $20\sqrt{2}$ **11.** -2

13. -1 **15.** 6 **17.** $\sqrt{6}-\sqrt{2}+\sqrt{3}-1$

19. $\sqrt{22}+\sqrt{55}-\sqrt{14}-\sqrt{35}$ **21.** $8-\sqrt{15}$ **23.** $9+4\sqrt{5}$

25. $26-2\sqrt{105}$ **27.** $4-\sqrt[3]{36}$ **29.** 10

31. $6x+3\sqrt{x}-2\sqrt{5x}-\sqrt{5}$ **33.** $9r-s$

35. $4\sqrt[3]{4y^2}-19\sqrt[3]{2y}-5$ **37.** $3x-4$ **39.** $4x-y$ **41.** $2\sqrt{6}-1$

43. $\sqrt{7}$ **45.** $5\sqrt{3}$ **47.** $\frac{\sqrt{6}}{2}$ **49.** $\frac{9\sqrt{15}}{5}$ **51.** $-\frac{7\sqrt{3}}{12}$ **53.** $\frac{\sqrt{14}}{2}$

55. $-\frac{\sqrt{14}}{10}$ **57.** $\frac{2\sqrt{6x}}{x}$ **59.** $\frac{-8\sqrt{3k}}{k}$ **61.** $\frac{-5m^2\sqrt{6mn}}{n^2}$

63. $\frac{12x^3\sqrt{2xy}}{y^5}$ **65.** $\frac{5\sqrt{2my}}{y^2}$ **67.** $-\frac{4k\sqrt{3z}}{z}$ **69.** $\frac{\sqrt[3]{18}}{3}$ **71.** $\frac{\sqrt[3]{12}}{3}$

73. $\frac{\sqrt[3]{18}}{4}$ **75.** $-\frac{\sqrt[3]{2pr}}{r}$ **77.** $\frac{x^2\sqrt[3]{y^2}}{y}$ **79.** $\frac{2\sqrt[4]{x^3}}{x}$ **81.** $\frac{\sqrt[4]{2yz^3}}{z}$

83. $\frac{3(4-\sqrt{5})}{11}$ **85.** $\frac{6\sqrt{2}+4}{7}$ **87.** $\frac{2(3\sqrt{5}-2\sqrt{3})}{33}$

89. $2\sqrt{3}+\sqrt{10}-3\sqrt{2}-\sqrt{15}$ **91.** $\sqrt{m}-2$

93. $\frac{4(\sqrt{x}+2\sqrt{y})}{x-4y}$ **95.** $\frac{x-2\sqrt{xy}+y}{x-y}$ **97.** $\frac{5\sqrt{k}(2\sqrt{k}-\sqrt{q})}{4k-q}$

99. $3-2\sqrt{6}$ **101.** $1-\sqrt{5}$ **103.** $\frac{4-2\sqrt{2}}{3}$ **105.** $\frac{6+2\sqrt{6p}}{3}$

107. $\frac{3\sqrt{x+y}}{x+y}$ **109.** $\frac{p\sqrt{p+2}}{p+2}$ **111.** Each expression is approximately

equal to 0.2588190451. **113.** $\frac{33}{8(6+\sqrt{3})}$ **115.** $\frac{4x-y}{3x(2\sqrt{x}+\sqrt{y})}$

117. $\left\{\frac{3}{8}\right\}$ **119.** $\left\{-\frac{1}{3},\frac{3}{2}\right\}$

Summary Exercises on Operations with Radicals and Rational Exponents (pages 642–643)

1. $-6\sqrt{10}$ **2.** $7-\sqrt{14}$ **3.** $2+\sqrt{6}-2\sqrt{3}-3\sqrt{2}$ **4.** $4\sqrt{2}$

5. $73+12\sqrt{35}$ **6.** $\frac{-\sqrt{6}}{2}$ **7.** $4(\sqrt{7}-\sqrt{5})$ **8.** $-3+2\sqrt{2}$

9. -44 **10.** $\frac{\sqrt{x}+\sqrt{5}}{x-5}$ **11.** $2abc^3\sqrt[3]{b^2}$ **12.** $5\sqrt[3]{3}$

13. $3(\sqrt{5}-2)$ **14.** $\frac{\sqrt{15x}}{5x}$ **15.** $\frac{8}{5}$ **16.** $\frac{\sqrt{2}}{8}$ **17.** $-\sqrt[3]{100}$

18. $11+2\sqrt{30}$ **19.** $-3\sqrt{3x}$ **20.** $52-30\sqrt{3}$ **21.** $\frac{\sqrt[3]{117}}{9}$

22. $3\sqrt{2}+\sqrt{15}+\sqrt{42}+\sqrt{35}$ **23.** $2\sqrt[4]{27}$ **24.** $\frac{1+\sqrt[3]{3}+\sqrt[3]{9}}{-2}$

25. $\frac{x\sqrt[3]{x^2}}{y}$ **26.** $-4\sqrt{3}-3$ **27.** $xy^{6/5}$ **28.** $x^{10}y$ **29.** $\frac{1}{25x^2}$

30. $7+4\cdot3^{1/2}$, or $7+4\sqrt{3}$ **31.** $3\sqrt[3]{2x^2}$ **32.** -2

33. **(a)** 8 **(b)** $\{-8,8\}$ **34.** **(a)** 10 **(b)** $\{-10,10\}$

35. **(a)** $\{-4,4\}$ **(b)** -4 **36.** **(a)** $\{-5,5\}$ **(b)** -5

37. **(a)** $-\frac{9}{11}$ **(b)** $\left\{-\frac{9}{11},\frac{9}{11}\right\}$ **38.** **(a)** $-\frac{7}{10}$ **(b)** $\left\{-\frac{7}{10},\frac{7}{10}\right\}$

39. **(a)** $\{-0.2,0.2\}$ **(b)** 0.2 **40.** **(a)** $\{-0.3,0.3\}$ **(b)** 0.3

Section 10.6 (pages 648–650)

1. **(a)** yes **(b)** no **3.** **(a)** yes **(b)** no **5.** No. There is no solution.

The radical expression, which is positive, cannot equal a negative number.

7. $\{11\}$ **9.** $\left\{\frac{1}{3}\right\}$ **11.** $\varnothing$ **13.** $\{5\}$ **15.** $\{18\}$ **17.** $\{5\}$ **19.** $\{4\}$

21. $\{17\}$ **23.** $\{5\}$ **25.** $\varnothing$ **27.** $\{0\}$ **29.** $\{0\}$ **31.** $\varnothing$ **33.** $\{1\}$

35. It is incorrect to just square each term. The right side should be $(8 - x)^2 = 64 - 16x + x^2$. The correct first step is $3x + 4 = 64 - 16x + x^2$, and the solution set is $\{4\}$. **37.** $\{1\}$ **39.** $\{-1\}$
41. $\{14\}$ **43.** $\{8\}$ **45.** $\{0\}$ **47.** $\emptyset$ **49.** $\{7\}$ **51.** $\{7\}$
53. $\{4, 20\}$ **55.** $\emptyset$ **57.** $\left\{\frac{5}{4}\right\}$ **59.** $\{9, 17\}$ **61.** $\left\{\frac{1}{4}, 1\right\}$

63. $L = CZ^2$ **65.** $K = \dfrac{V\sqrt{m}}{2}$ **67.** $M = \dfrac{r^2 F}{m}$ **69.** $r = \dfrac{a}{4\pi^2 N^2}$

71. $1 + x$ **73.** $2x^2 + x - 15$ **75.** $\dfrac{-7(5 + \sqrt{2})}{23}$

Section 10.7 (pages 655–657)

1. i **3.** -1 **5.** $-i$ **7.** $13i$ **9.** $-12i$ **11.** $i\sqrt{5}$ **13.** $4i\sqrt{3}$
15. $-\sqrt{105}$ **17.** -10 **19.** $i\sqrt{33}$ **21.** $\sqrt{3}$ **23.** $5i$ **25.** -2
27. Any real number a can be written as $a + 0i$, a complex number with imaginary part 0. **29.** $-1 + 7i$ **31.** 0 **33.** $7 + 3i$ **35.** -2
37. $1 + 13i$ **39.** $6 + 6i$ **41.** $4 + 2i$ **43.** -81 **45.** -16
47. $-10 - 30i$ **49.** $10 - 5i$ **51.** $-9 + 40i$ **53.** $-16 + 30i$
55. 153 **57.** 97 **59.** 4 **61.** $a - bi$ **63.** $1 + i$ **65.** $2 + 2i$
67. $-1 + 2i$ **69.** $-\frac{5}{13} - \frac{12}{13}i$ **71.** $1 - 3i$ **73.** $1 + 3i$ **75.** -1
77. i **79.** -1 **81.** $-i$ **83.** $-i$ **85.** Since $i^{20} = (i^4)^5 = 1^5 = 1$, the student multiplied by 1, which is justified by the identity property for multiplication. **87.** $\frac{1}{2} + \frac{1}{2}i$ **89.** Substitute both $1 + 5i$ and $1 - 5i$ for x, and show that the result is $0 = 0$ in each case. **91.** $\frac{37}{10} - \frac{19}{10}i$
93. $-\frac{13}{10} + \frac{11}{10}i$ **95.** $\left\{-\frac{13}{6}\right\}$ **97.** $\{-8, 5\}$ **99.** $\left\{-\frac{2}{5}, 1\right\}$

Chapter 10 Review Exercises (pages 662–665)

1. 42 **2.** -17 **3.** 6 **4.** -5 **5.** -3 **6.** -2 **7.** $\sqrt[n]{a}$ is not a real number if n is even and a is negative. **8. (a)** $|x|$ **(b)** $-|x|$ **(c)** x
9. -6.856 **10.** -5.053 **11.** 4.960 **12.** 0.009 **13.** -3968.503
14. -0.189

15. domain: $[1, \infty)$; range: $[0, \infty)$
$f(x) = \sqrt{x - 1}$

16. domain: $(-\infty, \infty)$; range: $(-\infty, \infty)$
$f(x) = \sqrt[3]{x} + 4$

17. B **18.** cube (third); 8; 2; second; 4; 4 **19.** A **20. (a)** m must be even. **(b)** m must be odd. **21.** no **22.** 7 **23.** -11 **24.** 32
25. -4 **26.** $-\frac{216}{125}$ **27.** -32 **28.** $\frac{1000}{27}$ **29.** It is not a real number.
30. $\left(\sqrt[3]{8}\right)^2$; $\sqrt[3]{8^2}$ **31.** The radical $\sqrt[n]{a^m}$ is equivalent to $a^{m/n}$. For example, $\sqrt[3]{8^2} = \sqrt[3]{64} = 4$, and $8^{2/3} = (8^{1/3})^2 = 2^2 = 4$.
32. $\sqrt{m + 3n}$ **33.** $\dfrac{1}{\left(\sqrt[3]{3a + b}\right)^5}$, or $\dfrac{1}{\sqrt[3]{(3a + b)^5}}$ **34.** $7^{9/2}$
35. $p^{4/5}$ **36.** 5^2, or 25 **37.** 96 **38.** $a^{2/3}$ **39.** $\dfrac{1}{y^{1/2}}$ **40.** $\dfrac{z^{1/2}x^{8/5}}{4}$
41. $r^{1/2} + r$ **42.** $s^{1/2}$ **43.** $r^{3/2}$ **44.** $p^{1/2}$ **45.** $k^{9/4}$ **46.** $m^{13/3}$
47. $z^{1/12}$ **48.** $x^{1/8}$ **49.** $x^{1/15}$ **50.** $x^{1/36}$ **51.** The product rule for exponents applies only if the bases are the same. **52.** $\sqrt{66}$ **53.** $\sqrt{5r}$

54. $\sqrt[3]{30}$ **55.** $\sqrt[4]{21}$ **56.** $2\sqrt{5}$ **57.** $5\sqrt{3}$ **58.** $-5\sqrt{5}$
59. $-3\sqrt[3]{4}$ **60.** $10y^3\sqrt{y}$ **61.** $4pq^2\sqrt[3]{p}$ **62.** $3a^2b\sqrt[3]{4a^2b^2}$
63. $2r^2t\sqrt[3]{79r^2t}$ **64.** $\dfrac{y\sqrt{y}}{12}$ **65.** $\dfrac{m^5}{3}$ **66.** $\dfrac{\sqrt[3]{r^2}}{2}$ **67.** $\dfrac{a^2\sqrt[4]{a}}{3}$
68. $\sqrt{15}$ **69.** $p\sqrt{p}$ **70.** $\sqrt[12]{2000}$ **71.** $\sqrt[10]{x^7}$ **72.** 10 **73.** $\sqrt{197}$
74. $-11\sqrt{2}$ **75.** $23\sqrt{5}$ **76.** $7\sqrt{3y}$ **77.** $26m\sqrt{6m}$ **78.** $19\sqrt[3]{2}$
79. $-8\sqrt[4]{2}$ **80.** $\left(16\sqrt{2} + 24\sqrt{3}\right)$ ft **81.** $\left(12\sqrt{3} + 5\sqrt{2}\right)$ ft
82. $1 - \sqrt{3}$ **83.** 2 **84.** $9 - 7\sqrt{2}$ **85.** $15 - 2\sqrt{26}$ **86.** 29
87. $2\sqrt[3]{2y^2} + 2\sqrt[3]{4y} - 3$ **88.** $4.801960973 \neq 66.28725368$
89. The denominator would become $\sqrt[3]{6^2} = \sqrt[3]{36}$, which is not rational.
90. $\dfrac{\sqrt{30}}{5}$ **91.** $-3\sqrt{6}$ **92.** $\dfrac{3\sqrt{7py}}{y}$ **93.** $\dfrac{\sqrt{22}}{4}$ **94.** $-\dfrac{\sqrt[3]{45}}{5}$
95. $\dfrac{3m\sqrt[3]{4n}}{n^2}$ **96.** $\dfrac{\sqrt{2} - \sqrt{7}}{-5}$ **97.** $\dfrac{5(\sqrt{6} + 3)}{3}$ **98.** $\dfrac{1 - \sqrt{5}}{4}$
99. $\dfrac{1 - 4\sqrt{2}}{3}$ **100.** $\dfrac{-6 + \sqrt{3}}{2}$ **101.** $\{2\}$ **102.** $\{6\}$ **103.** $\emptyset$
104. $\{0, 5\}$ **105.** $\{9\}$ **106.** $\{3\}$ **107.** $\{7\}$ **108.** $\left\{-\frac{1}{2}\right\}$
109. $\{-13\}$ **110.** $\{-1\}$ **111.** $\{14\}$ **112.** $\{-4\}$ **113.** $\emptyset$
114. $\emptyset$ **115.** $\{7\}$ **116.** $\{4\}$ **117. (a)** $H = \sqrt{L^2 - W^2}$ **(b)** 7.9 ft
118. $5i$ **119.** $10i\sqrt{2}$ **120.** no **121.** $-10 - 2i$ **122.** $14 + 7i$
123. $-\sqrt{35}$ **124.** -45 **125.** 3 **126.** $5 + i$ **127.** $32 - 24i$
128. $1 - i$ **129.** $4 + i$ **130.** $-i$ **131.** 1 **132.** -1 **133.** 1
134. -4 **135.** $\frac{1}{100}$ **136.** $\dfrac{1}{z^{3/5}}$ **137.** k^6 **138.** $3z^3t^2\sqrt[3]{2t^2}$
139. $57\sqrt{2}$ **140.** $-\dfrac{\sqrt{3}}{6}$ **141.** $\dfrac{\sqrt[3]{60}}{5}$ **142.** 1 **143.** $7i$
144. $3 - 7i$ **145.** $-5i$ **146.** $\dfrac{1 + \sqrt{6}}{2}$ **147.** $5 + 12i$ **148.** $6x\sqrt[3]{y^2}$
149. The expression cannot be simplified further.
150. $\sqrt{35} + \sqrt{15} - \sqrt{21} - 3$ **151.** $\{5\}$ **152.** $\{-4\}$ **153.** $\left\{\frac{3}{2}\right\}$
154. $\{2\}$ **155.** $\{1\}$ **156.** $\{2\}$ **157.** $\{9\}$ **158.** $\{4\}$ **159.** $\{7\}$
160. $\{6\}$

Chapter 10 Test (pages 665–666)

[10.1] **1.** -29 **2.** -8 [10.2] **3.** 5 [10.1] **4.** C **5.** 21.863
6. -9.405 **7.** domain: $[-6, \infty)$; range: $[0, \infty)$
$f(x) = \sqrt{x + 6}$

[10.2] **8.** $\frac{125}{64}$ **9.** $\frac{1}{256}$ **10.** $\dfrac{9y^{3/10}}{x^2}$ **11.** $x^{4/3}y^6$ **12.** $7^{1/2}$, or $\sqrt{7}$

[10.3] **13.** $a^3\sqrt[3]{a^2}$, or $a^{11/3}$ **14.** $\sqrt{145}$ **15.** 10 **16.** $3x^2y^3\sqrt{6x}$
17. $2ab^3\sqrt[4]{2a^3b}$ **18.** $\sqrt[6]{200}$ [10.4] **19.** $26\sqrt{5}$ **20.** $(2ts - 3t^2)\sqrt[3]{2s^2}$
[10.5] **21.** $66 + \sqrt{5}$ **22.** $23 - 4\sqrt{15}$ **23.** $-\dfrac{\sqrt{10}}{4}$ **24.** $\dfrac{2\sqrt[3]{25}}{5}$
25. $-2\left(\sqrt{7} - \sqrt{5}\right)$ **26.** $3 + \sqrt{6}$ [10.6] **27. (a)** 59.8

(b) $T = \dfrac{V_0^2 - V^2}{-V^2 k}$, or $T = \dfrac{V^2 - V_0^2}{V^2 k}$ **28.** $\{-1\}$ **29.** $\{3\}$

30. $\{-3\}$ [10.7] **31.** $-5 - 8i$ **32.** $-2 + 16i$ **33.** $3 + 4i$ **34.** i

35. (a) true **(b)** true **(c)** false **(d)** true

Chapters 1–10 Cumulative Review Exercises (pages 667–668)

[1.4–1.6] **1.** 1 **2.** $-\frac{14}{9}$ [2.3] **3.** $\{-4\}$ **4.** $\{-12\}$ **5.** $\{6\}$

[2.8] **6.** $(-6, \infty)$ [2.7] **7.** 36 nickels; 64 quarters

8. $2\frac{2}{39}$ L [3.2, 7.1] **9.**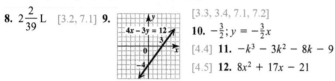

[3.3, 3.4, 7.1, 7.2]
10. $-\frac{3}{2}; y = -\frac{3}{2}x$

[4.4] **11.** $-k^3 - 3k^2 - 8k - 9$

[4.5] **12.** $8x^2 + 17x - 21$

[4.7] **13.** $3y^3 - 3y^2 + 4y + 1 + \dfrac{-10}{2y + 1}$

[5.2, 5.3] **14.** $(2p - 3q)(p - q)$

[5.4] **15.** $(3k^2 + 4)(k - 1)(k + 1)$

16. $(x + 8)(x^2 - 8x + 64)$ [5.5] **17.** $\left\{-3, -\frac{5}{2}\right\}$ **18.** $\left\{-\frac{2}{5}, 1\right\}$

[6.1] **19.** $x \neq -3, x \neq 3$ [6.2] **20.** $\dfrac{y}{y + 5}$ [6.4] **21.** $\dfrac{4x + 2y}{(x + y)(x - y)}$

[6.5] **22.** $-\frac{9}{4}$ **23.** $\dfrac{1}{xy - 1}$ [6.6] **24.** $\varnothing$ [6.7] **25.** Danielle: 8 mph;

Richard: 4 mph [7.4] **26.** -37 [7.6] **27.** \$9.92

[8.1–8.3, 8.6] **28.** $\{(7, -2)\}$ [8.4, 8.6] **29.** $\{(-1, 1, 1)\}$

[8.5] **30.** 2-oz letter: \$0.61; 3-oz letter: \$0.78 [9.1] **31.** $(2, 3)$

32. $(-\infty, 2) \cup (3, \infty)$ [9.2] **33.** $\left\{-\frac{10}{3}, 1\right\}$ **34.** $(-\infty, -2] \cup [7, \infty)$

[10.3] **35.** $2x\sqrt[3]{6x^2y^2}$ [10.4] **36.** $7\sqrt{2}$ [10.5] **37.** $\dfrac{\sqrt{10} + 2\sqrt{2}}{2}$

[10.3] **38.** $\sqrt{29}$ [10.6] **39.** $\{3, 4\}$ [10.7] **40.** $4 + 2i$

---

11 QUADRATIC EQUATIONS, INEQUALITIES, AND FUNCTIONS

Section 11.1 (pages 674–675)

1. B, C **3.** The zero-factor property requires a product equal to 0. The first step should have been to rewrite the equation with 0 on one side.

5. $\{-7, 8\}$ **7.** $\{-11, 11\}$, or $\{\pm 11\}$ **9.** $\left\{-\frac{5}{3}, 6\right\}$ **11.** $\{\pm 9\}$

13. $\{\pm\sqrt{14}\}$ **15.** $\{\pm 4\sqrt{3}\}$ **17.** $\left\{\pm\frac{5}{2}\right\}$ **19.** $\{\pm 1.5\}$

21. $\{\pm\sqrt{3}\}$ **23.** $\{\pm 2\sqrt{5}\}$ **25.** $\left\{\pm\dfrac{2\sqrt{7}}{7}\right\}$ **27.** $\{\pm 2\sqrt{6}\}$

29. $\left\{\pm\dfrac{2\sqrt{5}}{5}\right\}$ **31.** $\{\pm 3\sqrt{3}\}$ **33.** $\{\pm 2\sqrt{2}\}$ **35.** $\{-2, 8\}$

37. $\{4 \pm \sqrt{3}\}$ **39.** $\{8 \pm 3\sqrt{3}\}$ **41.** $\left\{-3, \frac{5}{3}\right\}$ **43.** $\left\{0, \frac{3}{2}\right\}$

45. $\left\{\dfrac{1 \pm \sqrt{7}}{3}\right\}$ **47.** $\left\{\dfrac{-1 \pm 3\sqrt{2}}{3}\right\}$ **49.** $\left\{\dfrac{5 \pm \sqrt{30}}{2}\right\}$

51. $\{-10 \pm 4\sqrt{3}\}$ **53.** $\left\{\dfrac{1 \pm 4\sqrt{3}}{4}\right\}$ **55.** $\{-4.48, 0.20\}$

57. $\{-3.09, -0.15\}$ **59.** $\{\pm 2i\sqrt{3}\}$ **61.** $\{5 \pm 2i\}$

63. $\left\{\dfrac{1}{6} \pm \dfrac{\sqrt{2}}{3}i\right\}$ **65.** 5.6 sec **67.** 9 in. **69.** 2% **71.** $\dfrac{4 + 4\sqrt{3}}{5}$

73. $\dfrac{3 + \sqrt{6}}{4}$ **75.** $(x - 5)^2$

Section 11.2 (pages 681–683)

1. Solve $(2x + 1)^2 = 5$ by the square root property. Solve $x^2 + 4x = 12$ by completing the square. **3.** $9; (x + 3)^2$

5. $36; (p - 6)^2$ **7.** $\frac{81}{4}; \left(q + \frac{9}{2}\right)^2$ **9.** $\frac{1}{64}; \left(x + \frac{1}{8}\right)^2$

11. $0.16; (x - 0.4)^2$ **13.** 4 **15.** 25 **17.** $\frac{1}{36}$ **19.** $\{1, 3\}$

21. $\{-1 \pm \sqrt{6}\}$ **23.** $\{-2 \pm \sqrt{6}\}$ **25.** $\{-5 \pm \sqrt{7}\}$

27. $\{4 \pm 2\sqrt{3}\}$ **29.** $\left\{\dfrac{-7 \pm \sqrt{53}}{2}\right\}$ **31.** $\left\{-\frac{3}{2}, \frac{1}{2}\right\}$ **33.** $\left\{-\frac{8}{3}, 3\right\}$

35. $\left\{\dfrac{-5 \pm \sqrt{41}}{4}\right\}$ **37.** $\left\{\dfrac{5 \pm \sqrt{15}}{5}\right\}$ **39.** $\left\{\dfrac{4 \pm \sqrt{3}}{3}\right\}$

41. $\{-4, 2\}$ **43.** $\{4 \pm \sqrt{3}\}$ **45.** $\{1 \pm \sqrt{6}\}$ **47.** $\left\{\dfrac{2 \pm \sqrt{3}}{3}\right\}$

49. $\{1 \pm \sqrt{2}\}$ **51. (a)** $\left\{\dfrac{3 \pm 2\sqrt{6}}{3}\right\}$ **(b)** $\{-0.633, 2.633\}$

53. (a) $\{-2 \pm \sqrt{3}\}$ **(b)** $\{-3.732, -0.268\}$ **55.** $\{-2 \pm 3i\}$

57. $\left\{-\dfrac{2}{3} \pm \dfrac{2\sqrt{2}}{3}i\right\}$ **59.** $\{-3 \pm i\sqrt{3}\}$ **61.** x^2 **62.** x **63.** $6x$

64. 1 **65.** 9 **66.** $(x + 3)^2$, or $x^2 + 6x + 9$ **67.** $\{\pm\sqrt{b}\}$

69. $\left\{\pm\dfrac{\sqrt{b^2 + 16}}{2}\right\}$ **71.** $\left\{\dfrac{2b \pm \sqrt{3a}}{5}\right\}$ **73.** $\sqrt{13}$ **75.** 1

Section 11.3 (pages 688–690)

1. The documentation was incorrect, since the fraction bar should extend under the term $-b$. The correct formula is $x = \dfrac{-b \pm \sqrt{b^2 - 4ac}}{2a}$.

3. The last step is wrong. Because 5 is not a common factor in the numerator, the fraction cannot be simplified. The solution set is $\left\{\dfrac{5 \pm \sqrt{5}}{10}\right\}$. **5.** $\{3, 5\}$ **7.** $\left\{\dfrac{-2 \pm \sqrt{2}}{2}\right\}$ **9.** $\left\{\dfrac{1 \pm \sqrt{3}}{2}\right\}$

11. $\{5 \pm \sqrt{7}\}$ **13.** $\left\{\dfrac{-1 \pm \sqrt{2}}{2}\right\}$ **15.** $\left\{\dfrac{-1 \pm \sqrt{7}}{3}\right\}$

17. $\{1 \pm \sqrt{5}\}$ **19.** $\left\{\dfrac{-2 \pm \sqrt{10}}{2}\right\}$ **21.** $\{-1 \pm 3\sqrt{2}\}$

23. $\left\{\dfrac{1 \pm \sqrt{29}}{2}\right\}$ **25.** $\left\{\dfrac{-4 \pm \sqrt{91}}{3}\right\}$ **27.** $\left\{\dfrac{-3 \pm \sqrt{57}}{8}\right\}$

29. $\left\{\dfrac{3}{2} \pm \dfrac{\sqrt{15}}{2}i\right\}$ **31.** $\{3 \pm i\sqrt{5}\}$ **33.** $\left\{\dfrac{1}{2} \pm \dfrac{\sqrt{6}}{2}i\right\}$

35. $\left\{-\dfrac{2}{3} \pm \dfrac{\sqrt{2}}{3}i\right\}$ **37.** $\left\{\frac{1}{2} \pm \frac{1}{4}i\right\}$ **39.** B; factoring

41. C; quadratic formula   **43.** A; factoring   **45.** D; quadratic formula

47. $\left\{-\frac{7}{5}\right\}$ **49.** $\left\{-\frac{1}{3}, 2\right\}$ **51.** **(a)** Discriminant is 25, or 5^2; solve by factoring; $\left\{-3, -\frac{4}{3}\right\}$ **(b)** Discriminant is 44; use the quadratic

formula; $\left\{\frac{7 \pm \sqrt{11}}{2}\right\}$ **53.** -10 or 10 **55.** 16   **57.** 25

59. $b = \frac{44}{5}; \frac{3}{10}$ **61.** $\{-8\}$ **63.** $\{5\}$

Section 11.4 (pages 697–700)

1. Multiply by the LCD, x.   **3.** Substitute a variable for $x^2 + x$.
5. The proposed solution -1 does not check. The solution set is $\{4\}$.

7. $\{-2, 7\}$ **9.** $\{-4, 7\}$ **11.** $\left\{-\frac{2}{3}, 1\right\}$ **13.** $\left\{-\frac{14}{17}, 5\right\}$

15. $\left\{-\frac{11}{7}, 0\right\}$ **17.** $\left\{\frac{-1 \pm \sqrt{13}}{2}\right\}$ **19.** $\left\{-\frac{8}{3}, -1\right\}$

21. $\left\{\frac{2 \pm \sqrt{22}}{3}\right\}$ **23.** $\left\{\frac{-1 \pm \sqrt{5}}{4}\right\}$ **25. (a)** $(20 - t)$ mph

(b) $(20 + t)$ mph   **27.** 25 mph   **29.** 50 mph   **31.** 3.6 hr   **33.** Rusty: 25.0 hr; Nancy: 23.0 hr   **35.** 3 hr; 6 hr   **37.** $\{2, 5\}$ **39.** $\{3\}$

41. $\left\{\frac{8}{9}\right\}$ **43.** $\{9\}$ **45.** $\left\{\frac{2}{5}\right\}$ **47.** $\{-2\}$ **49.** $\{\pm 2, \pm 5\}$

51. $\left\{\pm 1, \pm \frac{3}{2}\right\}$ **53.** $\left\{\pm 2, \pm 2\sqrt{3}\right\}$ **55.** $\{-6, -5\}$

57. $\left\{-\frac{16}{3}, -2\right\}$ **59.** $\{-8, 1\}$ **61.** $\{-64, 27\}$ **63.** $\left\{\pm 1, \pm \frac{27}{8}\right\}$

65. $\left\{-\frac{1}{3}, \frac{1}{6}\right\}$ **67.** $\left\{-\frac{1}{2}, 3\right\}$ **69.** $\left\{\pm \frac{\sqrt{6}}{3}, \pm \frac{1}{2}\right\}$ **71.** $\{3, 11\}$

73. $\{25\}$ **75.** $\left\{-\sqrt[3]{5}, -\frac{\sqrt[3]{4}}{2}\right\}$ **77.** $\left\{\frac{4}{3}, \frac{9}{4}\right\}$

79. $\left\{\pm \frac{\sqrt{9 + \sqrt{65}}}{2}, \pm \frac{\sqrt{9 - \sqrt{65}}}{2}\right\}$ **81.** $\left\{\pm 1, \pm \frac{\sqrt{6}}{2}i\right\}$

83. $W = \frac{P - 2L}{2}$, or $W = \frac{P}{2} - L$ **85.** $C = \frac{5}{9}(F - 32)$

Summary Exercises on Solving Quadratic Equations (page 700)

1. square root property   **2.** factoring   **3.** quadratic formula
4. quadratic formula   **5.** factoring   **6.** square root property

7. $\left\{\pm \sqrt{7}\right\}$ **8.** $\left\{-\frac{3}{2}, \frac{5}{3}\right\}$ **9.** $\left\{-3 \pm \sqrt{5}\right\}$ **10.** $\{-2, 8\}$

11. $\left\{-\frac{3}{2}, 4\right\}$ **12.** $\left\{-3, \frac{1}{3}\right\}$ **13.** $\left\{\frac{2 \pm \sqrt{2}}{2}\right\}$ **14.** $\left\{\pm 2i\sqrt{3}\right\}$

15. $\left\{\frac{1}{2}, 2\right\}$ **16.** $\{\pm 1, \pm 3\}$ **17.** $\left\{\frac{-3 \pm 2\sqrt{2}}{2}\right\}$ **18.** $\left\{\frac{4}{5}, 3\right\}$

19. $\left\{\pm \sqrt{2}, \pm \sqrt{7}\right\}$ **20.** $\left\{\frac{1 \pm \sqrt{5}}{4}\right\}$ **21.** $\left\{-\frac{1}{2} \pm \frac{\sqrt{3}}{2}i\right\}$

22. $\left\{-\frac{\sqrt[3]{175}}{5}, 1\right\}$ **23.** $\left\{\frac{3}{2}\right\}$ **24.** $\left\{\frac{2}{3}\right\}$ **25.** $\left\{\pm 6\sqrt{2}\right\}$

26. $\left\{-\frac{2}{3}, 2\right\}$ **27.** $\{-4, 9\}$ **28.** $\{\pm 13\}$ **29.** $\left\{1 \pm \frac{\sqrt{3}}{3}i\right\}$

30. $\{3\}$ **31.** $\left\{\frac{1}{6} \pm \frac{\sqrt{47}}{6}i\right\}$ **32.** $\left\{-\frac{1}{3}, \frac{1}{6}\right\}$

Section 11.5 (pages 705–709)

1. Find a common denominator, and then multiply both sides by the common denominator.   **3.** Write it in standard form (with 0 on one side, in decreasing powers of w).   **5.** $m = \sqrt{p^2 - n^2}$

7. $t = \frac{\pm \sqrt{dk}}{k}$ **9.** $d = \frac{\pm \sqrt{skI}}{I}$ **11.** $v = \frac{\pm \sqrt{kAF}}{F}$

13. $r = \frac{\pm \sqrt{3\pi Vh}}{\pi h}$ **15.** $t = \frac{-B \pm \sqrt{B^2 - 4AC}}{2A}$ **17.** $h = \frac{D^2}{k}$

19. $\ell = \frac{p^2 g}{k}$ **21.** $r = \frac{\pm \sqrt{S\pi}}{2\pi}$ **23.** $R = \frac{E^2 - 2pr \pm E\sqrt{E^2 - 4pr}}{2p}$

25. $r = \frac{5pc}{4}$ or $r = -\frac{2pc}{3}$ **27.** $I = \frac{-cR \pm \sqrt{c^2 R^2 - 4cL}}{2cL}$

29. 7.9, 8.9, 11.9   **31.** eastbound ship: 80 mi; southbound ship: 150 mi
33. 8 in., 15 in., 17 in.   **35.** length: 24 ft; width: 10 ft   **37.** 2 ft

39. 7 m by 12 m   **41.** 20 in. by 12 in.   **43.** 1 sec and 8 sec
45. 2.4 sec and 5.6 sec   **47.** 9.2 sec   **49.** It reaches its *maximum* height at 5 sec because this is the only time it reaches 400 ft.   **51.** \$0.80
53. 0.035, or 3.5%   **55.** 5.5 m per sec   **57.** 5 or 14
59. (a) \$420 billion **(b)** \$420 billion; They are the same.
61. 2004; The graph indicates that spending first exceeded \$400 billion in 2005.   **63.** 9   **65.** domain: $(-\infty, \infty)$; range: $[0, \infty)$

Section 11.6 (pages 715–718)

1. (a) B **(b)** C **(c)** A **(d)** D   **3.** $(0, 0)$ **5.** $(0, 4)$ **7.** $(1, 0)$
9. $(-3, -4)$ **11.** $(5, 6)$ **13.** down; wider   **15.** up; narrower
17. down; narrower   **19. (a)** D **(b)** B **(c)** C **(d)** A

21.   **23.**   **25.**

27. vertex: $(4, 0)$;   **29.** vertex: $(-2, -1)$;   **31.** vertex: $(2, -4)$;
axis: $x = 4$;   axis: $x = -2$;   axis: $x = 2$;
domain: $(-\infty, \infty)$;   domain: $(-\infty, \infty)$;   domain: $(-\infty, \infty)$;
range: $[0, \infty)$ range: $[-1, \infty)$ range: $[-4, \infty)$

33. vertex: $(-1, 2)$;   **35.** vertex: $(2, -3)$;   **37.** linear; positive

axis: $x = -1$;   axis: $x = 2$;   **39.** quadratic; positive

domain: $(-\infty, \infty)$;   domain: $(-\infty, \infty)$;   **41.** quadratic; negative

range: $(-\infty, 2]$ range: $[-3, \infty)$ **43. (a)**

$f(x) = -\frac{1}{2}(x + 1)^2 + 2$

$f(x) = 2(x - 2)^2 - 3$

Sales (in millions of dollars)

8000, 7000, 6000, 5000, 4000, 3000, 2000, 1000

0 1 2 3 4 5 6

Years Since 2000

(b) quadratic; positive   **(c)** $f(x) = 99.3x^2 + 400.7x + 1825$

(d) \$9496 million   **(e)** No. The number of digital cameras sold in 2007 is far below the number approximated by the model. Rather than continuing to increase, sales of digital cameras fell in 2007.   **45. (a)** 6105

(b) The approximation using the model is low.   **47.** $\{-4, 5\}$

49. -2 **51.** $\{-4, 1\}$ **53.** $\left\{-3 \pm 2\sqrt{3}\right\}$

Section 11.7 (pages 726–729)

1. If x is squared, it has a vertical axis. If y is squared, it has a horizontal axis.   **3.** Use the discriminant of the function. If it is positive, there are two x-intercepts. If it is 0, there is one x-intercept (at the vertex), and if it is negative, there is no x-intercept.   **5.** $(-4, -6)$ **7.** $(1, -3)$

9. $\left(-\frac{1}{2}, -\frac{29}{4}\right)$ **11.** $(-1, 3)$; up; narrower; no x-intercepts

13. $\left(\frac{5}{2}, \frac{37}{4}\right)$; down; same; two x-intercepts   **15.** $(-3, -9)$; to the right; wider   **17.** F   **19.** C   **21.** D

23. vertex: $(-4, -6)$;   **25.** vertex: $(1, -3)$;   **27.** vertex: $(1, -2)$;

axis: $x = -4$;   axis: $x = 1$;   axis: $y = -2$;

domain: $(-\infty, \infty)$;   domain: $(-\infty, \infty)$;   domain: $[1, \infty)$;

range: $[-6, \infty)$ range: $(-\infty, -3]$ range: $(-\infty, \infty)$

$f(x) = x^2 + 8x + 10$

$f(x) = -2x^2 + 4x - 5$

$x = (y + 2)^2 + 1$

29. vertex: $(1, 5)$; axis: $y = 5$;   **31.** vertex: $(-7, -2)$;

domain: $(-\infty, 1]$;   axis: $y = -2$; domain: $[-7, \infty)$;

range: $(-\infty, \infty)$ range: $(-\infty, \infty)$

$x = -\frac{1}{5}y^2 + 2y - 4$

$x = 3y^2 + 12y + 5$

33. 20 and 20   **35.** 140 ft by 70 ft; 9800 ft²   **37.** 16 ft; 2 sec

39. 2 sec; 65 ft   **41.** 20 units; \$210   **43. (a)** minimum

(b) 2003; \$825.8 billion   **45. (a)** The coefficient of x^2 is negative because a parabola that models the data must open down.

(b) (18.45, 3860)   **(c)** In 2018 Social Security assets will reach their maximum value of \$3860 billion.

47. (a) $R(x) = (100 - x)(200 + 4x) = 20,000 + 200x - 4x^2$

(b)

$R(x)$

22,500, 20,000, 15,000, 10,000, 5,000

(25, 22,500)

$R(x) = (100 - x)(200 + 4x)$

0   25 50 75 100 x

(c) 25   **(d)** \$22,500

49.

0 1   5

51.

0 1   5

53. $\left(-\frac{3}{2}, \infty\right)$

Section 11.8 (pages 735–736)

1. (a) $\{1, 3\}$ **(b)** $(-\infty, 1) \cup (3, \infty)$ **(c)** $(1, 3)$

3. (a) $\{-2, 5\}$ **(b)** $[-2, 5]$ **(c)** $(-\infty, -2] \cup [5, \infty)$

5. $(-\infty, -1) \cup (5, \infty)$

$-1\,0$ 5

7. $(-4, 6)$

-4 0   6

9. $(-\infty, 1] \cup [3, \infty)$

0 1   3

11. $\left(-\infty, -\frac{3}{2}\right) \cup \left[\frac{3}{5}, \infty\right)$

$-\frac{3}{2}$ 0 $\frac{3}{5}$ 1

13. $\left[-\frac{3}{2}, \frac{3}{2}\right]$

$-\frac{3}{2}$ 0 $\frac{3}{2}$

15. $\left(-\infty, -\frac{1}{2}\right) \cup \left[\frac{1}{3}, \infty\right)$

-1 $-\frac{1}{2}$ 0 $\frac{1}{3}$ 1

17. $(-\infty, 0] \cup [4, \infty)$

0   4

19. $\left[0, \frac{5}{3}\right]$

0   1 $\frac{5}{3}$

21. $\left(-\infty, 3 - \sqrt{3}\right] \cup \left[3 + \sqrt{3}, \infty\right)$

0 $3 - \sqrt{3}$ 3 $3 + \sqrt{3}$

23. $(-\infty, \infty)$ **25.** $\emptyset$ **27.** $(-\infty, 1) \cup (2, 4)$

0   1   2   4

29. $\left[-\frac{3}{2}, \frac{1}{3}\right] \cup [4, \infty)$

$-\frac{3}{2}$ 0 $\frac{1}{3}$ 2   4

31. $(-\infty, 1) \cup (4, \infty)$

0 1   4

33. $\left[-\frac{3}{2}, 5\right)$

$-\frac{3}{2}$ 0   5

35. $(2, 6]$

0   2   6

37. $\left(-\infty, \frac{1}{2}\right) \cup \left(\frac{5}{4}, \infty\right)$

0 $\frac{1}{2}$ $\frac{5}{4}$ 2

39. $[-7, -2)$

-7 -2 0

41. $(-\infty, 2) \cup (4, \infty)$

0   2   4

43. $\left(0, \frac{1}{2}\right) \cup \left(\frac{5}{2}, \infty\right)$

0 $\frac{1}{2}$ 1 $\frac{5}{2}$

45. $\left[\frac{3}{2}, \infty\right)$

0    $\frac{3}{2}$

47. $\left(-2, \frac{5}{3}\right) \cup \left(\frac{5}{3}, \infty\right)$

49. domain: $\{0, 1, 2, 3\}$; range: $\{1, 2, 4, 8\}$ **51.** function

Chapter 11 Review Exercises (pages 740–744)

1. $\{\pm 11\}$ **2.** $\{\pm \sqrt{3}\}$ **3.** $\left\{-\frac{15}{2}, \frac{5}{2}\right\}$ **4.** $\left\{\frac{2}{3} \pm \frac{5}{3}i\right\}$

5. By the square root property, the first step should be $x = \sqrt{12}$ or $x = -\sqrt{12}$. The solution set is $\{\pm 2\sqrt{3}\}$.   **6.** 5.8 sec

7. $\{-2 \pm \sqrt{19}\}$ **8.** $\left\{\frac{1}{2}, 1\right\}$ **9.** $\left\{\frac{-4 \pm \sqrt{22}}{2}\right\}$

10. $\left\{\frac{3}{8} \pm \frac{\sqrt{87}}{8}i\right\}$ **11.** $\left\{-\frac{7}{2}, 3\right\}$ **12.** $\left\{\frac{-5 \pm \sqrt{53}}{2}\right\}$

13. $\left\{\frac{1 \pm \sqrt{41}}{2}\right\}$ **14.** $\left\{-\frac{3}{4} \pm \frac{\sqrt{23}}{4}i\right\}$ **15.** $\left\{\frac{2}{3} \pm \frac{\sqrt{2}}{3}i\right\}$

16. $\left\{\frac{-7 \pm \sqrt{37}}{2}\right\}$ **17.** (a) C   (b) A   **18.** (a) D   (b) B

19. $\left\{-\frac{5}{2}, 3\right\}$ **20.** $\left\{-\frac{1}{2}, 1\right\}$ **21.** $\{-4\}$ **22.** $\left\{-\frac{11}{6}, -\frac{19}{12}\right\}$

23. $\left\{-\frac{343}{8}, 64\right\}$ **24.** $\{\pm 1, \pm 3\}$ **25.** 7 mph   **26.** 40 mph   **27.** 4.6 hr

28. Zoran: 2.6 hr; Claude: 3.6 hr   **29.** $v = \frac{\pm \sqrt{rFkw}}{kw}$ **30.** $y = \frac{6p^2}{z}$

31. $t = \frac{3m \pm \sqrt{9m^2 + 24m}}{2m}$ **32.** 9 ft, 12 ft, 15 ft

33. 12 cm by 20 cm   **34.** 1 in.   **35.** 18 in.   **36.** 5.2 sec   **37.** 3 min

38. (a) \$15,511 million; It is close to the number suggested by the graph.
(b) $x = 6$, which represents 2006; Based on the graph, the revenue in 2006 was closer to \$13,000 million than \$14,000 million.   **39.** $(1, 0)$

40. $(3, 7)$ **41.** $(-4, 3)$ **42.** $\left(\frac{2}{3}, -\frac{2}{3}\right)$

43. vertex: $(2, -3)$;
axis: $x = 2$;
domain: $(-\infty, \infty)$;
range: $[-3, \infty)$

44. vertex: $(2, 3)$;
axis: $x = 2$;
domain: $(-\infty, \infty)$;
range: $(-\infty, 3]$

45. vertex: $(-4, -3)$;
axis: $y = -3$;
domain: $[-4, \infty)$;
range: $(-\infty, \infty)$

$f(x) = -2x^2 + 8x - 5$

$y = 2(x - 2)^2 - 3$

$x = 2(y + 3)^2 - 4$

46. vertex: $(4, 6)$;
axis: $y = 6$;
domain: $(-\infty, 4]$;
range: $(-\infty, \infty)$

$x = -\frac{1}{2}y^2 + 6y - 14$

47. (a) $c = 2.9$
$100a + 10b + c = 24.3$
$400a + 20b + c = 56.5$
(b) $f(x) = 0.054x^2 + 1.6x + 2.9$
(c) \$60.3 billion; The result using the model is close, but slightly low.

48. 5 sec; 400 ft   **49.** length: 50 m; width: 50 m; maximum area: 2500 m²

50. $\left(-\infty, -\frac{3}{2}\right) \cup (4, \infty)$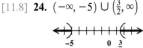

51. $[-4, 3]$

52. $(-\infty, -5] \cup [-2, 3]$ **53.** $\varnothing$

54. $\left(-\infty, \frac{1}{2}\right) \cup (2, \infty)$

55. $[-3, 2)$ **56.** $R = \frac{\pm \sqrt{Vh - r^2 h}}{h}$

57. $\left\{1 \pm \frac{\sqrt{3}}{3}i\right\}$ **58.** $\left\{\frac{-11 \pm \sqrt{7}}{3}\right\}$ **59.** $d = \frac{\pm \sqrt{SkI}}{I}$

60. $(-\infty, \infty)$ **61.** $\{4\}$ **62.** $\left\{\pm \sqrt{4 + \sqrt{15}}, \pm \sqrt{4 - \sqrt{15}}\right\}$

63. $\left(-5, -\frac{23}{5}\right]$ **64.** $\left\{-\frac{5}{3}, -\frac{3}{2}\right\}$ **65.** $\{-2, -1, 3, 4\}$

66. $(-\infty, -6) \cup \left(-\frac{3}{2}, 1\right)$ **67.** (a) F   (b) B   (c) C
(d) A   (e) E   (f) D

68. vertex: $\left(-\frac{1}{2}, -3\right)$; axis: $x = -\frac{1}{2}$;
domain: $(-\infty, \infty)$; range: $[-3, \infty)$

$f(x) = 4x^2 + 4x - 2$

69. 10 mph   **70.** length: 2 cm; width: 1.5 cm

Chapter 11 Test (pages 744–746)

[11.1] **1.** $\{\pm 3\sqrt{6}\}$ **2.** $\left\{-\frac{8}{7}, \frac{2}{7}\right\}$ [11.2] **3.** $\{-1 \pm \sqrt{5}\}$

[11.3] **4.** $\left\{\frac{3 \pm \sqrt{17}}{4}\right\}$ **5.** $\left\{\frac{2}{3} \pm \frac{\sqrt{11}}{3}i\right\}$ [11.1] **6.** A

[11.3] **7.** discriminant: 88; There are two irrational solutions.

[11.1–11.4] **8.** $\left\{\frac{2}{3}\right\}$ **9.** $\left\{-\frac{2}{3}, 6\right\}$ **10.** $\left\{\frac{-7 \pm \sqrt{97}}{8}\right\}$ **11.** $\left\{\pm \frac{1}{3}, \pm 2\right\}$

12. $\left\{-\frac{5}{2}, 1\right\}$ [11.5] **13.** $r = \frac{\pm \sqrt{\pi S}}{2\pi}$ [11.4] **14.** Terry: 11.1 hr;
Callie: 9.1 hr   **15.** 7 mph   [11.5] **16.** 2 ft   **17.** 16 m   [11.6] **18.** A

19. vertex: $(0, -2)$; axis: $x = 0$;   [11.7] **20.** vertex: $(2, 3)$; axis: $x = 2$;
domain: $(-\infty, \infty)$;
range: $[-2, \infty)$

domain: $(-\infty, \infty)$;
range: $(-\infty, 3]$

$f(x) = \frac{1}{2}x^2 - 2$

$f(x) = -x^2 + 4x - 1$

21. vertex: $(2, 2)$; axis: $y = 2$;
domain: $(-\infty, 2]$;
range: $(-\infty, \infty)$

$x = -(y - 2)^2 + 2$

22. (a) 139 million   (b) 2007;
145 million   **23.** 160 ft by 320 ft
[11.8] **24.** $(-\infty, -5) \cup \left(\frac{3}{2}, \infty\right)$

25. $(-\infty, 4) \cup [9, \infty)$

Chapters 1–11 Cumulative Review Exercises (pages 746–747)

[1.4, 10.7] **1. (a)** $-2, 0, 7$ **(b)** $-\frac{7}{3}, -2, 0, 0.7, 7, \frac{32}{3}$

(c) All are real except $\sqrt{-8}$.   **(c)** All are complex numbers.

[2.3] **2.** $\left\{\frac{4}{5}\right\}$ [9.2] **3.** $\left\{\frac{11}{10}, \frac{7}{2}\right\}$ [10.6] **4.** $\left\{\frac{2}{3}\right\}$ [6.6] **5.** $\emptyset$

[11.2, 11.3] **6.** $\left\{\dfrac{7 \pm \sqrt{177}}{4}\right\}$ [11.4] **7.** $\{\pm 1, \pm 2\}$ [2.8] **8.** $[1, \infty)$

[9.2] **9.** $\left[2, \frac{8}{3}\right]$ [11.8] **10.** $(1, 3)$ **11.** $(-2, 1)$

[3.2, 7.1, 7.3, 7.4] **12.** function;

domain: $(-\infty, \infty)$; range: $(-\infty, \infty)$;

$f(x) = \frac{4}{5}x - 3$

[7.3, 9.3] **13.** not a function

[11.6] **14.** function;

domain: $(-\infty, \infty)$;

range: $(-\infty, 3]$;

$f(x) = -2(x - 1)^2 + 3$

[3.2, 3.3, 7.1] **15.** $m = \frac{2}{7}$; x-intercept: $(-8, 0)$; y-intercept: $\left(0, \frac{16}{7}\right)$

[7.2] **16. (a)** $y = -\frac{5}{2}x + 2$ **(b)** $y = \frac{2}{5}x + \frac{13}{5}$ [4.1, 4.2] **17.** $\dfrac{x^8}{y^4}$

18. $\dfrac{4}{xy^2}$ [4.6] **19.** $\frac{4}{9}t^2 + 12t + 81$ [4.7] **20.** $4x^2 - 6x + 11 + \dfrac{4}{x + 2}$

[5.1–5.4] **21.** $(4m - 3)(6m + 5)$ **22.** $(2x + 3y)(4x^2 - 6xy + 9y^2)$

23. $(3x - 5y)^2$ [6.2] **24.** $-\frac{5}{18}$ [6.4] **25.** $-\dfrac{8}{x}$ [6.5] **26.** $\dfrac{r - s}{r}$

[8.1–8.3, 8.6] **27.** $\{(1, -2)\}$ [8.4, 8.6] **28.** $\{(3, -4, 2)\}$

[8.5] **29.** Microsoft: \$60.4 billion; Oracle: \$22.4 billion

[10.3] **30.** $\dfrac{3\sqrt[3]{4}}{4}$ [10.5] **31.** $\sqrt{7} + \sqrt{5}$

[11.5] **32.** southbound car: 57 mi; eastbound car: 76 mi

APPENDICES

Appendix A (pages 896–897)

1. $\{1, 2, 3, 4, 5, 6, 7\}$ **3.** $\{$winter, spring, summer, fall$\}$ **5.** $\emptyset$

7. $\{L\}$ **9.** $\{2, 4, 6, 8, 10, \dots\}$ **11.** The sets in **Exercises 9 and 10** are infinite sets.   **13.** true   **15.** false   **17.** true   **19.** true   **21.** true

23. true   **25.** true   **27.** false   **29.** true   **31.** true   **33.** false

35. true   **37.** true   **39.** false   **41.** false   **43.** true   **45.** $\{g, h\}$

47. $\{b, c, d, e, g, h\}$ **49.** $\{a, c, e\} = B$ **51.** $\{d\} = D$ **53.** $\{a\}$

55. $\{a, c, d, e\}$ **57.** $\{a, c, e, f\}$ **59.** $\emptyset$ **61.** B and D; C and D

Appendix B (pages 903–904)

1. $\dfrac{1}{a^2b}$ **3.** $\dfrac{100y^{10}}{x^2}$ **5.** 0   **7.** $\dfrac{x^{10}}{2w^{13}y^5}$ **9.** $\dfrac{a^{15}}{-64b^{15}}$ **11.** $\dfrac{x^{16}z^{10}}{y^6}$

13. $-6a^4 + 11a^3 - 20a^2 + 26a - 15$ **15.** $8x^3 - 18x^2 + 6x - 16$

17. $x^2y - xy^2 + 6y^3$ **19.** $-3x^2 - 62x + 32$

21. $10x^3 - 4x^2 + 9x - 4$ **23.** $6x^2 - 19x - 7$ **25.** $4x^2 - 9x + 2$

27. $16t^2 - 9$ **29.** $4y^4 - 16$ **31.** $16x^2 - 24x + 9$

33. $36r^2 + 60ry + 25y^2$ **35.** $c^3 + 8d^3$ **37.** $64x^3 - 1$

39. $14t^3 + 45st^2 + 18s^2t - 5s^3$ **41.** $4xy^3(2x^2y + 3x + 9y)$

43. $(x + 3)(x - 5)$ **45.** $(2x + 3)(x - 6)$ **47.** $(6t + 5)(6t - 5)$

49. $(4t + 3)^2$ **51.** $p(2m - 3n)^2$ **53.** $(x + 1)(x^2 - x + 1)$

55. $(2t + 5)(4t^2 - 10t + 25)$ **57.** $(t^2 - 5)(t^4 + 5t^2 + 25)$

59. $(5x + 2y)(t + 3r)$ **61.** $(6r - 5s)(a + 2b)$

63. $(t^2 + 1)(t + 1)(t - 1)$ **65.** $(2x + 3y - 1)(2x + 3y + 1)$

67. $4(x - 5)(x - 2)$

Appendix C (page 908)

1. $x - 5$ **3.** $4m - 1$ **5.** $2a + 4 + \dfrac{5}{a + 2}$ **7.** $p - 4 + \dfrac{9}{p + 1}$

9. $4a^2 + a + 3$ **11.** $x^4 + 2x^3 + 2x^2 + 7x + 10 + \dfrac{18}{x - 2}$

13. $-4r^5 - 7r^4 - 10r^3 - 5r^2 - 11r - 8 + \dfrac{-5}{r - 1}$

15. $-3y^4 + 8y^3 - 21y^2 + 36y - 72 + \dfrac{143}{y + 2}$ **17.** 7   **19.** -2

21. 0   **23.** By the remainder theorem, a 0 remainder means that $P(k) = 0$. That is, k is a number that makes $P(x) = 0$.   **25.** yes   **27.** no   **29.** yes

31. no   **33.** $(2x - 3)(x + 4)$ **34.** $\left\{-4, \frac{3}{2}\right\}$ **35.** 0   **36.** 0   **37.** a

38. Yes, $x - 3$ is a factor. $Q(x) = (x - 3)(3x - 1)(x + 2)$

Glossary

For a more complete discussion, see the section(s) in parentheses.

A

absolute value The absolute value of a number is the distance between 0 and the number on a number line. (Section 1.4)

absolute value equation An absolute value equation is an equation that involves the absolute value of a variable expression. (Section 9.2)

absolute value inequality An absolute value inequality is an inequality that involves the absolute value of a variable expression. (Section 9.2)

addition property of equality The addition property of equality states that the same number can be added to (or subtracted from) both sides of an equation to obtain an equivalent equation. (Section 2.1)

addition property of inequality The addition property of inequality states that the same number can be added to (or subtracted from) both sides of an inequality without changing the solution set. (Section 2.8)

additive inverse (opposite) The additive inverse of a number x, symbolized $-x$, is the number that is the same distance from 0 on the number line as x, but on the opposite side of 0. The number 0 is its own additive inverse. For all real numbers x, $x + (-x) = (-x) + x = 0$. (Section 1.4)

algebraic expression An algebraic expression is a sequence of numbers, variables, operation symbols, and/or grouping symbols (such as parentheses) formed according to the rules of algebra. (Section 1.3)

area Area is a measure of the surface covered by a two-dimensional (flat) figure. (Section 2.5)

associative property of addition The associative property of addition states that the grouping of terms in a sum does not affect the sum. (Section 1.7)

associative property of multiplication The associative property of multiplication states that the grouping of factors in a product does not affect the product. (Section 1.7)

axis (axis of symmetry) The axis of a parabola is the vertical or horizontal line (depending on the orientation of the graph) through the vertex of the parabola. (Sections 4.4, 11.6, 11.7)

B

base The base in an exponential expression is the expression that is the repeated factor. In b^x, b is the base. (Sections 1.2, 4.1)

binomial A binomial is a polynomial consisting of exactly two terms. (Section 4.4)

C

circle graph (pie chart) A circle graph (or pie chart) is a circle divided into sectors, or wedges, whose sizes show the relative magnitudes of the categories of data being represented. (Section 1.1)

coefficient (See **numerical coefficient.**)

combined variation A relationship among variables that involves both direct and inverse variation is called combined variation. (Section 7.6)

combining like terms Combining like terms is a method of adding or subtracting terms having exactly the same variable factors by using the properties of real numbers. (Section 1.8)

common factor An integer that is a factor of two or more integers is called a common factor of those integers. (Section 5.1)

commutative property of addition The commutative property of addition states that the order of terms in a sum does not affect the sum. (Section 1.7)

commutative property of multiplication The commutative property of multiplication states that the order of factors in a product does not affect the product. (Section 1.7)

complement of a set The set of elements in the universal set that are not in a set A is the complement of A, written A'. (Appendix A)

complementary angles (complements) Complementary angles are two angles whose measures have a sum of 90°. (Section 2.4)

completing the square The process of adding to a binomial the expression that makes it a perfect square trinomial is called completing the square. (Section 11.2)

complex conjugate The complex conjugate of $a + bi$ is $a - bi$. (Section 10.7)

complex fraction A complex fraction is a quotient with one or more fractions in the numerator, denominator, or both. (Section 6.5)

complex number A complex number is any number that can be written in the form $a + bi$, where a and b are real numbers and i is the imaginary unit. (Section 10.7)

components In an ordered pair (x, y), x and y are called the components of the ordered pair. (Section 7.1)

composite function If g is a function of x, and f is a function of $g(x)$, then $f(g(x))$ defines the composite function of f and g. It is symbolized $(f \circ g)(x)$. (Section 7.5)

composite number A natural number greater than 1 that is not prime is a composite number. It is composed of prime factors represented in one and only one way. (Section 1.1)

composition of functions The process of finding a composite function is called composition of functions. (Section 7.5)

conditional equation A conditional equation is true for some replacements of the variable and false for others. (Section 2.3)

conjugate The conjugate of $a + b$ is $a - b$. (Section 10.5)

consecutive integers Two integers that differ by 1 are called consecutive integers. (Sections 2.4, 5.6)

constant function A linear function of the form $f(x) = b$, where b is a constant, is called a constant function. (Section 7.4)

constant of variation In the variation equations $y = kx$, $y = \frac{k}{x}$, or $y = kxz$, the nonzero real number k is called the constant of variation. (Section 7.6)

contradiction A contradiction is an equation that is never true. It has no solution. (Section 2.3)

coordinate on a number line Every point on a number line is associated with a unique real number, called the coordinate of the point. (Section 1.4)

coordinates of a point The numbers in an ordered pair are called the coordinates of the corresponding point in the plane. (Sections 3.1, 7.1)

cross products The cross products in the proportion $\frac{a}{b} = \frac{c}{d}$ are ad and bc. (Section 2.6)

cube root A number b is a cube root of a if $b^3 = a$ is true. (Section 10.1)

cube root function The function defined by $f(x) = \sqrt[3]{x}$ is called the cube root function. (Section 10.1)

D

degree A degree is a basic unit of measure for angles in which one degree ($1°$) is $\frac{1}{360}$ of a complete revolution. (Section 2.4)

degree of a polynomial The degree of a polynomial is the greatest degree of any of the terms in the polynomial. (Section 4.4)

degree of a term The degree of a term is the sum of the exponents on the variables in the term. (Section 4.4)

denominator The number below the fraction bar in a fraction is called the denominator. It indicates the number of equal parts in a whole. (Section 1.1)

dependent variable In an equation relating x and y, if the value of the variable y depends on the value of the variable x, then y is called the dependent variable. (Section 7.3)

descending powers A polynomial in one variable is written in descending powers of the variable if the exponents on the variables of the terms of the polynomial decrease from left to right. (Section 4.4)

difference The answer to a subtraction problem is called the difference. (Section 1.1)

difference of cubes The difference of cubes, $x^3 - y^3$, can be factored as $x^3 - y^3 = (x - y)(x^2 + xy + y^2)$. (Section 5.4)

difference of squares The difference of squares, $x^2 - y^2$, can be factored as $x^2 - y^2 = (x + y)(x - y)$. (Section 5.4)

direct variation y varies directly as x if there exists a nonzero real number (constant) k such that $y = kx$. (Section 7.6)

discriminant The discriminant of the quadratic equation $ax^2 + bx + c = 0$ is the quantity $b^2 - 4ac$ under the radical in the quadratic formula. (Section 11.3)

disjoint sets Sets that have no elements in common are disjoint sets. (Appendix A)

distributive property of multiplication with respect to addition (distributive property)
For any real numbers a, b, and c, the distributive property states that $a(b + c) = ab + ac$ and $(b + c)a = ba + ca$. (Section 1.7)

domain The set of all first components (x-values) in the ordered pairs of a relation is called the domain. (Section 7.3)

E

elements (members) The elements (members) of a set are the objects that belong to the set. (Section 1.3, Appendix A)

empty set (null set) The empty set, denoted by { } or $\emptyset$, is the set containing no elements. (Section 2.3, Appendix A)

equation An equation is a statement that two algebraic expressions are equal. (Section 1.3)

equivalent equations Equivalent equations are equations that have the same solution set. (Section 2.1)

equivalent inequalities Equivalent inequalities are inequalities that have the same solution set. (Section 2.8)

exponent (power) An exponent, or power, is a number that indicates how many times its base is used as a factor. In b^x, x is the exponent (power). (Sections 1.2, 4.1)

exponential expression A number or letter (variable) written with an exponent is an exponential expression. (Sections 1.2, 4.1)

extraneous solution (extraneous value) A proposed solution to an equation, following any of several procedures in the solution process, that does not satisfy the original equation is called an extraneous solution. (Sections 7.6, 10.6)

extremes of a proportion In the proportion $\frac{a}{b} = \frac{c}{d}$, the a- and d-terms are called the extremes. (Section 2.6)

F

factor If a, b, and c represent numbers and $a \cdot b = c$, then a and b are factors of c. (Sections 1.1, 5.1)

factored A number is factored by writing it as the product of two or more numbers. (Section 1.1)

factor If a, b, and c represent numbers and $a \cdot b = c$, then a and b are factors of c. (Section 5.1)

factored form An expression is in factored form when it is written as a product. (Section 5.1)

factoring Writing a polynomial as the product of two or more simpler polynomials is called factoring. (Section 5.1)

factoring by grouping Factoring by grouping is a method for grouping the terms of a polynomial in such a way that the polynomial can be factored. It is used when the greatest common factor of the terms of the polynomial is 1. (Section 5.1)

factoring out the greatest common factor Factoring out the greatest common factor is the process of using the distributive property to write a polynomial as a product of the greatest common factor and a simpler polynomial. (Section 5.1)

first-degree equation A first-degree (linear) equation has no term with the variable to a power other than 1. (Section 7.1)

FOIL FOIL is a mnemonic device which represents a method for multiplying two binomials $(a + b)(c + d)$. Multiply **F**irst terms ac, **O**uter terms ad, **I**nner terms bc, and **L**ast terms bd. Then combine like terms. (Section 4.5)

formula A formula is an equation in which variables are used to describe a relationship among several quantities. (Section 2.5)

fourth root A number b is a fourth root of a if $b^4 = a$ is true. (Section 10.1)

function A function is a set of ordered pairs (x, y) in which each value of the first component x corresponds to exactly one value of the second component y. (Section 7.3)

function notation If a function is denoted by f, the notation $y = f(x)$ is called function notation. Here y, or $f(x)$, represents the value of the function at x. (Section 7.4)

G

graph of a number The point on a number line that corresponds to a number is its graph. (Section 1.4)

graph of an equation The graph of an equation in two variables is the set of all points that correspond to all of the ordered pairs that satisfy the equation. (Sections 3.2, 7.1)

graph of a relation The graph of a relation is the graph of its ordered pairs. (Section 7.3)

greatest common factor (GCF) The greatest common factor of a list of integers is the largest factor of all those integers. The greatest common factor of the terms of a polynomial is the largest factor of all the terms in the polynomial. (Sections 1.1, 5.1)

grouping symbols Examples of grouping symbols are parentheses ( ), brackets [ ], and fraction bars. (Section 1.2)

H

hypotenuse The side opposite the right angle in a right triangle is the longest side and is called the hypotenuse. (Sections 5.6, 10.3)

I

identity An identity is an equation that is true for all valid replacements of the variable. It has an infinite number of solutions. (Section 2.3)

identity element for addition For all real numbers a, $a + 0 = 0 + a = a$. The number 0 is called the identity element for addition. (Section 1.7)

identity element for multiplication For all real numbers a, $a \cdot 1 = 1 \cdot a = a$. The number 1 is called the identity element for multiplication. (Section 1.7)

identity property The identity property for addition states that the sum of 0 and any number equals the number. The identity property for multiplication states that the product of 1 and any number equals the number. (Section 1.7)

imaginary part The imaginary part of the complex number $a + bi$ is b. (Section 10.7)

imaginary unit The symbol i, which represents $\sqrt{-1}$, is called the imaginary unit. (Section 10.7)

independent variable In an equation relating x and y, if the value of the variable y depends on the value of the variable x, then x is called the independent variable. (Section 7.3)

index (order) In a radical of the form $\sqrt[n]{a}$, n is called the index or order. (Section 10.1)

inequality An inequality is a statement that two expressions are not equal. (Section 1.2)

inner product When using the FOIL method to multiply two binomials $(a + b)(c + d)$, the inner product is bc. (Section 4.5)

integers The set of integers is $\{\ldots, -3, -2, -1, 0, 1, 2, 3, \ldots\}$. (Section 1.4)

intersection The intersection of two sets A and B, written $A \cap B$, is the set of elements that belong to *both A and B*. (Appendix A)

interval An interval is a portion of a number line. (Section 2.8)

interval notation Interval notation is a simplified notation that uses parentheses ( ) and/or brackets [ ] and/or the infinity symbol ∞ to describe an interval on a number line. (Section 2.8)

inverse property The inverse property for addition states that a number added to its opposite (additive inverse) is 0. The inverse property for multiplication states that a number multiplied by its reciprocal (multiplicative inverse) is 1. (Section 1.7)

inverse variation y varies inversely as x if there exists a nonzero real number (constant) k such that $y = \frac{k}{x}$. (Section 7.6)

irrational number An irrational number cannot be written as the quotient of two integers, but can be represented by a point on a number line. (Section 1.4, 10.1)

J

joint variation y varies jointly as x and z if there exists a nonzero real number (constant) k such that $y = kxz$. (Section 7.6)

L

least common denominator (LCD) Given several denominators, the least multiple that is divisible by all the denominators is called the least common denominator. (Sections 1.1, 6.3)

legs of a right triangle The two shorter perpendicular sides of a right triangle are called the legs. (Sections 5.6, 10.3)

like radicals Like radicals are multiples of the same root of the same number or expression. (Section 10.3)

like terms Terms with exactly the same variables raised to exactly the same powers are called like terms. (Sections 1.8, 4.4)

linear equation in one variable A linear equation in one variable can be written in the form $Ax + B = C$, where A, B, and C are real numbers, with $A \neq 0$. (Section 2.1)

linear equation in two variables A linear equation in two variables is an equation that can be written in the form $Ax + By = C$, where A, B, and C are real numbers, and A and B are not both 0. (Sections 3.1, 7.1)

linear function A function defined by an equation of the form $f(x) = ax + b$, for real numbers a and b, is a linear function. The value of a is the slope m of the graph of the function. (Section 7.4)

linear inequality in one variable A linear inequality in one variable can be written in the form $Ax + B < C$, $Ax + B \leq C$, $Ax + B > C$, or $Ax + B \geq C$, where A, B, and C are real numbers, with $A \neq 0$. (Section 2.8)

line graph A line graph is a series of line segments in two dimensions that connect points representing data. (Section 3.1)

line of symmetry The axis of a parabola is a line of symmetry for the graph. It is a line that can be drawn through the vertex of the graph in such a way that the part of the graph on one side of the line is an exact reflection of the part on the opposite side. (Section 4.4)

lowest terms A fraction is in lowest terms if the greatest common factor of the numerator and denominator is 1. (Sections 1.1, 6.1)

M

mathematical model In a real-world problem, a mathematical model is one or more equations (or inequalities) that describe the situation. (Section 3.1)

means of a proportion In the proportion $\frac{a}{b} = \frac{c}{d}$, the b- and c-terms are called the means. (Section 2.6)

mixed number A mixed number includes a whole number and a fraction written together and is understood to be the sum of the whole number and the fraction. (Section 1.1)

monomial A monomial is a polynomial consisting of exactly one term. (Section 4.4)

multiplication property of equality The multiplication property of equality states that the same nonzero number can be multiplied by (or divided into) both sides of an equation to obtain an equivalent equation. (Section 2.2)

multiplication property of inequality The multiplication property of inequality states that both sides of an inequality may be multiplied (or divided) by a positive number without changing the direction of the inequality symbol. Multiplying (or dividing) by a negative number reverses the direction of the inequality symbol. (Section 2.8)

multiplicative inverse (reciprocal) The multiplicative inverse (reciprocal) of a nonzero number x, symbolized $\frac{1}{x}$, is the real number which has the property that the product of the two numbers is 1. For all nonzero real numbers x, $\frac{1}{x} \cdot x = x \cdot \frac{1}{x} = 1$. (Section 1.6)

N

natural numbers The set of natural numbers is the set of numbers used for counting: $\{1, 2, 3, 4, \ldots\}$. (Sections 1.1, 1.4)

negative number A negative number is located to the left of 0 on a number line. (Section 1.4)

number line A line that has a point designated to correspond to the real number 0, and a standard unit chosen to represent the distance between 0 and 1, is a number line. All real numbers correspond to one and only one number on such a line. (Section 1.4)

numerator The number above the fraction bar in a fraction is called the numerator. It shows how many of the equivalent parts are being considered. (Section 1.1)

numerical coefficient (coefficient) The numerical factor in a term is called the numerical coefficient, or simply, the coefficient. (Sections 1.8, 4.4)

O

ordered pair An ordered pair is a pair of numbers written within parentheses in the form (x, y). (Sections 3.1, 7.1)

origin The point at which the x-axis and y-axis of a rectangular coordinate system intersect is called the origin. (Sections 3.1, 7.1)

outer product When using the FOIL method to multiply two binomials $(a + b)(c + d)$, the outer product is ad. (Section 4.5)

P

parabola The graph of a second-degree (quadratic) equation in two variables is called a parabola. (Sections 4.4, 11.6)

parallel lines Parallel lines are two lines in the same plane that never intersect. (Sections 3.3, 7.1)

percent Percent, written with the symbol %, means per one hundred. (Section 2.6)

percentage A percentage is a part of a whole. (Section 2.6)

perfect cube A perfect cube is a number with a rational cube root. (Section 10.1)

perfect square A perfect square is a number with a rational square root. (Section 10.1)

perfect square trinomial A perfect square trinomial is a trinomial that can be factored as the square of a binomial. (Section 5.4)

perimeter The perimeter of a two-dimensional figure is a measure of the distance around the outside edges of the figure—that is, the sum of the lengths of its sides. (Section 2.5)

perpendicular lines Perpendicular lines are two lines that intersect to form a right (90°) angle. (Sections 3.3, 7.1)

plot To plot an ordered pair is to locate it on a rectangular coordinate system. (Sections 3.1, 7.1)

point-slope form A linear equation is written in point-slope form if it is in the form $y - y_1 = m(x - x_1)$, where m is the slope and (x_1, y_1) is a point on the line. (Sections 3.4, 7.2)

polynomial A polynomial is a term or a finite sum of terms in which all coefficients are real, all variables have whole number exponents, and no variables appear in denominators. (Section 4.4)

polynomial function A function defined by a polynomial in one variable, consisting of one or more terms, is called a polynomial function. (Section 7.5)

polynomial in x A polynomial whose only variable is x is called a polynomial in x. (Section 4.4)

positive number A positive number is located to the right of 0 on a number line. (Section 1.4)

prime factor A prime factor of a number is a factor greater than 1 whose only factors are 1 and itself. For example, the prime factors of 12 are $2 \cdot 2 \cdot 3$. (Section 1.1)

prime number A natural number greater than 1 is prime if it has only 1 and itself as factors. (Section 1.1)

prime polynomial A prime polynomial is a polynomial that cannot be factored into factors having only integer coefficients. (Section 5.2)

principal root (principal nth root) For even indexes, the symbols $\sqrt{\ }$, $\sqrt[4]{\ }$, $\sqrt[6]{\ }, \ldots, \sqrt[n]{\ }$ are used for nonnegative roots, which are called principal roots. (Section 10.1)

product The answer to a multiplication problem is called the product. (Section 1.1)

product of the sum and difference of two terms The product of the sum and difference of two terms is the difference of the squares of the terms, or $(x + y)(x - y) = x^2 - y^2$. (Section 4.6)

proportion A proportion is a statement that two ratios are equal. (Section 2.6)

proportional If y varies directly as x and there exists some nonzero real number (constant) k such that $y = kx$, then y is said to be proportional to x. (Section 7.6)

proposed solution A value that appears as an apparent solution after a rational, radical, or logarithmic equation has been solved according to standard methods is called a proposed solution for the original equation. It may or may not be an actual solution and must be checked. (Sections 6.6, 10.6)

pure imaginary number If $a = 0$ and $b \neq 0$ in the complex number $a + bi$, the complex number is called a pure imaginary number. (Section 10.7)

Pythagorean theorem The Pythagorean theorem states that the square of the length of the hypotenuse of a right triangle equals the sum of the squares of the lengths of the two legs. (Sections 5.6, 10.3)

Q

quadrant A quadrant is one of the four regions in the plane determined by the axes in a rectangular coordinate system. (Sections 3.1, 7.1)

quadratic equation A quadratic equation is an equation that can be written in the form $ax^2 + bx + c = 0$, where a, b, and c are real numbers, with $a \neq 0$. (Sections 5.5, 11.1)

quadratic formula The quadratic formula is a general formula used to solve a quadratic equation of the form $ax^2 + bx + c = 0$, where $a \neq 0$. It is $x = \dfrac{-b \pm \sqrt{b^2 - 4ac}}{2a}$. (Section 11.3)

quadratic function A function defined by an equation of the form $f(x) = ax^2 + bx + c$, for real numbers a, b, and c, with $a \neq 0$, is a quadratic function. (Section 11.6)

quadratic inequality A quadratic inequality is an inequality that can be written in the form $ax^2 + bx + c < 0$ or $ax^2 + bx + c > 0$ (or with $\leq$ or $\geq$), where a, b, and c are real numbers, with $a \neq 0$. (Section 11.8)

quadratic in form An equation is quadratic in form if it can be written in the form $au^2 + bu + c = 0$, for $a \neq 0$ and an algebraic expression u. (Section 11.4)

quotient The answer to a division problem is called the quotient. (Section 1.1)

R

radical An expression consisting of a radical symbol, root index, and radicand is called a radical. (Section 10.1)

radical equation A radical equation is an equation with a variable in at least one radicand. (Section 10.6)

radical expression A radical expression is an algebraic expression that contains radicals. (Section 10.1)

radical symbol The symbol $\sqrt{\ }$ is called a radical symbol. (Section 10.1)

radicand The number or expression under a radical symbol is called the radicand. (Section 10.1)

range The set of all second components (y-values) in the ordered pairs of a relation is called the range. (Section 7.3)

ratio A ratio is a comparison of two quantities using a quotient. (Section 2.6)

rational expression The quotient of two polynomials with denominator not 0 is called a rational expression. (Section 6.1)

rational inequality An inequality that involves rational expressions is called a rational inequality. (Section 11.8)

rationalizing the denominator The process of rewriting a radical expression so that the denominator contains no radicals is called rationalizing the denominator. (Section 10.5)

rational numbers Rational numbers can be written as the quotient of two integers, with denominator not 0. (Section 1.4)

real numbers Real numbers include all numbers that can be represented by points on the number line—that is, all rational and irrational numbers. (Section 1.4)

real part The real part of a complex number $a + bi$ is a. (Section 10.7)

reciprocal (See **multiplicative inverse.**)

rectangular (Cartesian) coordinate system The x-axis and y-axis placed at a right angle at their zero points form a rectangular coordinate system. It is also called the Cartesian coordinate system. (Sections 3.1, 7.1)

relation A relation is a set of ordered pairs. (Section 7.3)

right angle A right angle measures 90°. (Section 2.4)

rise Rise refers to the vertical change between two points on a line—that is, the change in y-values. (Sections 3.3, 7.1)

run Run refers to the horizontal change between two points on a line—that is, the change in x-values. (Sections 3.3, 7.1)

S

scatter diagram A scatter diagram is a graph of ordered pairs of data. (Section 3.1)

scientific notation A number is written in scientific notation when it is expressed in the form $a \times 10^n$, where $1 \leq |a| < 10$ and n is an integer. (Section 4.3)

set A set is a collection of objects. (Appendix A)

set-builder notation The special symbolism $\{x \mid x$ has a certain property$\}$ is called set-builder notation. It is used to describe a set of numbers without actually having to list all of the elements. (Section 1.4)

signed numbers Signed numbers are numbers that can be written with a positive or negative sign. (Section 1.4)

simplified radical A simplified radical meets four conditions:

1. The radicand has no factor (except 1) that is a perfect square (if the radical is a square root), a perfect cube (if the radical is a cube root), and so on.

2. The radicand has no fractions.

3. No denominator contains a radical.

4. Exponents in the radicand and the index of the radical have greatest common factor 1.

(Section 10.3)

slope The ratio of the change in y to the change in x for any two points on a line is called the slope of the line. (Sections 3.3, 7.1)

slope-intercept form A linear equation is written in slope-intercept form if it is in the form $y = mx + b$, where m is the slope and $(0, b)$ is the y-intercept. (Sections 3.4, 7.2)

solution of an equation A solution of an equation is any replacement for the variable that makes the equation true. (Section 1.3)

solution set The set of all solutions of an equation is called the solution set. (Section 2.1)

square of a binomial The square of a binomial is the sum of the square of the first term, twice the product of the two terms, and the square of the last term: $(x + y)^2 = x^2 + 2xy + y^2$ and $(x - y)^2 = x^2 - 2xy + y^2$. (Section 4.6)

square root The inverse of squaring a number is called taking its square root. That is, a number a is a square root of k if $a^2 = k$ is true. (Section 10.1)

square root function The function defined by $f(x) = \sqrt{x}$, with $x \geq 0$, is called the square root function. (Section 10.1)

square root property The square root property (for solving equations) states that if $x^2 = k$, with $k > 0$, then $x = \sqrt{k}$ or $x = -\sqrt{k}$. (Section 11.1)

squaring property The squaring property (for solving equations) states that if each side of a given equation is squared, then all solutions of the given equation are *among* the solutions of the squared equation. (Section 10.6)

standard form of a complex number The standard form of a complex number is $a + bi$. (Section 10.7)

standard form of a linear equation A linear equation in two variables written in the form $Ax + By = C$, with A and B not both 0, is in standard form. (Sections 3.4, 7.2)

standard form of a quadratic equation A quadratic equation written in the form $ax^2 + bx + c = 0$, where a, b, and c are real numbers with $a \neq 0$, is in standard form. (Sections 5.5, 11.1)

straight angle A straight angle measures 180°. (Section 2.4)

subscript notation Subscript notation is a way of indicating nonspecific values. In x_1 and x_2, 1 and 2 are subscripts on the variable x. (Sections 3.3, 7.1)

subset If all elements of set A are in set B, then A is a subset of B, written $A \subseteq B$. (Appendix A)

sum The answer to an addition problem is called the sum. (Section 1.1)

sum of cubes The sum of cubes, $x^3 + y^3$, can be factored as $x^3 + y^3 = (x + y)(x^2 - xy + y^2)$. (Section 5.4)

supplementary angles (supplements) Supplementary angles are two angles whose measures have a sum of 180°. (Section 2.4)

synthetic division Synthetic division is a shortcut procedure for dividing a polynomial by a binomial of the form $x - k$. (Appendix C)

T

table of values A table of values is an organized way of displaying ordered pairs. (Section 3.1)

term A term is a number, a variable, or the product or quotient of a number and one or more variables raised to powers. (Section 1.8)

terms of a proportion The terms of the proportion $\frac{a}{b} = \frac{c}{d}$ are a, b, c, and d. (Section 2.6)

three-part inequality An inequality that says that one number is between two other numbers is called a three-part inequality. (Section 2.8)

trinomial   A trinomial is a polynomial consisting of exactly three terms. (Section 4.4)

U

union   The union of two sets A and B, written $A \cup B$, is the set of elements that belong to *either A or B*, or both. (Section 9.1, Appendix A)

universal set   The set that includes all elements under consideration is the universal set, symbolized U. (Appendix A)

unlike terms   Unlike terms are terms that do not have the same variable, or terms with the same variables but whose variables are not raised to the same powers. (Section 1.8)

V

variable   A variable is a symbol, usually a letter, used to represent an unknown number. (Section 1.3)

vary directly (is proportional to) y varies directly as x if there exists a nonzero real number (constant) k such that $y = kx$. (Section 7.6)

vary inversely y varies inversely as x if there exists a nonzero real number (constant) k such that $y = \frac{k}{x}$. (Section 7.6)

vary jointly   If one variable varies as the product of several other variables (possibly raised to powers), then the first variable is said to vary jointly as the others. (Section 7.6)

Venn diagram   A Venn diagram consists of geometric figures, such as rectangles and circles, that illustrate the relationships among sets. (Appendix A)

vertex   The point on a parabola that has the least y-value (if the parabola opens up) or the greatest y-value (if the parabola opens down) is called the vertex of the parabola. (Sections 4.4, 11.6)

vertical angles   When two intersecting lines are drawn, the angles that lie opposite each other have the same measure and are called vertical angles. (Section 2.5)

vertical line test   The vertical line test states that any vertical line will intersect the graph of a function in at most one point. (Section 7.3)

volume   The volume of a three-dimensional figure is a measure of the space occupied by the figure. (Section 2.5)

W

whole numbers   The set of whole numbers is $\{0, 1, 2, 3, 4, \ldots\}$. (Sections 1.1, 1.4)

X

x-axis   The horizontal number line in a rectangular coordinate system is called the x-axis. (Sections 3.1, 7.1)

x-intercept   A point where a graph intersects the x-axis is called an x-intercept. (Sections 3.2, 7.1)

Y

y-axis   The vertical number line in a rectangular coordinate system is called the y-axis. (Sections 3.1, 7.1)

y-intercept   A point where a graph intersects the y-axis is called a y-intercept. (Sections 3.2, 7.2)

Z

zero-factor property   The zero-factor property states that if two numbers have a product of 0, then at least one of the numbers is 0. (Sections 5.5, 11.1)

Index

Triangles and Angles

Right Triangle

Triangle has one 90° (right) angle.

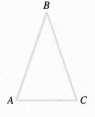

Pythagorean Theorem (for right triangles)

$a^2 + b^2 = c^2$

Right Angle

Measure is 90°.

Isosceles Triangle

Two sides are equal.

$AB = BC$

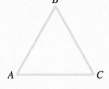

Straight Angle

Measure is 180°.

Equilateral Triangle

All sides are equal.

$AB = BC = CA$

Complementary Angles

The sum of the measures of two complementary angles is 90°.

Angles ① and ② are complementary.

Sum of the Angles of Any Triangle

$A + B + C = 180°$

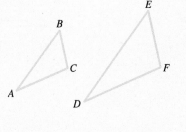

Supplementary Angles

The sum of the measures of two supplementary angles is 180°.

Angles ③ and ④ are supplementary.

Similar Triangles

Corresponding angles are equal. Corresponding sides are proportional.

$A = D, B = E, C = F$

$\dfrac{AB}{DE} = \dfrac{AC}{DF} = \dfrac{BC}{EF}$

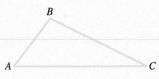

Vertical Angles

Vertical angles have equal measures.

Angle ① = Angle ③

Angle ② = Angle ④

Formulas

Figure	Formulas	Illustration
Square	Perimeter: $P = 4s$ Area: $A = s^2$	
Rectangle	Perimeter: $P = 2L + 2W$ Area: $A = LW$	
Triangle	Perimeter: $P = a + b + c$ Area: $A = \dfrac{1}{2}bh$	
Parallelogram	Perimeter: $P = 2a + 2b$ Area: $A = bh$	
Trapezoid	Perimeter: $P = a + b + c + B$ Area: $A = \dfrac{1}{2}h(b + B)$	
Circle	Diameter: $d = 2r$ Circumference: $C = 2\pi r$ $C = \pi d$ Area: $A = \pi r^2$	

Formulas

Figure	*Formulas*	*Illustration*
Cube	Volume: $V = e^3$ Surface area: $S = 6e^2$	
Rectangular Solid	Volume: $V = LWH$ Surface area: $\mathcal{A} = 2HW + 2LW + 2LH$	
Right Circular Cylinder	Volume: $V = \pi r^2 h$ Surface area: $S = 2\pi rh + 2\pi r^2$ (Includes both circular bases)	
Cone	Volume: $V = \frac{1}{3}\pi r^2 h$ Surface area: $S = \pi r \sqrt{r^2 + h^2} + \pi r^2$ (Includes circular base)	
Right Pyramid	Volume: $V = \frac{1}{3}Bh$ $B =$ area of the base	
Sphere	Volume: $V = \frac{4}{3}\pi r^3$ Surface area: $S = 4\pi r^2$	

Other Formulas

Distance: $d = rt$ ($r =$ rate or speed, $t =$ time)

Percent: $p = br$ ($p =$ percentage, $b =$ base, $r =$ rate)

Temperature: $F = \frac{9}{5}C + 32$ $C = \frac{5}{9}(F - 32)$

Simple Interest: $I = prt$ ($p =$ principal or amount invested, $r =$ rate or percent, $t =$ time in years)